H. A. Dixon
Room 908
Fed. Dorma
NYU
Sect 11·D

5.50

D1130257

Technical Drawing

BOOKS BY THE AUTHORS

THE BLUEPRINT LANGUAGE, by H. C. Spencer and H. E. Grant
(The Macmillan Co., 1947)

DESCRIPTIVE GEOMETRY, by F. E. Giesecke and A. Mitchell (Technical Book Co.,
Austin, Texas, 1943)

DESCRIPTIVE GEOMETRY PROBLEMS, by F. E. Giesecke and A. Mitchell (Technical
Book Co., Austin, Texas, 1937)

ENGINEERING PREVIEW, by L. E. Grinter, H. C. Spencer, et al. (The Macmillan Co.,
1945)

HOT WATER HEATING, RADIANT HEATING, AND RADIANT COOLING, by
F. E. Giesecke (Technical Book Co., Austin, Texas, 1947)

LETTERING EXERCISES FROM TECHNICAL DRAWING PROBLEMS, by F. E.
Giesecke, A. Mitchell, and H. C. Spencer (The Macmillan Co., 1948)

TECHNICAL DRAWING, by F. E. Giesecke, A. Mitchell, and H. C. Spencer (The Macmillan Co., 1949)

TECHNICAL DRAWING FOR HIGH SCHOOLS, WORKBOOKS I AND II, By
E. L. Williams and H. C. Spencer (The Macmillan Co., 1935)

TECHNICAL DRAWING PROBLEMS, by F. E. Giesecke, A. Mitchell, and H. C. Spencer
(The Macmillan Co., 1947)

TECHNICAL DRAWING PROBLEMS—SERIES 2, by H. C. Spencer and H. E. Grant
(The Macmillan Co., 1948)

Courtesy Ford Motor Company

TECHNICAL
DRAWING

FREDERICK E. GIESECKE, M.E., B.S. in ARCH., C.E., PH.D.
Consulting Engineer. Formerly Professor of Drawing, Agricultural and Mechanical College of Texas.

ALVA MITCHELL, B.C.E. *Professor Emeritus of Engineering Drawing, Agricultural and Mechanical College of Texas.*

HENRY CECIL SPENCER, A.B., B.S. in ARCH., M.S.
Professor of Technical Drawing. Director of Department, Illinois Institute of Technology.

THIRD EDITION

THE MACMILLAN COMPANY : NEW YORK

Preface

This volume is intended as a class text and reference book in technical drawing. It contains a very large number of problems covering every phase of the subject, and it constitutes a complete teaching unit in itself. In addition to the problems in the text, two complete workbooks have been prepared especially for use with this text. The first, *Technical Drawing Problems*, by Giesecke, Mitchell and Spencer, was introduced in 1936, and is now available in its Second Edition, 1947. The second, *Technical Drawing Problems—Series 2*, by Spencer and Grant, was published in 1948. Thus, there are three alternate sources of problems available, and problem assignments can be varied easily from year to year.

The extensive use of this text during the last twelve years in college classes and in drafting rooms has encouraged the authors in their original aim, which was, and still is, to prepare a book *which teaches the language of the engineer*, and to keep it in step with the developments in industry. The idea has been to illustrate and explain each basic principle from the standpoint of the student, to make it so clear that the student is certain to understand, and to make it interesting enough so that he will read and study on his own initiative. Thus, it was hoped to free the teacher of a great deal of labor in teaching every student individually those things which the textbook can teach, and to permit him to give his attention to students having real difficulties.

This edition is a complete revision and not a reprinting. A large part of the text matter has been rewritten. A considerable number of new illustrations and problems have been added, and several hundred of the old ones have been re-drawn. Throughout, the book has been brought into agreement with the latest revision of the *American Standard Drawings and Drafting Room Practice* (ASA Z14.1—1946), and a complete facsimile of this standard is given in the Appendix.

Over half the page area of the book is taken up by drawings. This large area is due not only to the fact that there are well over one thousand figures, but also to the careful elimination of all "eye-killers." The aim was to reproduce every drawing large enough to be read with ease.

Another important objective has been to maintain and, where possible, to improve the quality of the drafting in the illustrations. It seems logical to say that in a drawing book the drawings are more important than anything else. A special effort has been made to place illustrations and related text matter on the same page or on facing pages. All instructions for problems are given directly adjacent to the figures.

The basic chapters on Lettering, Multiview Drawing, Sectioning, Auxiliary Views, and Dimensioning have been completely rewritten and expanded. Special attention has been given to the problems of the left-handed student.

The most complete revision has been devoted to the subject of Dimensioning. This chapter has been approximately doubled in size, with special attention given to limit dimensioning.

A feature of the chapter on Axonometric Projection is the new simplified presentation of Dr. L. Eckhart's "method of intersections," by means of which trimetrics can be drawn almost as easily as isometrics. Attention is called to the difference between normal and oblique axonometric projections.

The chapter on Fasteners has been revised to conform with the latest American Standards. The chapter on Shop Processes has been revised and enlarged by Professor J. George H. Thompson of Texas A & M College to relate shop processes more closely to drafting. A considerable number of new advanced problems have been added to the chapter on Working Drawings. Problems which were small and difficult to read have all been enlarged. The chapter on Gearing and Cams was prepared by Professor B. Leighton Wellman, of Worcester Polytechnic Institute.

The chapters on Pipe, Fittings, and Valves; Welding; Graphs; Architectural Drawing; Structural Drawing; Topographic Drawing; and Reproduction of Drawings have all been rewritten and expanded. The chapter on Architectural Drawing was expanded by the addition of a section on Dimensional or Modular Coordination and a section on the functions of the Federal Housing Administration. The chapter on Aeronautical Drafting has been revised by Mr. W. N. Wright, engineer of the Boeing Airplane Company, to bring it abreast of the latest developments in that industry.

All problem layouts have been re-drawn to agree with the American Standard sizes $8\frac{1}{2}'' \times 11''$, $11'' \times 17''$, and so on.

Through the cooperation of leading engineers and manufacturers, this volume includes many commercial drawings of value in developing the subject. The authors wish to express their thanks to these and others too numerous to mention who have contributed to the production of the book.

Especial appreciation is due to Mr. Angelus Duros, who skilfully prepared most of the new drawings, to Mr. O. C. Kluge, who made a number of the drawings, and to Professors H. E. Grant and H. C. Hesse for their valuable contributions. The authors also wish to acknowledge a certain continued indebtedness to the late Dr. E. R. Hedrick for contributions to the original edition which are residual in this revision.

F. E. Giesecke
A. Mitchell
H. C. Spencer

Chicago, Illinois

CONTENTS

Technical Drawing

CHAPTER 1

Introduction

1. Introductory. Technical drawing is a *universal graphic language* by means of which the form, size, finish, color, and construction of an object can be described accurately and clearly. It is the language used by engineers and architects to develop and record their ideas and to transmit them to those who are to execute their designs. For example, if a highway, a bridge, a building, or a machine is to be constructed, the designing engineers or architects prepare drawings with specifications which completely describe the structure to be built. Anyone who is competent to read the drawings and is qualified to build the structures can then carry out the designs in every detail without any additional instructions from the designer.

History indicates that drawings were used in ancient times to delineate the exact forms and sizes of structures. The Bible states that Solomon's Temple was "built of stone made ready before it was brought thither," indicating that drawings were used to describe the forms and sizes of the individual members of that historic structure. The ancient Greek temples, so complex in arrangement and refined in detail, as the Parthenon, for example, could not have been constructed without accurate drawings to guide the artisans in forming the structural elements and the builders in assembling them.

Vitruvius, in 30 B.C., wrote a treatise on architecture in which he referred to projection drawings for structures. But it was not until the early part of the fifteenth century that the theory of projections was well developed by the Italian architects Brunelleschi, Alberti, and others.

The theory of projection drawing was advanced to an academic study by the introduction of two planes of projection at right angles to each other by the French mathematician Gaspard Monge, near the end of the eighteenth century. This development provides the basis of *descriptive geometry*, the science which treats of the graphical description of objects of three dimensions and provides problems designed to develop the ability to visualize and to solve space problems.

The original and natural method of describing the forms of objects is by means of drawings. Written or spoken language is inadequate to describe

1

any but the most elementary forms. Specifications which accompany the drawings used in the building of structures are worthless without the drawings for which they were prepared. Together, the drawings and the specifications are the instruments which enable the designer to convey his ideas to the builder, and which enable the builder and the owner to agree on a definite undertaking.

Technical drawing has become highly specialized according to the particular branch of the engineering sciences to which it applies. The fundamental principles of technical drawing, common to all branches, are presented in this text and should be mastered by all who are directly concerned with technical work. The student of technical drawing should attain a knowledge of these fundamental principles and as much skill as possible in drawing. To become a finished draftsman, he must also acquire a knowledge of the details of construction employed in the branch of engineering in which he plans to work. No draftsman can prepare accurate and complete drawings of machines, bridges, or buildings if he is not thoroughly familiar with the construction of these structures.

Technical drawings may be made with instruments, or freehand, or partly with instruments and partly freehand. *Instrumental drawing* is the term usually applied to technical drawings executed with instruments; *technical sketching* applies to such drawings executed without the aid of instruments.

Technical drawing is the art and science of describing structures and structural details completely and accurately by graphical means.

Engineering drawing and *architectural drawing* are those branches of technical drawing which apply primarily to engineering and architectural structures.

CHAPTER 2

Instruments and Materials

2. Typical Equipment. The principal items of equipment needed by students in technical schools and by draftsmen in professional practice are shown in Fig. 1. To secure the most satisfactory results, the drawing equip-

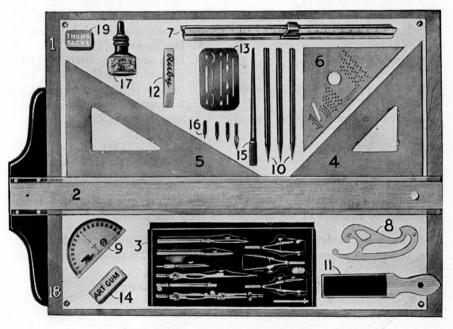

FIG. 1 Principal Items of Equipment.

ment should be of high grade. When instruments are to be purchased, the advice of an experienced draftsman or a reliable manufacturer* should be

* Keuffel & Esser Co., New York, Eugene Dietzgen Co., New York, Theo. Alteneder & Sons, Philadelphia, and Frederick Post Co., Chicago, are some of the larger manufacturers of this equipment; their products are available through local dealers.

sought, because it is impossible for beginners to distinguish high-grade instruments from those which are inferior. Each student should scratch some neat mark of identification on his instruments.

A complete list of equipment, which should provide a satisfactory selection for students of technical drawing, follows:

1. Drawing board (§ 3).
2. T-square (§ 4).
3. Set of instruments (§ 23).
   (1) 6″ compass including pen attachment and lengthening bar (§ 24).
   (2) 6″ hairspring dividers (§ 24).
   (3) Two ruling pens (§ 27).
   (4) Three bow instruments (§ 20).
   (5) Box of leads (§ 60).
4. 45° triangle (§ 10).
5. 30° × 60° triangle (§ 10).
6. Lettering triangle or Ames Lettering Instrument (§ 144).
7. Triangular Architects' scale (§ 13).
8. Irregular curve (§ 34).
9. Protractor (§ 36).
10. Drawing pencils (HB, F, 2H and 4H to 6H) (§ 7).
11. Pencil pointer (sandpaper pad, or file) (§ 8).
12. Pencil eraser (§ 9).
13. Erasing shield (§ 9).
14. Art gum or other cleaning eraser (§ 9).
15. Pen staff.
16. Pen points (Gillott's 303, 404; Hunt's 512; Leonardt's ball-pointed 516 F) (§ 140).
17. Drawing ink (black, waterproof) and pen wiper (§ 33).
18. Drawing paper, tracing paper, or tracing cloth (§§ 18–20).
19. Thumbtacks, drafting tape or draftsman's stapler (§ 22).

In addition (not illustrated above) these items may be included if necessary:

20. Dusting brush (§ 9).
21. Drop pen (§ 31), detail pen (§ 27), proportional dividers (§ 32), beam compass (§ 30), contour pen (§ 29).
22. Arkansas oil stone (for sharpening ruling pens) (§ 28).
23. Pocket knife.
24. Slide rule (§ 41).
25. Dust cloth (about 18″ square).

The following detailed description of the instruments and materials will be helpful to students in the selection of their equipment.

3. Drawing Boards. Drawing boards (Fig. 2) are usually made of white pine, but are sometimes made of other soft woods. To prevent warping, the

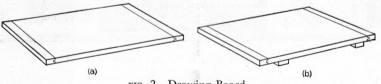

(a)   (b)

FIG. 2   Drawing Board.

board should be made of narrow strips glued edge-to-edge, rather than from one piece. Cleats should be joined to both ends with tongue-and-groove joints to allow for expansion and to prevent warping (Fig. 2, a). For elementary drawing, a board 18″ × 24″ is sufficiently large.

Many draftsmen prefer cleats or ledges on the underside of the board to give it rigidity and to raise it above the surface of the drawing table (Fig. 2, b).

The top face of the board should be smooth and the *working edge* should be straight. See also § 6.

The increasing use of drafting tape to fasten drawings to the drawing board has now made it possible to use drawing boards made of masonite or other smooth, hard wallboards, or even steel. Some have found that white battleship linoleum, glued to the table top, affords a fine working surface.

4. T-Squares. The T-square is composed of a long strip called the *blade*, fastened rigidly to a shorter piece called the *head* (Fig. 3, a). The upper edge of the blade and the inner edge of the head are the *working edges;* they should be perfectly straight and should be at right angles to each other, or nearly so.

Most T-squares have black walnut heads and maple blades, but other woods, such as pearwood, mahogany, ash, and boxwood, are frequently used. A T-square made entirely of bakelite has been introduced on the market. Wooden T-squares should be varnished or shellacked to exclude moisture and thereby prevent warping, and to make them easy to keep clean. They are available in lengths from 18″ to 72″; the length that is used depends somewhat upon the length of the drawing board (Fig. 2) and the size of the drawing.

The most popular T-square is that shown in Fig. 3 (a). It is made of hardwood, and its blade has celluloid edges through which the draftsman can see his work. The fixed-head types are used for all ordinary work, but occasionally the adjustable-head type is useful. The adjustable head shown in Fig. 3 (b) is intended for use in drawing parallel inclined lines. The type shown in Fig. 3 (c) is seldom used, perhaps because of the unusual design of the blade, but it has the advantage of great *rigidity.* A stainless steel T-square, with adjustable head and vernier, is shown at (d).

The T-square is a very important and rather delicate instrument. It should not be used for driving thumb-tacks, for cutting paper along its working edges, or for other improper purposes. When not in use, it should be suspended from the hole in the end of the blade or left flat on the drawing board. *Drafting machines* (§ 38) and *parallel-rule attachments* (§ 39) are widely used in industrial

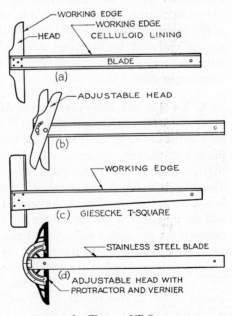

FIG. 3 Types of T-Squares.

drafting rooms in place of the T-square. They have definite advantages but are comparatively expensive.

A *straghtedge* is similar to the blade of a T-square, with the head removed. A steel straightedge is heavy enough to maintain its position on a drawing while triangles are being used with it. Such straightedges are often used instead of T-squares for map drawing.

Long T-squares for large drawing boards are not satisfactory, due to the excessive "give" or swing of the blade. In such cases, the parallel-rule attachment (§ 39) is recommended.

5. Testing the T-Square. The blade of the T-square can be tested for

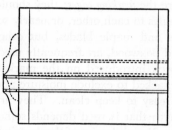

FIG. 4   Testing the T-Square.

straightness by drawing, very carefully, with a sharp, hard pencil a line along the entire length of the working edge, and then turning the T-square over and drawing the line again along the same edge (Fig. 4). If the edge of the T-square is straight, the lines as drawn will coincide; if they do not coincide, the error in the blade is half that shown by the space between the lines, and must be corrected before the T-square is used.

If the head of the T-square is held firmly against the working edge of the board with the left hand, the blade may be tested for horizontal "swing" by moving the end of the blade with the right hand. If any swing exists, it is the result of a loose joint of the blade and head, or of a curvature in the edge of the drawing board or in the edge of the T-square head. The former defect can be remedied by re-gluing the joint and tightening the screws and the latter by scraping and sandpapering the defective edge, as explained for triangles in § 12.

6. Testing the Drawing Board. After the blade of the T-square has been tested for straightness and has been found to be correct, the working edge of the drawing board should be tested by holding the board in a vertical plane and placing the tested edge of the T-square blade upon the edge of the board (Fig. 5). If the edge of the board is straight, the blade of the T-square will touch the edge of the board along its entire length. Any defect will be apparent if the edges are held between the eye and a window or light, and this defect must be corrected by planing or sandpapering the edge before the board is used. A drawing board should be flat so that it will not "rock" when placed on the drawing table.

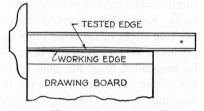

FIG. 5   Testing the Working-Edge of the Drawing Board.

7. Grades of Drawing Pencils. Drawing pencil leads are made chiefly of graphite, mixed with varying quantities of clay to produce eighteen degrees of hardness: 7B (very soft), 6B, 5B, 4B, 3B, 2B, B, HB, F, H, 2H, 3H, 4H, 5H, 6H, 7H, 8H, 9H (very hard). For the different uses of these grades, see § 46.

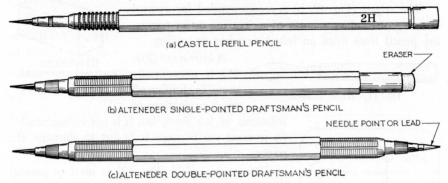

(a) CASTELL REFILL PENCIL

ERASER

(b) ALTENEDER SINGLE-POINTED DRAFTSMAN'S PENCIL

NEEDLE POINT OR LEAD

(c) ALTENEDER DOUBLE-POINTED DRAFTSMAN'S PENCIL

FIG. 6   Mechanical Pencils.

The degree of hardness of leads may be judged roughly by a comparison of the diameters (Fig. 60). Drawing pencils are hexagonal in shape, so that three planes may be in contact with the thumb, forefinger, and second finger, and so that the pencil will not easily roll off the drawing board or desk.

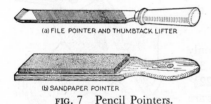

(a) FILE POINTER AND THUMBTACK LIFTER

(b) SANDPAPER POINTER

FIG. 7   Pencil Pointers.

Mechanical pencils (Fig. 6) are now widely used. They are popular because their length is constant, they can be easily refilled with new leads, and only the lead requires sharpening. See also §§ 46 and 47.

8. Pencil Sharpeners. Various pencil sharpeners, which produce results as shown in Fig. 61 (b), are available for draftsmen's use. However, a pencil pointer (Fig. 7) is necessary to dress the lead to the desired point. A simple sharpener is shown in Fig. 8, and an automatic feed sharpener in Fig. 9.

TO SHARPEN LEAD ONLY

TO CUT WOOD ONLY

FIG. 8 Simple Pencil Sharpener.

NOTE: WOOD ONLY IS CUT AWAY BY SPECIAL DRAFTSMAN'S CUTTERS

FIG. 9   Pencil Sharpener with Draftsman's Special Cutters.

9. Erasers. Erasers are available in many different degrees of hardness and abrasiveness. For general drafting, the Eberhard-Faber Ruby eraser (Fig. 10, a), a *hard eraser*, is recommended. This eraser is used for erasing both pencil and ink. Gritty ink erasers should be avoided as they invariably damage the working surface of the paper. A soft pencil eraser is preferred by many draftsmen to erase light lines during the construction stage of a drawing. See § 67, Step 2.

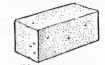

(a) RUBY ERASER
FOR GENERAL USE-PENCIL & INK

The *artgum* (Fig. 10, b) is recommended for general cleaning of the larger areas of a drawing or for removing pencil lines from an inked drawing or tracing.

FIG. 11   Knife Eraser.

(b) ARTGUM
FOR CLEANING PURPOSES ONLY

FIG. 10   Erasers.

A *knife eraser* (Fig. 11) is occasionally useful in clipping off small projections or segments of ink lines, but it is not recommended for general use because it is apt to damage the paper.

The *erasing shield* (Fig. 12) is used to protect the lines around those to be erased. See § 73. It is made of nickel silver, steel, or plastic.

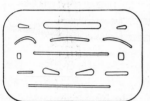

FIG. 12   Erasing Shield.

The *electric erasing machine* (Fig. 13) saves time and is very convenient if much drafting is being done.

A *dusting brush* (Fig. 14) is useful for removing eraser crumbs without smearing the drawing.

10. Triangles. The triangles commonly employed in drafting are the 45° and the 30° × 60° triangles. The 15° × 75° and the $22\frac{1}{2}°$ × $67\frac{1}{2}°$ triangles are

FIG. 14   Draftsman's Dusting Brush.

sometimes found to be convenient, but they are rarely necessary.

FIG. 13   Electric Erasing Machine.

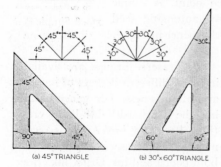

(a) 45° TRIANGLE

(b) 30°× 60° TRIANGLE

FIG. 15   Celluloid Triangles.

The best triangles are made of celluloid (Fig. 15) and are available in several sizes, thicknesses, and colors (such as amber and green). The amber-colored triangle, about 0.08″ in thickness, is most popular. A 30° × 60° triangle having its longest leg 10″ or 12″ long, and a 45° triangle having each of its legs 6″ or 8″ long, make a very satisfactory combination. Triangles are also made of metal, but these are seldom used. *Lettering triangles* are illustrated and described in § 144.

11. Testing the Triangles. Perhaps the only disadvantage of celluloid triangles is that they will not necessarily remain true, even if they are true at first. Celluloid triangles must therefore be tested and made true periodically. Triangles should always be kept flat, to prevent warping.

The edges may be tested with a steel straightedge, or in the same manner as the T-square (§ 5).

The right angle of the 45° or the 30° × 60° triangle may be tested (Fig. 16, a) by drawing a vertical line with the triangle against the T-square, and then turning the triangle over without moving the T-square and drawing the line again along the same edge. If the two lines thus drawn do not coincide, the right angle is not true, the actual error being half the angle between the two lines.

The 45° angle may be tested (Fig. 16, b) by drawing a line at 45° with the horizontal with one of the 45° angles, and then drawing a 45° line with the other 45° angle. If the two lines do not coincide, there is an error in one or both of the 45° angles. A direct test of either 45° angle can be made by drawing a right triangle; the sides adjacent to the right angle will be equal if the two 45° angles are correct (assuming the 90° angle to be correct).

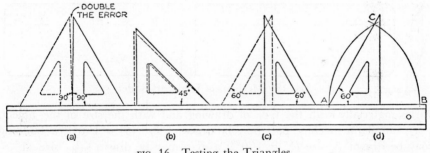

FIG. 16   Testing the Triangles.

The 60° angle may be tested (Fig. 16, c) by using the 30° × 60° triangle to draw an equilateral triangle. If the sides are not exactly equal in length, the 60° angle is not correct. Another method of testing the 60° angle (Fig. 16, d) is to draw a horizontal line *AB* slightly shorter than the hypotenuse of the triangle, and to draw arcs with *A* and *B* as centers and *AB* as radius, intersecting at *C*. When the triangle is placed as shown, its hypotenuse should pass through *C*.

When a triangle has been tested and found to be incorrect, it may be corrected by scraping, sandpapering, or filing the edges where necessary (§ 12).

12. Correcting the Triangles. After it has been determined in what respect a triangle needs correcting (Fig. 16), a "rough cut" may be made by

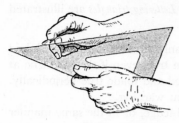

FIG. 17   Scraping the Triangle.

scraping the edge with a sharp pocket knife or a piece of broken window glass (Fig. 17).   A block plane also serves well for this purpose.   The edge may be finally trued by holding the triangle flat against the edge of a table top, with the edge of the triangle level with it, and smoothing with fine sandpaper, such as #00 or #000.   T-squares with celluloid edges (§ 4) may be similarly corrected.

13. Types of Scales.   A drawing of an object may be the same size as the object, or it may be larger or smaller than the object; in most cases, the drawing is made smaller than the object represented.   The rate of reduction

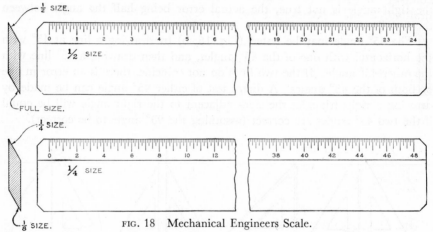

FIG. 18   Mechanical Engineers Scale.

varies materially with the type of drawing and with the size of the object. For example, a machine part may be drawn $\frac{1}{2}$ size ($6'' = 1'\text{-}0''$); a building may be drawn $\frac{1}{48}$ size ($\frac{1}{4}'' = 1'\text{-}0''$); a map may be drawn $\frac{1}{1200}$ size ($1'' = 100'\text{-}0''$).

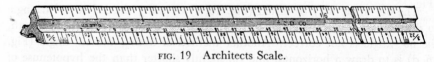

FIG. 19   Architects Scale.

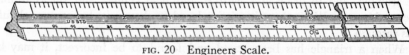

FIG. 20   Engineers Scale.

Scales are classified as Mechanical Engineers Scales (Fig. 18), Architects Scales (Fig. 19), Engineers Scales or Chain Scales (Fig. 20), and Metric Scales (Fig. 21).

A *full-divided scale* is one in which basic units are subdivided throughout the length of the scale (Fig. 18); an *open-divided scale* is one in which the end unit only is subdivided (Fig. 19).

FIG. 21   Metric Scale.

Scales are generally made of boxwood; the better ones have white celluloid-composition edges. Steel scales are also available but are seldom used in drafting. Scales are either flat (Figs. 18 and 21) or triangular (Figs. 19 and

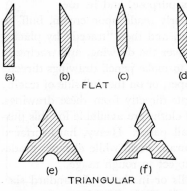

(a)   (b)   (c)   (d)
FLAT

(e)   (f)
TRIANGULAR

FIG. 22   Cross Sections of Scales.

20). The various sections of both scales are shown in Fig. 22. The triangular scales have the advantage of combining eleven scales on one stick, but the user will waste much time looking for the required scale if a scale guard (Fig. 23) is not used. The flat scale is almost universally used by professional draftsmen, because its shape makes it easy to handle, and it is easy to locate the scale to be used. However, several flat scales are necessary to replace one triangular scale. Since a draftsman generally uses one scale for extended periods, however, the use of several scales has no disadvantage other than larger initial cost. Some professional draftsmen prefer only one scale per stick and keep a complete set of 4″, 6″, 8″, or 12″ scales. Many machine draftsmen use only two flat scales (Fig. 18), usually of the *opposite-bevel type*, full-divided: one with the full- and the half-size scales, and the other with the quarter- and the eighth-size scales.

Special scales with any kind of graduations can be furnished by manufacturers.

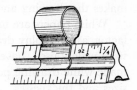

FIG. 23   Scale Guard.

14. Mechanical Engineers Scales.—Fig. 18. These scales are used for drawings of machines and machine parts which can be represented on a standard size sheet either full size, one-half, one-fourth, or one-eighth size. *The scales are divided so that each main division represents one inch.*

15. Architects Scales.—Fig. 19. These scales are used for drawings of buildings and other large structures which can be represented on a sheet of ordinary size only to a small scale, frequently to a scale of $\frac{1}{4}'' = 1'\text{-}0''$, i.e., $\frac{1}{48}$ size. The scales are divided into major units, from $3''$ to $\frac{3}{32}''$, *each representing one foot and subdivided to represent inches and fractions thereof.*

16. Chain Scales or Engineers Scales.—Fig. 20. These scales are used in making maps, plats, and graphical constructions. They are available with divisions of 10, 20, 30, 40, 50, 60, or 80 parts to the inch. These scales are used in drawing maps to scales of $1'' = 50'$; $1'' = 500'$; $1'' = 5$ miles, etc., and in drawing stress diagrams to scales of $1'' = 20$ lbs., or $1'' = 4000$ lbs., etc.

17. Metric Scales.—Fig. 21. These scales are divided into centimeters, millimeters, and half millimeters for full-size drawings, and in the ratios of $\frac{1}{100}, \frac{2}{100}, \frac{3}{100}, \frac{5}{100}, \frac{25}{1000},$ and $\frac{125}{10000}$, for reduced-scale drawings.

18. Drawing Paper. The paper to be used for a drawing depends entirely upon the character of the drawing, its purpose, and its use.

Practically all pencil drawings were formerly made upon cream, buff, or green drawing paper, or upon "detail" paper, and then "traced" by placing tracing paper (§ 19) or tracing cloth (§ 20) over the drawing, and tracing in pencil or in ink. At present it is customary to make pencil drawings directly on tracing paper or vellum, on light bond paper, or on the dull side of tracing cloth, and to make blueprints or other prints directly from these drawings. Many excellent tracing papers, vellums, and cloths are available for this purpose. Ink is rarely applied directly to detail paper. Heavy, hard-surfaced detail paper is available for high-grade, accurate work, while cheaper grades may be used for drawings which are not subject to rough usage.

All such papers can be purchased in rolls or in sheets of standard size, as $9'' \times 12''$, $12'' \times 18''$, $18'' \times 24''$, and $24'' \times 36''$. Most companies buy their paper in sizes suitable to their particular filing systems (§470). Usually a standard border and title strip or box containing such information as would appear on all drawings are printed on each sheet (§ 472). The draftsman makes the drawing and merely fills in the blanks in the title box.

White papers are used for drawings where the appearance is an important factor, as in display drawings. Whatman's handmade papers, which formerly were widely used, have been almost entirely replaced by high-grade machine-made white drawing papers. They are available in rolls or in sheets of various sizes and thicknesses.

Hot-pressed (HP) paper is used mostly for pencil and fine-line drawings, *cold-pressed* (CP) for water-color and general drawing, and *rough* (R) for water-color sketches. Bristol board has an ideal surface for accurate ink work, and has the advantages of being stiff, hard, and smooth. Although Bristol board is available in several thicknesses, as 2-ply, 3-ply, 4-ply, etc., the 3-ply is most widely used.

Patent Office drawings must be made on a "pure white paper of a thickness corresponding to two-ply or three-ply Bristol board," according to detailed instructions contained in the *Guide for Patent Draftsmen* issued by the United States Patent Office (§ 529). Patent Office sheets cut to standard size and containing the standard border and printing are available.

19. Tracing Papers. Tracing paper is a thin, transparent paper, upon which copies or "tracings" of drawings are made for the purpose of reproducing by blueprinting or by other similar processes. Tracings may be made in pencil or in ink, usually in pencil. Most tracing papers will "take" pencil or ink, but some are especially suited to one or to the other. Most architectural working drawings are made in pencil on special lightweight pencil tracing paper.

Tracing papers are of two kinds: (1) those treated with oils, waxes, or similar substances to render them more transparent, called *vellums;* (2) those not so treated, but which may be quite transparent, owing to the high quality of the raw materials and the methods of manufacture. Some treated papers deteriorate rapidly with age, becoming brittle in many cases within a few months, but some excellent vellums are available. Untreated papers made entirely of good rag stock will last indefinitely and will remain tough. For a discussion of tracing methods, see §§ 68–71.

20. Tracing Cloth. Tracing cloth is a thin, transparent muslin (cotton) fabric sized with a starch compound to provide a good working surface. It is much more expensive than tracing paper. Tracing cloth is available in rolls of standard widths, as 30″, 36″, and 42″, and also in sheets of standard sizes, with and without printed borders and title forms (§ 472).

For pencil tracings, special pencil tracing cloths are available. Many concerns make their drawings in pencil directly on this cloth, dispensing entirely with the preliminary pencil drawing on detail paper, thus saving a great deal of time. *Fixatif* or a similar compound may be used to "fix" the lines and prevent smudging.

Some tracing cloths are suitable for either pencil or ink drawing. Combination drawings, which are drawn partly in pencil and partly in ink, are possible on this cloth. An instance of this practice is seen where information for the pattern shop is shown in pencil, which prints lightly, and information for the machine shop in ink, which prints more clearly.

21. Standard Sheets. The American Standard* trimmed sizes of drawing paper and cloth are as follows (see Fig. 24):

A	$8\frac{1}{2} \times 11$		D	22×34
B	11×17		E	34×44
C	17×22			

"The use of the basic sheet size $8\frac{1}{2} \times 11$ in. and its multiple permits filing of small tracings and folded prints in commercial standard files with or with-

---

* See A S A Z14.1—1946 (Appendix 2). All problems in this book have been designed for American Standard sheets. See "Layouts" in Appendix 1.

out correspondence. These sheet sizes also cut without waste from the present 36 in. rolls of paper and cloth. These standard sizes are based on the dimensions of the commercial letter head, $8\frac{1}{2} \times 11$ in., in general use in the United States.

"Drawings larger than standard sheet sizes may be made as 'rolled' drawings. Widths are controlled by standard paper sizes, and lengths are in multiples of 11 in.

"The title block with appropriate space for the identifying number should be located at the lower right hand corner of the sheet. Accordion folding of prints with the printed side out is recommended when prints are filed in a standard letter size file. . . . [see Fig. 24].

"In order to file prints which have been accordion folded so that the closed fold will be up and the number still be visible, it is necessary to add a supplementary number block (approximately 1.75 in. by 0.5 in.) to each size sheet as shown in Fig. 24. This supplementary number block may be either parallel or normal to the border line of the drawing. If change notes or general notes reach this supplementary number block a minimum clearance of 0.25 in. should be left above and below the block."

For information regarding the American Standard recommendations regarding change records and the zoning system of locating changes, see Appendix 2.

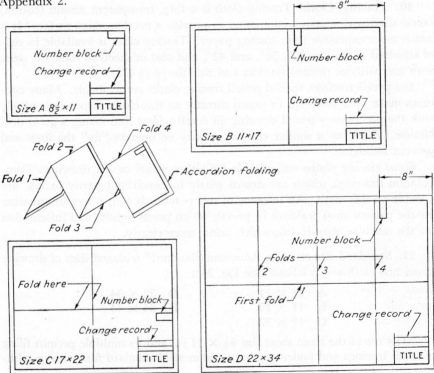

FIG. 24   American Standard Sheets (ASA Z14.1—1946).

22. Paper Fasteners. For holding paper to the drawing board, thumbtacks are still generally used (Fig. 25), though their use seems to be decreasing. They are made in a variety of sizes and forms. A thumbtack should have a shank long enough to hold the paper firmly, yet short enough to allow the tack to be removed easily. The head should be thin, to allow the T-square and the triangles to glide over it easily, and should be large enough to make

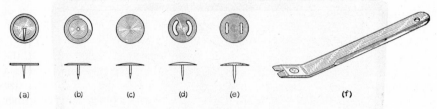

(a) (b) (c) (d) (e) (f)

FIG. 25 Thumbtacks and Tack Lifter.

it easy to remove. The cheaper kinds of thumbtacks are stamped from a sheet of metal (Fig. 25, a) or are made by bradding the shank into a hole in the head (Fig. 25, b). The points break off the stamped tacks easily, and the thick heads prevent free movement of the T-square and triangles. The bradded shank frequently presses through the head into the user's thumb. The best thumbtacks have a steel shank screwed into a German silver head and riveted (Fig. 25, c). Several special tacks are on the market. The one shown in Fig. 25 (d) is provided with fingernail slots, and the one shown in Fig. 25 (e) is withdrawn with a special lifter. A thumbtack may be removed by grasping the head between the nails of the thumb and the second finger and applying a twisting motion. A common thumbtack lifter is shown in Fig. 25 (f). Many draftsmen prefer to use *wire staples*, forced through the paper into the board by a stapler (Fig. 26). Others prefer *drafting tape* (Fig. 27), which is available in rolls, strips of which may be used to tape the drawing securely to the drawing board. The adhesive material is of such composition that it does not dry out quickly and the strips can be used repeatedly. Its advantage over thumbtacks or wire brads is that it eliminates the

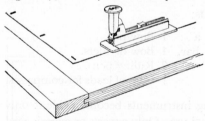

FIG. 26 Draftsman's Stapler.

punching of holes in the board. It is ideal for use on a glass-top tracing table.

23. Drawing Instruments. The principal parts of high-grade instruments are made of nickel

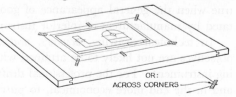

OR:
ACROSS CORNERS

FIG. 27 Drafting Tape.

silver, which has a silvery luster, is noncorrosive, and can be readily machined into the desired shapes. Tool steel is used for the blades of ruling pens, for spring parts, for divider points, and for the various screws.

Drawing instruments are generally sold in "sets" in velvet-lined cases, but they may be purchased separately. A case of instruments which is elaborate enough for usual school or professional requirements is shown in Fig. 28.

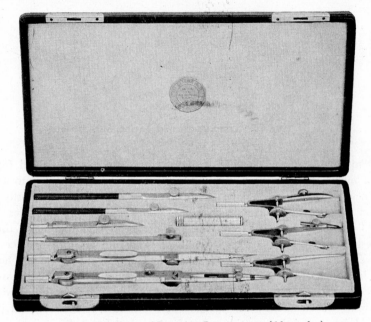

FIG. 28   The Case of Drawing Instruments (Alteneder).

This set contains the following instruments:

1 Compass, with a pencil attachment, a pen attachment, and a lengthening bar.	1 Bow pen.
	1 Bow dividers.
1 Dividers.	2 Ruling pens.
1 Bow pencil.	1 Case of leads for compasses.

Many of the qualities of good drawing instruments become evident only after the instruments have been put to actual use. Only experts or experienced draftsmen can recognize fine instruments by inspection. This is particularly true when the general appearance of good instruments has been closely imitated by manufacturers of inferior instruments.

In technical drawing, *accuracy*, *neatness*, and *speed* are essential. These objectives are not likely to be attained with the use of cheap or inferior drawing instruments. For the professional draftsman or the student, it is advisable, and in the end more economical, to purchase the best instruments available. Good instruments will satisfy the most rigid requirements; and the satisfaction, the saving in time, and the improved quality of work which the use of good instruments can produce will justify the higher prices. Sometimes fine tools are not sturdy in design, though capable of minute adjustment. Hence, deli- cate instruments should be avoided; the best designs are simple and strong. One good criterion by which to judge drawing instruments is the reputation of the manufacturer (see footnote, page 3).

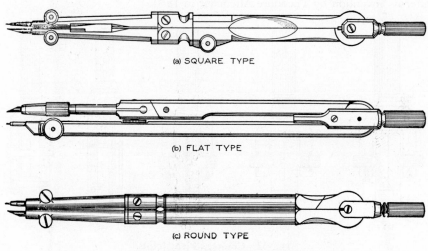

(a) SQUARE TYPE

(b) FLAT TYPE

(c) ROUND TYPE

FIG. 29   Three Types of Compasses.

24. Compasses and Dividers. The three common types of compasses and dividers are shown in Figs. 29 and 30. The square form (Fig. 29, a) is probably most popular in America; the flat and round forms, (b) and (c), are most common in Europe. Excellent instruments are obtainable in each of the three forms.

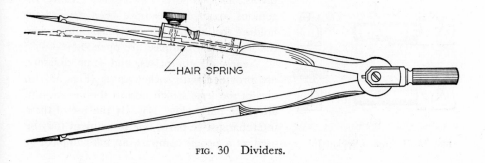

HAIR SPRING

FIG. 30   Dividers.

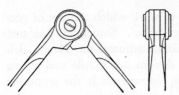

FIG. 31   The Compass "Tongue Joint."

The two legs of the old-time compasses and dividers were fastened by means of the "tongue joint" (Fig. 31), held together by a single screw. Because there was no way of taking up the wear on the tongue, which frequently rendered the instruments unfit for use after a short time, the tongue joint was superseded by the "pivot joint" (Fig. 32) soon after its invention by Theodore Alteneder in 1850.

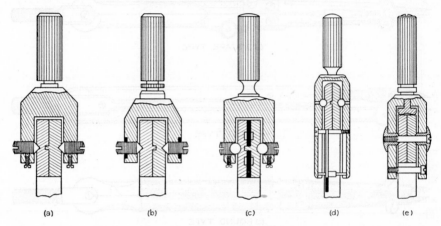

(a)   (b)   (c)   (d)   (e)

FIG. 32   Compass Pivot Joints.

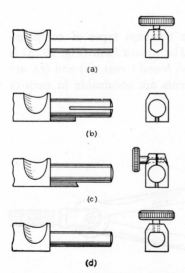

(a)

(b)

(c)

(d)

FIG. 33   Compass Socket Joints.

By the use of the adjustable pivots on each side of the head of the compass and dividers, sufficient friction can be maintained to hold the legs rigidly throughout the life of the instrument. Various locking devices, such as small set screws (Fig. 32, a) or locknuts (b) are used to maintain the adjustment.

The yoke (Fig. 32), besides supporting the pivots, also supports the handle. Many ingenious arrangements have been devised for holding the handle in a vertical position when the legs of the compass are opened.

Nearly all compasses, and some dividers, are provided with socket joints (Fig. 33) on one of the legs, which permit the insertion of alternate parts (Fig. 34). By the use of these interchangeable parts, one instrument may be used as a pencil compass, an ink compass, or

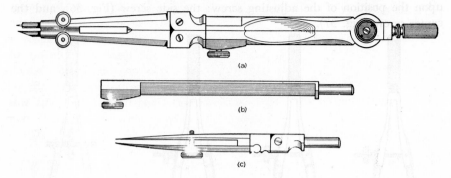

FIG. 34   Compass and Attachments.

as dividers. Many dividers (Fig. 30) and some compasses are equipped with a *hairspring* to facilitate minute adjustments. A lengthening bar (Fig. 34, b) is useful for increasing the possible radius of the compass (Fig. 78).

25. Testing Compasses and Dividers. The tension in the pivot joint of the compasses and dividers should be checked by holding the legs of the instruments and slowly opening and closing them. The tension should be constant throughout the motion and just enough to maintain a "setting" of the instrument at any desired point. If the tension is insufficient, the instrument will not maintain its setting; if the tension is too great, it cannot be readily adjusted. In both cases an adjustment must be made by loosening the locknuts, adjusting the tension by the adjusting screws, and then tightening the locknuts. A small screwdriver is provided in the set of instruments for this purpose. Adjusting the

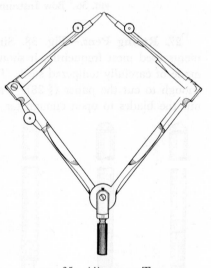

FIG. 35   Alignment Test.

tension of instruments is a delicate operation and should be performed very carefully. Oil should not be applied to the joint, because the tension depends on the friction between the moving parts.

When the legs of the compass are "broken," as shown in Fig. 35, the extreme points should meet. If they do not, the instrument may be out of adjustment, or has been damaged, or is of inferior quality.

26. Bow Instruments. Except for the handles, screws, and nuts, *bow instruments* are made of tool steel. There are two general designs, depending upon the position of the adjusting screw: the side screw (Fig. 36), and the center screw (Fig. 37).

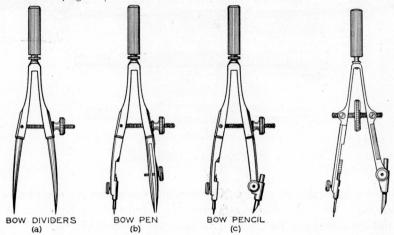

BOW DIVIDERS   BOW PEN   BOW PENCIL
(a)   (b)   (c)

FIG. 36   Bow Instruments.

FIG. 37   Bow Pencil with Center Wheel.

27. Ruling Pens.—Fig. 38. Since the ruling pen is one of the instruments used most frequently, it should be of highest quality. The blades are made of carefully tempered steel. The points should be sharp, but not sharp enough to cut the paper (§ 28). Various devices have been invented to permit the blades to open enough for easy cleaning (Fig. 38).

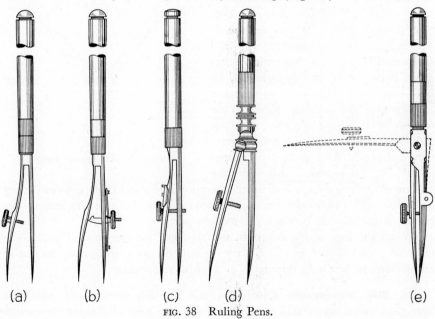

(a)   (b)   (c)   (d)   (e)

FIG. 38   Ruling Pens.

The *detail pen*, capable of holding a considerable quantity of ink, is extremely useful for drawing very long or very heavy lines (Fig. 39).

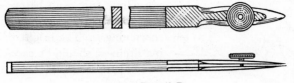

FIG. 39　Detail Pen.

28. To Sharpen the Ruling Pen. If a ruling pen is subjected to frequent or extended use, its nibs will become so worn that good lines cannot be drawn with it. The correct point is shown in Fig. 40 (a), and a characteristic worn point is shown at (b).

CORRECT　WORN
NIB　　NIB

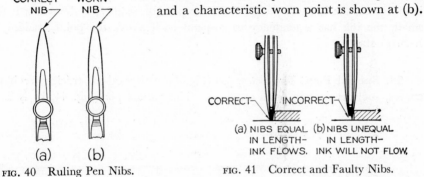

CORRECT　INCORRECT

(a) NIBS EQUAL　(b) NIBS UNEQUAL
IN LENGTH–　　IN LENGTH–
INK FLOWS.　INK WILL NOT FLOW.

(a)　　(b)

FIG. 40　Ruling Pen Nibs.　　　　FIG. 41　Correct and Faulty Nibs.

An examination of the tip of the nibs of a worn ruling pen reveals a bright point on each nib, which reflects light like a small mirror. Such a condition first manifests itself to the student in his inability to draw fine lines. Another indication of a defective ruling pen is a scratchy contact with the paper, or the necessity of pressing the points firmly into the paper to get the ink to flow. The reason for this condition is illustrated in Fig. 41 (b), which shows one nib much longer than the other. This may result, to some extent, from wear or from dropping the pen and chipping away small segments of the nibs.

It is in respect to these matters that the difference between inferior and superior instruments is most noticeable. The material in good ruling pens does not wear quickly and is not apt to chip, and the pen is more easily sharpened.

A hard Arkansas oil stone is excellent for sharpening ruling pens. If the nibs of the ruling pen are unequal in length, they should first be equalized by moving the pen, with the nibs together, across the stone lightly with an oscillating movement from left to right as shown in Fig. 42. To sharpen the nibs, they

FIG. 42　Equalizing the Lengths of Nibs.

should be opened and each nib sharpened on the outside, as shown in Fig. 43, rolling the pen slightly from side to side to preserve the convex surface of the

nib. Great care must be exercised to prevent oversharpening one nib and thus shortening it. The bright points, indicating dullness, should be carefully observed, and the nibs should be sharpened until the bright points disappear. No attempt should ever be made to sharpen the inside of the nibs, for this always results in a slight convexity, which will ruin the pen.

FIG. 43   Sharpening the Ruling Pen.

If the pen is sharpened so that the width of the elliptical nib (Fig. 40, a) is too great, the ink will "feed" from the pen too readily; if the width is too small, the ink has a tendency to suspend itself above the point, making it hard to start.

29. Special Pens. The *contour pen* (Fig. 44, a) is used for tracing freehand curves, such as contour lines on maps. The *railroad pen* (Fig. 44, b) is used

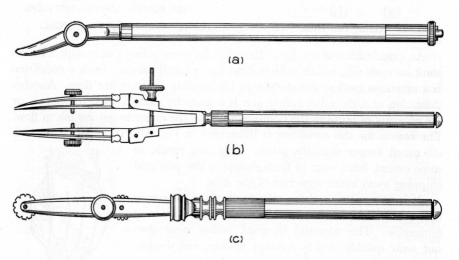

(a)

(b)

(c)

FIG. 44   Special Pens.

for drawing two parallel lines straight or moderately curved, as for roads and railroads. The *dotting pen* (Fig. 44, c) is used for drawing lines composed of dots or short dashes. Other special pens are sold by the various manufacturers.

30. Beam Compass. The *beam compass* or *trammel* (Fig. 45) is used in drawing circular arcs or circles larger than can be drawn with the regular

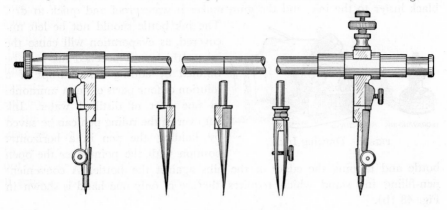

FIG. 45   Beam Compass.

compass, and for transferring distances too great for the regular dividers. Besides steel points, pencil and pen attachments are provided. The "beams" may be made of nickel silver, steel, or wood, and are procurable in various lengths.

31. Drop Spring Bow Instruments. These instruments (Fig. 46) are designed for drawing many duplicate circles of small diameter, such as rivets and rivet heads. The center rod, or needle point, remains stationary, while the tube to which the pencil or pen is attached is rotated upon it. Since the needle point does not revolve, it cannot wear a hole in the paper. Some draftsmen prefer these instruments for drawing all small arcs or circles.

32. Proportional Dividers. For enlarging or reducing a drawing, proportional dividers (Fig. 47) are convenient. They may be used for dividing straight lines or circles into equal parts. For this purpose, points of division are marked on the instrument so as to secure the required subdivisions readily. They may also be used for securing many special ratios, such as $1 : \sqrt{2}$, the diameter of a circle to the side of an equal square, feet to meters, etc.

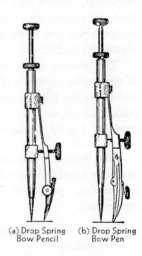

(a) Drop Spring   (b) Drop Spring
Bow Pencil   Bow Pen

FIG. 46   Drop Spring
Bow Instruments.

FIG. 47   Proportional Dividers.

33. Drawing Ink. Drawing ink (Fig. 48) is composed chiefly of carbon in colloidal suspension and gum. The fine particles of carbon give the deep, black luster to the ink, and the gum makes it waterproof and quick to dry.

(a) DRAWING INK (b) INKSTAND

FIG. 48 Drawing Ink.

The ink bottle should not be left uncovered, as evaporation will cause the ink to thicken. Thickened ink may be thinned by adding a few drops of a solution of four parts of aqua ammonia to one part of distilled water. Ink left over in the ruling pen can be saved by holding the pen in a horizontal position with the point over the open bottle and tapping the edges of the nibs against the bottle. A convenient pen-filling ink stand which requires the use of only one hand is shown in Fig. 48 (b).

34. Irregular Curves. When it is required to draw mechanical curves other than circles or circular arcs, an *irregular*, or *French*, *curve* is generally employed. Many different forms and sizes of curves are manufactured, as suggested by the more common forms illustrated in Fig. 49.

The curves are composed largely of successive segments of the geometric curves, as the ellipse, parabola, hyperbola, involute, etc. The best curves are made of highly transparent celluloid.

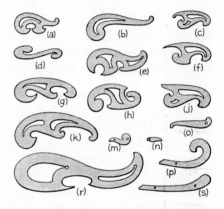

FIG. 49 Irregular, or French, Curves.

35. Special Curves. Besides the irregular curves discussed in § 34, many special curves are available, including hyperbolas, parabolas, ellipses, logarithmic spirals, ship curves, railroad curves, etc.

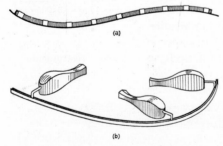

(a)

(b)

FIG. 50 Adjustable Curve Rulers.

Adjustable curves (Fig. 50) are also available. The curve shown at (a) consists of a core of lead, enclosed by a coil spring, to which is attached a metal strip. The one at (b) consists of a *spline*, to which *ducks* (weights) are attached. The spline can be bent to form any desired curve, limited only by the elasticity of the material.

36. Protractors. For measuring or setting off angles other than those obtainable with the triangles, the protractor is used. The best protractors are made of nickel silver and are capable of most accurate work (Fig. 51, a). For ordinary work the celluloid or stamped sheet-metal protractor is satisfactory and is much cheaper (Fig. 51, b).

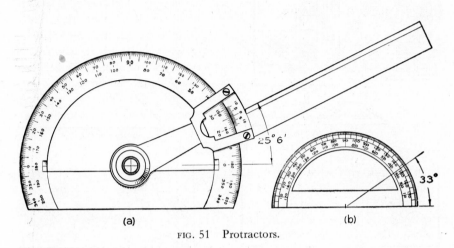

FIG. 51   Protractors.

37. Drafting Devices. A number of clever devices are available for specialized needs (Fig. 52). The *Engineers Triangle* (a) may be used as an ordinary 30° × 60° triangle and also in drawing standard bolt heads and

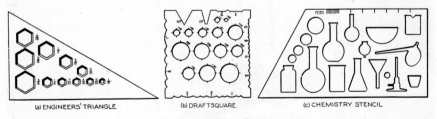

(a) ENGINEERS' TRIANGLE   (b) DRAFTSQUARE   (c) CHEMISTRY STENCIL

FIG. 52   Drafting Devices.

nuts. The *Draftsquare* (b) is useful in drawing bolt heads and nuts, fillets of various sizes, circles, thread forms, and inclined guide lines for lettering. The *Chemistry Stencil* (c) is convenient for drawing chemical symbols.

The *Draft-Scale-Angle* (Fig. 53, a) is a versatile and practical drafting aid whose applications are apparent in the illustration. The *Lesh Angle* is illustrated in Figs. 53 (b) and 54.

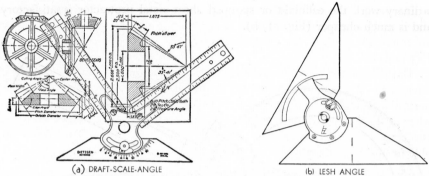

(a) DRAFT-SCALE-ANGLE   (b) LESH ANGLE

FIG. 53   Drafting Angles.

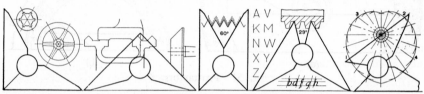

FIG. 54   Uses of the Lesh Angle.

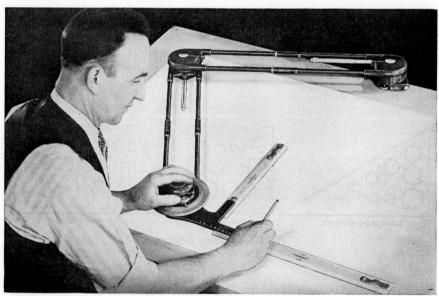

FIG. 55   Universal Drafting Machine.

38. Drafting Machines. The drafting machine (Fig. 55) is an ingenious device which replaces the T-square, triangles, scales, and protractor. The links, or bands, are arranged so that the controlling head is always in any desired fixed position, regardless of where it is placed on the board; thus the horizontal straightedge will remain horizontal if so set. The controlling head is graduated in degrees (including a vernier in certain machines), which allows the straightedges, or scales, to be set and locked at any angle. There are automatic stops at the most frequently used angles, as 15°, 30°, 45°, 60°, 75°, and 90°.

Drafting machines* have been greatly improved in recent years. The chief advantage of the drafting machine is that it speeds up drafting. Since its parts are made of metal, their accurate relationships are not subject to change, whereas T-squares, triangles, and working edges of drawing boards must be checked and corrected frequently. Drafting machines for left handers are available from the manufacturers.

39. Parallel-Rule Attachment. As a substitute for the T-square, the *parallel-rule attachment* (Fig. 56) is used in many commercial drafting rooms. The straightedge is attached to the board by a combination of pulleys and cords so that the straightedge remains parallel to its original position as it is moved over the board, and thus replaces the T-square with sufficient accuracy for ordinary drafting.

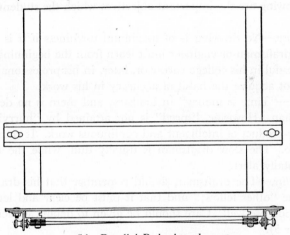

FIG. 56   Parallel Rule Attachment.

40. Planimeter. The *planimeter* is an instrument used for measuring areas on drawings. Principal uses include measurement of indicator diagrams in mechanical engineering, and of plats of tracts of land in civil engineering.

41. Slide Rule. The *slide rule* is a mechanical device for making calculations. Its use is very general in all technical fields, particularly in the drafting room, and it is rightly considered a symbol of the engineering profession.

* Universal Drafting Machine Co., Bruning Co., Keuffel & Esser Co., Eugene Dietzgen Co., Frederick Post Co., are some of the manufacturers.

CHAPTER 3

Instrumental Drawing*

42. Objectives in Drafting. In the following paragraphs the correct methods to be used in instrumental drawing are explained. The student should learn and practice correct manipulation of the drawing instruments to the end that correct habits may be formed and maintained. The instructor should insist upon absolutely correct form at all times, making exceptions only in cases of physical disability.

The following are the important objectives which the student should strive to attain:

1. *Accuracy.*—No drawing is of maximum usefulness if it is not accurate. The young draftsman or engineer must learn from the beginning that he cannot be successful in his college career or, later, in his professional employment if he does not acquire the habit of accuracy in his work.

2. *Speed.*—"Time is money" in industry, and there is no demand for the slow draftsman. However, "speed" is not attained by "hurrying"; it is an unsought by-product of intelligent and continuous work. It comes with study and practice. The slow draftsman is usually dull, while the fast worker is usually mentally alert.

3. *Legibility.*—The draftsman should remember that his drawing is being made for the "other fellow," and that it must be clear and legible in order to serve its purpose well. Care should be given to details, especially to lettering (Chapter 5).

4. *Neatness.*—A drawing should not only be accurate and legible but should also be clean, and the student should strive to acquire the habit of neatness in his work. Untidy drawings are the result of faulty methods (§ 74) and should not be accepted by the instructor.

43. Arrangement of Equipment. *Orderliness promotes efficiency.* Before beginning a drawing, the draftsman should place the items of the equipment he expects to use in an orderly manner on the drawing table (Fig. 57). Each article should be placed so that it may be used with the greatest convenience,

*See Chapter 14 for technical sketching.

and should be kept in that place when not in actual use. Systematic arrangement of equipment becomes habitual and effects a great saving in time and an increase in efficiency.

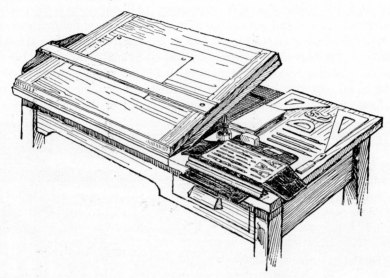

FIG. 57   Orderly Arrangement of Equipment.

44. Lighting. The best light for drafting is natural north light. In general, drafting rooms should be oblong in shape with a bank of windows on a long side, facing north. In this way all sunlight is avoided, and the light is "cool" and pleasant. The ceiling should be painted a very light color, such as matt white or cream. The walls may be slightly darker, but still very light, of "cool" colors in tints predominantly green or blue.

Window areas on the north side should be as large as practicable and not less than 20 per cent of the floor area. If windows are not on the north side, double shades (both rollers in the middle of the window, one operating upward, and the other downward) or Venetian blinds are helpful.

The draftsman should have his table placed so that light comes from the left. Enough light should also come over the left shoulder and from the front-left to avoid shadows cast by the triangles, the T-square, or the hands. In other words, a diffused light from the left is advisable.

The left-handed person (if the light is not greatly diffused) will have to turn his table so that light comes from his right, to keep his equipment and hands from casting shadows on his work.

In addition to the best natural light obtainable, correct artificial light should be provided; in most localities many days are so dark, especially in winter, that artificial lighting is necessary.

The lighting of a drafting room should be such that the draftsmen can pursue their work without eyestrain. An illumination of fifty foot-candles* at the drawing-board level is generally specified as the minimum, but individual requirements differ widely.

The lighting should be such that the degree of illumination is high enough to permit good vision, but not so high as to make the cost of lighting excessive.

"Brightness ratios" should be as low as possible; that is, there should be as little contrast as possible between the various lighted areas within the field of vision. For this reason, light fixtures should be as high in the room as possible to prevent their brightness from causing eye discomfort. On this same basis, large window areas may be objectionable rather than advantageous if

Courtesy General Electric Co.

FIG. 58   Fluorescent Lighting.

they are unshaded. Venetian blinds are most satisfactory, since they allow light to come into the room but prevent the high brightnesses outdoors from coming into the field of view of those within the room.

A lighting system highly recommended by illumination engineers is the "single lamp recessed troffer" system, an installation of which is shown in Fig. 58. Here the face of the fixture is flush with the ceiling, and the light

---

* A *foot-candle* is the degree of illumination provided by a standard candle on a surface one foot away from it. A *luminometer* is used to measure the degree of illumination in foot-candles.

source is generally above the field of vision and does not offer a great deal of direct brightness in the field of vision. The great ceiling brightness usually resulting from indirect lighting is largely eliminated and there is a higher utilization of the light produced by the lamps. Also shown in this figure are the "vertical" drawing boards which are highly recommended by lighting experts and favored by many draftsmen. In this case there is no problem with shadows, since those along the horizontal straightedge fall below the drafting instruments. Reflected glare is practically eliminated, due to the angle of the working surface. By-products of the vertical boards are improved posture and consequent comfort of the draftsman, better access to all parts of the drawing by the draftsman, and the decreased floor space required.

Automatic lighting controls are available in which the rows of lights parallel to the windows are turned on or off automatically by means of a photoelectric cell as the natural light from the windows increases or decreases. The saving in current is said to be sufficient to pay for the installation of the control.

The most important recent development in illumination is the *vapor lamp*. The ordinary neon tube used in signs is one of many types of vapor lamps. Vapor lamps are now available with mercury, carbon-dioxide, sodium, neon, and helium gases. These give lights of many colors, including "daylight." In the future, according to illumination engineers, there will undoubtedly continue to be some indirect and semi-indirect lighting, both with filament and fluorescent lamps. But the majority of the lighting will probably have a considerable "downward component," that is, direct light from above, and the lighting systems will be almost exclusively fluorescent.

The introduction of the *polaroid* screen is also having its effect upon illumination. This material eliminates glare, which is one of the chief causes of eyestrain.

45. Fastening Paper to the Board. Drawing paper should be placed close enough to the working edge of the board to reduce to a minimum any error resulting from a slight "swing" in the blade of the T-square, and close enough to the upper edge of the board to permit room at the bottom of the sheet for using the T-square and supporting the arm while drawing (Fig. 59).

To thumbtack the paper in place, the T-square head is pressed firmly against the working edge of the drawing board with the left hand, while the paper is adjusted with the right hand until the top edge "lines up" with the upper edge of the T-square. The first fastening is made in the upper left corner, and the second

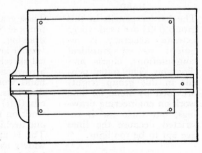

FIG. 59 Placing Paper on Drawing Board.

in the upper or lower right corner, depending upon the condition of the paper. Generally, four fastenings are required; but in very large sheets more than four may be required, while in very small sheets, if thumbtacks are used, only two tacks in the upper corners of the paper may be sufficient.

The method of applying drafting tape is illustrated in Fig. 27. Some draftsmen prefer to use two thumbtacks at the top of the paper and small pieces of drafting tape placed diagonally across the bottom corners.

Architects employ a method of fastening sheets (especially large sheets) to drawing boards, known as a *stretch*. First, the paper is thoroughly wetted with a sponge on both sides, leaving a dry strip approximately $1\frac{1}{2}''$ wide around the edge on the "under" side. To this dry strip a special *drawing board glue* is applied with the fingertips. The edges are then pressed firmly against the board, using first the fingers, and finally a smooth hard object. The sheet is then allowed to dry, and shrinkage of the paper makes the "stretch" tight and smooth.

Ordinary glue tape such as is used in wrapping packages, instead of the special vegetable glue, is used a great deal in making stretches.

The advantage of the stretch is that the paper is taut and smooth, presenting a most agreeable working surface, and there is no obstruction to the T-square or triangles.

46. Choice of Grade of Pencil. A general classification of the various grades of drawing pencils and their uses is shown in Fig. 60. However, other factors besides hardness of lead should affect the choice for any given purpose, as follows:

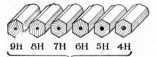

9H 8H 7H 6H 5H 4H

3H 2H H F HB B   2B 3B 4B 5B 6B 7B

HARD	MEDIUM	SOFT
The harder pencils in this group (left) are used where extreme accuracy is required, as on graphical computations, charts and diagrams. The softer pencils in this group (right) are used by some for line work on engineering drawings, but their use is restricted because the lines are apt to be too light.	These grades are for general-purpose work in technical drawing. The softer grades (right) are used for technical sketching, for lettering, arrowheads, and other freehand work on mechanical drawings. The harder pencils (left) are used for line work on machine drawings and architectural drawings. The H and 2H pencils are widely used on pencil tracings for blueprinting.	These pencils are too soft to be useful in mechanical drafting. Their use for such work results in smudged, rough lines which are hard to erase, and the pencil must be sharpened continually. These grades are used for art work of various kinds, and for full-size details in architectural drawing.

FIG. 60   Pencil Grade Chart.

1. Type of work—amount of accuracy, etc.
2. Texture of paper—hardness, roughness, etc.
3. Atmospheric conditions — humidity.
4. Reproduction — by blueprinting or otherwise.

An excellent combination of pencils for machine drafting on ordinary high-quality detail paper is a 4H to 6H for construction lines and an F, H, or 2H for brightening required lines, and for freehand work such as lettering, arrowheads, break lines, etc. In general, the pencil for construction lines should be hard, and the pencil for required lines should be soft enough to make a "bright" black line, yet not soft enough to smudge easily. A slightly softer pencil, such as HB or F, is recommended for technical sketching (§ 314).

47. Pencil Points. The *unlettered end* of the pencil is the end to be sharpened to preserve the grade mark and to enable one to identify the pencil in use. For general use the *conical point* (Fig. 61, c) is preferred. First, the wood

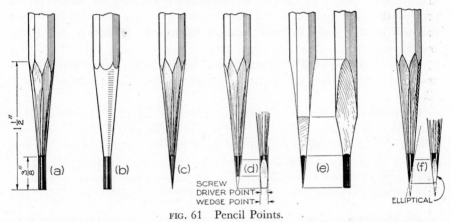

FIG. 61   Pencil Points.

should be cut away with a sharp knife, starting about $1\frac{1}{2}''$ from the end, and leaving about $\frac{3}{8}''$ of lead uncut (Figs. 61, a, and 62, a). Or the pencil sharpener with draftsman's cutters (Fig. 9) may be used to cut the wood away, leaving

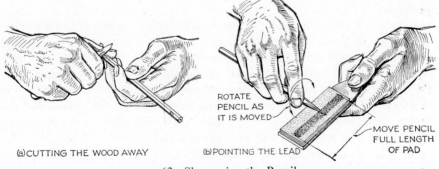

FIG. 62   Sharpening the Pencil.

the lead uncut as shown in Fig. 61 (b). The pencil should then be brought to a sharp conical point on a *pencil pointer* (sandpaper pad or a small file, Figs. 61, c, and 62, b), and *the lead wiped clean to remove loose particles of graphite.* Many draftsmen then "burnish" the point on a piece of hard paper to obtain a smoother, sharper point. The sandpaper pad, when not in use, should be kept in a container, such as an envelope with one end open, to prevent the particles of graphite from falling upon the drawing or drawing equipment.

The pencil pointer should be kept close by, as frequent pointing of the pencil is necessary.

For straight-line drawing, some draftsmen prefer the *wedge point* (Fig. 61, d). This point is produced by cutting the wood away, as in Fig. 61 (a) or (b), and then sharpening on opposite sides, as shown at (d). In drawing a line with this point, the flat face of the lead is held against the straightedge. Some prefer to sharpen slightly on the edges of the wedge so as to produce a "screwdriver" point, as shown. If pronounced flat cuts are made in the wood on the same sides as the flat cuts in the lead as shown at (e), the draftsman will be able easily to "feel" when a flat face of the lead is against the straightedge.

A quick method of sharpening a good wedge point is to produce first a conical point and then cut a flat face on one side. The resulting point is elliptical in contour (Fig. 61, f).

If a good mechanical pencil (Fig. 6) is used, much time may be saved in sharpening, since the lead can be "fed" from the pencil, as needed, and pointed on the sandpaper pad in the same manner as the regular wooden pencil. It is also more economical since the lead is used for its entire length, while ordinary wooden pencils are difficult to use when shorter than about three inches.

48. Horizontal Lines. Horizontal lines are drawn along the working edge of the T-square, from left to right. The left hand should hold the head of the T-square firmly against the working edge of the board (Fig. 63), or, after pressing the head against the board, the hand may slide to the position shown in Fig. 64. The latter position is preferable for drawing accurate lines, but the former is faster.

The pencil should lean in the direction in which the line is being drawn, at an angle of about 60° with the paper. Care should be taken to keep the pencil in a vertical plane; otherwise the line may not be straight. The little finger of the hand holding the pencil should glide lightly on the blade of the T-square. In order to keep the conical point symmetrical during use, the pencil should be rotated slowly back and forth between the thumb and the fingers throughout the extent of the line. This will preserve the symmetry of the point and produce a line of uniform width.

In general, the left-handed person will exactly reverse the above procedure, doing with the left hand what is described for the right hand. He will place the T-square head against the right-hand edge of the board, and, with the pencil in the left hand, draw horizontal lines from *right to left*. The right-hand edge is, for him, the *working edge*, and should be tested for straightness and corrected if necessary (§ 6).

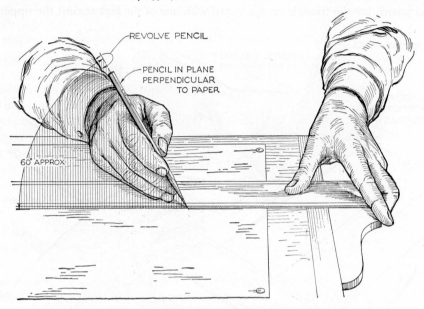

FIG. 63   Drawing Horizontal Lines.

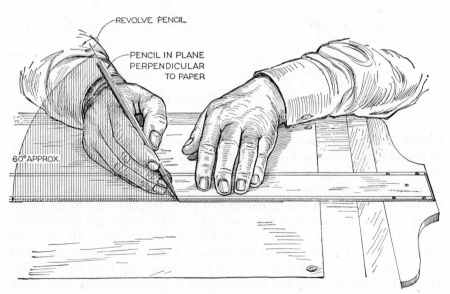

FIG. 64   Drawing Horizontal Lines.

49. Vertical Lines. Since both the 45° triangle and the 30° × 60° triangle contain right angles (§ 10), either may be used against the T-square to draw vertical lines (Fig. 65). To draw vertical lines in this manner, the draftsman should press the head of the T-square against the working edge of the board, lay the triangle on the board with one of the legs against the upper

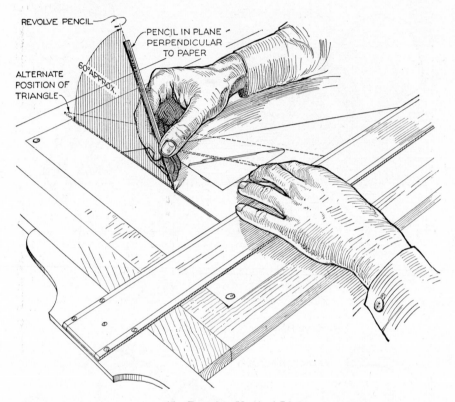

FIG. 65   Drawing Vertical Lines.

edge of the T-square, then slide the left hand to the position shown in Fig. 65, so that it holds both the T-square and triangle firmly in position, and draw the line *upward* along the vertical leg of the triangle. The pencil should lean at an angle of approximately 60° with the paper in the direction in which the line is being drawn and be moved in a plane perpendicular to the paper.

In general, the left-handed person will exactly reverse the above procedure, doing with the left hand what is described for the right. He will press the head of the T-square against the right-hand edge of the board, and place the triangle against the T-square so that the vertical edge is on the *right* side. He will hold the T-square and triangle firmly in position with the right hand, and draw vertical lines *upward* along the vertical leg of the triangle.

50. Inclined Lines. Most inclined lines in instrumental drawing are drawn at standard angles, obtainable from the triangles used singly or in combination (Fig. 66). The directions in which inclined lines should be drawn are indicated by the arrows in Fig. 66.

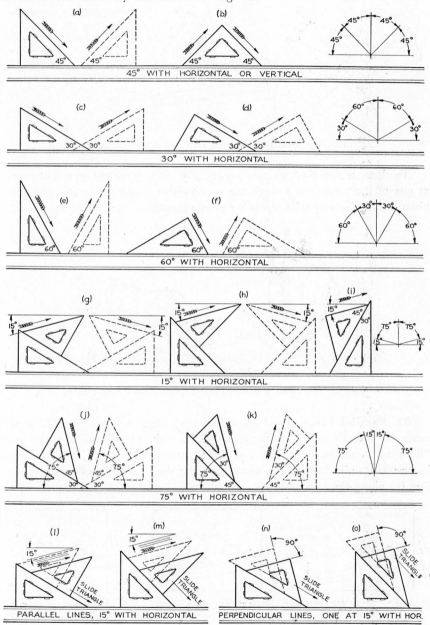

FIG. 66 Drawing Inclined Lines with the Triangles.

To draw a line at any other angle it is necessary to construct the angle geometrically or to set it off with a protractor (§ 36).

The methods of drawing lines making 30°, 75°, and 15° with any given ine are shown in Fig. 67.

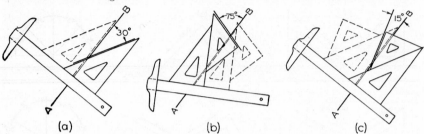

FIG. 67   Drawing Inclined Lines with the Triangles.

To draw a line through two points (Fig. 68), place the pencil vertically at one of the points, and move the straightedge about the pencil point as a pivot until it lines up with the other point; then draw the line along the edge.

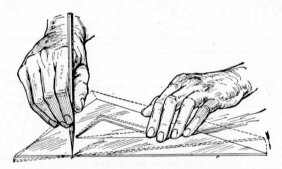

FIG. 68   To Draw a Pencil Line through Two Given Points.

51. Parallel Lines. To draw a line parallel to a given line (Fig. 69), move the triangle and T-square as a unit until the hypotenuse of the triangle "lines up" with the given line (Fig. 69, a); then, holding the T-square firmly in position, slide the triangle away from the line (b) and draw the required line (c) along the hypotenuse.

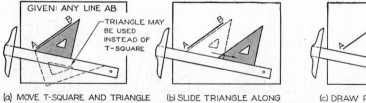

(a) MOVE T-SQUARE AND TRIANGLE   (b) SLIDE TRIANGLE ALONG   (c) DRAW REQUIRED LINE
    TO LINE UP WITH AB.   T-SQUARE   PARALLEL TO AB

FIG. 69   To Draw a Line Parallel to a Given Line.

Obviously any straightedge, such as one of the triangles, may be substituted for the T-square in this operation. Figure 69 (a) shows how the triangle can be effectively substituted.

52. Perpendicular Lines. To draw a line perpendicular to a given line, move the T-square and triangle as a unit until one edge of the triangle "lines up" with the given line (Fig. 70, a); then slide the triangle across the line (b) and draw the required line (c).

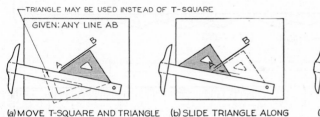
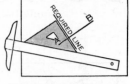

(a) MOVE T-SQUARE AND TRIANGLE   (b) SLIDE TRIANGLE ALONG   (c) DRAW REQUIRED LINE
    TO LINE UP WITH AB   T-SQUARE   PERPENDICULAR TO AB

FIG. 70   To Draw a Line Perpendicular to a Given Line.

53. Use of the Mechanical Engineers Scale.—Fig. 18. The objects represented in machine drawing vary in size from small parts, an inch or so in size, to machines of large dimensions. By drawing these objects full size, $\frac{1}{2}$ size, $\frac{1}{4}$ size, or $\frac{1}{8}$ size, the drawings will readily come within the limits of the standard-size sheets. For this reason the mechanical engineers scales, shown in Fig. 18, are divided into units representing inches and fractions thereof to scales of full size, $\frac{1}{2}$ size, $\frac{1}{4}$ size, or $\frac{1}{8}$ size (§ 14). To make a drawing of an object to a scale of $\frac{1}{4}$ size, for example, use the mechanical engineers scale marked $\frac{1}{4}$ size, which is graduated so that every $\frac{1}{4}$ inch represents 1 inch.

54. Use of the Architects Scales.—Fig. 19. The objects represented in architectural and structural drawing vary in size up to several hundred feet. In order to draw such large objects on a standard-size sheet, it is frequently necessary to make the drawing to a very small scale. For such drawings the architects scale (Fig. 19) is used.

Figures 71 and 73 illustrate the use of the usual scales found on the triangular architects scale. By means of these scales a drawing may be made to various scales from full size to one-hundred-twenty-eighth size. Note that in all the reduced scales the major divisions represent feet and their subdivisions represent inches and fractions thereof. Thus the scale marked "$\frac{3}{4}$" means $\frac{3}{4}''$ equals $1'$, not $\frac{3}{4}''$ equals $1''$; that is, one-sixteenth size, not three-fourths size. Similarly, the scale marked "$\frac{1}{2}$" means $\frac{1}{2}''$ equals $1'$, not $\frac{1}{2}''$ equals $1''$; that is, one-twenty-fourth size, not half size.

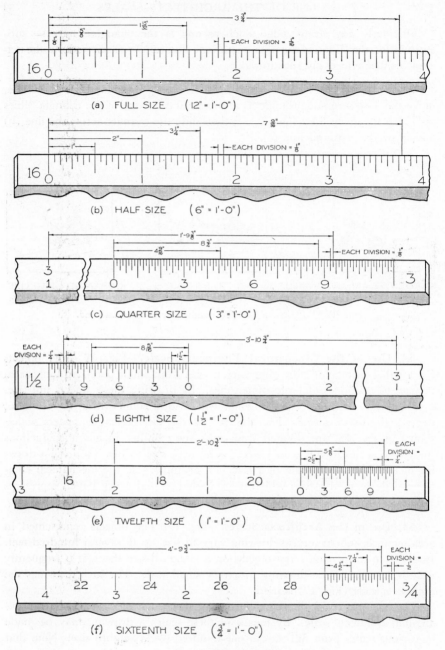

FIG. 71 Architects Scales.

40

Full Size.—Fig. 71 (a). Each division in the full-size scale equals $\frac{1}{16}''$. Each inch is divided first into halves, then quarters, eighths, and finally, sixteenths; the division lines diminishing in length with each division (Fig. 73). To set off $\frac{1}{32}''$, estimate one-half of $\frac{1}{16}''$; to set off $\frac{1}{64}''$, estimate one-fourth of $\frac{1}{16}''$.

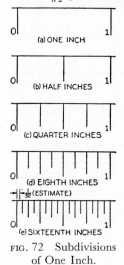

FIG. 72 Subdivisions of One Inch.

(a) ONE INCH

(b) HALF INCHES

(c) QUARTER INCHES

(d) EIGHTH INCHES
$\frac{1}{32}$ (ESTIMATE)

(e) SIXTEENTH INCHES

Half Size.—Fig. 71 (b). Use the full-size scale and divide every dimension mentally by two. Do not use the $\frac{1}{2}''$ scale which is intended for drawing to a scale of $\frac{1}{2}''$ equals $1'$, or one-twenty-fourth size. To set off $1''$, measure $\frac{1}{2}''$; to set off $2''$, measure $1''$; to set off $3\frac{1}{4}''$ measure $1\frac{1}{2}''$ (half of 3), then $\frac{1}{8}''$ (half of $\frac{1}{4}''$); to set off $7\frac{9}{16}''$, measure $3\frac{1}{2}''$ (half of 7), then $\frac{9}{32}''$ ($\frac{4\frac{1}{2}}{16}''$, or half of $\frac{9}{16}''$).

Quarter Size.—Fig. 71 (c). Use the three-inch scale in which $3''$ equals $1'$. The subdivided portion to the right of zero represents one foot, and is divided into inches, then half inches, quarter inches, and finally, eighth inches. The entire portion representing one foot would actually measure three inches; therefore: $3''$ equals $1'$. To set off anything less than twelve inches, start at zero and measure to the right.

To set off more than twelve inches, for example, $1'-9\frac{3}{8}''$ (Fig. 71, c), find the $1'$ mark to the left of 0, and the $9\frac{3}{8}''$ mark to the right of 0; the required distance is the distance between these marks, and *represents* $1'-9\frac{3}{8}''$, being actually one-fourth of $1'-9\frac{3}{8}''$.

Eighth Size.—Fig. 71 (d). Use the $1\frac{1}{2}''$ scale in which $1\frac{1}{2}''$ equals $1'$. The subdivided portion to the left of zero represents $1'$, and is divided into inches, then half inches, and finally, quarter inches. The entire portion, representing $1'$, actually is $1\frac{1}{2}''$; therefore: $1\frac{1}{2}''$ equals $1'$. To set off anything less than twelve inches, start at zero and measure to the left.

To set off more than twelve inches, for example, $3'-10\frac{3}{4}''$ (Fig. 71, d), find the $3'$ mark to the right of 0, and the $10\frac{3}{4}''$ mark to the left of 0; the required distance is the distance between these marks, and *represents* $3'-10\frac{3}{4}''$, being one-eighth of $3'-10\frac{3}{4}''$.

Double Size.—Fig. 71 (a). Use the full-size scale and multiply every dimension mentally by two. To set off $1''$, measure $2''$; to set off $3\frac{1}{4}''$, measure $6\frac{1}{2}''$, and so on. The double-size scale is occasionally used to represent small objects. In such cases, a small actual-size outline view should be shown near the bottom of the sheet to help the shop man visualize the actual size of the object.

Other Sizes.—Figs. 71 and 73. The other scales besides those described above are used chiefly by architects. Machine drawings are customarily made only double size, full size, $\frac{1}{2}$ size, $\frac{1}{4}$ size, or $\frac{1}{8}$ size.

Do not abuse the scale by using it as a straightedge, hammering thumbtacks with it, pricking holes in it with dividers to take off dimensions, or using it in ways other than its intended use, which is to make measurements.

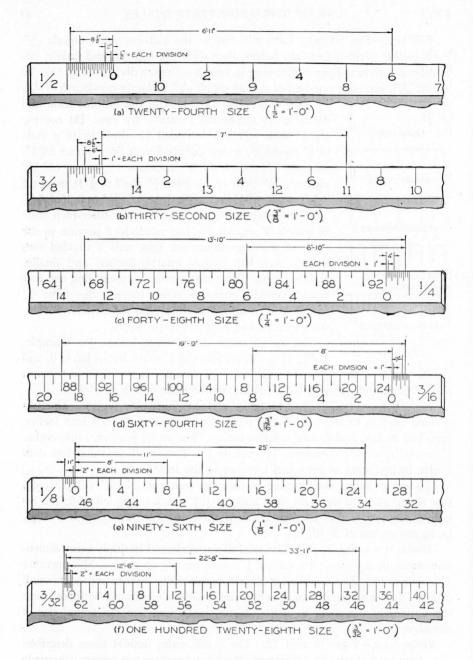

FIG. 73 Architects Scales.

55. Use of the Engineers Scale.—Fig. 20. The *engineers scale* is graduated in the decimal system, and is therefore often called the *decimal scale*. It is also frequently called the *civil engineers scale* because it was originally used mainly in civil engineering. The name *chain scale* also persists because it was originally derived from the use of the surveyors' chain composed of 100 links, used for land measurements. The name *engineers scale* is perhaps best, because the scale is used by engineers wherever decimal measurements are used.

The engineers scale is especially suitable for map drawing, because when a tract of land is surveyed, distances are measured with a flexible steel tape graduated in feet and tenths of a foot. The engineers scale is graduated in units of one inch divided into 10, 20, 30, 40, 50, and 60 parts. In using the scale, each unit may represent $10'$, $20'$, $30'$, etc., depending upon the size or scale of drawing desired.

The engineers scale is also convenient in machine drawing to set off dimensions expressed in decimals. For example, to set off 5.650 inches full size, use the "10 scale" and simply set off 5 main divisions plus $6\frac{1}{2}$ subdivisions. To set off the same dimension half size, use the "20 scale" in the same manner, since the "20 scale" is exactly half the size of the "10 scale."

56. Use of the Metric Scales.—Fig. 21. Metric scales are divided into units and decimal fractions thereof, as described in § 17. They are used in place of the chain scales for graphical constructions or calculations, and instead of the mechanical engineers scales in representing objects whose dimensions are in metric units.

During recent years the use of the metric scale has increased considerably because American and European manufacturers are producing interchangeable machine parts, particularly for military equipment.

57. To Indicate the Scale on a Drawing. The American Standards Association recommends the designation of scales on drawings as indicated in Fig. 74. Practice is not uniform, however, and the terms Quarter Size, Half Size, and Full Size are also widely used. For examples of indication of scale on drawings, see Figs. 844-846. For map scales, see § 578.

DRAWING SMALLER THAN OBJECT

Scale $1\frac{1}{2}''=1'-0''$ Scale $\frac{3}{4}'' =1''$

Scale $3''=1'-0''$ Full Scale

Quarter Scale   Scale $\frac{1}{2}''=1'-0''$

Scale $\frac{3}{8}''=1''$ Scale $1''=1'-0''$

Half Scale   Scale $1''=100'-0''$

DRAWING LARGER THAN OBJECT

Scale $\frac{1.5}{1}$ Scale $\frac{2}{1}$

MAP SCALES

Scale $\frac{1}{62500}$ (Representative fraction)

400   0   400   800 Ft (Graphic scale)

FIG. 74   Designation of Scales
(ASA Z14.1—1946).

58. Accurate Measurements. Accurate drafting depends largely upon correct use of the scale in setting off distances. Measurements should not be taken off the scale with the dividers or compass, as this will result in damage to the scale. Place the scale on the drawing with the edge parallel to the line on which the measurement is to be made and, with a sharp pencil having a conical point, make a short dash at right angles to the scale and opposite the correct graduation mark, as shown in Fig. 75 (a). If extreme accuracy is required, a *tiny* prick mark may be made at the required point with the needle point or stylus, as shown in Fig. 75 (b), or by means of one leg of the dividers.

FIG. 75   Accurate Measurements.

The student must avoid cumulative errors in the use of the scale. If a number of distances are to be set off, end-to-end, all should be set off at one setting of the scale, by adding each successive measurement to the preceding one. Never set off the distances individually, moving the scale to a new position each time, since slight errors in the measurements may accumulate and give rise to a large error.

59. Use of the Compass. The compass (§ 24), with pencil and inking points, is used for drawing circles having radii of approximately 1″ or larger. The needle point should be inserted in the compass so that the end having the shoulder will be in contact with the paper. The point should be adjusted so that it is a little longer than the pencil point (Fig. 79, d) or the pen attachment, if the latter is used.

To draw a pencil circle, (1) set off the required radius on one of the center lines, (2) place the needle point at the exact intersection of the center lines, (3) adjust the compass to the required radius,

FIG. 76   Using the Compass.

(4) lean the compass forward at an angle of about 60° with the paper, and draw the circle in a clockwise direction, beginning at the lowest point and rotating the handle between the thumb and forefinger. The hands should not touch the compass legs during this operation, since that is apt to change the adjustment.

When inked circles are being drawn, it is important that the legs of the compass stand approximately in a plane perpendicular to the drawing board, in order that both nibs of the pen may be in contact with the paper. The method of "breaking" the legs of the compass for this purpose is shown in Fig. 77.

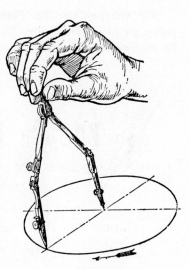

FIG. 77 "Breaking" the Legs of the Compass.

The compass is opened and closed with the fingers of the hand which holds the compass, as illustrated for the dividers in Fig. 81. On drawings containing circular arcs and tangent straight lines, it is best to draw the arcs first, whether the drawing is in pencil or ink, as it is much easier to connect a straight line to an arc than to adjust the arc to the straight line. For circles of very large radii the lengthening bar is used (Figs. 34, b, and 78). Both hands are used to draw a circle, but care must be exercised not to change the adjustment of the instrument.

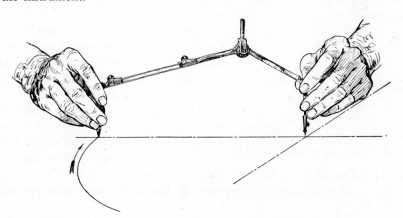

FIG. 78   Drawing Circles of Large Radii.

The grade of lead to use in the compass for pencil drawing varies with the type of work. In general it should conform to the grade of pencils used on the straight-line work (§ 46). However, since heavy pressure cannot be exerted on the compass as can be done in the use of the pencil, it may be necessary to use a compass lead about one grade softer than the pencil used for the straight-line work. For example, if an H pencil is used for the final straight lines on the drawing, then an F lead might be found suitable for the compass work.

60. Sharpening the Compass Lead. Various forms of compass lead points are illustrated in Fig. 79. At (a) a single elliptical face has been formed by rubbing on the sandpaper pad, as shown in Fig. 80. At (b) the point is

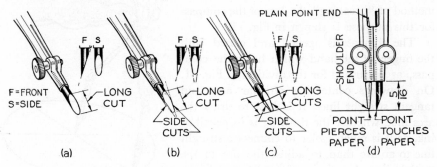

FIG. 79 Compass Lead Points.

narrowed by small side cuts. At (c) two long cuts and two small side cuts have been made, so as to produce a point similar in appearance to a sharp screwdriver.

FIG. 80 Sharpening Compass Lead.

The shoulder end of the needle point should be used, as shown at (d), and the tiny needle point should extend about half-way into the paper when the compass lead just touches the paper.

As the lead is reduced in length, due to sharpening, do not change the needle point; instead, move the lead out each time an adjustment is needed. This habit will prevent the use of stubby leads, so common in beginners' work.

The pen attachment is sharpened in the same manner as the ruling pen (§ 28).

61. Use of the Dividers. The dividers (Fig. 30), as the name implies, are used for *dividing* distances into a number of equal parts. They are used also for *transferring* distances, or for *setting off* a series of equal distances. The dividers are adjusted with one hand only. Figure 81 shows the position of the fingers in adjusting the dividers.

To divide a given distance into a number of equal parts (Fig. 82), the method is one of trial and error. The dividers are adjusted with the fingers of the hand which holds them, to the approximate unit of division, estimated by eye. The dividers are then rotated counterclockwise through 180°, and then clockwise through 180°, and so on, until the desired number of units

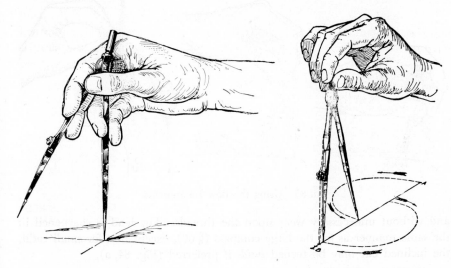

FIG. 81   Adjusting the Dividers.   FIG. 82   Using the Dividers.

has been stepped off. If the last prick of the dividers falls short of the end of the line to be divided, the distance between the divider points is increased proportionately. For example, to divide the line *AB* (Fig. 82) into three equal parts, the dividers are set by eye to approximately one-third the length *AB*. When it is found that the trial radius is too small, the distance between the divider points is increased by one-third the remaining distance. If the last prick of the dividers is beyond the end of the line, a similar decreasing adjustment is made. Dividers with a hairspring and a thumbscrew, for small adjustments, are recommended (Fig. 30).

The student must avoid *cumulative errors* which may result when the dividers are used to set off a series of distances, end-to-end. For this purpose the scale should be used if possible, as described in § 58. Many large errors are the result of cumulative slight errors in measurement.

62. Use of the Bow Instruments. The bow pencil (Fig. 36, c) is used for drawing penciled circles having a radius of about 1″ or smaller. Whether the center-wheel instrument (Fig. 37) or the side-wheel instrument (Fig. 36) is used, the adjustment should be made with the fingers of the hand which holds the instrument (Fig. 83, a).

When adjustment of any of the side-screw bow instruments must be made directly from a large to a small radius, or vice versa, it is best to press the two legs together with the fingers of the left hand (Fig. 83, c), thus relieving the pressure upon the thumbscrew, so that it may be spun to position quickly

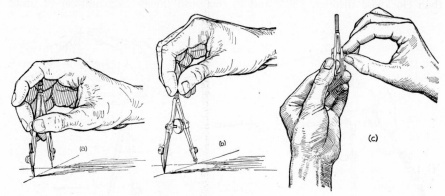

FIG. 83   Using the Bow Instruments.

and without unnecessary wear upon the threads. The lead is sharpened in the same manner as for the large compass (§ 60), except that for small radii, the inclined cut may be turned *inside* if preferred (Fig. 84, a).

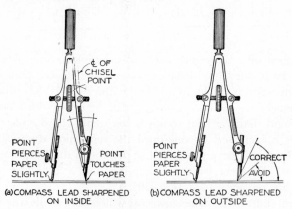

FIG. 84   Compass Lead Points.

Be sure to avoid the use of a blunt compass lead caused by lack of frequent sharpening or of incorrect sharpening.

The bow pen (Figs. 36, b, and 83, b) is used for drawing inked circles of approximately 1″ radius or smaller, and is manipulated in the same manner as the bow pencil.

In adjusting the needle point of the bow pencil or bow pen, the point should be slightly longer than the lead or pen (Fig. 84).

The bow dividers (Fig. 36, a) are used for the same purposes as the large dividers, but for smaller and more accurate work.

63. Use of Drop Spring Bow Instruments. The tube of the drop spring bow instrument (Fig. 46) is free to move up and down or to rotate upon the pin or needle point. To use the instrument, hold the lower knurled head between the thumb and second finger, placing the first finger on top of the upper knurled head. Place the needle point at the desired center, allow the pen or pencil point to come in contact with the paper, and twirl the instrument clockwise with the thumb and second finger. Then lift the pen or pencil independently of the needle point, and finally, lift the entire instrument.

64. Conventional Lines. Technical drawings are composed chiefly of symbolic lines. The American Standards Association* has adopted a set of line symbols, as shown in Fig. 85. According to these standards, "Three widths of line, thick, medium and thin, are shown and are considered desirable on finished drawings in ink, both for legibility and appearance, although in rapid practice and in particular on penciled tracings from which prints are to be made this may be simplified to two widths, medium and thin, both of which must be dense black in order to print. For pencil tracings, the lines should be in proportion to the ink lines, medium for outlines, hidden, cutting plane, short breaks, adjacent part and alternate position lines; and thin for section, center, extension, dimension, long break, and ditto lines."

The standard lines for pencil drawing are shown in Fig. 85, and those for ink drawing in Fig. 86. An *object line* or outline of parts is defined as a visible contour of the object or the visible intersection of two surfaces of the object. A *hidden line* is an invisible object line. See § 202.

Professor Clair V. Mann has devised the *draftsman's line gauge*† (Fig. 87), in which the various widths of lines are designated in fractions of an inch, which is convenient when referring to lines of various widths.

The lines shown in Figs. 85 and 86 are reproduced *full size*, and will be found suitable for ordinary work. According to the American Standard, "The actual width of each type of line should be governed by the size and style of the drawing, the relative widths of the lines should approximate those shown. . . ." See Appendix 2.

All ink lines should be clean and black, and all pencil lines except construction lines should be dark. *Construction lines should be extremely light* (Fig. 85).

65. To Lay Out a Sheet.—Fig. 88. After the sheet has been attached to the board as explained in § 45, proceed as follows: ‡

---

* See ASA Z14.1—1946. These American Standards are heartily endorsed by the authors, have been followed throughout this book, and are reproduced in full in Appendix 2.

† Used by permission.

‡ Most large concerns have the border and title block printed, in which case alignment is made with the printed border.

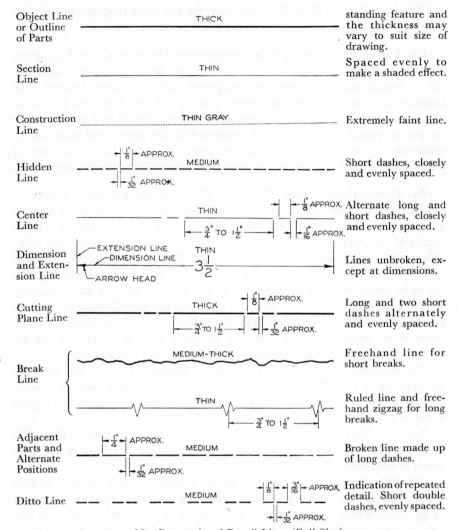

Object Line or Outline of Parts — THICK — standing feature and the thickness may vary to suit size of drawing.

Section Line — THIN — Spaced evenly to make a shaded effect.

Construction Line — THIN GRAY — Extremely faint line.

Hidden Line — MEDIUM — Short dashes, closely and evenly spaced.

Center Line — THIN — Alternate long and short dashes, closely and evenly spaced.

Dimension and Extension Line — EXTENSION LINE / DIMENSION LINE / ARROW HEAD / THIN — Lines unbroken, except at dimensions.

Cutting Plane Line — THICK — Long and two short dashes alternately and evenly spaced.

Break Line — MEDIUM-THICK — Freehand line for short breaks.
— THIN — Ruled line and freehand zigzag for long breaks.

Adjacent Parts and Alternate Positions — MEDIUM — Broken line made up of long dashes.

Ditto Line — MEDIUM — Indication of repeated detail. Short double dashes, evenly spaced.

FIG. 85   Conventional Pencil Lines (Full Size).

I. Using the T-square, draw a horizontal *trim line* near the lower edge of the paper; and then, using the T-square and a triangle, draw a vertical trim line near the left edge of the paper. Both should be *light construction* lines (Fig. 85).

II. Place the scale along the lower trim line with the full-size scale up. Draw short, light dashes *perpendicular* to the scale at the required distances. See Fig. 75 (a).

III. Place the scale along the left trim line with the full-size scale to the

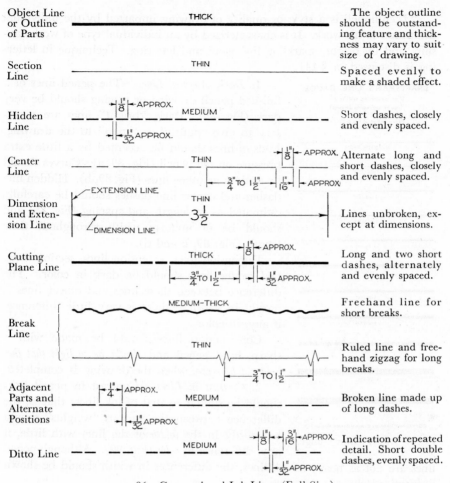

Object Line or Outline of Parts	THICK	The object outline should be outstanding feature and thickness may vary to suit size of drawing.
Section Line	THIN	Spaced evenly to make a shaded effect.
Hidden Line	MEDIUM	Short dashes, closely and evenly spaced.
Center Line	THIN	Alternate long and short dashes, closely and evenly spaced.
Dimension and Extension Line	THIN	Lines unbroken, except at dimensions.
Cutting Plane Line	THICK	Long and two short dashes, alternately and evenly spaced.
Break Line	MEDIUM–THICK	Freehand line for short breaks.
	THIN	Ruled line and freehand zigzag for long breaks.
Adjacent Parts and Alternate Positions	MEDIUM	Broken line made up of long dashes.
Ditto Line	MEDIUM	Indication of repeated detail. Short double dashes, evenly spaced.

FIG. 86   Conventional Ink Lines (Full Size).

left, and mark the required distances with short, light dashes, perpendicular to the scale. See Fig. 75 (a).

IV. Draw horizontal construction lines with the aid of the T-square (Fig. 63) through the marks at the left of the sheet.

V. Draw vertical construction lines, from the bottom upward, along the edge of the triangle (Fig. 65) through the marks at the bottom of the sheet.

VI. Retrace the border and the title strip to make them heavier. Notice that the layout is made independently of the edges of the paper.

66. Technique of Pencil Drawing. The greater part of commercial drafting is executed in pencil. Most blueprints are made from pencil tracings and all ink tracings must be preceded by a pencil drawing. It should therefore be evident that skill in drafting implies, chiefly, skill in pencil drawing.

"Technique" is a style or quality of drawing imparted by the individual draftsman to his work. It is characterized by an individual type of workmanship, and by bright, sparkling line work and lettering. Technique in lettering is discussed in § 141.

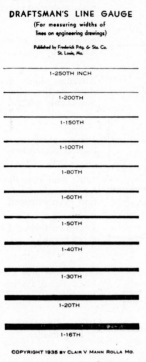

DRAFTSMAN'S LINE GAUGE
(For measuring widths of
lines on engineering drawings)

Published by Frederick Ptg. & Sta. Co.
St. Louis, Mo.

1-250TH INCH

1-200TH

1-150TH

1-100TH

1-80TH

1-60TH

1-50TH

1-40TH

1-30TH

1-20TH

1-16TH

COPYRIGHT 1935 BY CLAIR V MANN ROLLA MO.

FIG. 87 Mann's Line Gauge.

1. *Dark, Accented Lines.*—The pencil lines of a finished pencil drawing or tracing should be very dark (Fig. 89). Dark, "bright" lines are necessary to give "punch" or "snap" to the drawing. Ends of lines should be accented by a little extra pressure on the pencil (Fig. 89, a). Curves should be as dark as other lines (Fig. 89, b). Hidden line dashes and center line dashes should be carefully estimated as to length and spacing (Fig. 85) and should be of uniform width throughout their length (Fig. 89, c and d).

Dimension lines, extension lines, section lines, and center lines should be dark in color. The difference between these lines and object lines is mostly in width — there is very little difference, if any, in color.

Construction lines should be made with a sharp, hard pencil and *should be so light that they need not be erased* when the drawing is completed.

2. *Contrast in Lines.*—Contrast in pencil lines should be similar to that of ink lines; that is, the difference between the various "weights" should be mostly in the *width* of the line, with little, if any, difference in *color* (Fig. 90). Although pencil lines are not as heavy as ink lines, the differences in width should be shown proportionately.

67. Order of Penciling. The proper order of penciling a working drawing is illustrated in Fig. 91. The drawing is carried through two stages: **first,** the construction stage, shown in spaces 1, 2, and 3, in which the drawing is completely constructed with a hard pencil, such as 4H to 6H, with *extremely light lines;* and **second,** the finishing stage, shown in space 4, in which the lines are "brightened" and the lettering added with a softer pencil such as an F, H, or 2H.

The detailed procedure is as follows:

After a choice of the number, arrangement, and kind of views has been made, draw the border, and title strip if any, with light construction lines.

1. Draw the center lines. These may be drawn as construction lines and later retraced as center lines.

2. "Block in" the views with construction lines, drawing circles and im-

portant arcs first, and then the straight lines. Allow construction lines to cross at corners (Fig. 90, a).

3. Construct fillets, rounds, and other details.

4. Darken object lines (F, H, or 2H pencil); draw extension lines and dimension lines (2H or 3H pencil); add arrowheads, dimensions, and notes (F, H, or 2H pencil).

Construction lines need not be erased if they are drawn lightly.

68. Pencil Tracing. While some pencil tracings are made from a drawing placed underneath the tracing paper (usually when a great deal of erasing and changing is necessary on the original drawing), most drawings today are made directly on pencil tracing paper, cloth, vellum, or bond paper. These are not "tracings" but pencil drawings, and the methods and technique are the same as heretofore described for pencil drawing (§§ 66 and 67).

In making a drawing directly on tracing paper or cloth, a stiff, smooth sheet of heavy, white paper should be placed underneath. Such a sheet is known as a *platten sheet*. The whiteness of the platten sheet improves the visibility of the lines, and the hardness of the surface makes it possible to exert pressure on the pencil and produce dense black lines without excessive grooving of the paper.

These "tracings" or drawings are intended to be reproduced by blueprinting or by other kindred processes (Chapter 30), and all lines must be dark and sharply drawn (§ 66). The techniques of pencil tracing and pencil drawing are identical. The order of tracing should also conform to that for pencil drawing (§ 67).

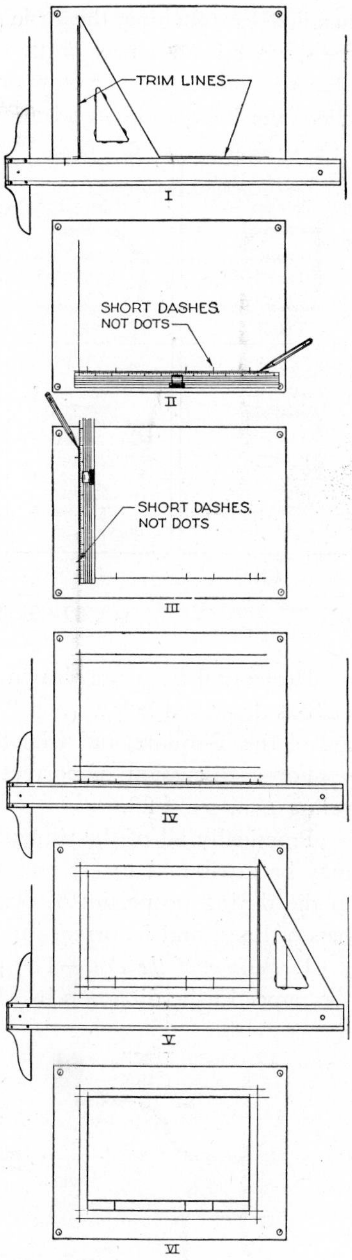

69. Use of the Ruling Pen. The ruling pen (Fig. 38) is used to ink lines

FIG. 88   To Lay Out a Sheet.

drawn with instruments, never to ink freehand lines or freehand lettering. The proper method of filling the pen is shown in Fig. 92. The hands may be steadied by touching the little fingers together. Twisting instead of pulling the stopper from a new bottle of ink or one that has not been used for some time will often save the stopper from being broken. After the pen has been filled, the ink should stand about $\frac{1}{4}''$ deep in the pen (Fig. 93, b).

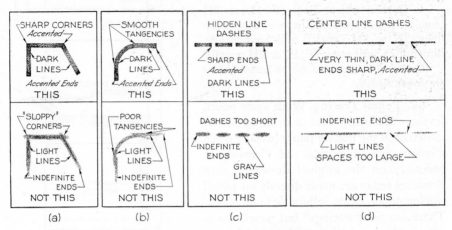

FIG. 89   Technique of Lines (Magnified).

Horizontal lines are drawn with the aid of the T-square, the pen being held as described below (Fig. 93, a and b). Vertical lines are drawn with the aid of the T-square and triangle, as shown in Fig. 65.

For a discussion of correct shaping and sharpening of the nibs of the ruling pen, see § 28.

Practically all of the difficulties encountered in the use of the ruling pen may be attributed to (1) incorrect position of the pen, (2) lack of attention to the drying properties of drawing ink, and (3) improper control of thickness of lines, and incorrect junctures.

1. *Position of the Pen.*—The pen should lean at an angle of about 60° with the paper in the direction in which the line is being drawn, and in a vertical

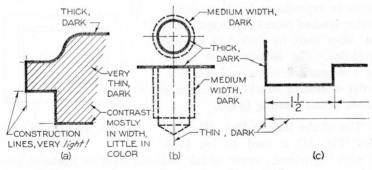

FIG. 90   Contrast of Lines (Magnified).

plane containing the line (Fig. 93, a and b). In general, the more the pen is leaned toward the paper, the thicker the line will be; and the more nearly vertical the pen is held, the thinner the line will be. The thumbscrew is faced away from the straight edge, and is adjusted (Fig. 93, c) with the thumb and forefinger of the same hand which holds the instrument. The correct position of the pen and the resulting correct line are shown at (a) in Fig. 94.

If the nibs are pressed tightly against the T-square or triangle, the effect is to close the nibs and thus reduce the thickness of the lines (Fig. 94, b). If the pen is held as shown at (c), the ink will come in contact with the T-square and paper at the same time and will run under the T-square and cause a blot on the drawing. The same result may occur if, in filling the pen, ink is deposited on the outside of the nib next to the T-square. If the pen is held as shown at (d), the outside nib of the ruling pen may not touch the paper and the line is apt to be ragged.

When the line has been correctly drawn, care must be exercised not to touch the wet ink when removing the T-square or triangle. The triangle or T-square should be carefully drawn away from the line before being picked up. If more than $\frac{1}{4}''$ of ink is placed in the pen, the ink will flow too readily, thus increasing the danger of a blot.

2. *Correct Use of Drawing Ink.*—One of the most common difficulties is that the pen will not "feed." This will occur if the nibs are screwed too close together, or if the ink has been allowed to dry between the nibs.

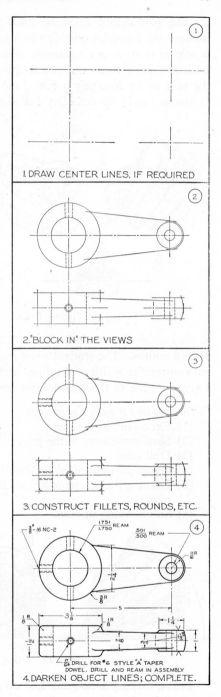

1. DRAW CENTER LINES, IF REQUIRED

2. "BLOCK IN" THE VIEWS

3. CONSTRUCT FILLETS, ROUNDS, ETC.

4. DARKEN OBJECT LINES; COMPLETE.

FIG. 91   Order of Penciling.

The pen should never be filled until the draftsman is ready to use it, because the ink dries quickly when not flowing from the pen. *Ink should never be allowed to dry in any instrument. Never lay a ruling pen down with ink in it.* The student should clean the pen frequently by slipping a stiff blotter between the nibs or by inserting a folded cloth between them. *Sandpaper should never be used to remove dry ink.* Dry ink should be removed by scraping *very lightly* with a pen knife. Ruling pens constructed so that the nibs will separate for cleaning are available in a number of good designs (Fig. 38).

FIG. 92   Filling the Ruling Pen.

The stopper should always be kept in the bottle when it is not in use, since exposure of the ink to the air causes it to become thick and difficult to use.

3. *How to Control Thickness of Lines.*—The various widths of lines used for inked drawings or tracings are shown in Fig. 86. The draftsman must first develop a trained eye to distinguish fine variations, and must also acquire skill in producing the desired widths. The student must remember that the thumbscrew alone does not control the width of the line. Factors affecting the width of a line with a given setting of the thumbscrew are:

Factors that tend to make line heavier:
    (1) Excess ink in the pen.
    (2) Slow movement of the pen.
    (3) Dull nibs.
    (4) Caked particles of ink on the nibs.
    (5) Leaning the pen more toward the paper.
    (6) Soft working surface.

Factors that tend to make line finer:
    (1) Small amount of ink in the pen.
    (2) Rapid movement of the pen.
    (3) Sharp nibs.
    (4) Fresh ink and clean pen.
    (5) Pen approaching the perpendicular.
    (6) Hard working surface.

(a) FRONT VIEW   (b) SIDE VIEW   (c) ADJUSTING THUMB SCREW

FIG. 93   Using the Ruling Pen.

Before making a new ink line on a drawing, the thickness of line should be tested by drawing a test line on a separate piece of paper under the same conditions. *Never test the pen freehand, or on a different kind of paper.* Always use a straightedge, and use identical paper.

If excess ink is in the pen or if wet lines are allowed to intersect previously drawn lines which are still wet, teardrop ends and rounded corners will result (Fig. 95).

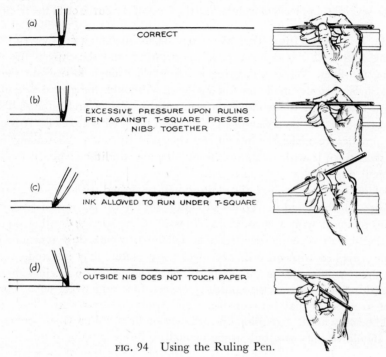

FIG. 94   Using the Ruling Pen.

The ruling pen is used in inking irregular curves, as well as straight lines, as shown in Figs. 98 and 99. The pen should be held more nearly perpendicular when used with an irregular curve than when used with the T-square or a triangle. The ruling pen should lean slightly in the direction in which

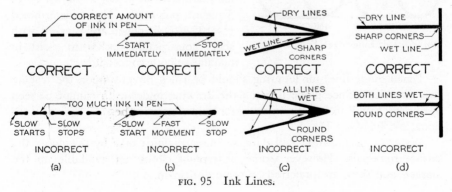

FIG. 95   Ink Lines.

the line is being drawn. It should be in a vertical plane containing a tangent to the curve at the position of the pen.

Some draftsmen insert a small piece of cardboard, or a triangle, under the irregular curve, back from the line, in order to raise the curve from the paper and prevent ink running under the edge. Another effective method is to glue several thin pieces of celluloid to the faces of the curve or to the triangles.

70. Tracing in Ink. To make a tracing in ink, tracing paper (§ 19) or tracing cloth (§ 20) is fastened over the drawing, and the copy is made by tracing the lines. When a drawing is important enough to warrant the use of ink, it is generally made on tracing cloth. Although the glazed side of the cloth is intended as the working surface, most draftsmen prefer the dull side, because it takes ink better and can be marked upon with a pencil. It is common practice to make the pencil drawing directly upon the tracing cloth and then trace it with ink, thus eliminating the traditional pencil drawing on detail paper.

Before the ink is applied, the cloth should be dusted with a small quantity of *pounce*, which should be rubbed in lightly with a soft fabric and then thoroughly removed with a clean cloth. Instead of the special drafting pounce, any slightly abrasive powder, such as talcum or chalk dust (calcium carbonate), applied with an ordinary blackboard eraser, may be used.

A greater difference in the width of lines is necessary on tracings than on pencil drawings, because the contrast between blue and white on blueprints is not so great as that between black and white on drawings. Object lines should be very **bold.** Extension lines, dimension lines, section lines, and center lines should be very *fine*, but strong enough to insure positive printing.

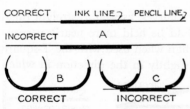

FIG. 96   Ink Lines over Pencil Lines.

In inking or tracing a pencil line, the ink line should be drawn so that the middle of the ink line is over the middle of the pencil line (Fig. 96). Arcs should be drawn tangent to straight lines as shown at *B*, not as shown at *C*. Tangent points should be determined (§§ 105-107) in pencil and marked with short construction dashes to assist in making smooth connections.

Pencil guide lines for lettering should be ruled directly upon the tracing paper or cloth, since guide lines on the drawing underneath cannot be seen distinctly enough to furnish an accurate guide for letter-heights. For conventional ink lines, see Fig. 86.

Water or perspiration will damage most tracing cloths by dissolving the surface materials. However, some waterproof cloths are available on the market, and these are preferred by some draftsmen.

71. Order of Inking. A definite order should be followed in inking a drawing or tracing. The recommended order is as follows (see Fig. 97):

1. Mark all tangent points in pencil directly on tracing.
2. Indent all compass centers (with pricker or divider point).
3. Full circles and arcs (smallest first).
4. Hidden circles and arcs (smallest first).
5. Irregular curves.
6. Full straight lines.

1st Horizontal
2nd Vertical
3rd Inclined

7. Hidden straight lines.
8. Center lines.
9. Extension and dimension lines.
10. Dimension figures and arrowheads.
11. Section lines.
12. Lettering, notes and titles (pencil guide lines directly on tracing).

Some draftsmen prefer to ink center lines before indenting the compass centers because of the possibility of ink going through the holes and causing blots on the back of the sheet.

72. Use of the Irregular Curve. The irregular curve is a device for the *mechanical drawing of curved lines and should not be applied directly to the points,* or used for purposes of producing an initial curve. The proper use of the irregular curve requires skill, especially when the lines are to be drawn in ink. After points have been plotted through which the curve is to pass, a light pencil line should be sketched freehand smoothly through the points (Fig. 99, a).

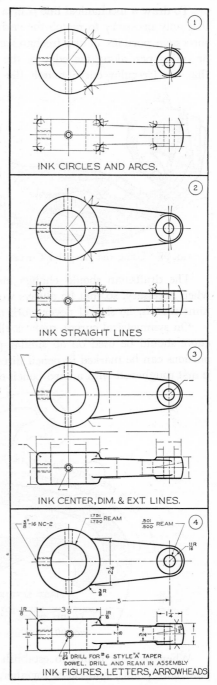

INK CIRCLES AND ARCS.

INK STRAIGHT LINES

INK CENTER, DIM. & EXT. LINES.

INK FIGURES, LETTERS, ARROWHEADS

FIG. 97 Order of Inking.

To draw a mechanical line over a freehand line using the irregular curve, it is only necessary to match the various segments of the irregular curve with successive portions of the freehand curve and to draw the line with pencil or ruling pen along the edge of the curve (Fig. 98). It is very important that the irregular curve match the curve to be drawn for some distance

at each end beyond the segment to be drawn for any one setting of the curve. See Fig. 99 (b), (c), (d). When this rule is observed, the successive sections of the curve will be tangent to each other, without any abrupt change in the curvature of the resulting line. In placing the irregular curve, the short-radius end of the curve should be turned toward the short-radius part of the curve to be drawn. This will prevent abrupt changes in direction.

FIG. 98 Using the Irregular Curve.

The draftsman should change his position with respect to the drawing when necessary, so that he always works on the side of the curve away from him; that is, he should never work on the "under" side of the curve.

On symmetrical curves, such as ellipses, the same portion of the irregular curve should be used on all similar parts of the curve to be drawn. These portions can be marked in pencil directly on the irregular curve if the surface is first roughened with a hard pencil eraser.

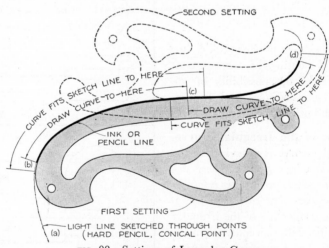

FIG. 99 Settings of Irregular Curve.

When plotting points to establish the path of a curve, it is desirable to plot more points, and closer together, where sharp turns in the curve occur.

Curves may also be drawn with the compass, as shown in Fig. 141.

73. Erasing. Mistakes are certain to occur in drafting, and correct methods of erasing should be considered a part of the technique of drafting.

For erasing pencil and ink lines on drawing paper, tracing paper, or tracing cloth, the Ruby pencil eraser (Fig. 10, a) is recommended. Ink erasers are usually highly abrasive; hence their use may destroy the surface of the paper. It is especially important not to use gritty erasers upon tracing cloth, tracing paper, or any surface which must take ink after the erasures. Better results are obtained from erasing if a hard surface, such as a triangle, is placed under the paper. If the surface has been injured by erasers or if grooves remain in the paper where lines were erased, the surface can be improved by burnishing with an object having a hard, smooth surface, or with the back of the fingernail.

An application of pounce or chalk dust will improve the surface and prevent running of the ink. The erasing shield (Figs. 12 and 100) should be used to protect lines adjacent to the area to be erased.

When an ink blot is made, the excess ink should be taken up with a blotter or smeared with the finger if a blotter is not available, and not allowed to soak into the paper. When

FIG. 100 Using the Erasing Shield.

the spot is thoroughly dry the remaining ink can be erased easily.

A knife eraser (Fig. 11) or a common penknife may be used to remove small segments of inked lines, especially on tracing cloth. *This will always injure the surface of the paper and should be used only as a last resort.* For cleaning untidy drawings, or for removing the original pencil lines from an inked drawing, a sponge rubber, kneaded rubber, or artgum is useful. The artgum is recommended for general use. Pencil lines or dirt can be removed from tracing cloth by rubbing lightly with a cloth moistened with carbon tetrachloride (Carbona), or benzine (Energine). Dusting brushes (Fig. 14), for use in removing eraser crumbs, can be obtained from manufacturers of drawing materials.

When erasure on cloth damages the surface, it may be restored by rubbing the spot with soapstone and then applying pounce or chalk dust. If the damage is not too great, an application of the powder will be sufficient.

When a gap in a thick ink line is made by erasing, the gap should be filled in with a series of fine lines which are allowed to run together. A single heavy line is likely to "run" and cause a blot.

In commercial drafting rooms, the electric erasing machine (Fig. 13) is usually available to save the time of the draftsmen.

74. Keeping Drawings Clean. Cleanliness in drafting is very important and should become a habit. It results only from a conscious effort to observe correct procedures.

FIRST, the draftsman should keep his *hands clean at all times*. Oily or perspiring hands should be frequently washed with *soap and water*. Talcum powder on the hands tends to counteract excessive perspiration.

SECOND, all drafting equipment, such as drawing board, T-square, triangles, and scale, should be cleaned frequently. For this purpose water should not be used, since it may cause warping of wooden or celluloid articles. Artgum or other soft erasers are recommended for cleaning drawing equipment.

THIRD, the largest contributing factor to dirty drawings is *not dirt, but graphite* from the pencil; hence the draftsman should observe the following precautions:

1. Never sharpen a pencil over the drawing.

2. Always wipe the pencil point with a clean cloth, after sharpening or pointing, to remove small particles of loose graphite.

3. Never place the sandpaper pad in contact with any other drawing equipment unless it is completely enclosed in an envelope or similar cover.

4. Never work with the sleeves or hands resting upon a penciled area. Keep such parts covered with clean paper (not a cloth). In lettering a drawing, always place a piece of paper under the hand.

5. Avoid sliding anything across lines on the drawing. A certain amount of sliding of T-square and triangles is necessary, but triangles should be picked up by their tips and the T-square blade tilted upward slightly before moving.

6. Never rub across the drawing with the palm of the hand to remove eraser particles; use a dust brush (Fig. 14) or flick—don't rub—the particles off with a clean cloth.

When the drawing is completed, it is not necessary to "clean it" if the above rules have been observed. The practice of making a pencil drawing, scrubbing it with artgum, and then re-tracing the lines, is poor technique and this habit should not be acquired.

At the end of the period or of the day's work, the drawing should be covered to protect it from dust.

PROBLEMS

75. Instrumental Exercises. The following constructions should be made accurately in pencil. If desired, they may be inked to provide practice in inking. They should first be drawn lightly with a hard pencil (4H to 6H). The lines forming the required figures should then be re-traced with a softer pencil (F to 2H). Construction lines need not be erased if they are very light and fine.

The problems of Chapter 4, Geometry of Technical Drawing, provide excellent additional practice to develop skill in the use of drawing instruments.

Problems in convenient form for solution may be found in *Technical Drawing Problems*, by Giesecke, Mitchell, and Spencer, and in *Technical Drawing Problems—Series 2*, by Spencer and Grant, both designed to accompany this text, and published by The Macmillan Company.

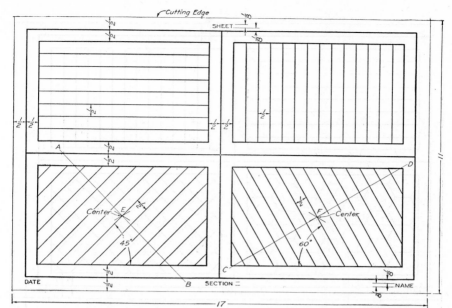

FIG. 101 STRAIGHT LINES. Divide sheet into four equal rectangles, and draw object lines in pencil as shown. Draw border lines slightly thicker than the object lines. In the lower spaces, draw construction lines AB and CD first, and set off $\frac{1}{2}''$ spaces along them; then draw required object lines at right angles to them. Omit all dimensions and instructional notes.

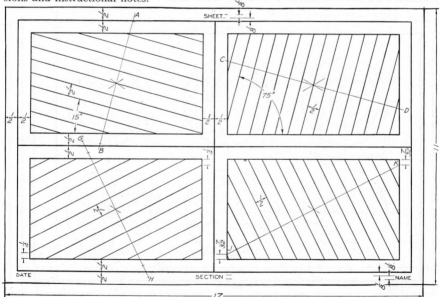

FIG. 102 STRAIGHT LINES. Divide sheet into four equal parts, and draw lines as shown. In each space, draw construction lines AB, CD, GH and JK perpendicular to required lines; then, along each construction line, set off $\frac{1}{2}''$ spaces and draw required object lines as shown. Omit all dimensions and instructional notes.

63

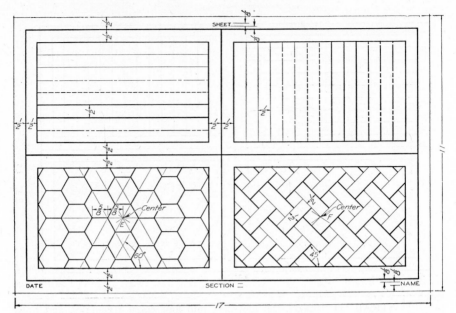

FIG. 103 STRAIGHT LINES. Divide sheet into four equal rectangles, and draw lines shown, in the manner described for Fig. 101. In top spaces, draw conventional lines to match those in Fig. 85. In lower spaces, first locate centers *E* and *F* by diagonals, and then work constructions out from them. Omit all dimensions and instructional notes.

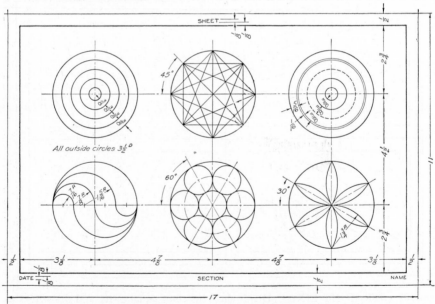

FIG. 104 CIRCLES AND ARCS. Draw horizontal and vertical center lines to locate centers of the six figures; then draw the figures in pencil as shown. Omit all dimensions and instructional notes.

64

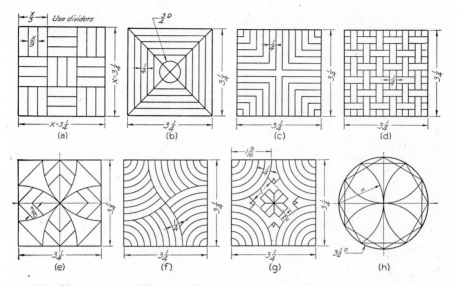

FIG. 105 Using layout of Fig. 104, draw any six assigned figures in pencil. Omit all dimensions and instructional notes.

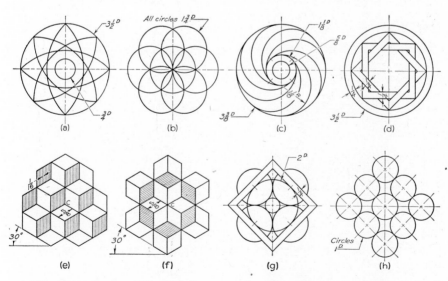

FIG. 106 Using layout of Fig. 104, draw any six assigned figures in pencil. Omit all dimensions and instructional notes.

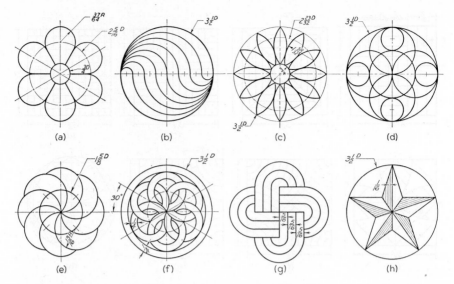

FIG. 107 Using layout of Fig. 104, draw any six assigned figures in pencil. Omit all dimensions and instructional notes.

CHAPTER 4

Geometry of Technical Drawing

76. Introduction. The following pages are intended to present definitions of terms and geometric constructions of importance in technical drawing, suggest simplified methods of construction, point out practical applications, and afford opportunity for practice in accurate instrumental drawing. The mathematical proofs of the several constructions are generally omitted.

Every draftsman should be sufficiently familiar with plane geometry to be able to apply its principles to the solutions of problems, and to use intelligently modified and simplified constructions based on it.

The articles which immediately follow include definitions of some of the more common terms related to lines, circles, arcs, angles, and other plane figures.

· 77. Circles, Arcs, and Angles. A *circle* is generated by a point moving in a plane at a fixed distance from a point called the center. The common terms with reference to the related parts of a circle are illustrated in Fig. 108 (a) and (b).

An *angle* is formed by two intersecting lines (Fig. 108, c to f). Angles are measured in degrees, minutes, and seconds. One degree is $\frac{1}{360}$ of a circle; one minute is $\frac{1}{60}$ of a degree; and one second is $\frac{1}{60}$ of a minute. A 90° angle is called a *right* angle (e). Two right angles form a *straight* angle of 180° (f). If an angle is less than 90° it is called an *acute* angle; if more than 90°, it is an *obtuse* angle.

Certain commonly used angles, such as 90°, 30°, 45°, 15°, and so on, are laid out with the ordinary triangles (Fig. 66). Other angles are drawn with the aid of the protractor (Fig. 51).

78. Plane Figures. A plane figure bounded by three straight lines is a *triangle*, the three included angles always totalling 180°. A *right* triangle has one 90° angle, and the square of the hypotenuse is equal to the sum of the squares of the two sides (Fig. 108, k). Other kinds of triangles are shown from (g) to (m) in the same figure.

A plane figure bounded by four straight lines is a *quadrilateral*, as shown in Fig. 108 (n) to (t).

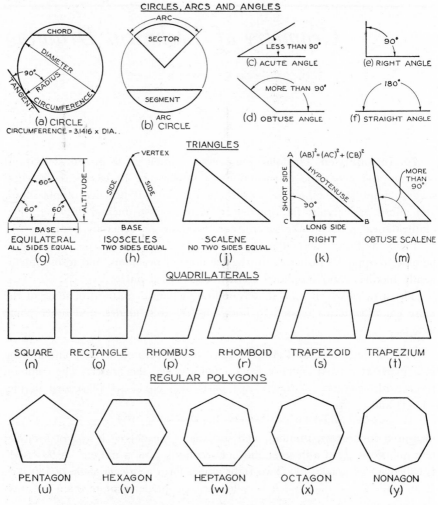

FIG. 108   Circles, Arcs, Angles, and Plane Figures.

Any plane figure bounded by straight lines is a *polygon*, including triangles and quadrilaterals mentioned above. A polygon having equal sides and equal angles is called a *regular polygon*, as shown in Fig. 108 (u) to (y), their names depending upon the number of sides.

79. To Bisect a Straight Line *AB* or a Circular Arc *AB*.—Fig. 109.

(a) With *B* as center and with any radius greater than half of *AB*, strike arcs as shown; with *A* as center and the same radius, strike arcs to intersect the first arcs at points C and D. The straight line joining these points bisects the straight line at F and the circular arc at E.

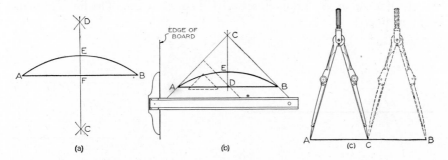

FIG. 109   To Bisect a Straight Line or an Arc.

(b) With the hypotenuse of the 45° triangle against the blade of the T-square placed parallel to the given line, or parallel to the chord of the given arc, draw two 45° lines, as shown in Fig. 109 (b). With one side of the triangle against the blade of the T-square, draw a vertical line along the other side and through the intersection of the two 45° lines. This line bisects the arc at E and the straight line at D.

(c) *Preferred by Draftsmen.*—Using dividers, bisect the line AB by trial. The general method of dividing a line into any number of equal parts with the dividers is explained in § 61.

80. To Bisect an Angle.—Fig. 110 (a). With A as center and any radius, strike the arc BC. With B and C as centers and a radius slightly larger than half BC, strike arcs to intersect at D. The line AD bisects the angle A.

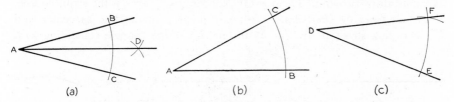

FIG. 110   Bisecting an Angle and Transferring an Angle.

81. To Transfer an Angle.—Fig. 110 (b) and (c). Let CAB at (b) be the angle and DE at (c) one side of the transferred angle. With A as center and any convenient radius, strike the arc CB. With D as center and the same radius, strike the arc FE. With E as center and BC as radius, strike an arc intersecting the arc EF at F. The angle EDF is the required angle, since straight lines joining CB and FE complete two congruent triangles.

82. To Draw a Line through a Point Parallel to a Line.—Fig. 111. Let P be the point and AB the line.

(a) With P as center and any radius, strike the arc CD to intersect the line AB at E. With E as center and the same radius, strike the arc FP to intersect the line AB at G. From E, set off EH equal to GP. The line PH is the required line.

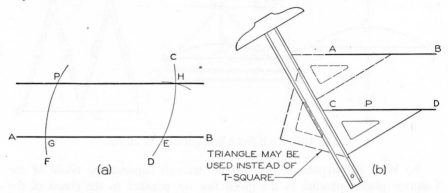

FIG. 111   To Draw a Line through a Point Parallel to a Line.

(b) *Preferred by Draftsmen.*—Place one edge of a triangle against the blade of the T-square, or against another triangle, so that another edge coincides with the line AB. Hold the T-square in place and slide the triangle along the blade of the T-square until the required line CD can be drawn along the edge of the triangle and through the point P, as shown.

83. To Draw a Line Parallel to a Line and at a Given Distance.—Fig. 112. Let AB be the line and CD the given distance.

(a) With points E and F near A and B, respectively, as centers and CD as radius, draw two arcs. The line GH, tangent to the arcs, is the required line.

(b) *Preferred by Draftsmen.*—With any point E of the line as center and CD as radius, strike an arc JK. With one side of the triangle coinciding with

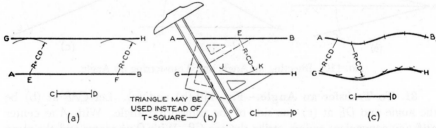

FIG. 112   To Draw a Line Parallel to a Line at a Given Distance.

the line AB and the other side resting against the blade of the T-square, slide the triangle along the blade of the T-square; then draw the required line GH along the triangle tangent to the arc JK.

(c) With centers selected at random on the line AB, and with CD as radius, draw a series of arcs; then draw the required line tangent to these arcs as explained in § 72.

84. To Divide a Straight Line into Any Number of Equal Parts.— Fig. 113. Let it be required to divide the line *AB* into seven equal parts.

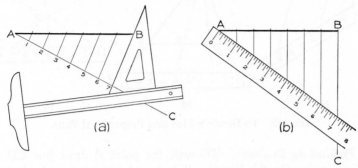

FIG. 113   To Divide a Line into Any Number of Equal Parts.

(a) Through one end of the line draw line *AC* at any convenient angle and along it set off seven equal spaces. Number the division points as shown. Draw the line *7B* and through the remaining division points, draw lines parallel to *7B*, using a triangle and T-square, as explained in § 51. These parallel lines divide the line *AB* into seven equal parts.

(b) *Preferred by Draftsmen.*—Through one end of the line, draw any convenient line *CB*, preferably a vertical line. Place a scale so that one division point of the scale is at the end of the given line and the seventh consecutive division point is on the line *BC*. Mark the six intervening division points

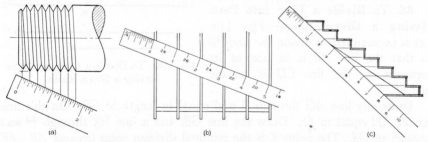

FIG. 114   Practical Applications of Dividing a Line into Equal Parts.

with tiny dots and through these points draw lines parallel to *CB*. These parallel lines divide the line *AB* into seven equal parts.

(c) *Preferred by Draftsmen.*—Divide the line by trial, using the bow dividers or the hairspring dividers as explained in § 61, Fig. 82.

Practical Applications.—The problem of dividing a line into a number of equal parts occurs frequently in drafting. Figure 114 illustrates three common cases.

85. To Divide a Line into Proportional Parts.—Fig. 115. Let it be required to divide the line *AB* into three parts proportional to *2, 3,* and *4.*

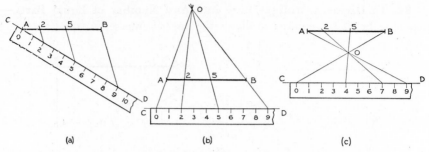

(a)   (b)   (c)

FIG. 115   To Divide a Line into Proportional Parts.

(a) *Preferred by Draftsmen.*—Through the point *A* draw line *CD* at any convenient angle. On this line set off 2, 3, and 4 units of convenient size by means of the scale as shown. Draw the line *9B*, and then, parallel thereto, the lines *5–5* and *2–2* as explained for Fig. 113 (a).

(b) and (c) Draw a line *CD* parallel to *AB* and at any convenient distance. On this line set off 2, 3, and 4 units as shown. Draw lines through the ends of the two lines to intersect at the point *O*. Draw lines through *O* and the points *2* and *5* to divide *AB* into the required proportional parts.

Constructions of this type are useful in the preparation of graphs, Chapter 25.

86. To Divide a Line into Parts Having a Given Ratio.—Fig. 116. Let it be required to divide the line *AB* so that the line *AB* is to one of its segments as the line *CD* is to the line *EF.*

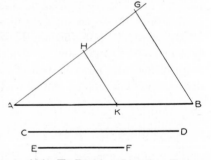

FIG. 116   To Divide a Line into Parts Having a Given Ratio.

Draw any line *AG* through *A* and equal in length to *CD*. On this line set off *AH* equal to *EF*. Draw the line *GB*, and a line *HK* through *H* and parallel to *GB*. The point *K* is the required division point because $AB : AK$ $= AG$ (or CD) $: AH$ (or EF).

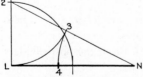

FIG. 117   To Divide a Line into Mean and Extreme Ratio—the Golden Section.

87. To Divide a Line into Extreme and Mean Ratio.—Fig. 117. Let *LN* be the line. Construct on *LN* the right triangle *L2N*, making *L2* half of *LN*. With *2* as center and *2L* as radius, draw the arc *L3*. With *N* as center and *N3* as radius, draw the arc *3–4*. Then $L4 : 4N = 4N : LN$, or $N4 = 0.618\ NL$. This section is called the *golden section.*

If *NL* is the radius of a circle, *N4* is the side of the regular inscribed deca-gon. This construction is the basis for the method of inscribing a regular pentagon in a circle (§ 94).

The golden section is sometimes used in aesthetic design because it pro-duces pleasing proportions. When it is applied to the design of letters, the height of small letters becomes 0.618 the height of large letters. This corre-sponds to the statement in § 158 that this ratio should vary from three-fifths to two-thirds.

88. To Find the Mean Proportional of Two Lines.—Fig. 118. Let *S* and *R* be the lines. Set off *AC* equal to *S* and *CG* equal to *R*, as shown. Upon

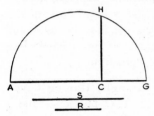

AG as the diameter, draw a semicircle and erect the perpendicular *CH*; this is the required mean proportional, since $AC : CH = CH : CG$.

89. To Draw a Line through a Point Per-pendicular to a Line.—Fig. 119.

(a) When the point is not on the line. From the point *P* draw any convenient oblique line to intersect the given line at *D*. Bisect the line *DP*

FIG. 118   To Find Mean Proportional of Two Lines.

at *C*. With center at *C* and radius *CP*, strike the arc *DEP*. The line *EP* is the required perpendicular.

(b) With *P* as center, strike an arc to intersect the given line at *C* and *D*. With *C* and *D* as centers and radius slightly greater than half *CD*, strike arcs to intersect at *E*. The line *PE* is the required perpendicular.

(c) When the point is on the given line. Let *AB* be the line and *P* the point. With *P* as center and any radius, strike arcs to intersect *AB* at *D* and *G*. With *D* and *G* as centers and radius slightly greater than half *DG*, strike arcs to intersect at *F*. The line *PF* is the required perpendicular.

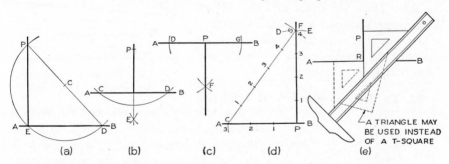

FIG. 119   To Draw a Line Through a Point Perpendicular to a Line.

(d) Select any convenient unit of length, a quarter-inch, for example. With *P* as center and three units as radius, strike an arc to intersect the given line at *C*. With *P* as center and four units as radius, strike the arc *DE*. With

C as center and five units as radius, strike an arc to intersect *DE* at *F*. The line *PF* is the required perpendicular.

(e) *Preferred by Draftsmen.*—With the hypotenuse of a triangle against the blade of the T-square and one side of the triangle along the line *AB*, slide the triangle along the blade of the T-square until the required line *RP* can be drawn along the side of the triangle and through the point *P* or the point *R*, whichever is the given point, as shown.

Practical Applications.—The method of constructing a right angle illustrated in Fig. 119 (d) is frequently used in laying off rectangular foundations for machines or buildings, and in similar cases. For this purpose a wooden frame (Fig. 120) may be constructed and used like a large steel square; or a steel or metallic tape may be used and distances of 30, 40, and 50 feet measured as the three sides of the right triangle.

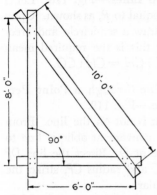

FIG. 120   Practical Method of Constructing a Right Triangle.

90. To Draw a Triangle, Having Given Its Three Sides.

—Fig. 121. Let *R*, *S*, and *T* be the three given sides. Draw a line *AB* equal in length to one of the three given sides, as *T*. With *A* and *B* as centers and radii equal to *S* and *R*, respectively, draw arcs intersecting at *C*. The triangle *ACB* is the required triangle. This problem is especially useful in obtaining the developments of surfaces by triangulation (§ 340).

91. To Draw a Right Triangle, Having Given the Hypotenuse and One Side.

—Fig. 122. Let *S* be the hypotenuse and *R* the side. Draw *AB* equal to *S* and on *AB* as diameter, construct a semicircle. With *A* as center and *R* as radius, draw an arc intersecting the semicircle at *C*. Draw *AC* and *CB* to complete the triangle.

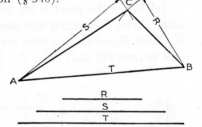

FIG. 121   To Draw a Triangle Having Given Its Three Sides.

92. To Draw an Equilateral Triangle.

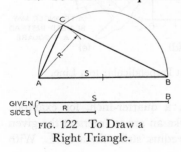

FIG. 122   To Draw a Right Triangle.

—Fig. 123. (a) Given the side *AB*. With *A* and *B* as centers and *AB* as radius, strike the two arcs to intersect at *C*. Draw the lines *AC* and *BC* to complete the required equilateral triangle.

(b) *Preferred by Draftsmen.*—Given the side *AB*. Through the points *A* and *B* draw lines making angles of 60° with the given line, as shown, and intersecting at *C*.

(c) Given the circumscribed circle. Let O be the center of the given circle. Draw the diameter AB. With A as center and the radius of the circle as radius, strike an arc intersecting the circumference at C and at D. Draw the required triangle CBD.

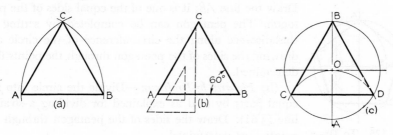

FIG. 123   To Draw an Equilateral Triangle.

93. To Draw a Square.—Fig. 124.

(a) Given one side AB. Through the point A draw a perpendicular to the line AB (§ 89, c). With A as center and AB as radius, draw the arc to intersect the perpendicular in the point C. With B and C as centers and AB as radius, strike the arcs to intersect at D. Draw the lines CD and BD to complete the required square.

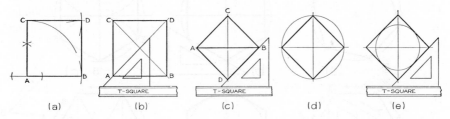

FIG. 124   To Draw a Square.

(b) *Preferred by Draftsmen.*—Given one side AB. Using the T-square and the 45° triangle, draw the lines AC and BD perpendicular to AB, and the lines AD and BC at an angle of 45° with AB. Draw the line CD with the T-square to complete the required square.

(c) *Preferred by Draftsmen.*—Given the diagonal AB. Using the T-square and the 45° triangle, draw lines through A and B at angles of 45° with AB and to intersect each other in the points C and D, thus completing the square.

(d) Given the circumscribed circle. Draw two diameters at right angles to each other. The intersections of these diameters with the circumference of the given circle are the vertices of an inscribed square.

(e) *Preferred by Draftsmen.*—Given the inscribed circle (distance "across flats," as in drawing bolt heads). Using the T-square and the 45° triangle, draw the four sides tangent to the circle. See Fig. 779.

94. To Draw a Regular Pentagon.—Fig. 125. Let the circumscribed circle be given.

(a) Bisect the radius OD (§ 79) at C. With C as center and CA as radius, strike the arc AE. With A as center and AE as radius, strike the arc EB.

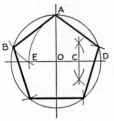

Draw the line AB; it is one of the equal sides of the pentagon. The pentagon can be completed by setting off this distance along the circumference of the circle and drawing the sides of the pentagon through the points thus determined.

(b) *Preferred by Draftsmen.*—Divide the circle into five equal parts by trial as explained for dividing a straight line (§ 61). Draw the sides of the pentagon through the points thus determined.

FIG. 125   To Draw a Pentagon.

95. To Draw a Regular Hexagon.—Fig. 126.

(a) Let the circumscribed circle be given. Each side of a hexagon is equal to the radius of the circumscribed circle. Set off the six sides of the hexagon along the circumference of the circle with the compass or dividers, using the

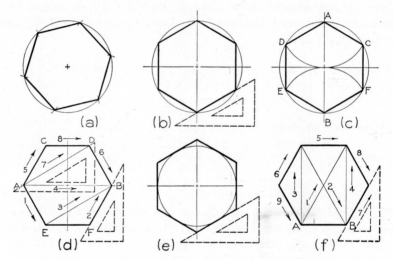

FIG. 126   To Draw a Regular Hexagon.

radius of the circle as the length of the sides. Join the points on the circumference with straight lines to complete the hexagon.

(b) *Preferred by Draftsmen.*—Draw two diameters, one vertical and the other horizontal. Using the 30° × 60° triangle and the T-square, draw lines at an angle of 30° with the horizontal through the ends of the vertical diameter, and complete the hexagon as shown.

(c) Draw two diameters, as in (b). With centers at A and B and radius equal to that of the circle, draw arcs to intersect the circumference at *C*, *D*, *E*, and *F*, and complete the hexagon as shown.

(d) Let one side, as *EF*, be given. At end points *E* and *F*, and using the T-square and 30° × 60° triangle, draw lines 1 and 2 at 60° with horizontal. Line 3 is drawn at 30° with horizontal to intersect line 2 at *B*. Horizontal line 4 is drawn to intersect line 1 at *A*, and so on, in the order indicated.

(e) *Preferred by Draftsmen.*—Let the diameter of the inscribed circle, that is, the distance "across flats" of the hex-agon, be given. Using the 30° × 60° triangle and the T-square, draw the sides of the hexagon tangent to the circle. See Fig. 778.

(f) Let one side of the hexagon be given. Draw the given side *AB*, and, using the 30° × 60° triangle, draw the lines in the order indicated in the figure.

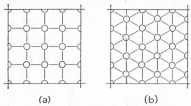

(a)   (b)

FIG. 127   The Hexagon.

Practical Applications.—The problem of constructing hexagons occurs in drawing hexagonal bolt heads and nuts (§ 427) and in many other cases in engineering. For example, if the maximum number of holes, spaced a given distance apart, are to be drilled in a ceiling panel to improve the sound-absorbing property of the panel, the hexagonal arrangement is the best. Figure 127 shows two panels in which the holes are placed, respectively, in squares and in hexagons. If the distance between centers of holes is *d*, the area occupied by one hole is, respectively, d^2 and $d^2\sqrt{\frac{3}{4}}$ in the two cases and the number of holes in the two panels are to each other as 866 is to 1000.

96. To Draw a Regular Octagon.—Fig. 128.

(a) Given the circumscribed square. Draw the diagonals *CA* and *DB*; then draw the center lines *EF* and *GH*. With *O* as center and *OB* as radius, strike

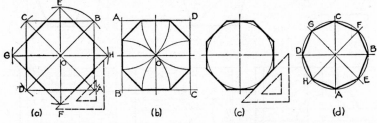

(a)   (b)   (c)   (d)

FIG. 128   To Draw an Octagon.

arcs to intersect the center lines at *E*, *H*, *F*, and *G*. Through *E* draw the 45° lines *EG* and *EH*. Through *G* and *H* draw 45° lines *GF* and *HF*. These lines form a second square of the same size as the given square. The sides of the octagon are formed by the interior segments of the sides of the two squares.

(b) Given the circumscribed square. With the corners of the given square as centers and with half the diagonal as radius, draw arcs cutting the sides as shown. Join the points thus found.

(c) *Preferred by Draftsmen.*—Given the inscribed circle. Using the 45° triangle and the T-square, draw the sides of the octagon tangent to the given circle as indicated.

(d) Given the circumscribed circle. Draw four diameters 45° apart as shown. The points of intersection of these diameters and the given circle are the vertices of an inscribed octagon. Join the points thus found.

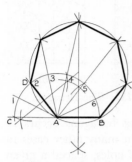

FIG. 129 To Draw a
Regular Polygon.

97. To Draw Any Regular Polygon upon a Side.—Fig. 129. Let the number of sides be seven and let *AB* be the side. With *A* as center and *AB* as radius, draw a semicircle *CDB*. Using the dividers, divide the semicircle by trial into seven equal parts (the number of sides of the polygon). *D* is the second division point; draw the line *AD*, which is another side of the required heptagon. Draw a circle through the three points *B*, *A*, and *D* (Fig. 135); it circumscribes the required heptagon. Find the remaining vertices by setting off the chord *AB* along this circle or by drawing lines from the point *A* through the division points of the semicircle *CDB* as shown.

98. To Transfer Plane Figures.—Fig. 130.

(a) and (b) *To Transfer a Triangle to a New Location.*—Set off any side, as *AB*, in the new location (b). With the extremities of the line as centers and

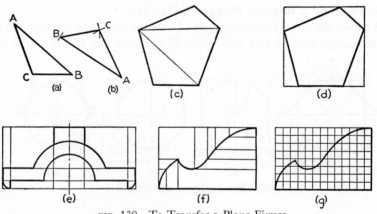

FIG. 130 To Transfer a Plane Figure.

the lengths of the other sides of the given triangle (a) as radii, strike two arcs to intersect at *C*. Join point *C* with points *A* and *B* to complete the triangle.

(c) *To Transfer a Polygon by the Triangle Method.*—Divide the polygon into triangles and transfer each triangle as explained above.

(d) *To Transfer a Polygon by the Rectangle Method.*—Circumscribe a rectangle about the given polygon. Draw a congruent rectangle in the new location and locate the vertices of the polygon by transferring location measurements along the sides of the rectangle to the new rectangle. Join the points thus found to complete the figure.

(e) *To Transfer Irregular Figures.*—Figures composed of rectangular and circular forms are readily transferred by enclosing the elementary features in rectangles and determining centers of arcs and circles. These may then be transferred to the new location.

(f) *To Transfer Figures by Offset Measurements.*—*Offset location measurements* are frequently useful in transferring figures composed of free curves. When the figure has been enclosed by a rectangle, the sides of the rectangle are used as reference lines for the location of points along the curve.

(g) *To Transfer Figures by a System of Rectangles.*—Figures involving free curves are easily copied, enlarged, or reduced by the use of a system of rectangles. For example, to enlarge a figure to double size, draw the containing rectangle and all small rectangles double their size in the original figure. The line is then drawn through the corresponding points in the new set of rectangles.

99. To Enlarge or Reduce a Drawing.—Fig. 131. Let it be required to enlarge Drawing I in the proportion of *a:b*. Assume the corner of the enlarged drawing at *A* and draw the rectangle *ABHE*. Draw the two triangles *BCD* and *FGH* so that their sides are equal to *a* and *b*, respectively. To obtain heights in Drawing II, project down from Drawing I to intersect *DB*, and then across to Drawing II. To obtain widths in Drawing II, project across from Drawing I to *GJ*, and then down to Drawing II as shown.

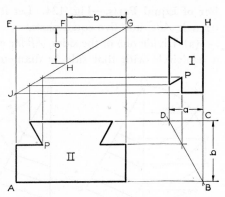

FIG. 131   To Enlarge or Reduce a Drawing.

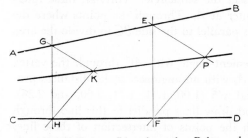

FIG. 132 To Draw a Line through a Point and the Inaccessible Intersection of Two Lines.

100. To Draw a Line through a Point and through the Inaccessible Intersection of Two Lines.— Fig. 132. Let *P* be the point and *AB* and *CD* the lines. Construct any triangle *EFP* having its vertices, respectively, in the two lines and in the point. Construct a triangle *GHK* similar and its corresponding sides parallel to the triangle *EFP* and having two of its vertices, respectively, in the two lines. The line *PK* is the required line.

Figure 132 may be considered the projection of a triangular pyramid. This construction is useful in perspective drawing when it is desired to draw a line toward an inaccessible vanishing point, when at least two other lines have already been drawn toward that point (§ 306).

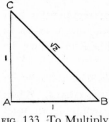

FIG. 133 To Multiply or Divide a Line by $\sqrt{2}$.

101. To Multiply or Divide a Line by $\sqrt{2}$.— Fig. 133. Construct an isosceles right triangle *ABC*. If the side *AB* is the line, the hypotenuse *CB* will be the line multiplied by $\sqrt{2}$.

If the hypotenuse *CB* is the line, the side *AB* (or *AC*) will be the line divided by $\sqrt{2}$.

This construction is useful in drawing an octagon circumscribed about a required ellipse. See § 116 and Fig. 150 (b).

102. To Divide the Area of a Triangle or Trapezoid into Any Number of Equal Parts.—Fig. 134. Let it be required to divide the area of the triangle *ABC* into five equal parts.

(a) Divide one of the sides, *AB* for example, into five equal parts and draw a semicircle with that side as diameter. Through the division points draw

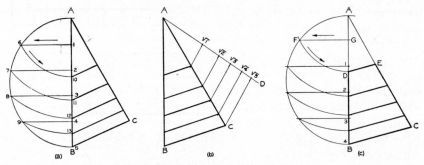

FIG. 134   To Divide the Area of a Triangle or a Trapezoid into Equal Parts.

lines perpendicular to *AB*, to intersect the semicircle. Through these intersections draw circular arcs with center at *A*. Through the points where the arcs intersect the side *AB*, draw lines parallel to the side *BC* to divide the area of the triangle into five equal parts.

(b) Draw line *AD* at any convenient angle with *AC* through the vertex *A* and set off, along this line from *A*, with an engineers scale, distances proportional to $\sqrt{1}$, $\sqrt{2}$, $\sqrt{3}$, $\sqrt{4}$, and $\sqrt{5}$ (1.00, 1.41, 1.71, 2.00, and 2.24). Join the last division point to *C* and draw lines parallel to this line through the other division points. Through the points of intersection of these lines with the side *AC*, draw lines parallel to *CB*, to divide the area of the triangle into five equal parts.

(c) Let it be required to divide the area of the trapezoid *DECB* into four equal parts. Produce the sides of the trapezoid to form the triangle *ABC*. With *AB* as diameter, draw a semicircle. With *A* as center and *AD* as radius, strike an arc to intersect the semicircle at *F*. From *F* draw a perpendicular to *AB* to intersect it at *G*. Divide *GB* into four equal parts and complete the construction as shown and as described for (a). Obviously, the method of (b) could also be used.

Practical Applications.—Constructions (a) and (b) can be used to determine the centers of hydraulic pressure on dams and retaining walls. Construction (c) can be used to determine the correct locations of stirrups in uniformly loaded reinforced concrete beams; for example, if *AB* represents the semi-length of the beam and *DB* the portion of the beam needing shear reinforcement, divide the trapezoid *DECB* into twice as many equal parts as stirrups are required. The stirrups are located at the first and every other following division point on the line *DB*.

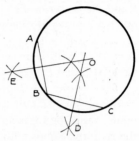

FIG. 135   To Draw a Circle through Three Points.

103. To Find the Center of a Circle Passing through Three Points Not in a Straight Line and to Draw the Circle.—Fig. 135. Let *A*, *B*, and *C* be the three points. Draw the lines *AB* and *BC*; they are chords of the required circle. Draw *EO* and *DO*, the perpendicular

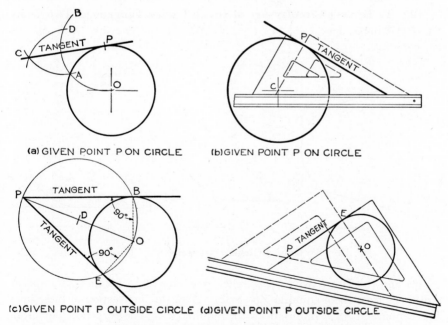

(a) GIVEN POINT P ON CIRCLE   (b) GIVEN POINT P ON CIRCLE

(c) GIVEN POINT P OUTSIDE CIRCLE   (d) GIVEN POINT P OUTSIDE CIRCLE

FIG. 136   To Draw a Tangent to a Circle through a Point.

bisectors of the chords (§ 79). The intersection O of the bisectors is the required center of the circle. With O as center and OA, OB, or OC as radius,
draw the required circle.

104. To Draw a Line Tangent to a Circle through a Point.—Fig. 136.

(a) Let P be the point *on the circle*. With P as center and PO as radius,
strike the arc OAB. With A as center and the same radius, strike the arc CD.
With D as center and the same radius, strike the arc AC. Through the intersection C of these arcs, and the point P, draw the required tangent line.

(b) *Preferred by Draftsmen.*—Let P be the point *on the circle*. Move the T-
square and triangle as a unit until one leg of the triangle passes through point
P and the center of the circle (dotted triangle); then slide the triangle until the
other leg passes through point P, and draw the required tangent as shown.

(c) Let P be the point *outside the circle*. Draw the line PO and bisect it at
D (§ 79). With D as center and DO as radius, strike an arc to cut the given
circle at B and E. Draw the lines PB and PE, the required tangent lines.

(d) *Preferred by Draftsmen.*—Let P be the point *outside the circle*. Move the
T-square and triangle as a unit until one leg of the triangle passes through
point P and, by inspection, is tangent to the circle (solid triangle); then draw
the required tangent line. To locate the point of tangency, slide the triangle
until the other leg passes through the center of the circle (dotted triangle) and
mark the tangent point E. The second tangent and its point of tangency may
be determined in a similar manner.

**105. To Draw a Circular Arc of Given Radius Tangent to Two Non-
Parallel Lines.**—Fig. 137. Let LN and MO be the two lines and AB the
given radius.

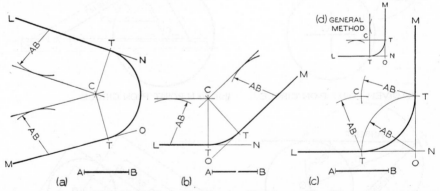

FIG. 137   To Draw a Circular Arc Tangent to Two Lines.

(a) and (b) Draw two lines parallel, respectively, to LN and MO and at
a distance from them equal to AB (§ 83). With the intersection of these lines
C as center and AB as radius, draw the required arc. The perpendiculars from
C to LN and MO determine the points of tangency.

(c) Let the two lines be at right angles to each other (special case). With the intersection of the two lines as center and with AB as radius, draw an arc to intersect the lines at the tangent points T. With these points as centers and the same radius, draw arcs to intersect at C, the center of the required arc. Obviously, the general method of (a) and (b) could be used as shown at (d).

These constructions are useful in drawing fillets and rounds of machine parts, §§ 444 and 467.

106. To Draw a Circular Arc of Given Radius Tangent to a Circular Arc and to a Straight Line.—Fig. 138. Let AB be the arc and O its center; let CD be the straight line; and let EF be the radius of the required circular arc.

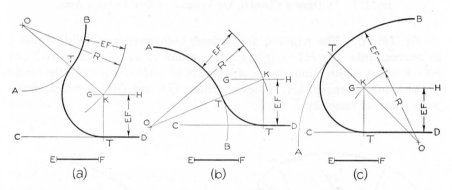

FIG. 138   To Draw a Circular Arc Tangent to a Circular Arc
and to a Straight Line.

(a), (b), and (c) Draw the line GH parallel to the line CD and at a distance EF from it. With O as center, draw an arc parallel to the arc AB and at a distance EF from it, to intersect the line GH in the point K. With K as center and radius EF, draw the required circular arc. A perpendicular from K to CD determines the point of tangency T on the line CD. The line of centers OK determines the point of tangency T on the circular arc AB.

This construction is useful in drawing fillets and rounds of machine parts. See §§ 444 and 467.

107. To Draw a Circular Arc of Given Radius Tangent to Two Circular Arcs.

Fig. 139 (a), (b), and (c) Let E and F be the centers of the two given circular arcs and HK the radius of the required circular arc. With E and F as centers draw arcs parallel to the given arcs and at a distance HK from them; their intersection G is the center of the required arc. The lines of centers EG and FG determine the points of tangency T.

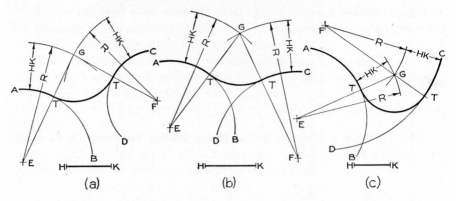

FIG. 139   To Draw a Circular Arc Tangent to Two Circular Arcs.

Fig. 140 (a).—The required arc encloses both given arcs. With A and B as centers, strike arcs $HK-r$ (given radius minus radius of small circle) and $HK-R$ (given radius minus radius of large circle) intersecting at G, the center of the required tangent arc. Lines of centers GA and GB (extended) determine points of tangency T.

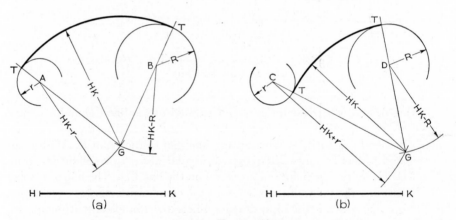

FIG. 140   Tangent Arcs.

Fig. 140 (b).—The required arc encloses one given arc. With C and D as centers, strike arcs $HK+r$ (given radius plus radius of small circle) and $HK-R$ (given radius minus radius of large circle) intersecting at G, the center of the required tangent arc. Lines of centers GC and GD (extended) determine points of tangency T.

The number of solutions in such cases equals the number of intersections G, which can be constructed in this general manner.

108. To Draw a Series of Tangent Circular Arcs Forming a Curved Line through Given Points.—Fig. 141. Let *A*, *B*, *C*, *D*, *E*, and *F* be the

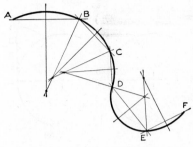

points. First, sketch lightly a smooth pleasing curve through the points. The lines joining consecutive points are chords of the required circular arcs. Draw their perpendicular bisectors (§ 79). Beginning with one of the bisectors, preferably that of the longest chord, assume the radius of this arc and its center on this bisector and draw the arc. Draw the extreme radius of this arc. The centers of the adjacent arcs are at the intersections of these radii with the bisectors of the adjacent chords. Complete the figure as shown.

FIG. 141   A Series of Tangent Arcs.

109. To Draw a Reverse or Ogee Curve Connecting Two Parallel Lines.—Fig. 142. Let *NA* and *BM* be the two parallel lines. At *A* and *B*, the termini of the reverse curve, erect perpendiculars *AF* and *BC* to the lines *NA*

and *BM*, respectively. Draw *AB* and assume a point *E* in which it is desired the ogee curve should intersect *AB*. Draw the perpendicular bisectors of *AE* and *BE*. The intersections *F* and *C* of these bisectors and the perpendiculars, respectively, are the centers of the required arcs. With *F* as center and *AF* as radius, draw

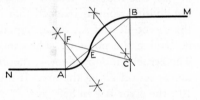

FIG. 142   Ogee Curve.

the arc *AE*. With *C* as center and *CB* as radius, draw the arc *EB*. The curve *AEB* is the desired curve.

This construction is useful in drawing architectural moldings.

110. To Draw a Curve Tangent to Three Intersecting Lines.—Fig. 143 (a) and (b). Let *AB*, *BC*, and *CD* be the lines. Select the point of tangency *P* at any point on the line *BC*. Make *BT* equal to *BP* and *CS* equal to *CP* and erect perpendiculars at the points *P*, *T*, and *S*. Their intersections *O* are the centers of the required arcs.

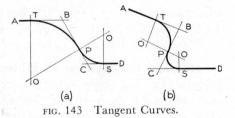

(a)   (b)

FIG. 143   Tangent Curves.

111. To Rectify a Circular Arc on Its Tangent and to Set Off a Given Length on a Circular Arc.—Fig. 144.

Let it be required to rectify the arc AB.

(a) Draw the tangent at *B*. Draw the diameter *BC* and extend it to *D*, making *CD* equal to the radius *OB*. Draw the line *DA* and produce it to intersect the tangent at E. The tangent BE is slightly shorter than the arc BA. For an angle of 30°, the difference in length is 1 in 2326 ±; for 45°, it is 1 in 420 ±; and for 60°, it is 1 in 132 ±.

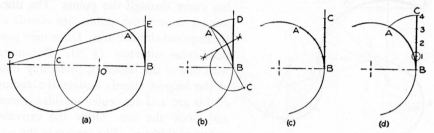

FIG. 144   To Rectify a Circular Arc.

(b) Draw the tangent at B. Draw the chord AB and extend it to C, making BC equal to one-half BA. With C as center and radius CA, strike the arc AD. The tangent BD is slightly shorter than the arc BA. For an angle of 45° the difference in length is about 1 in 2866 ±.

(c) Use the bow dividers and, beginning at A, set off equal distances until the division point is reached that is nearest the point B. At this point, reverse the direction and set off an equal number of distances along the tangent to determine the point C. The tangent BC is slightly shorter than the arc AB. The error is independent of the angle of the arc AB and varies with the distances set off along the arc. If the angle subtended by one of the divisions is 10°, the error is 1 in 830 ±.

Let it be required to set off a given length along a given arc.

(a) and (c) Reverse the methods used for rectifying the arc on the tangent.

(d) To set off the length BC along the arc BA, draw BC tangent to the arc at B. Divide BC into four equal parts. With center at *1*, the first division point, and radius *1C*, draw the arc CA. The arc BA is practically equal to BC for angles not larger than 30°. For larger angles, the arc is slightly longer; for 45° the difference is 1 in 3232 ± and for 60° it is 1 in 835 ±.

The constructions shown above are empirical.

112. The Construction of Ellipses.—Fig. 145.   (a) *An ellipse may be generated by a point moving so that the sum of its distances from two points (foci) is constant and equal to the major axis.* For example, an ellipse may be constructed by placing a looped string around two points E and F, the foci of the ellipse, and around a pencil point P and moving the pencil along its maximum orbit while the string is kept taut.

(b) An ellipse may also be constructed with a "trammel" made from a strip of stiff paper or other material. The trammel may be prepared in two ways, as shown. In each case, distances equal to the semi-major and semi-minor axes are set off on the edge of the trammel; in one case, these distances overlap, and in the other, they are end-to-end. To use either method, place the trammel so that two of the points are on the respective axes, as shown; the third point will then be on the curve, and can be marked with a small dot. Additional points are obtained by moving the trammel to other positions,

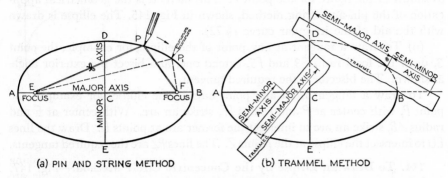

(a) PIN AND STRING METHOD   (b) TRAMMEL METHOD

FIG. 145   Ellipses.

always keeping the two points on the respective axes. Extend the axes to use the long trammel. The more points found, the more accurate will be the ellipse. The final curve is drawn with the aid of the irregular curve (§ 72).

113. To Draw an Ellipse by the Foci Method.—Fig. 146.

(a) Let *AB* and *CD* be the axes of the ellipse. Foci *E* and *F* are found by striking arcs *R*, with radius equal to half the major axis and with centers at *C* and *D* Then, between *E* and *O* on the major axis, mark at random a number of points equal to the number of points desired in each quadrant of the

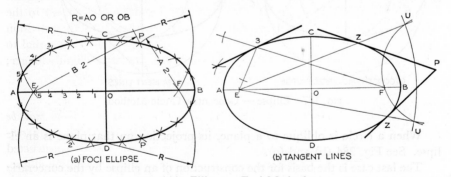

(a) FOCI ELLIPSE   (b) TANGENT LINES

FIG. 146   Ellipse — Foci Method.

ellipse. In Fig. 146 (a) five points were selected as sufficient. For larger ellipses, more than five points should be used; that is, enough to insure the production of a smooth, accurate curve. Begin construction with any one of these points, as *2*. With *E* and *F* as centers and radii *B2* and *A2*, respectively, strike arcs to intersect at *P*, thus determining two points of the required ellipse.

With the same radii, but with reversed centers *F* and *E*, strike arcs to intersect at 2, thus determining two other points. Using each of the remaining points 1, 3, 4, and 5, as explained for the point 2, find additional points of the ellipse as shown in the figure for the point *P*. This method is the geometrical application of the pin-and-string method, shown in Fig. 145. The ellipse is drawn with the aid of the irregular curve (§ 72).

(b) To draw a tangent at any point of the ellipse, for example, the point 3, draw the focal radii *E3* and *F3*, extend one, and bisect the exterior angle as shown. The bisector is the required tangent.

To draw a tangent from any point outside the ellipse, for example, the point *P*, with center at *P* and radius *PF*, strike an arc. With center at *E* and radius *AB*, strike an arc to intersect the former arc at points *U*. Draw the lines *EU* to intersect the ellipse at the points *Z*. The lines *PZ* are the required tangents.

114. To Draw an Ellipse by the Concentric Circle Method.—Fig. 147.

When a circle is parallel to a plane, its projection on that plane is a circle. See Fig. 284 (a).

When a circle is perpendicular to a plane, its projection on that plane is a straight line. See Fig. 284 (a) and (b).

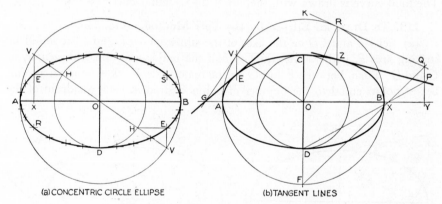

(a) CONCENTRIC CIRCLE ELLIPSE   (b) TANGENT LINES

FIG. 147   Ellipse — Concentric Circle Method.

When a circle is oblique to a plane, its projection on that plane is an ellipse. See Fig. 284 (b) and (c).

The last case is the basis for the construction of an ellipse by the concentric circle method (Fig. 147, a). The circle of diameter *AB* is inclined to the plane of projection at an angle so that the diameter of the circle at right angles to *AB* is reduced in length to *CD*, and all chords of the circle parallel to *CD* are reduced in the same ratio.

(a) To draw the ellipse when the axes *AB* and *CD* are given, describe circles on the two axes as diameters and draw any diagonal *VV* through center *O*. From the points *V*, in which the diagonal intersects the larger circle, draw lines VE parallel to the minor axis, and from the points H, in which it intersects the smaller circle, draw lines HE parallel to the major axis. The intersections E of these lines are points of the required ellipse. Four points can thus be determined for each diameter drawn, since the points S and R can be determined by extending lines VE and HE. Additional points on the ellipse are found by drawing other diagonals through center O, each diagonal accounting for four more points. While in Fig 147 (a) six points in each quadrant were deemed sufficient, more points would be necessary for larger ellipses, or where more accuracy is desired. Notice, in Fig. 147 (a), that where the curve is sharpest near the ends of the ellipse, the points were constructed closer together to better determine the curve.

When sufficient points have been found, the ellipse is drawn with the aid of the irregular curve (§ 72).

It is evident from the figure that the ordinate EX of the ellipse is to the corresponding ordinate VX of the circle as b is to a, where b represents the semi-minor axis and a the semi-major axis. Thus the area of the ellipse is equal to the area of the circumscribed circle multiplied by $\frac{b}{a}$; hence it is equal to πab.

(b) To draw a tangent at a point on the ellipse, for example, the point E, draw the ordinate at E and produce it to intersect the circumscribed circle at V. Draw a tangent to the circle at V (§ 104), and produce it to intersect the major axis produced at G. The line GE is the required tangent.

To draw a tangent on a point outside the ellipse, for example, the point P, draw the ordinate PY and elongate it in the ratio $b : a$ (§ 86), to find the corresponding ordinate QY. Make use of radii OD and OF in this construction, as follows: Draw DP and find its intersection X with the axis AB, produced if necessary. Draw FX and produce it to intersect the ordinate through P at Q. Then, from similar triangles, $QY : PY = FO : DO = a : b$. Draw a tangent to the circumscribed circle from Q (§ 104). Find the point of tangency R, and draw the ordinate at R to intersect the ellipse in Z. The line ZP is the required tangent. As a check on the drawing, the tangents RQ and ZP should intersect in the major axis of the ellipse produced. Two tangents can be drawn from P to the ellipse.

115. To Draw an Ellipse by the Tangent Method.—
Fig. 148. A curve can be drawn more accurately if a series of tangents and the points of

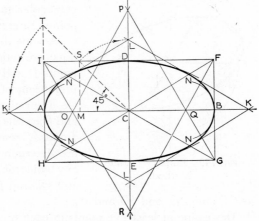

FIG. 148   Ellipse — Tangent Method.

tangency are given than if only a series of points is given. The tangents may
be straight lines or circular arcs. At any point of an ellipse an infinite number
of tangent circles can be drawn. One of these circles, the osculating circle, has
a higher order of contact with the ellipse than any other, and should be
used as the tangent circular arc.

To draw the required ellipse, having given the axes AB and DE, draw the
circumscribed rectangle $IFGH$ and its diagonals. From the vertices of the rectangle draw perpendiculars to the diagonals to find the centers O, P, Q, and
R of the four osculating circles at the vertices of the axes. With O and Q as
centers and radius OA, draw two tangent arcs as shown. With P and R as
centers and radius RD, draw two tangent arcs as shown. In most cases, it is
sufficiently accurate to join these four tangent arcs by smooth curves (§ 72).
When greater accuracy is required, four straight line-tangents KL should be
drawn by making KC equal to AC multiplied by $\sqrt{2}$ and CL equal to CD
multiplied by $\sqrt{2}$ (§ 101), since the diagonal of a square is equal to a side
multiplied by $\sqrt{2}$. This is shown graphically in Fig. 148 (dotted lines). From
C, draw 45° line CST, and, using center C, strike arcs SL and TK. The other
two corners of the rhombus are located in a similar manner.

The radius of the osculating circle at the vertex of the major axis is $b^2 \div a$
if b and a represent, respectively, the semi-minor and semi-major axes. From
the similar triangles OAH and IAC, it is evident that $OA : AH = IA : AC$;
hence $OA = b^2 \div a$. Similarly, $PE = a^2 \div b$.

116. To Draw an Ellipse, Having Given Two Conjugate Diameters.—
Figs. 149 and 150.

Fig. 149. Let AB and DE be the given conjugate diameters. Two diameters
are conjugate when each is parallel to the tangents at the extremities of the
other. With center at C and radius CA,
draw a circle; draw the diameter GF perpendicular to AB and draw lines joining the
points D and F, and G and E.

Assume that the required ellipse is an oblique projection of the circle just drawn; the
points D and E of the ellipse are the oblique
projections of the points F and G of the circle, respectively; and similarly, the points P
and R are the oblique projections of the points
I and S, respectively. The points P and R
are determined by assuming the point X at
any point on AB and drawing the lines IS
and PR, and IP and SR, parallel, respectively,
to GF and DE, and FD and GE.

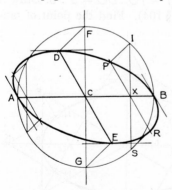

FIG. 149   Ellipse — Circle
Method.

Determine at least five points in each quadrant (more for larger ellipses)
by assuming additional points in the major axis and proceeding as explained

above for the point X. Draw the tangents at the extremities of the conjugate diameters, and then draw the required ellipse through the points with the aid of the irregular curve (§ 72).

Fig. 150 (a).—On the given conjugate diameters AB and DE, draw a parallelogram with sides parallel to them. Divide AC and AJ each into the same number of equal parts, and draw lines through these points as shown. The ellipse will pass through the intersection points. Points in the remaining three quadrants may be found in a similar manner.

Fig 150 (b).—Let AB and DE be the given conjugate diameters. Assume that the required ellipse is the oblique projection of a circle and that the circle is circumscribed by two squares whose sides make 45° with each other. The

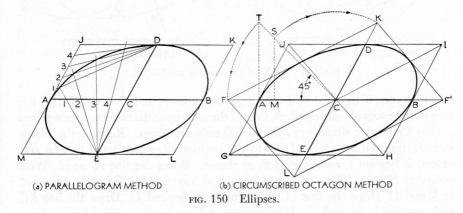

(a) PARALLELOGRAM METHOD   (b) CIRCUMSCRIBED OCTAGON METHOD

FIG. 150   Ellipses.

two squares will be projected as two parallelograms, circumscribed about the required ellipse, as shown, the sides of each square being parallel to the diagonals of the other.

Draw the parallelogram GJIH as shown. Draw parallelogram FKF′L by making FC equal to AC multiplied by √2 and CK equal to CD multiplied by √2 (§ 101) since the diagonal of a square is equal to a side multiplied by √2. This is shown graphically in Fig. 150 (b) with dotted lines. From C, draw the 45° line CST. Make CM equal to CD, and draw MS and AT perpendicular to FC. Using center C, strike arcs TF and SK. The other two corners of the parallelogram are located in a similar manner.

Inscribe the required ellipse in the octagon which is formed by the interior segments of the sides of the two parallelograms, as shown, with the aid of the irregular curve (§ 72).

117. Having Conjugate Diameters of an Ellipse Given, to Find the Axes.—Fig. 151.

(a) Conjugate diameters AB and CD and the ellipse are given. With the intersection O of the conjugate diameters (center of ellipse) as center, and any convenient radius, draw a circle to intersect the ellipse in four points. Join these points with straight lines, as shown; the resulting quadrilateral will be a rectangle whose sides are parallel, respectively, to the required major and minor axes. Draw the axes *EF* and *GH* parallel to the sides of the rectangle.

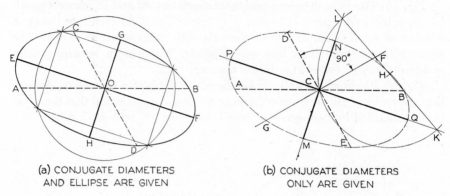

(a) CONJUGATE DIAMETERS
AND ELLIPSE ARE GIVEN

(b) CONJUGATE DIAMETERS
ONLY ARE GIVEN

FIG. 151   To Find the Axes of an Ellipse.

Obviously, if the center of the ellipse *O* is known, or is found by trial, the axes may be located as described, even if the conjugate diameters are not given.

(b) Conjugate diameters *AB* and *CD* only are given. Revolve the diameter *DE* through an angle of 90° to the position *FG*. Draw the line *FB* and extend it beyond *F* and beyond *B*, as shown. Bisect the line *FB* at *H*. With center at *H* and radius *HC*, draw an arc to intersect the line *FB*, produced, in *K* and *L*. Draw the line *LC* and produce it beyond *C*. Draw the line *KC* and produce it beyond *C*. With center at *C* and radius equal to *FL*, draw arcs to intersect *LC* in *M* and *N*. The line *MN* is the required minor axis. With center at *C* and radius *FK*, draw arcs to intersect *KC* in *P* and *Q*. The line *PQ* is the required major axis.

118. A General Method for Drawing Conic Sections.—Fig. 152.

Since the circle, ellipse, parabola, and hyperbola are curves which may be determined by the intersection of a plane with a cone of revolution (§ 330), it follows that all graphical constructions relating to points on the curves, tangents, etc., must be similar in the four cases. Figure 152 shows such related constructions when the axes and three points of the arcs are given, and it is required to find additional points on the arcs.

For the circle the diameters are given, for the ellipse the axes, for the parabola the axis, and for the hyperbola the transverse axis. In all cases the points *F*, *B*, and *G* are given. Draw the circumscribed rectangle *FHKG*. Divide *FH*, the side, into any number of equal parts (four, for example) and *FN*, half the bottom, into the same number of equal parts.

Draw lines through the division points as shown; the intersections of these lines are points of the curves. Note that one group of lines is the same in all four cases, while the lines in the other groups radiate inward and downward

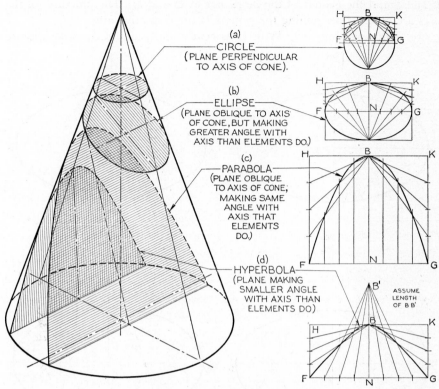

(a)
—CIRCLE—
(PLANE PERPENDICULAR
TO AXIS OF CONE).

(b)
—ELLIPSE—
(PLANE OBLIQUE TO AXIS
OF CONE, BUT MAKING
GREATER ANGLE WITH
AXIS THAN ELEMENTS DO.)

(c)
—PARABOLA—
(PLANE OBLIQUE
TO AXIS OF CONE,
MAKING SAME
ANGLE WITH
AXIS THAT
ELEMENTS
DO.)

(d)
—HYPERBOLA—
(PLANE MAKING
SMALLER ANGLE
WITH AXIS THAN
ELEMENTS DO)

ASSUME
LENGTH
OF B B'

FIG. 152   Conic Sections.

for the circle and ellipse, remain parallel for the parabola, and radiate inward and upward for the hyperbola.

119. To Draw Approximate Ellipses by Means of Circular Arcs.— Fig. 153. *Let AB and DE be the axes.*

There are a number of constructions available. The following are recommended for their simplicity and for the close approximation of the resulting curves to true ellipses. The deviations from the true ellipse increase as the difference between the lengths of the axes increase.

(a) Sketch the semi-ellipse DAE and choose the center K of the small arc. Make DL equal to AK; draw KL and its perpendicular bisector; its point of intersection M with the minor axis produced is the center of the large arc. Find the centers N and O by setting off CN equal to CK and CO equal to CM. With centers at K and N and radius KA, draw the two small arcs; with centers at M and O and radius DM, draw the two large arcs. The junctures of the arcs are on the lines joining the centers of the respective arcs.

(b) Make CG and CH equal to the difference of the axes. Make CK and CL equal to three-fourths of CG or CH. The centers of the small arcs are at

K and L and the centers of the large arcs at G and H. The junctures of the arcs are on the lines joining the centers of the respective arcs.

(c) Draw the line AD. With C as center and radius CA, strike the arc

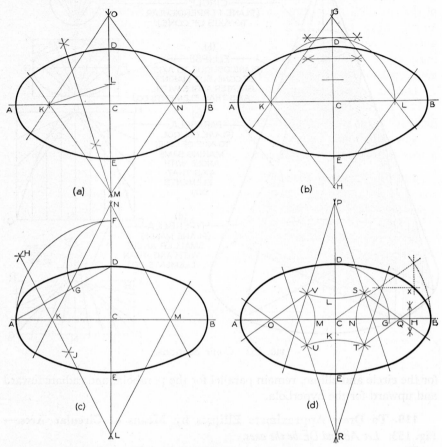

FIG. 153 Approximate Ellipses.

AF. With D a center and radius DF, strike the arc FG. Draw the perpendicular bisector HJ of the line AG; the points K and L, where it intersects the axes, are the centers of two of the required arcs. Find the centers M and N by setting off CM equal to CK, and CN equal to CL. The junctures of the arcs are on the lines joining the centers of the respective arcs.

(d) Find the centers O, Q, R, and P of the osculating circles of the required ellipse as explained for Fig. 148. Circles drawn with centers at R and P and radius RD would entirely enclose the required ellipse. Circles drawn with centers at O and Q and radius OA would be entirely within the required ellipse. It is necessary, therefore, to draw four circular arcs connecting the four circles referred to, in order to secure the required ellipse. An infinite number of different radii may be used for these arcs. Good results may always be secured if the radius is the mean of the two semi-axes AC and CD. See § 88. Therefore, make CG equal CD, bisect GB at H, and take CH as the radius of the circular arcs to connect the four arcs drawn with centers at O, Q, P, and R. Make DK, EL, AM, and BN equal to CH. With centers at O, Q, R, and P draw arcs as shown to find the centers S, T, U, and V of the four connecting arcs. Draw lines through the centers as shown to find the points of tangency of the several arcs and draw the arcs as shown.

Having drawn the approximate ellipse, the method of concentric circles (§ 114) can be used to check the accuracy of a few points of the curve, as indicated for the point X in the upper right quadrant.

The approximate ellipse constructed by this method differs so little from a true ellipse that the construction may be used quite generally in practice.

120. To Draw a Parabola.—Fig. 154. The curve of intersection of a cone of revolution with a plane parallel to one of the elements of the cone is a parabola (§ 118, Fig. 152). Such a curve is generated by a point moving so

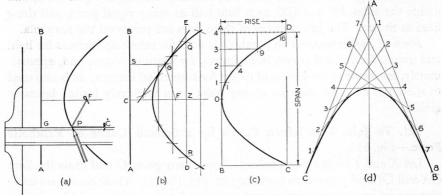

FIG. 154   To Draw a Parabola.

that its distances from a fixed point, the focus, and from a fixed line, the directrix, remain equal. The parabola, in each case below, is drawn with the aid of the irregular curve (§ 72).

(a) Let F be the focus and AB the directrix. The curve may be generated by a pencil guided by a string, as shown. The string is fastened at F and C; its length is GC; the point C is selected at random; its distance from G depends on the desired extent of the curve. The string must be kept taut, and the pencil must be kept against the T-square, as shown.

(b) Draw a line DE parallel to the directrix and at any distance CZ from it. With center at F and radius CZ strike arcs to intersect the line DE in the points Q and R, which are points of the required curve. Determine as many additional points as are necessary to draw the required parabola accurately by selecting other points similar to point Z along the axis, drawing lines through them parallel to *AB*, and continuing as described for line *DE*. A tangent to the parabola at any point *G* bisects the angle formed by the focal line *FG* and the line *SG* perpendicular to the directrix.

(c) Given the *rise* and *span* of the parabola. Divide *AO* into any number of equal parts and divide *AD* into a number of equal parts amounting to the square of that number. From line *AB*, each point is offset by a number of units equal to the square of the number of units from point *O*. Thus, point *1* projects 1 unit (the square of *1*), point *2* projects 4 units (the square of *2*), point *3* projects 9 units (the square of *3*), and point *4* projects 16 units (the square of *4*). This method is generally used for drawing parabolic arches.

(d) Let *B* and *C* be two given points of the parabola and *AB* and *AC* tangents at those points. Divide the segments *AB* and *AC* into the same number of equal parts, for example, eight. Number the division points as shown and connect corresponding points. These lines are tangents of the required parabola and form its envelope. Draw the curve as shown.

Fig. 152 (c).—Given the *span* and *rise*, or the width and height of the enclosing rectangle. Divide the base, *FG*, into any number of equal parts, and divide the sides, *HF* and *GK*, each into half as many equal parts, and draw lines as shown. The intersections of these lines are points on the parabola.

Practical Applications.—The parabola is used for reflecting surfaces for light and sound, for vertical curves in highways, for forms of arches, and, approximately, for forms of the curves of cables for suspension bridges. It is also used to show the bending moment at any point on a uniformly loaded beam or girder.

121. To Join Two Given Points by a Smooth Curve of Parabolic Form.—Fig. 155.

Let *X* and *Y* be the given points. Assume any point *O* and draw the lines *OX* and *OY* and proceed as explained for Fig. 154 (d). These curves are more pleasing in appearance than circular arcs and are useful in machine design. If the tangents *OX* and *OY* are equal, the axis of the parabola will bisect the angle between the two tangents.

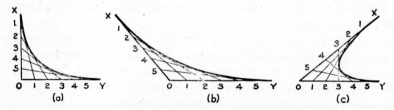

FIG. 155   To Join Two Points by a Parabolic Curve.

122. To Draw a Hyperbola.—Fig. 156. The curve of intersection of a cone of revolution with a plane making an angle with the axis of the cone smaller than that made by the elements is a *hyperbola* (§ 330, Figs. 649 and

152, d). Such a curve is generated by a point moving so that the difference of its distances from two fixed points, the foci, is constant and equal to the transverse axis of the hyperbola.

Fig. 156 (a).—Let *F* and *F'* be the foci and *AB* the transverse axis. The curve may be generated by a pencil guided by a string, as shown. The string is fastened at *F'* and *C*; its length is *FC* minus *AB*; the point *C* is chosen at pleasure; its distance from *F* depends on the desired extent of the curve.

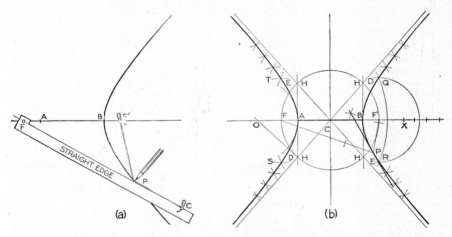

FIG. 156   To Draw a Hyperbola.

The straightedge is fastened at *F*. If it is revolved about *F*, with the pencil point moving against it and with the string taut, the hyperbola may be drawn, as shown.

Fig. 156 (b).—To construct the curve geometrically, select any point *X* in the transverse axis produced. With centers at *F* and *F'* and *BX* as radius, strike the arcs *DE*. With the same centers and *AX* as radius, strike arcs to intersect the arcs first drawn in the points *Q*, *R*, *S*, and *T*, which are points of the required hyperbola. Find as many additional points as are necessary to draw the curves accurately by selecting other points similar to point *X* along the transverse axis, and proceeding as described for point *X*.

To draw the tangent to a hyperbola at a given point *P*, bisect the angle between the focal radii *FP* and *F'P*. The bisector is the required tangent.

To draw the asymptotes *HCH* of the hyperbola, draw a circle with the diameter *FF'* and erect perpendiculars to the transverse axis at the points *A* and *B* to intersect the circle in the points *H*. The lines *HCH* are the required asymptotes.

To find the center *O* of the osculating circle at the vertex of the transverse diameter, erect a perpendicular *HO* to the asymptote at *H*. Its intersection *O* with the transverse axis produced is the required center.

To draw the curve accurately, it is important to draw the asymptotes, the osculating circles at the vertices, and tangents at several points.

123. To Draw an Equilateral Hyperbola.—Fig. 157. Let the asymptotes OB and OA, at right angles to each other, and the point P on the curve, be given.

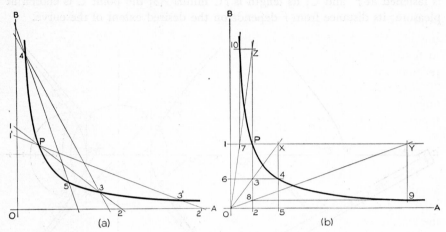

FIG. 157   Equilateral Hyperbola.

(a) In an equilateral hyperbola the asymptotes, at right angles to each other, may be used as the axes to which the curve is referred. If a chord of the hyperbola is extended to intersect the axes, the intercepts between the curve and the axes are equal. For example, a chord through given point P intersects the axes at points 1 and 2, intercept $P,1$ and $2,3$ are equal, and point 3 is a point on the hyperbola. Likewise, another chord through P provides equal intercepts $P,1'$ and $3',2'$, and point $3'$ is a point on the curve. All chords need not be drawn through given point P, but as new points are established on the curve, chords may be drawn through them to obtain more points. After enough points are found to insure an accurate curve, the hyperbola is drawn with the aid of the irregular curve (§ 72).

(b) In an equilateral hyperbola, the coordinates are related so that their products remain constant. Through given point P, draw lines $1,P,Y$ and $2,P,Z$ parallel, respectively, to the axes. From the origin of coordinates O, draw any diagonal intersecting these two lines at points 3 and X. At these points draw lines parallel to the axes, intersecting at point 4, a point on the curve. Likewise, another diagonal from O intersects the two lines through P at points 8 and Y, and lines through these points parallel to the axes intersect at point 9, another point of the curve. A third diagonal similarly produces point 10 on the curve, and so on. Find as many points as necessary for a smooth curve, and draw the parabola with the aid of the irregular curve (§ 72). It is evident from the similar triangles $0,X,5$ and $0,3,2$ that $P,1 \times P,2 = 4,5 \times 4,6$.

The equilateral hyperbola can be used to represent varying pressure of a gas as the volume varies, because the pressure varies inversely as the volume; i.e., pressure × volume is constant.

124. To Draw a Spiral of Archimedes.—Fig. 158. This spiral may be generated by a point moving around a fixed point, called the pole, and away from it in such a manner that the distance from the pole increases uniformly with the angle. Hence, to find points of the curve, draw lines through the pole making equal angles with each other, such as 30° angles, and, beginning with any one line, set off any distance, such as $\frac{1}{16}$ inch; set off twice that distance on the next line, three times on the third, and so on. Through the points thus determined draw a smooth curve, using the irregular curve (§ 72).

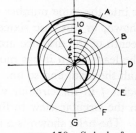

FIG. 158   Spiral of Archimedes.

125. To Draw a Helix.—Fig. 159. A *helix* is generated by a point moving around and along the surface of a cylinder or cone with a uniform angular velocity about the axis, and with a uniform linear velocity in the direction of the axis. A cylindrical helix is generally known simply as a "helix." The distance measured parallel to the axis traversed by the point in one revolution is called the *lead*.

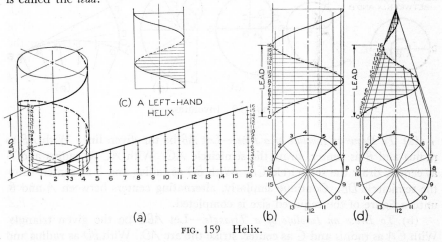

(C) A LEFT-HAND HELIX

(a)   (b)   (d)

FIG. 159   Helix.

If the cylindrical surface upon which a helix is generated is rolled out into a plane, the helix becomes a straight line, as shown in Fig. 159 (a), and the portion below the helix becomes a right triangle, the altitude of which is equal to the lead of the helix and the length of the base equal to the circumference of the cylinder. Such a helix can, therefore, be defined as the shortest line which can be drawn on the surface of a cylinder connecting two points not on the same element.

To draw the helix, draw two views of the cylinder upon which the helix is generated (b), and divide the circle of the base into any number of equal parts. On the rectangular view of the cylinder, set off the lead, and divide it into the same number of equal parts as the base. Number the divisions as shown, in this case sixteen. When the generating point has moved one-sixteenth of the distance around the cylinder, it will have risen one-sixteenth of the lead; when it has moved half-way around the cylinder, it will have risen half the lead, and so on. Points on the helix are found by projecting up from point *1* in the circular view to line *1* in the rectangular view, from point *2* in the circular view to line *2* in the rectangular view, and so on.

The helix shown is a *right-hand helix.* In a *left-hand helix,* the solid portions of the curve would be inclined in the opposite direction, i.e., downward to the right, as shown at (c). The helix shown at (b) could be converted into a left-hand helix by interchanging the visible and hidden lines.

The helix finds many applications in industry, as in screw threads, worm gears, conveyors, "spiral" stairways, and so on. The stripes of a barber pole are helical in form.

126. To Draw an Involute.—Fig. 160. The path of a point on a cord, as the cord unwinds from a line, a polygon, or a circle, is an involute.

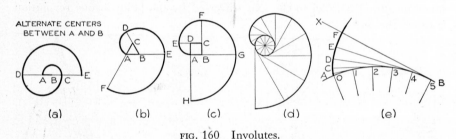

FIG. 160   Involutes.

(a) *To Draw an Involute of a Line.*—Let *AB* be the given line. With *AB* as radius and *B* as center, draw the semicircle *AC*. With *AC* as radius and *A* as center, draw the semicircle *CD*. With *BD* as radius and *B* as center, draw the semicircle *DE*. Continue similarly, alternating centers between *A* and *B*, until a figure of the required size is completed.

(b) *To Draw an Involute of a Triangle.*—Let *ABC* be the given triangle. With *CA* as radius and *C* as center, strike the arc *AD*. With *BD* as radius and *B* as center, strike the arc *DE*. With *AE* as radius and *A* as center, strike the arc *EF*. Continue similarly until a figure of the required size is completed.

(c) *To Draw an Involute of a Square.*—Let *ABCD* be the given square. With *DA* as radius and *D* as center, draw the 90° arc *AE*. Proceed as for the involute of a triangle until a figure of the required size is completed.

(d) *To Draw an Involute of a Circle.*—A circle may be regarded as a polygon with an infinite number of sides. The involute is constructed, as shown, by dividing the circumference into a number of equal parts, drawing a tangent at each division point, setting off along each tangent the length of the corresponding circular arc (§ 111), and drawing the required curve through the points set off on the several tangents.

(e) The involute may be generated by a point in a straight line which is rolled on a fixed circle. Points on the required curve may be determined by setting off equal distances 0–1, 1–2, 2–3, etc., along the circumference, drawing a tangent at each division point, and proceeding as explained for (d).

The involute of a circle is used in the construction of involute gear teeth (§ 488). In this system, the involute forms the face and a part of the flank of the teeth of gear wheels; the outlines of the teeth of racks are straight lines.

127. To Draw a Cycloid.—Fig. 161. A cycloid may be generated by a point P in the circumference of a circle which rolls along a straight line.

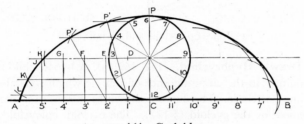

FIG. 161 Cycloid.

Given the generating circle and the straight line AB tangent to it, make the distances CA and CB each equal to the semi-circumference of the circle (§ 111). Divide these distances and the semi-circumference into the same number of equal parts, six for instance, and number them consecutively as shown. Suppose the circle to roll to the left; when point 1 of the circle reaches point 1' of the line, the center of the circle will be at D, point 7 will be the highest point of the circle and the generating point 6 will be at the same distance from the line AB as point 5 is when the circle is in its central position. Hence to find the point P', draw a line through point 5 parallel to AB and intersect it with an arc drawn from the center D with a radius equal to that of the circle. To find the point P'', draw a line through point 4 parallel to AB, and intersect it with an arc drawn from the center E, with a radius equal to that of the circle. Points J, K, and L are found in a similar manner.

Another method which may be employed is shown in the right half of the figure. With center at 11' and the chord 11–6 as radius, strike an arc. With 10' as center and the chord 10–6 as radius, strike an arc. Continue similarly with centers 9', 8', and 7'. Draw the required cycloid tangent to these arcs.

The student may use either method; the second is the shorter one, and is preferred. It is evident, from the tangent arcs drawn in the manner just described, that the line joining the generating point and the point of contact of the generating circle is a normal of the cycloid; the lines $1'P'$ and $2'P''$, for instance, are normals; this property makes the cycloid suitable for the outlines of gear teeth.

128. To Draw an Epicycloid.—Fig. 162 (a). An epicycloid may be generated by a point P in the circumference of a circle which rolls along the convex side of another circle. The curve is drawn as shown, in a manner similar to that described for the cycloid (§ 127).

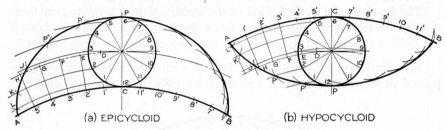

(a) EPICYCLOID   (b) HYPOCYCLOID

FIG. 162   Epicycloid and Hypocycloid.

129. To Draw a Hypocycloid.—Fig. 162 (b). A hypocycloid may be generated by a point P in the circumference of a circle which rolls along the concave side of another circle. The curve is drawn as shown, in a manner similar to that described for the cycloid (§ 127). The cycloid, epicycloid, and hypocycloid are used to form the outlines of cycloidal gear teeth and are, therefore, of great practical importance in machine design.

GEOMETRICAL CONSTRUCTION PROBLEMS*

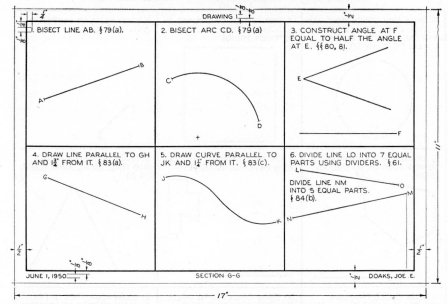

FIG. 163 GEOMETRICAL CONSTRUCTION PROBLEMS. Divide sheet into six equal parts as shown and draw constructions accurately, using a fairly hard pencil (2H to 4H) with a long, sharp, conical point. Draw required lines black, and construction lines *very light*. Letter points as shown. Omit spacing dimensions. Letter problem instructions if assigned.

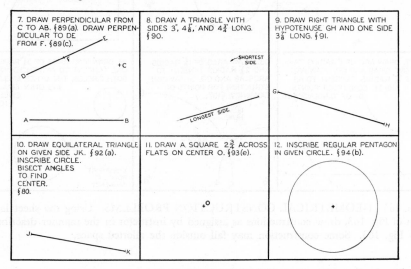

FIG. 164 GEOMETRICAL CONSTRUCTION PROBLEMS. Using the sheet layout of Fig. 163, draw constructions as assigned in the manner described for Fig. 163.

* Problems in convenient form for solution may be found in *Technical Drawing Problems*, by Giesecke, Mitchell and Spencer, and in *Technical Drawing Problems—Series 2*, by Spencer and Grant, both designed to accompany this text, and published by The Macmillan Co.

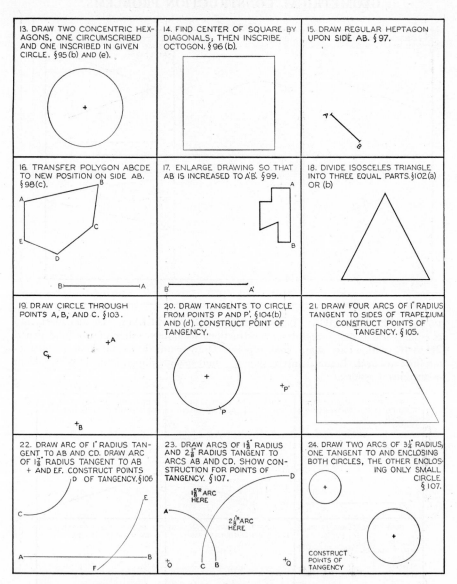

13. DRAW TWO CONCENTRIC HEX-AGONS, ONE CIRCUMSCRIBED AND ONE INSCRIBED IN GIVEN CIRCLE. §95 (b) AND (e).

14. FIND CENTER OF SQUARE BY DIAGONALS; THEN INSCRIBE OCTOGON. §96 (b).

15. DRAW REGULAR HEPTAGON UPON SIDE AB. §97.

16. TRANSFER POLYGON ABCDE TO NEW POSITION ON SIDE AB. §98(c).

17. ENLARGE DRAWING SO THAT AB IS INCREASED TO A'B'. §99.

18. DIVIDE ISOSCELES TRIANGLE INTO THREE EQUAL PARTS.§102.(a) OR (b)

19. DRAW CIRCLE THROUGH POINTS A, B, AND C. §103.

20. DRAW TANGENTS TO CIRCLE FROM POINTS P AND P'. §104(b) AND (d). CONSTRUCT POINT OF TANGENCY.

21. DRAW FOUR ARCS OF 1" RADIUS TANGENT TO SIDES OF TRAPEZIUM. CONSTRUCT POINTS OF TANGENCY. §105.

22. DRAW ARC OF 1" RADIUS TAN-GENT TO AB AND CD. DRAW ARC OF 1⅞" RADIUS TANGENT TO AB + AND EF. CONSTRUCT POINTS D OF TANGENCY.§106

23. DRAW ARCS OF 1⅜" RADIUS AND 2⅛" RADIUS TANGENT TO ARCS AB AND CD. SHOW CON-STRUCTION FOR POINTS OF TANGENCY. §107.
1⅝"R ARC HERE
2⅛"R ARC HERE
CONSTRUCT POINTS OF TANGENCY

24. DRAW TWO ARCS OF 3¼" RADIUS, ONE TANGENT TO AND ENCLOSING BOTH CIRCLES, THE OTHER ENCLOS-ING ONLY SMALL CIRCLE §107.
CONSTRUCT POINTS OF TANGENCY

FIG. 165 GEOMETRICAL CONSTRUCTION PROBLEMS. Using the sheet lay-out of Fig. 163, draw constructions as assigned by instructor in the manner described for Fig. 163. Some construction may fall outside the allotted space.

104

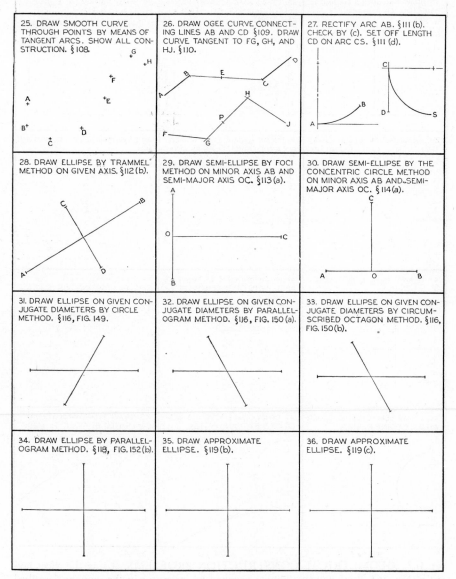

25. DRAW SMOOTH CURVE THROUGH POINTS BY MEANS OF TANGENT ARCS. SHOW ALL CONSTRUCTION. § 108.	26. DRAW OGEE CURVE CONNECTING LINES AB AND CD § 109. DRAW CURVE TANGENT TO FG, GH, AND HJ. § 110.	27. RECTIFY ARC AB. § 111 (b). CHECK BY (c). SET OFF LENGTH CD ON ARC CS. § 111 (d).
28. DRAW ELLIPSE BY TRAMMEL METHOD ON GIVEN AXIS. § 112 (b).	29. DRAW SEMI-ELLIPSE BY FOCI METHOD ON MINOR AXIS AB AND SEMI-MAJOR AXIS OC. § 113 (a).	30. DRAW SEMI-ELLIPSE BY THE CONCENTRIC CIRCLE METHOD ON MINOR AXIS AB AND SEMI-MAJOR AXIS OC. § 114 (a).
31. DRAW ELLIPSE ON GIVEN CONJUGATE DIAMETERS BY CIRCLE METHOD. § 116, FIG. 149.	32. DRAW ELLIPSE ON GIVEN CONJUGATE DIAMETERS BY PARALLELOGRAM METHOD. § 116, FIG. 150 (a).	33. DRAW ELLIPSE ON GIVEN CONJUGATE DIAMETERS BY CIRCUMSCRIBED OCTAGON METHOD. § 116, FIG. 150 (b).
34. DRAW ELLIPSE BY PARALLELOGRAM METHOD. § 118, FIG. 152 (b).	35. DRAW APPROXIMATE ELLIPSE. § 119 (b).	36. DRAW APPROXIMATE ELLIPSE. § 119 (c).

FIG. 166   GEOMETRICAL CONSTRUCTION PROBLEMS. Using the sheet layout of Fig. 163, draw constructions as assigned by instructor in the manner described for Fig. 163. Some construction may fall outside the allotted space.

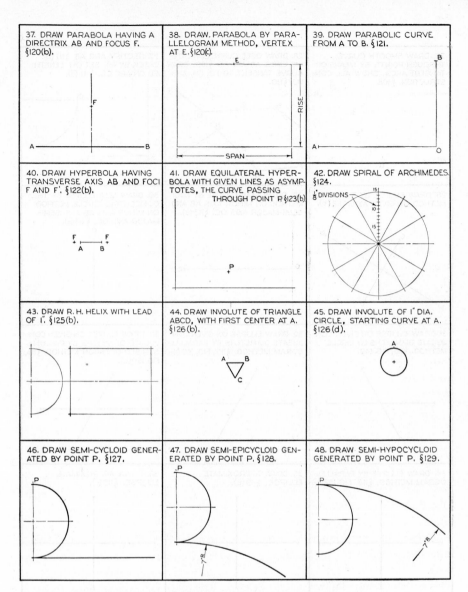

37. DRAW PARABOLA HAVING A DIRECTRIX AB AND FOCUS F. §120(b).	38. DRAW. PARABOLA BY PARALLELOGRAM METHOD, VERTEX AT E. §120(c).	39. DRAW PARABOLIC CURVE FROM A TO B. §121.
40. DRAW HYPERBOLA HAVING TRANSVERSE AXIS AB AND FOCI F AND F'. §122(b).	41. DRAW EQUILATERAL HYPERBOLA WITH GIVEN LINES AS ASYMPTOTES, THE CURVE PASSING THROUGH POINT P. §123(b)	42. DRAW SPIRAL OF ARCHIMEDES. §124.
43. DRAW R. H. HELIX WITH LEAD OF 1". §125(b).	44. DRAW INVOLUTE OF TRIANGLE ABCD, WITH FIRST CENTER AT A. §126(b).	45. DRAW INVOLUTE OF 1" DIA. CIRCLE, STARTING CURVE AT A. §126(d).
46. DRAW SEMI-CYCLOID GENERATED BY POINT P. §127.	47. DRAW SEMI-EPICYCLOID GENERATED BY POINT P. §128.	48. DRAW SEMI-HYPOCYCLOID GENERATED BY POINT P. §129.

FIG. 167   GEOMETRICAL CONSTRUCTION PROBLEMS. Using the sheet layout of Fig. 163, draw constructions as assigned by instructor in the manner described or Fig. 163. Some construction may fall outside allotted space.

CHAPTER 5

*Lettering**

130. Origin of Letter Forms. Modern European alphabets had their origin in Egyptian hieroglyphics, which were developed into a cursive hieroglyphic or hieratic writing. This was adopted by the Phoenicians, and was developed by them into an alphabet of twenty-two letters. This Phoenician alphabet was adopted by the Greeks, but it evolved into two distinct types in different sections of that country: an Eastern Greek type, used also in Asia Minor, and a Western Greek type, used in the Greek colonies in and near Italy. In this manner the Western Greek alphabet became the Latin alphabet about 700 B.C. The Latin alphabet came into general use throughout the Old World.

Originally the Roman capital alphabet consisted of twenty-two characters which have remained practically unchanged to this day. They may still be seen on Trajan's Column and other Roman monuments. The letter *V* was used for both *U* and *V* until the tenth century. The last of the twenty-six characters, *J*, was adopted at the end of the fourteenth century as a modification of the letter *I*. The dot over the lower-case *j* still indicates its kinship to the *i*; in Old English the two letters are very similar. The numerous modern styles of letters were derived from the original Roman capitals.

Before the invention of printing by Gutenberg in the fifteenth century, all letters were made by hand and were modified and decorated according to the taste of the individual writer. These letters were introduced into England, where they became known as Old English. The early German printers adopted these letters, and they are still in use in Germany. The early Italian printers used Roman letters, which were later introduced into England, where they gradually replaced the block letters of German origin. Thus the Roman capital has come down to us virtually in its original form.

131. Letter Styles. A general classification of letter styles is shown in Fig. 168. These were all made with Speedball pens, as indicated, and are therefore largely single-stroke letters.

---

* *Lettering*, and not "printing," is the correct term to denote the act of making letters by hand. *Printing* means the production of printed material on a printing press.

If the letters are drawn in outline and filled in, they are called "filled-in" letters (Figs. 212 and 219). The plainest and most legible style is the GOTHIC from which our single-stroke engineering letter is derived. The term ROMAN

Classification of letter styles by division of groups

ABCDEFGH
abcdefgh

GOTHIC *All letters having the elementary strokes of even width are classified as Gothic* ⌐
——*Made with Style A or B Speedball Pen*

ABCDEFGH
abcdefghij

Roman *All letters having elementary strokes "accented" or consisting of heavy and light lines, are classified as Roman.*
——*Made with Style C or D Speedball Pen*

ABCDEFGHI
abcdefghijklm

Italic- All slanting letters are classified as Italics~ These may be further designated as Roman-Italics, Gothic Italics or Text Italic.
——*Made with Style C or D Speedball Pen*

𝕬𝕭𝕮𝕯𝕰𝕱𝕲
𝖆𝖇𝖈𝖉𝖊𝖋𝖌𝖍𝖎𝖏𝖐𝖑

Text—*This term includes all styles of Old English, German text, Bradley text or others of various trade names ~ Text styles are too illegible for commercial purposes.*
——*Made with Style C or D Speedball Pen*

FIG. 168   Classification of Letter Styles.

refers to any letter having wide downward strokes and thin connecting strokes, as would result from the use of a wide pen, while the ends of the strokes are terminated with spurs called *serifs*. Roman letters include Old Roman and Modern Roman, and may be vertical or inclined. Inclined letters are also referred to as *Italic*, regardless of the letter style; those shown in Fig. 168 are inclined Modern Roman. *Text* letters are often loosely referred to as 𝖮𝖑𝖽 𝕰𝖓𝖌𝖑𝖎𝖘𝖍, though these letters as well as the other similar letters such as German Text, are actually Gothic. The Commercial Gothic shown at the top of Fig. 168 is a relatively modern development which originates from the earlier Gothic forms. German Text is the only commercially used form of medieval Gothic in use today.

For more extensive and detailed information regarding the styles of letters, see §§ 169-174.

132. Extended and Condensed Letters. To meet design or space requirements, letters may be extremely narrow and spaced close together, in

which case they are called "compressed" or "condensed" letters. If the letters
are wider than normal, they are referred to as "extended" letters. See Fig. 169.

CONDENSED LETTERS
EXTENDED LETTERS
Condensed Letters

Extended Letters

FIG. 169   Extended and Condensed Letters.

133. Lightface and Boldface Letters. Letters also vary as to the thickness of the stems or strokes. Letters having very thin stems are called LIGHT-
FACE, while those having heavy stems are called **BOLDFACE** (Fig. 170).

LIGHTFACE
BOLDFACE

FIG. 170   Lightface and Boldface Letters.

134. Single-Stroke Gothic Letters. During the latter part of the nine-
teenth century the development of industry and of technical drawing in the
United States made evident a need for a simple, legible letter which could be
executed with single strokes of an ordinary pen. To meet this need C. W. Reinhardt, formerly Chief Draftsman for the *Engineering News*, developed alphabets
of capital and lower-case inclined and "upright" letters,[*] based upon the old
Gothic letters (Fig. 214). For each letter he worked out a systematic series of
strokes. The single-stroke Gothic letters used on technical drawings today are
based upon Reinhardt's work.

A complete working drawing of an engineering structure must not only
describe graphically the form of the structure but it must show also, by figured
dimensions, the size of the structure, and, by written specifications, the material to be used in its construction, the finish of the surfaces, processes or
methods of construction, and much other necessary information. The supplying
of the dimensions and written specifications with notes of instruction, title,
etc., is an important part of working drawings. Well-executed lettering con-
tributes more than any other single factor to an attractive and legible drawing.
See Figs. 742, 885, 911, and 912.

[*] Published in the *Engineering News* about 1893, and in book form in 1895.

135. Standardization of Lettering. The first step toward standardization of technical lettering was made by C. W. Reinhardt when he developed single-stroke letters with a systematic series of strokes (§ 134). However, since that time there has been an unnecessary and confusing diversity of lettering styles and forms, and the American Standards Association, in 1935, suggested letter forms which are now generally considered as standard. The present Standard (ASA Z14.1—1946) is exactly the same as that given in 1935, except that vertical lower-case letters have now been added. Facsimile reproductions of American Standard lettering are given in Appendix 2 of this book.

The letters in this chapter and throughout this text conform to the American Standard.. Vertical letters are perhaps slightly more legible, but are more difficult to execute than inclined letters. Both vertical and inclined letters are standard, and the engineer or draftsman may be called upon to use either. Students should, therefore, learn to execute both forms well, though they may give more attention to the style which they like and can do better.

According to the American Standard, "The most important requirement for lettering as used on working drawings is legibility. The second is ease and rapidity of execution. . . . It is not desirable to grade the size of lettering with the size of the drawing except when a reduced photographic reproduction of the drawing is to be made. In other words the size and weight of the lettering should be such as will produce legible prints from tracings either in pencil or in ink. Lettering should not be underlined except for particular emphasis."*

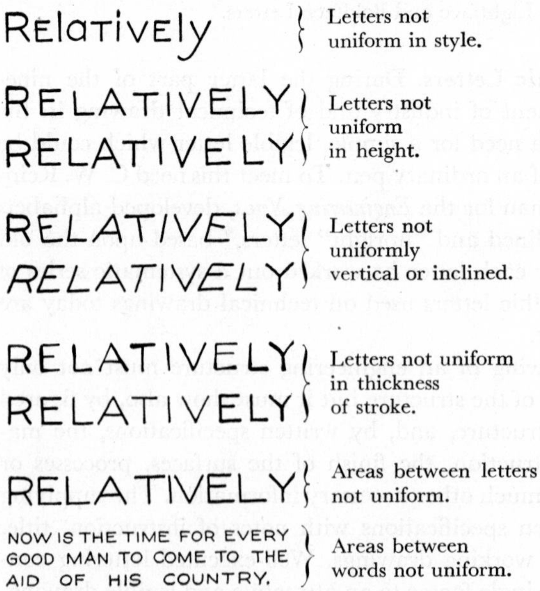

Relatively   } Letters not uniform in style.

RELATIVELY } Letters not uniform in height.
RELATIVELY }

RELATIVELY } Letters not uniformly vertical or inclined.
RELATIVELY }

RELATIVELY } Letters not uniform in thickness of stroke.
RELATIVELY }

RELATIVELY } Areas between letters not uniform.

NOW IS THE TIME FOR EVERY } Areas between words not uniform.
GOOD MAN TO COME TO THE }
AID OF HIS COUNTRY. }

FIG. 171   Uniformity in Lettering.

*ASA Z14.1—1946.

136. Uniformity. In any style of lettering, *uniformity* is essential. Uniformity in height, proportion, inclination, strength of lines, spacing of letters, and spacing of words insures a pleasing appearance (Fig. 171).

Uniformity in height and inclination is promoted by the use of light guide lines (Figs. 180 and 199). Uniformity in strength of lines can be acquired only by the skillful use of properly selected pencils and pens (§§ 139 and 140).

137. Optical Illusions. Good lettering involves

artistic design, in which the white and black areas are carefully balanced to produce a pleasing effect. Letters are designed to *look* well, and many allowances must be made for incorrect perception. Some of the more striking optical illusions are shown in Fig. 172. Note that in Fig. 182 the standard *H* is narrower, and the *W* is wider than those shown in Fig. 172; and that the numeral *8* in Fig. 195 is narrower at the top than is that shown in Fig. 172. Note that the very acute angles in the *W* give the letter a compressed appearance; such acute angles should be avoided in letter design. Other optical illusions are shown in Fig. 106 (e) and (f).

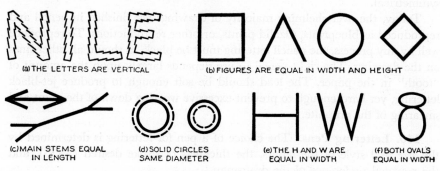

(a) THE LETTERS ARE VERTICAL   (b) FIGURES ARE EQUAL IN WIDTH AND HEIGHT

(c) MAIN STEMS EQUAL IN LENGTH   (d) SOLID CIRCLES SAME DIAMETER   (e) THE H AND W ARE EQUAL IN WIDTH   (f) BOTH OVALS EQUAL IN WIDTH

FIG. 172   Optical Illusions.

138. Stability. If the upper portions of certain letters and figures are equal in width to the lower portions, the letters and figures appear top-heavy. To correct this, the upper portions of these characters are reduced in size where possible, thereby producing the effect of *stability* and a more pleasing appearance (Fig. 173).

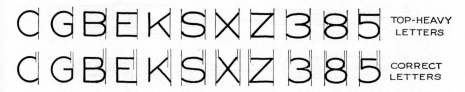

TOP-HEAVY LETTERS

CORRECT LETTERS

FIG. 173   Stability of Letters.

If the central horizontal strokes of the letters *B*, *E*, *F*, and *H* are placed at mid-height, they will appear to be below center. To overcome this optical illusion, these strokes should be drawn slightly above the center.

On account of the lack of width at the bottom of the letter *P*, if the central horizontal stroke, or stroke *2* (Fig. 190) is placed at mid-height it will *appear* to be above the center. To overcome this illusion, this stroke should be drawn slightly below the center.

The letter *R* is of such form that a similar illusion to that of the letter *P* does not exist, and the central horizontal stroke, or stroke *2* (Fig. 190) can be drawn at mid-height.

139. Lettering Pencils. Pencil letters can be best made with a medium-soft pencil with a conical point (Fig. 61, c). The pencil is first sharpened to a needle point, then the point is dulled *very slightly* by marking on paper, the pencil being rotated to keep the point symmetrical. An F, H, or a 2H pencil is suitable for use on ordinary drawing paper of smooth surface. While lettering, the draftsman should rotate the pencil occasionally in order to keep the point symmetrical.

Today, the overwhelming majority of drawings are finished in pencil and reproduced as blueprints, Ozalid prints, or other reproductions. To reproduce well by any process, the pencil lettering must be black, as should all other lines on the drawing. The right pencil to use depends largely upon the amount of "tooth" in the paper. The lead should be soft enough to produce jet-black lettering, yet hard enough to prevent excessive wearing down of the point and smearing of the graphite.

140. Lettering Pens. The choice of a pen for lettering is determined by the size and style of the letters, the thickness of stroke desired (§ 133), and the personal preference of the draftsman.

These conditions vary so much that it is impossible to specify any certain pen to use. The student who is zealous in his efforts to develop his ability to letter will learn by experience which pen is best suited to his purpose. Figure 174 shows a variety of the best pen points in a range from the *tit-quill*, the finest,

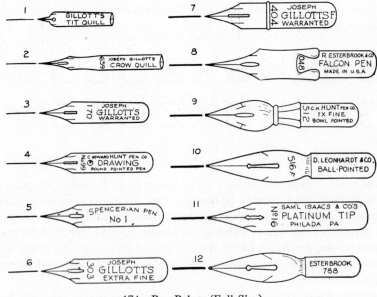

FIG. 174   Pen Points (Full Size).

to the *ball-pointed*, the coarsest. The widths of the lines made by the several pens are shown full-size in this figure. The medium widths, represented in the figure by the *Gillott's 303 and 404* (or equivalent) are most widely used for lettering notes and dimensions on drawings, in which case the letters are usually $\frac{1}{8}''$ high. For lettering $\frac{3}{16}''$ to $\frac{1}{4}''$ high, as for titles (§ 472), the ball-pointed pens are commonly used.

A very flexible pen should not be used for lettering, because the downward stroke is apt to be shaded. A good lettering pen is one with which it is easy to make a stroke of uniform width. New pen points have a thin film of oil, which should be removed with a cloth—not burned off with a match flame. The best results are secured from a pen which has been used for some time, that is, "broken in" with use. Hence, when a pen point has proved satisfactory, it should be carefully wiped after using and taken care of as a valuable instrument.

Letters more than about $\frac{1}{2}''$ in height generally require a special pen (Fig. 175). The *Speedball* pens are excellent for Gothic letters (Fig. 168), and are often used for titles and for the large drawing numbers in the corner of the title

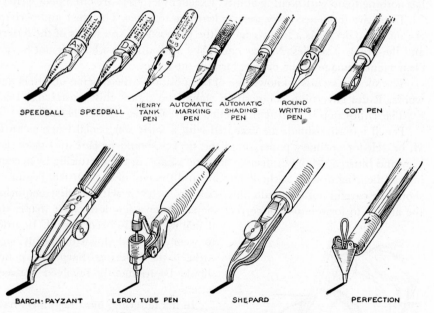

FIG. 175   Special Pens for Freehand Lettering.

block (Fig. 846). Other styles of Speedball pens are suitable for Roman or text letters. These pens have the additional advantage of being low in cost. The *Barch-Payzant Lettering Pen* is available in eleven sizes ranging from 000 (very coarse) to 8 (very fine). The size 8 pen produces a stroke fine enough to be used for the usual lettering on technical drawings, and is satisfactory for letters from $\frac{1}{8}''$ to $\frac{3}{16}''$ high.

The *Henry Tank Pen* (Fig. 175) is available in both plain and ball points, and has a simple device under the pen to hold ink. This device also prevents the points from spreading, and produces a uniform line.

The *Leroy Pen* is also available in a wide range of sizes, and is highly recommended. It can be used in a regular pen staff for freehand lettering or in the Leroy Lettering Instrument (Fig. 207) for mechanical lettering.

Several other popular patented pens are shown in Fig. 175. *Every lettering pen must be kept clean.* Drawing ink corrodes the point of the pen if allowed to dry, and thereby renders the pen unfit for use.

141. Technique of Lettering. *All normal persons can learn to letter if they are persistent and intelligent in their efforts.* While it is true that "practice makes perfect," it must be understood that practice alone is not enough; it must be accompanied by *continuous effort to improve.*

Lettering is freehand drawing and not writing. Good lettering is always accomplished by conscious effort and is never done well subconsciously, though correct habits of muscular co-ordination are of great assistance. Ability to letter has nothing to do with writing ability. Excellent letterers are often poor writers.

There are three necessary steps in learning to letter. The FIRST and perhaps the most important is a knowledge of the proportions and forms of the letters, and the order of strokes. No one can make a good letter who does not have a clear mental image of the correct form of the letter.

The SECOND step is a knowledge of composition—the spacing of letters and words. Rules governing composition should be thoroughly mastered (§ 166).

The THIRD step is persistent practice with *continuous effort to improve.*

Pencil lettering should be executed with a fairly soft pencil (such as an F, H, or 2H, for ordinary paper), and the strokes should be *dark* and *sharp*, not grey and blurred. Many draftsmen acquire "snap" in their lettering by accenting or "bearing down" at the beginning and the end of each stroke. Beginners should be careful not to overdo this trick or to try it without first acquiring the ability to form letters of correct shape. After a few letters are made, the pencil will tend to become dull. In order to wear the lead down uniformly, and to keep the lettering sharp, the pencil should be frequently revolved between letters.

FIG. 176 Position of Hand in Lettering.

In ink lettering, most beginners have a tendency toward excessive pressure on the pen point, thus producing strokes of varying widths. The pen point selected should make the strokes of desired thickness without spreading the nibs.

The correct position of the pen is shown in Fig. 176. The pen should be moved with light, uniform pressure, and the ink should *flow off* instead of being forced off by pressure upon the point. In general, vertical strokes should be drawn downward with a finger movement, and horizontal strokes to the right with a wrist movement, without turning the paper.

If the board upon which the drawing is fastened is small enough, it should be revolved to a position such that the lines of lettering are approximately at right angles to the forearm of the hand holding the pen. If the board is larger, the draftsman should shift his body to approximate this position as nearly as possible. *At no time should lettering be attempted when the forearm has no surface upon which to rest.*

Some draftsmen "ink" the pen with a quill from the ink bottle, but this is generally unnecessary unless some ink-holding device (such as that on the Henry Tank Pen, Fig. 175) is used. Excess ink, however, should be removed from the point by lightly touching it against the opening of the bottle.

Before an inked tracing is lettered, all guide lines should be drawn in pencil directly upon the tracing paper or cloth, as guide lines underneath are too indistinct to serve their purpose well as a guide for inking.

142. Left-Handers. All evidence indicates that the left-handed draftsman is just as skillful as the right-hander, and this includes skill in lettering. The most important step in learning to letter is to learn the correct shapes and proportions of letters, and these can be learned as well by the left-hander as by anyone else. The left-hander does have a problem of developing a system of strokes which seem most suitable for himself. The strokes shown in Figs. 182 to 203 are for right-handers, and the left-hander should experiment with each letter to find out which strokes are best for him. The habits of left-handers vary so much that it is futile to suggest a standard system of strokes for all left-handers.

The left-hander, in developing his own system of strokes, should decide upon strokes which he can make best with the pen, and he should then use the same strokes for pencil lettering as well. Pen strokes can be drawn in the direction the pen is leaned, or at right angles to this, or in curved paths between these two. The pen should never be "pushed" in the direction contrary to the way the pen is leaned, as the point has a tendency to dig into the paper. The strokes should, therefore, be those which are in harmony with the natural and intended use of the pen point.

The regular left-hander assumes a natural position exactly opposite to that of the right-hander, but he will be able to use the same strokes as shown for right-handers in Fig. 182 and those which follow, with perhaps some minor differences. As prescribed for right-handers, he will draw all vertical strokes downward, and may also draw all horizontal strokes from left to right. He may, however, prefer to draw horizontal strokes from right to left, and he should do this if it seems more natural to him. Also, he may wish to change the order of drawing horizontal strokes, so that in the case of the *E*, for example, the top stroke would be drawn first, and the bottom stroke drawn last. If this is done, the pen or pencil will not tend to hide strokes already drawn. Curved strokes will be essentially the same as for right-handers, with perhaps some adjustments of the starting and ending points of the curves.

The hooked-wrist left-hander has a more serious problem, and each such person will have to adopt a system which seems best for his own particular habits. Vertical strokes may be drawn downward as for right-handers, but many hooked-wrist left-handers will find it easier to draw vertical strokes upward. Horizontal strokes will most certainly be drawn from right to left with a finger movement, for the pen will dig into the paper if pushed in the other direction. Furthermore, the order of horizontal strokes will be to do those at the bottom first, and those at the top last, as, for instance, in the case of the *E*.

The left-handed student should advise his instructor at once that he is left-handed. On examinations where lettering is tested, he should letter a statement thereon to the effect that he is left-handed, and he should use strokes that he has found most suitable for his own use.

143. Guide Lines. Extremely light horizontal guide lines are necessary to regulate the height of the letters. Vertical letters do not look well if all letters are not uniformly vertical, and inclined letters do not look well if all letters are not inclined uniformly. Therefore, in addition to horizontal guide lines, light vertical or inclined guide lines should be used. These guide lines are not used to space the letters (as this should always be done by eye while lettering), but only to assist in securing uniform uprightness or inclination, and they should, accordingly, *be drawn at random*. Where several lines of letters are to be made, these vertical or inclined guide lines should be continuous lines from the bottom to the top of the lettered area (Fig. 180).

Guide lines are absolutely essential for good lettering, and the student should regard them as a welcome aid, and not as an unnecessary time-consuming requirement. Paradoxically, the better draftsman never fails to use guide lines, while the poor letterer who needs them most is inclined to slight this important step.

Guide lines for finished pencil lettering should be *made so lightly that they need not be erased*, as indeed they cannot be after the lettering has been completed. A relatively hard pencil, such as 4H to 6H, with a long, sharp conical point, should be used (Fig. 61, c). If the letters are inked, the guide lines may be removed after the ink is dry, with the artgum (Fig. 10).

In preparation for ink lettering, complete guide lines should be drawn, and the letters first drawn lightly in pencil. Experienced letterers often draw the complete guide lines, and then letter directly in ink, without first penciling the letters.

144. Spacing of Guide Lines. On working drawings, letters are commonly made $\frac{1}{8}''$ high. A simple method for drawing the guide lines is to use the scale in a vertical position, and simply set off $\frac{1}{8}''$ spaces, making both the letters and the spaces between lines of letters $\frac{1}{8}''$ high.

If it is desired to make the spaces between lines of letters less than the height of the letters, the methods shown in Fig. 177 will be found convenient. At (a), a scale is used diagonally, the letters in this case being four units high and the spaces between lines of letters being three units. If the scale is moved clockwise about the zero mark as center, the height of the letters and the spaces between lines of letters diminish but remain proportional. If moved counterclockwise, the spaces are increased. At (b), in Fig. 177, distances x are set off with bow dividers so that each is equal to $a + b$.

Special devices are often used for spacing guide lines. *Lettering triangles*, which are made in a variety of shapes and sizes, are provided with sets of holes in which the pencil point is inserted and the guide lines produced by moving

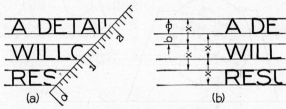

FIG. 177   Spacing of Guide Lines.

the triangle with the pencil point along the T-square. The *Braddock-Rowe Lettering Triangle* (Fig. 178) is convenient for drawing guide lines for lettering and dimension figures, and for drawing section lines. In addition, the triangle is

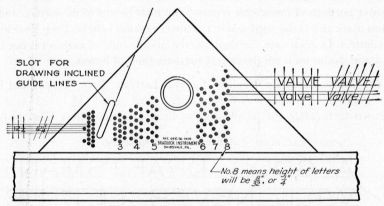

FIG. 178   Braddock-Rowe Lettering Triangle.

used as a utility 45° triangle. The numbers at the bottom of the triangle indicate spacings of guide lines in thirty-seconds of an inch. The column of holes at the left is used to draw guide lines for dimension figures $\frac{1}{8}''$ high, and for drawing section lines $\frac{1}{16}''$ apart.

The *Ames Lettering Instrument* (Fig. 179) is an ingenious transparent plastic device composed of a frame holding a disc which contains three columns of holes. The vertical distances between the holes may be adjusted quickly to the desired spacing for guide lines or section lines by simply turning the disc to one of the settings indicated at the bottom of the disc. These numbers indicate height of letters in thirty-seconds of an inch. Thus, for $\frac{1}{8}''$ high letters, the No. 4 setting would be used. The center column of holes is used to draw guide lines for numerals and fractions, the height of the whole number being two units, and the height of the fraction four units. Thus, for $\frac{1}{8}''$ whole numbers, the fraction would be twice as high, or $\frac{1}{4}''$. Since the spaces are equal, these holes can also be used to draw section lines for cast iron (§ 223).

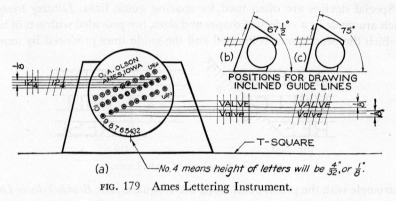

FIG. 179 Ames Lettering Instrument.

The two outer columns of holes are used to draw guide lines for capitals or lower-case letters, the column marked $\frac{3}{5}$ being used where it is desired to make the lower portions of lower-case letters $\frac{3}{5}$ the total height of the letters, and the column marked $\frac{2}{3}$ being used where the lower portion is to be $\frac{2}{3}$ the total height of the letters. In each case, for capitals, the middle hole of each set is not used. The $\frac{2}{3}$ and $\frac{3}{5}$ also indicate the spaces between lines of letters.

145. Guide Lines for Vertical Capital Letters. Both vertical and horizontal guide lines, drawn very lightly with a hard pencil (§§ 143, 144) should be drawn to regulate the height and verticality of the letters (Fig. 180).

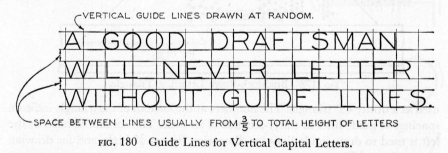

FIG. 180 Guide Lines for Vertical Capital Letters.

For lettering on working drawings the height of letters commonly used is $\frac{1}{8}''$. If the space between lines of letters is also taken at $\frac{1}{8}''$, the guide lines may be set off quickly by placing the scale in a vertical position, marking off $\frac{1}{8}''$ spaces, and drawing the guide lines with the T-square. The bow dividers may also be used by simply setting off $\frac{1}{8}$ spaces along a vertical line.

The space between two lines of lettering may vary from $\frac{3}{5}$ to the entire height of the letters, according to personal preference. If the space is less than the height of the letters, either of the methods shown in Fig. 177 may be used when guide-line devices for lettering are not available.

If the No. 4 holes on the Braddock-Rowe triangle are used, the letters will be $\frac{1}{8}''$ high, and the space between lines of lettering will be $\frac{2}{3}$ of this (§ 144). If the No. 4 setting of the Ames Lettering Instrument is used, the letters will be $\frac{1}{8}''$ high and the spaces between lines of lettering will be $\frac{2}{3}$ or $\frac{3}{5}$ of this, depending upon which column of holes is used.

However the horizontal guide lines are drawn, vertical guide lines should also be drawn, at random, to help keep the letters uniformly vertical.

When a combination of large and small capitals is used, the small capitals should be $\frac{3}{5}$ or $\frac{2}{3}$ as high as the large capitals (Fig. 181), which conforms to the guide-line devices mentioned above.

FIG. 181   Large and Small Capital Letters.

146. Vertical Capital Letters. The alphabet of vertical single-stroke Gothic letters of Fig. 182 is given for reference. The proportions of the letters

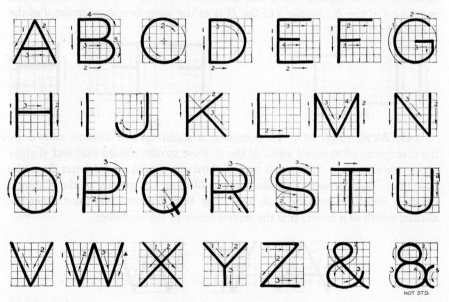

FIG. 182   Vertical Capital Letters.

are indicated by the small squares, and arrows with numbers show the directions and order of strokes. Note that the letters are six unit-squares high. A letter which is six units wide, therefore, is as wide as it is high, as for example the letter *A*. Horizontal strokes are made from left to right, and vertical strokes from the top downward.

Most of the strokes are natural and do not require memorizing, but it should be understood that it is a decided mistake for the student to practice lettering before he knows the proportions and strokes of the letters he desires to execute.

It is suggested that the student learn the forms of the letters by sketching them on cross-section paper, making each letter six squares high.

For purposes of analysis and practice, letters may be classified as (1) straight-line combinations and (2) curved-line combinations. They are explained on pages 120 and 121.

STRAIGHT-LINE LETTERS

147. ILT.—Fig. 183. The *I* and the vertical strokes of the *L* and *T* are drawn downward with a finger movement. The horizontal strokes are drawn from left to right.

The normal width of the *L* is $4\frac{1}{2}$ units as shown, but when it is followed in a word by a capital *A* its width should be reduced to about $4\frac{1}{4}$ spaces to compensate for the large area between the letters.

148. FEH.—Fig. 184. Stroke *4* of the *E* is about three-fifths as long as stroke *2*, and is slightly above the mid-point. Stroke *3* of the *F* is the same as stroke *4* of the *E*. Stroke *3* of the *H* is at the same height as stroke *4* of the *E* and stroke *3* of the *F*.

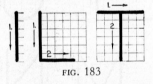

FIG. 183

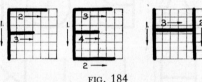

FIG. 184

149. AVW.—Fig. 185. To overcome a slight optical illusion caused by the divergence of strokes *1* and *2* of the *A*, those strokes should intersect slightly above the cap line. Stroke *3* is at one-third the height of the letter from the base line. To overcome a similar optical illusion, the strokes of the *V* should intersect slightly below the base line. The *W* is one and one-third times the normal width of a letter; it is the widest letter in the alphabet.

FIG. 185

150. MNZ.—Fig. 186. There is a decided advantage in drawing the parallel strokes of the *M* and *N* before drawing the diagonal strokes, as shown. Strokes *3* and *4* of the *M*, and strokes *2* and *3* of the *N*, should intersect in the base line.

151. KXY.—Fig. 187. Strokes *1* and *2* of the *K* intersect at a point one-third the height of the letter from the base line. Stroke *3*, extended, intersects stroke *1* at the top and should be approximately perpendicular to stroke *2*. The three strokes of the *Y* intersect a little below mid-point.

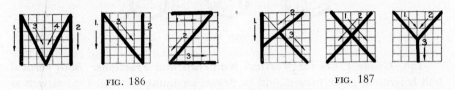

FIG. 186   FIG. 187

CURVED-LINE LETTERS

152. OCQG.—Fig. 188. The letters *O*, *C*, *Q*, and *G* are formed with circles as bases. The *O* and *Q* are complete circles. The *C* and *G* are not complete circles and, therefore, their widths are slightly less than their heights. Stroke *3* of the *Q* is a radial line making an angle of 30° with a vertical. The horizontal part of stroke *3* of the *G* begins at the center of the circle.

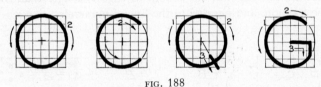

FIG. 188

153. JUD.—Fig. 189. The *J* is a modification of the *U* but is one-half space less in width. Stroke *3* of the *U* is elliptic and begins at a point one-third the height of the letter above the base line. Stroke *2* and the straight part of stroke *3* of the *D* are horizontal lines. The right side of the *D* is circular, but the bottoms of the *J* and *U* are elliptical.

154. PRB.—Fig. 190. Stroke *2* of the *P* is slightly below mid-height of the letter, while stroke *2* of the *R* is at mid-height, and stroke *3* of the *B* is slightly above mid-height.

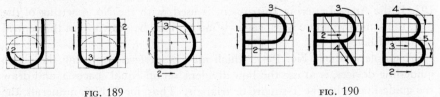

FIG. 189   FIG. 190

155. S and &.—Fig. 191. The upper and lower portions of the *S* are elliptic, the ellipses being tangent to a common vertical line on the left side. Compare the *S* with the numerals *8* and *3* (Fig. 195). The ampersand (&) has a variety of forms, the one on the left being American Standard. The second form is similar to a figure 8 with stroke *5* added.

FIG. 191

156. Guide Lines for Vertical Numerals and Fractions. Both vertical and horizontal guide lines should be drawn for numerals (Fig. 195) as well as for letters, and this is particularly necessary for beginners. However, even the expert letterer will be able to do better lettering if he uses guide lines, and he therefore is more likely to use them than the beginner who thinks they are "too much trouble."

The total height of a fraction is twice the height of the whole number (Fig. 194). The numerator and the denominator of a fraction are each from $\frac{3}{4}$ to $\frac{5}{6}$ the height of the whole number. These should never be allowed to touch the fraction bar. The fraction bar should be slightly longer than the greatest width of the fraction, and parallel to the line of numerals.

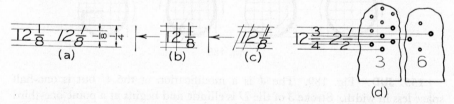

FIG. 192　Guide Lines for Dimension Figures.

For dimensioning on working drawings the commonly-used height of whole numbers is $\frac{1}{8}''$ and of fractions is double this, or $\frac{1}{4}''$, as shown in Fig. 192 (a). If the Braddock-Rowe triangle (Fig. 178) is used, the column of holes at the left produces five guide lines, each $\frac{1}{16}''$ apart, the central line being used to locate the fraction bar. The use of the Braddock-Rowe triangle is illustrated in Fig. 193. If the Ames Lettering Instrument is used, with the No. 4 setting of the disc, the same five guide lines, each $\frac{1}{16}''$ apart, may be drawn from the central column of holes.

A simple method (Fig. 194), which may be preferred to using the above guide-line devices, is to use the bow dividers, set off equal spaces *a*, and draw the guide lines with the T-square or triangle. Thus, for $\frac{1}{8}''$ high numerals, the bow dividers are set at $\frac{1}{8}''$, and two swings are taken to locate the top and bottom of the fraction, making the fraction $\frac{1}{4}''$ high.

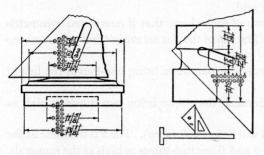

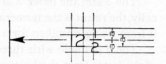

FIG. 194　Spacing Guide Lines with Bow Dividers.

FIG. 193　Guide Lines for Numerals — Braddock-Rowe Triangle.

If it is desired to draw guide lines for the bottom of the numerator and the top of the denominator, seven guide lines will be needed, and these can be drawn with the Braddock-Rowe triangle as shown in Fig. 192 (d).

In addition to the horizontal guide lines, it is important to draw, for each numeral and fraction, several vertical guide lines at random, as shown in Fig. 192 (b), and Fig. 194.

157. Vertical Numerals and Fractions.—Fig. 195. Since nearly all values on technical drawings are expressed by numerals, the student should make a careful study of their strokes and proportions. All numerals on drawings should be perfectly legible. The chief failure of students in lettering numerals and fractions is in making them too small and attempting to crowd them into spaces which are too small for legibility.

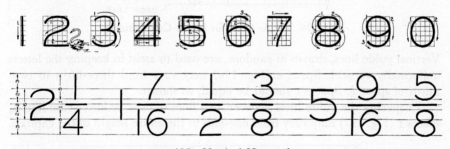

FIG. 195　Vertical Numerals.

The widths of numerals are easy to remember, since all except the *1* are five units wide (Fig. 195).

The numeral *1* is exactly like the letter *I*, made with a single downward stroke.

The *2* is made in two strokes, the first resembling a swan's neck or a question mark, and intersecting stroke two nearly at right angles. Note that stroke one passes through the center of the grid.

The *3* and the letter *S* are both of such shape that if completed symmetrically, the result is the numeral *8*. The top of the *3* is *not straight*, but *curved* to keep it from being mistaken for a *5*.

The *4* is made with three strokes, stroke three being one-fourth the height of the letter from the bottom.

The lower part of the *5* is elliptical, the ellipse being two-thirds as high as the numeral.

The *6* and *9* are elliptical and will fit in the *0* (zero). The *9* is the same as the *6* upside down. The loops in the *6* and *9* are two-thirds as high as the numerals.

Stroke one of the *7* is straight, like the bottom of the *2*. Stroke two is very slightly curved.

The *8* is composed of a small ellipse on top of a larger ellipse. If certain segments are cut out, the letter *S* or the numeral *3* may be formed. The tangency of the two ellipses is slightly above center.

The *0* (zero) is an ellipse, five units wide, and should be compared to the letter *O*, which is a circle six units in diameter.

The tops of the numerals *3*, *5*, *6*, and *8* are narrower than the bottoms to give stability to the characters (§ 138).

158. Guide Lines for Vertical Lower-Case Letters. Four horizontal guide lines and vertical guide lines drawn at random are used for lower-case lettering (Fig. 196). The *drop line* may be omitted by all except beginners.

FIG. 196   Guide Lines for Lower-Case Letters.

Vertical guide lines, drawn at random, are used to assist in keeping the letters uniformally vertical. Space *a* (Fig. 196) may vary from three-fifths to two-thirds of space *b*. Spaces *c* should be equal, as shown.

In spacing the guide lines between two lines of caps or lower-case letters, spaces *z* (Fig. 197) may vary from one-half to the entire height of the capitals.

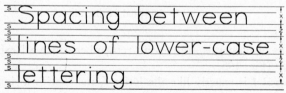

FIG. 197   Spacing of Guide Lines for Lower-Case Letters.

A convenient spacing is to make spaces *s* (Fig. 197) all equal. The spacing described may be obtained with the aid of the Braddock-Rowe triangle (Fig. 178) or the Ames Lettering Instrument (Fig. 179), as discussed in § 144.

159. Vertical Lower-Case Letters.—Fig. 198. Vertical lower-case letters are used largely on map drawings, and very seldom on machine drawings. The shapes are based upon a repetition of the circle or circular arc and the straight line, with some variations. The lower part of the letter is usually two-thirds the height of the capital letter.

Horizontal and vertical guide lines should be drawn (§ 158). The drop line is usually omitted, since comparatively few letters extend below the base line.

Strokes of the letters extending above the waist line (Fig. 196) are known as *ascenders*, and those extending below the base line as *descenders*. All ascenders except that of the *t* extend to the cap line. All descenders extend to the drop line.

FIG. 198   Vertical Lower-Case Letters.

Stroke *3* of the *e* is slightly above mid-height.   The dots over the *i* and *j* are slightly below the cap line.

The crosses on the *f* and *t* are on the waist line and are symmetrical with respect to strokes *1*. The curved strokes of *h*, *m*, *n*, and *r* intersect strokes *1* approximately two-thirds of the distance from the base line to the waist line.

The descenders of the *g*, *j*, and *y* terminate in curves which are tangent to the drop line, while those of *p* and *q* terminate in the drop line without curves.

160. Guide Lines for Inclined Capital Letters. Light horizontal guide lines and inclined guide lines drawn at random, made with a sharp, hard pencil, are used for inclined lettering (Fig. 200). The spacing of the horizontal guide lines is the same as for vertical capitals (§ 145). The American Standard slope of 2 in 5 for inclined guide lines may be established by drawing a slope triangle, as shown in Fig. 199 (a), and drawing the guide lines at random with the T-square and triangle, as shown in (b). Special triangles for the purpose are available, as shown at (c). If a protractor is available, any desired inclination may be easily set off (Fig. 51).

FIG. 199   Guide Lines for Inclined Capital Letters.

The Braddock-Rowe triangle (Fig. 178) has an inclined slot for drawing inclined guide lines. The Ames Lettering Instrument may be turned on its side to draw inclined guide lines at $67\frac{1}{2}$ ° or 70° with horizontal, as shown in Fig. 179 (b) and (c).

161. Inclined Capitals.—Fig. 200. The order and direction of the strokes and the proportions of the inclined letters are the same as those for vertical letters. The method of drawing inclined guide lines to assist in maintaining a uniform slant is explained in § 160, and is illustrated in Fig. 199.

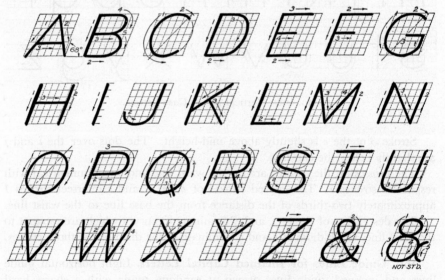

FIG. 200   Inclined Capital Letters.

Inclined letters may be regarded as *oblique projections* (§§ 178 and 286) of vertical letters. The circular parts of the vertical letters are elliptical in the inclined letters, the major axes of all the ellipses making angles of 45° with a horizontal (Fig. 200). This is illustrated by the letter *O*, where it is seen that the sharpest curves of the ellipse are in the upper-right and lower-left corners of the grid, and the flattest curves are in the upper-left and lower-right corners of the grid.

The letters having sloping sides, such as *V*, *W*, *X* and *Y* are difficult to make as inclined letters. To be made properly, they must be balanced symmetrically about a central inclined guide line.

162. Guide Lines for Inclined Numerals and Fractions. The inclined numerals and fractions (Fig. 201) are inclined at the same angle (approxi-

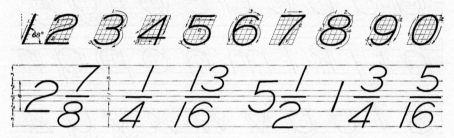

FIG. 201   Inclined Numerals and Fractions.

mately 68° with horizontal) as inclined letters (Figs. 192 and 199). In addition to the horizontal guide lines, inclined guide lines should be drawn, at random, as shown in Fig. 192 (c). The slope may be determined as shown in Fig. 199, or with the aid of the inclined slot in the Braddock-Rowe triangle (Figs. 178 and 193), or with the Ames Lettering Instrument as shown in Fig. 179 (b) and (c).

163. Inclined Numerals and Fractions.—Fig. 201. The inclined numerals and fractions may be regarded as oblique projections (§§ 178 and 286) of vertical numerals and fractions, and the general proportions and strokes are the same (§ 157). In lettering a fraction, the numerator and denominator should be balanced symmetrically about a central inclined guide line.

164. Guide Lines for Inclined Lower-Case Letters. Four horizontal guide lines and inclined guide lines drawn at random are used for inclined lower-case letters (Figs. 202 and 203).

FIG. 202   Guide Lines for Lower-Case Letters.

The spacing between the horizontal guide lines is the same as for vertical lower-case letters (§ 158). The slope of the inclined guide lines may be determined by drawing the slope triangle of *2* in *5,* as shown in Fig. 202, or with the aid of the inclined slot in the Braddock-Rowe triangle (Fig. 178), or with the Ames Lettering Instrument, as shown in Fig. 179 (b) and (c).

165. Inclined Lower-Case Letters.—Fig. 203. The order and direction of the strokes and the proportions of inclined lower-case letters are the same as those of vertical lower-case letters. The inclined lower-case letters may be

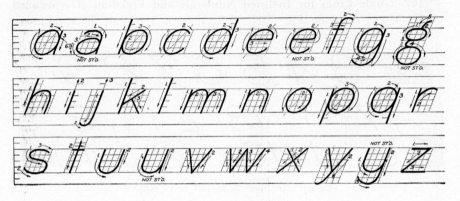

FIG. 203   Inclined Lower-Case Letters.

regarded, like the inclined capital letters, as oblique projections of vertical letters, in which all circles in the vertical alphabet become ellipses in the inclined alphabet. As in the inclined capital letters, all ellipses have their major axes inclined at an angle of 45° with a horizontal.

Some authorities recommend a slightly different slant for the axes of the *c, e,* and *o,* but the resulting difference in appearance does not justify the lack of uniformity in the inclination.

The forms of the letters *c, o, s, v, w, x,* and *z* are almost identical with those of the corresponding capitals.

166. Spacing. Uniformity in spacing of letters and words is a matter of balancing spaces with the eye. *The areas, and not the clearances between letters, must appear approximately equal.* In Fig. 204 (a) the letters are incorrectly spaced

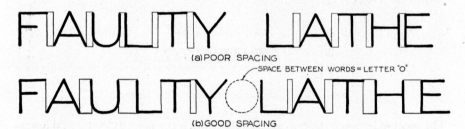

FIG. 204   Spacing Capital Letters.

at equal distances. At (b) they are correctly spaced so that the *areas* between the letters are approximately equal. The spacing of *L* and *T*, and *H* and *E*, at (a), illustrates this defect.

Some letters in combination, such as *L* and *T*, and *V* and *A*, may even be overlapped, if necessary to secure good spacing. In some cases the width of a letter may be decreased: for example, the lower stroke of the *L* may be shortened when followed by *A*.

Words should be spaced a distance apart approximately equal to the basic width of a letter (letter *O* for example).

The inexperienced letterer has a tendency to space letters too far apart, and to space words too close together. Each word should be compact and appear as a distinct unit. Correct and incorrect spacing of lower-case letters is illustrated in Fig. 205. It is especially important to allow ample space between letters *i*, *l*, and *t*, so that the areas between all letters will appear equal.

POOR SPACING

illiterate

GOOD SPACING

FIG. 205   Spacing of Lower-Case Letters.

When it is necessary to letter to a stop-line as in Fig. 206 (a), each letter should be spaced off from *right to left*, as shown in step II, the widths of letters

FIG. 206   Spacing to a Stop-Line and "On Center."

being estimated by eye. Then the letters should be lettered from *left to right*, and finally the spacing marks should be erased.

When it is necessary to space a line of letters symmetrically about a center line, as in Fig. 206 (b), which is frequently the case in titles (Figs. 210 and 211), the letters should be numbered, as shown, with the space between words considered as one letter. Then the middle letter should be placed on center, allowance being made for narrow letters (*I*'s) or wide letters (*W*'s) on either side. The *X* in Fig. 206 (b) is placed slightly to the left of the center to compensate for the letter *I*, which has no width. The dividers should be used to make the distances *a* exactly equal.

A trial line of letters may be roughly lettered on the bottom edge of a scrap of paper and placed in a balanced position immediately above, as shown in Fig. 206 (c), and the required letters spaced accordingly by eye.

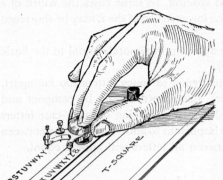

167. Lettering Devices. The *Leroy Lettering Instrument* (Fig. 207) is perhaps the most successful lettering device in use. A pin follows grooved letters in a guide, and the inking point moves on the paper. By adjusting the arm on the instrument, the letters may be made vertical or inclined. A variety of templates and sizes of pens is available. Inside of each pen is a cleaning pin used to keep the small tube open. These pins are easily broken, especially the small ones, when the pen is not promptly cleaned. To clean a pen, draw it across a blotter until all ink has been absorbed.

FIG. 207   Leroy Lettering Instrument.

The *Wrico* (Fig. 208) consists of a lettering pen which is moved along the edges of a guide in which parts of letters are perforated. Wrico letters more

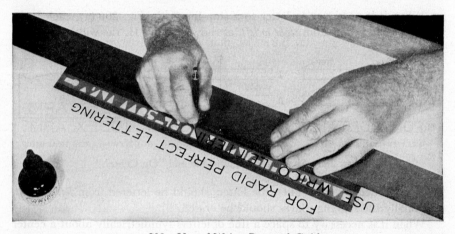

FIG. 208   Use of Wrico Pen and Guide.

closely resemble American Standard freehand letters than those of any other lettering device. The Wrico is recommended second only to the Leroy, and is preferred by many draftsmen.

FIG. 209   Lettering Angle.

The simplest device to assist in lettering is a piece of celluloid having all the convenient angles (Fig. 209). Curves are filled in freehand or with the compass.

Such mechanical aids are of value only in certain cases, and should not be relied upon for anything but large letters in titles, and elsewhere in which artistic effect is not essential, as such letters are invariably stiff, and generally not as pleasing to the eye as good freehand letters.

168. Titles. The composition of titles on machine drawings (§ 472) is important but not very difficult. Artistic effects are not necessary; only legibility and speed are important. On display drawings, however, as on highly finished maps and architectural designs, titles are made of "built-up" letters, and title design is important. The uses of the various letters are discussed in the following articles.

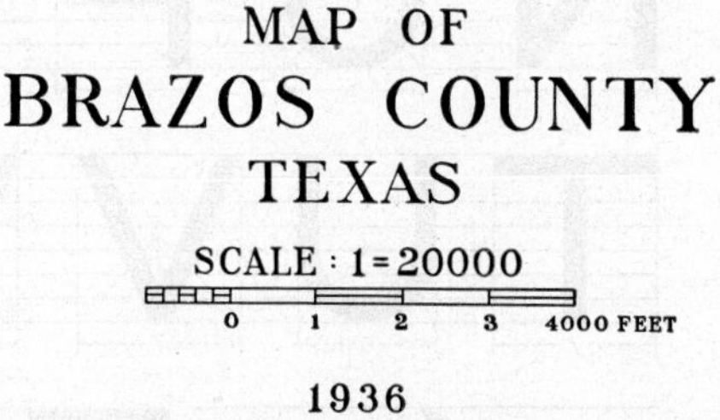

Two suggestive titles are shown in Figs. 210 and 211. Notice that the most important words are given most prominence, such as the name of the county which has been mapped, or the name of the structure represented. Other data, such as scale, date, etc., are not so important, and should not be given much prominence.

MAP OF

BRAZOS COUNTY

TEXAS

SCALE : 1 = 20000

0   1   2   3   4000 FEET

1936

FIG. 210   A Map Title.

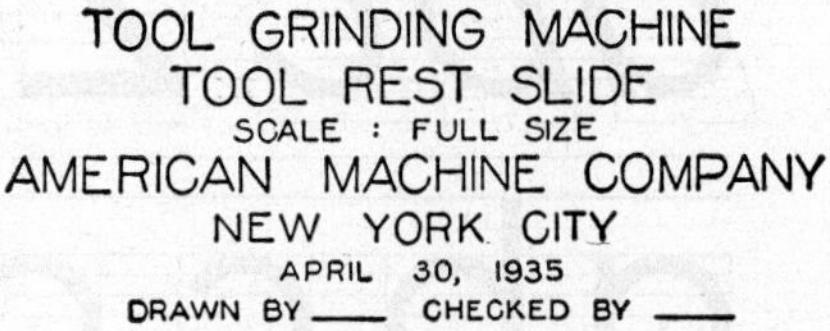

TOOL GRINDING MACHINE

TOOL REST SLIDE

SCALE : FULL SIZE

AMERICAN MACHINE COMPANY

NEW YORK CITY

APRIL 30, 1935

DRAWN BY ____   CHECKED BY ____

FIG. 211   A Machine-Drawing Title.

Such titles are always symmetrical about a vertical centerline. These titles take such forms as the rectangle, the oval, the inverted pyramid, or any other simple symmetrical form (Figs. 210 and 1093).

Most titles today are lettered within "boxes" or "title-strips" which are printed directly on the drawing paper, tracing paper, or cloth (Figs. 843 to 847).

GOTHIC

(a)

GOTH

(b)

FIG. 212   Gothic-Letter Construction.

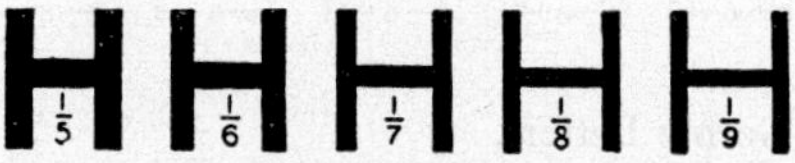

H H H H H
$\frac{1}{5}$ $\frac{1}{6}$ $\frac{1}{7}$ $\frac{1}{8}$ $\frac{1}{9}$

FIG. 213   Varying Thicknesses of Stems.

FIG. 214   Gothic Letters.

132

169. Gothic Letters.—Fig. 214. Among the many forms of Gothic styles, including Old English, German Gothic, etc., the so-called san-serif Gothic letter is the only one of interest to draftsmen. It is from this style that the modern single-stroke engineering letters, discussed in the early part of this chapter, are derived. While they are admittedly not so beautiful as many other styles, they are very legible and comparatively easy to make.

These letters should be used, therefore, on drawings where legibility and not beauty is the determining factor. They should be drawn in outline and then filled in (Fig. 212), the thickness of the stems being from one-fifth to about one-tenth the height of the letter (Fig. 213). An attractive letter may be produced by making heavy outlines, and not filling in, as for the letter *H* in Fig. 212 (a). A slight spur may be added to the ends of the stem, as for the letter *T*, in Fig. 212 (a). An example of condensed Gothic is shown at (b). A complete alphabet of Gothic letters is shown in Fig. 214.

170. Old Roman Letters.—Fig. 216. The Old Roman letter is the basis of all of our letters, and is still regarded as the most beautiful of all. The letters on the base of Trajan's Column, in Rome, are regarded by many as the finest example of Old Roman letters.

This letter is used mostly by architects (§ 171). Because of its great beauty, it is used almost exclusively on buildings, and for inscriptions on bronze or stone. Full-size "details" of the letter are usually drawn for such inscriptions.

Originally this letter was made on manuscript with a broad-point reed pen; the wide stems were produced by downward strokes, and the narrow stems by upward strokes. A brief examination of any Roman letter will show why certain strokes are wide while others are narrow.

Several styles of steel broad-nib pens are available and are suitable for making Roman, Gothic, or Text letters (Figs. 168 and 215). If necessary, an ordinary pen may be used to "touch up" after using the broad-nib pen, or to add fine-line flourishes, as in Text letters.

As in the case of the Gothic, the Old Roman letters may be drawn in outline and filled in, or may be left in outline. If a third line is added, an *incised* letter results, such as in Fig. 217 (top).

FIG. 215　Use of Broad-Nib Pen.

171. Architectural Lettering.—Fig. 217. Architectural lettering is derived directly from the Old Roman (Fig. 216). The *incised* letter shown at the top of Fig. 217 is much used in titles, as well as the outline letter, which is the same with the middle line omitted.

ABCDEFG
HIJKLMN
OPQRST
UVWXYZ

1234567890

abcdefghijklm
nopqrstuvwxyz

FIG. 216   Old Roman Letters and Numerals.

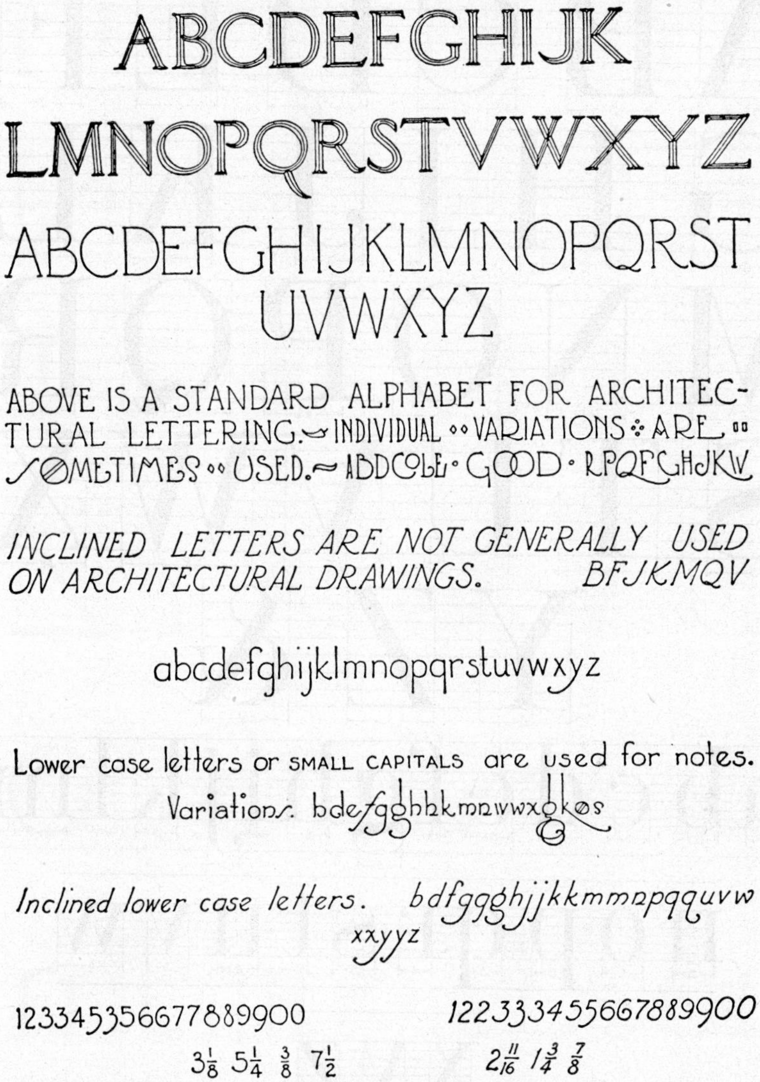

ABCDEFGHIJK

LMNOPQRSTVWXYZ

ABCDEFGHIJKLMNOPQRST
UVWXYZ

ABOVE IS A STANDARD ALPHABET FOR ARCHITEC-
TURAL LETTERING.— INDIVIDUAL ∞ VARIATIONS ∴ ARE ∞
√ØMETIMES ∞ USED.— ABDCϴLE · GϴϴD · RPQFϚHJKW

*INCLINED LETTERS ARE NOT GENERALLY USED
ON ARCHITECTURAL DRAWINGS.　　BFJKMQV*

abcdefghijklmnopqrstuvwxyz

Lower case letters or SMALL CAPITALS are used for notes.
Variations. bdefgghhkmnvwxǫkøs

*Inclined lower case letters.　bdfggghjjkkmmnpqquvw
xxyyz*

123345356677889900　　　122333455667889900
$3\frac{1}{8}$　$5\frac{1}{4}$　$\frac{3}{8}$　$7\frac{1}{2}$　　　　$2\frac{11}{16}$　$1\frac{3}{4}$　$\frac{7}{8}$

FIG. 217　Architectural Letters.

The single-stroke letters are used for general purposes on architectural
working drawings. While the purest architectural lettering is that which is
closest to the Old Roman, individuality in design of letters is permissible, or
even desirable, if the lettering is well done. Only those who have thoroughly
mastered the standard Roman form should attempt any variations and, even
then, they should proceed with care, avoiding any extreme or meaningless
"curly-cues."

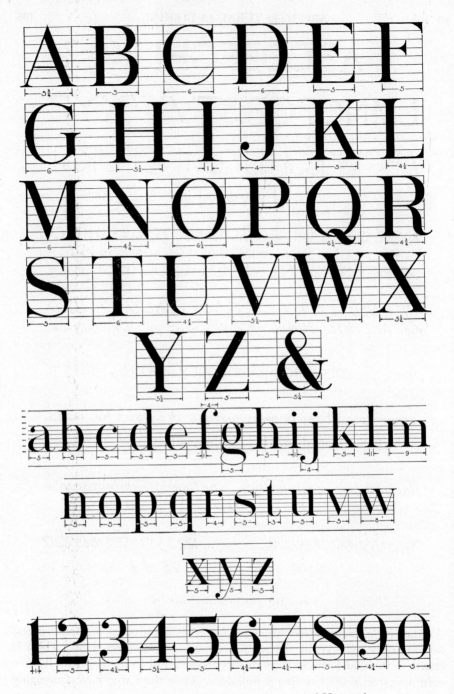

FIG. 218 Vertical Modern Roman Letters and Numerals.

172. Modern Roman Letters.—Figs. 218 and 220. The Modern Roman (commonly known as "Roman") letters were evolved during the eighteenth century by the type founders, and the letters used in most modern newspapers, magazines, and books are of this style. The text of this book is set in Modern Roman letters. These letters have been used for many years by the United States Government in its various publications, and are widely used on maps. Vertical Modern Roman letters are shown in Fig. 218, and Italic Modern Roman letters in Fig. 220. They may be drawn in outline and then filled in, as shown in Fig. 219, or they may be produced with one of the broad-point

MODERN Ror

(a)　　　　　　　　　　　　　　　　　　　　　　(b)

FIG. 219　Modern Roman Letter Construction.

pens shown in Fig. 175. The lower-case italics are known as *stump letters;* they are easily made freehand and are widely used on maps (§ 173).

If drawn in outline and filled in, the straight lines may be drawn with the ruling pen, and the fillets and other curves drawn freehand. The curves are subtle and the compass cannot be used satisfactorily. The thickness of the stem varies widely, but the usual thickness is from one-sixth to one-eighth of the height of the letter.

A typical example of the use of Modern Roman in titles is shown in Fig. 210. Their use on maps is discussed below.

173. Lettering on Maps. Modern Roman letters are generally used on maps, as follows:

(1) *Vertical Capitals.*—Names of states, countries, townships, capitals, large cities, and titles of maps. See § 168.

(2) *Vertical Lower-Case* (First letter of each word a capital).—Names of small towns, villages, post offices, etc.

(3) *Inclined Capitals.*—Names of oceans, bays, gulfs, sounds, large lakes, and rivers.

(4) *Inclined Lower-Case or "Stump Letters"* (First letter of each word a capital). —Names of rivers, creeks, small lakes, ponds, marshes, brooks, and springs.

Prominent land features, such as mountains, plateaus, and canyons, are lettered in vertical Gothic (Fig. 182), while the names of small land features, such as small valleys, islands, and ridges, are lettered in vertical lower-case Gothic (Fig. 198). Names of railroads, tunnels, highways, bridges, and other public structures are lettered in inclined Gothic capitals (Fig. 200).

FIG. 220 Inclined Modern Roman Letters and Numerals.

Vertical lettering on circular curves (Fig. 221) should have the axes of the letters, and not the stems, parallel to the radii of the arcs, as in (a). Also the horizontal strokes should be straight lines and not arcs.

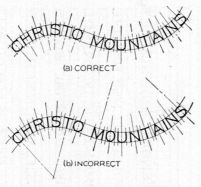

FIG. 221   Lettering on a Curve.

174. Old English Letters. English Gothic letters, commonly called "Old English" (Fig. 222), are little used where legibility is important, but only where

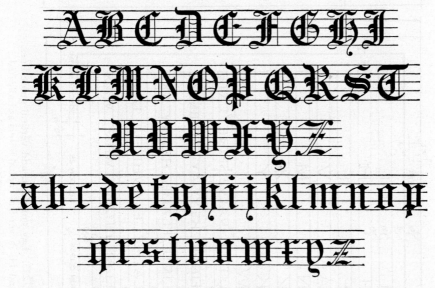

FIG. 222   Old English Letters.

a decorative effect is sought. These letters may be easily and rapidly made with a broad-nib pen (Fig. 215). The Old English letters were developed early in the middle ages, and the letter *J* was not differentiated from the letter *I* until the sixteenth century. Hence, in classical inscriptions, the letter *I* is often used for the letter *J*.

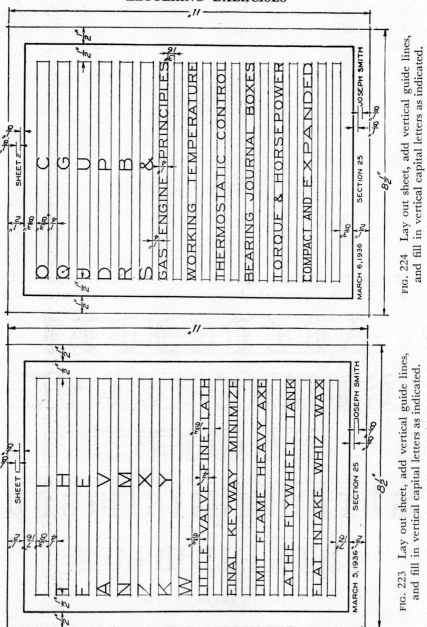

FIG. 224 Lay out sheet, add vertical guide lines, and fill in vertical capital letters as indicated.

FIG. 223 Lay out sheet, add vertical guide lines, and fill in vertical capital letters as indicated.

*Lettering sheets in convenient form for lettering practice may be found in *Technical Drawing Problems*, by Giesecke, Mitchell, and Spencer, and in *Technical Drawing Problems—Series 2*, by Spencer and Grant, both designed to accompany this text, and published by The Macmillan Co.

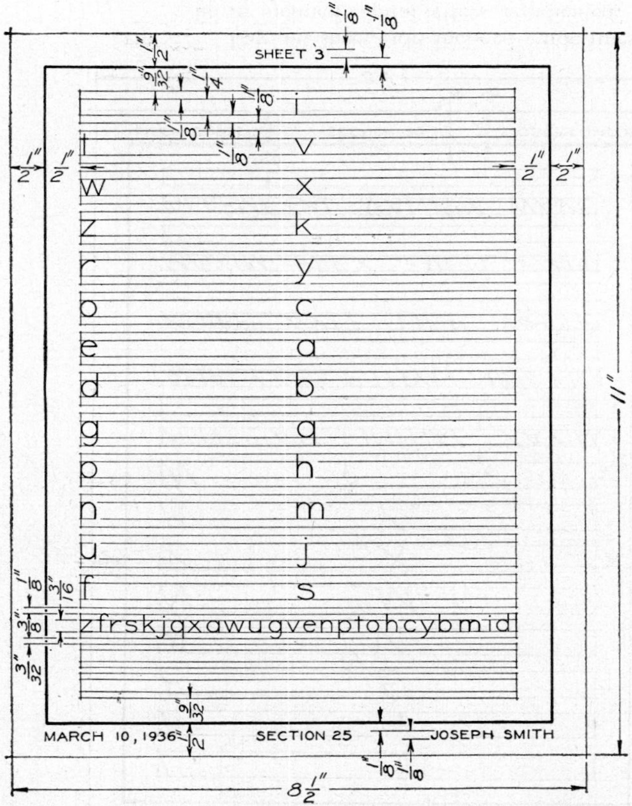

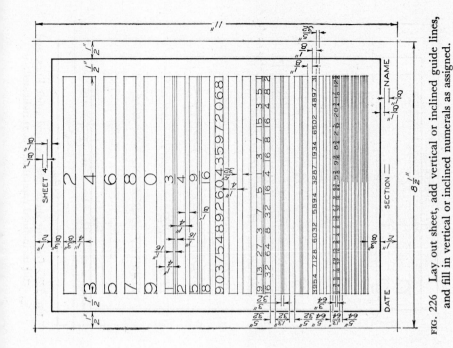

FIG. 226 Lay out sheet, add vertical or inclined guide lines, and fill in vertical or inclined numerals as assigned.

FIG. 225 Lay out sheet, add vertical or inclined guide lines, and fill in vertical or inclined lower-case letters as assigned.

141

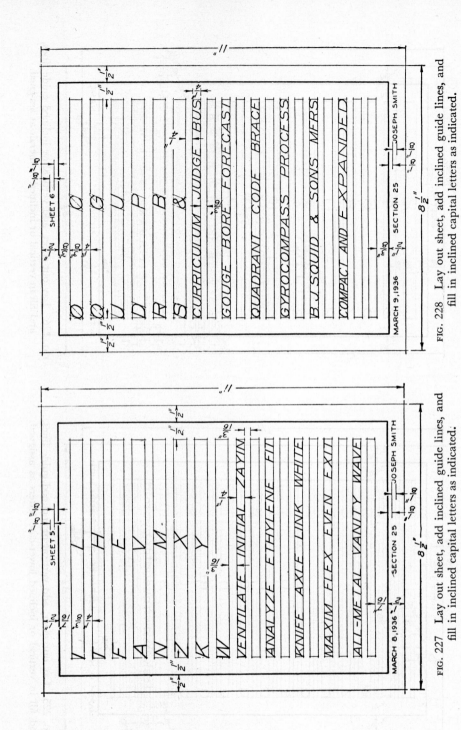

FIG. 227 Lay out sheet, add inclined guide lines, and fill in inclined capital letters as indicated.

FIG. 228 Lay out sheet, add inclined guide lines, and fill in inclined capital letters as indicated.

142

CHAPTER 6

Projections

175. Projection. The *projection* of an object on a plane is the representation of the object on that plane as it would appear to an observer stationed at the point from or toward which the projection is made.

In Fig. 229, the drawing *EFGH* is the projection on the plane *A* of the square *ABCD* as viewed by an observer whose eye is at the point *O*.

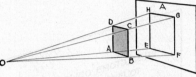

FIG. 229   Central Projection or Perspective.

176. Central Projection, or Perspective. In Fig. 230, the drawing *EFGH* is the projection on the plane *A* of the square *ABCD*. It is a *central projection*, or a *perspective* of the object.

The plane *A* is the *plane of projection*, or *picture plane*. The point *O* is the point from which the observer is assumed to view the object; it is called the *station point* or the *center of projection*. The lines *OA, OB, OC,* and *OD* are *visual rays, projectors, lines of sight,* or *sight lines.*

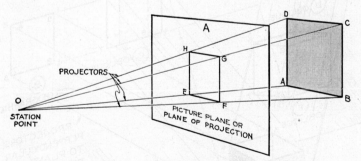

FIG. 230   Central Projection or Perspective.

The projection shown in Fig. 229 is also a central projection or perspective. In this case the object is in front of the picture plane and in Fig. 230 it is behind the picture plane. Note that the projection in Fig. 229 is larger than the object, while in Fig. 230 the projection is smaller than the object.

177. Parallel Projection. If the station point O (Figs. 229 and 230) is infinitely distant from the plane A, the projectors OA, OB, OC, and OD are

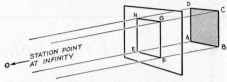

parallel, as shown in Fig. 231, and the projection is a *parallel projection*. In this case the projection $EFGH$ is of the same form and size as the square $ABCD$ if the latter is parallel to the *plane of projection*.

FIG. 231 Parallel Projectors.

178. Oblique Projection. If the parallel projectors are oblique to the plane of projection, the resulting projection is an *oblique projection* (Fig. 232, C, D, E, and F). If the parallel projectors are perpendicular to the plane of projection, the resulting view is an *orthographic projection*, as shown at B. The cube A can have only one orthographic projection on the plane, as shown at B, since only one perpendicular line can be drawn from any point in the cube

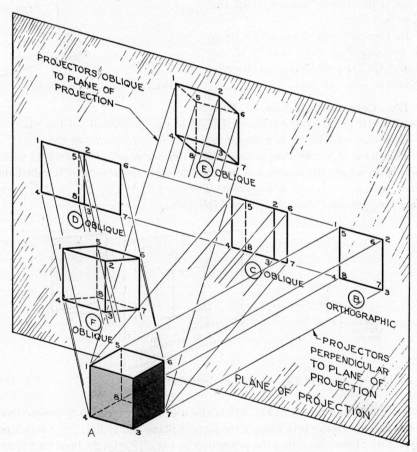

FIG. 232 Orthographic and Oblique Projections.

to that plane; but it can have any number of oblique projections on the plane since any number of lines can be drawn through any point in the cube oblique to that plane.

The oblique projections C and D are obtained by drawing the parallel projectors in the same horizontal planes as the corresponding perpendicular projectors but oblique to the plane of projection—at angles of, approximately, 66° and 40°, respectively. The oblique projection E is obtained by drawing the parallel projectors upward and toward the left. The oblique projection F is obtained by drawing the parallel projectors downward and toward the left.

In all five projections the front and rear faces of the cube are shown in their true forms and sizes, since they are parallel to the plane of projection. In the oblique projections E and F, the remaining four faces of the cube are shown as parallelograms, and not in their true forms and sizes. In the oblique projections C and D the right and left faces are shown as rectangles, but not in their true forms and sizes; and the upper and lower faces are shown as straight lines, because the projectors of all points in those faces lie in the planes of the respective faces.

It is evident that every oblique projection shows all lines and figures, which are parallel to the plane of projection, in their true forms and sizes. Moreover, all lines of the object which are perpendicular to the plane of projection may be shown in any desired direction and of any desired length by choosing the proper direction for the parallel projectors.

The cube A and its orthographic projection B present a natural appearance in Fig. 232, but the oblique projections C, D, E, and F are distorted because they are themselves in pictorial projection. The true forms of the oblique projections are shown in Fig. 233 together with that of the orthographic projection B.

For a more detailed treatment of oblique projection, see Chapter 12.

179. Orthographic Projection. The special case of parallel projection in which the projectors are perpendicular to the plane of projection is *orthographic* or *orthogonal* projection.* The orthographic projection of a cube, as B in Fig. 233, shows the front and rear faces of the cube in their true form and size and the four adjoining faces as straight lines. In order to show these four faces other than as straight lines, it is necessary to turn the cube so that its faces are inclined to the plane of projection, as in axonometric projection (§ 180), or to show additional *views* of the cube, as in multiview projection (§§ 186 and 190), in which case the faces will be shown as squares.

180. Axonometric Projection. If the faces of the cube are inclined to the plane of projection and the *projectors are perpendicular to the plane of projection* (Fig. 234), the resulting orthographic projection is a *normal axonometric projec-*

* *Orthogonal* means "right angles." *Orthographic* means "to write or to draw at right angles." Both terms, therefore, refer to the same type of projection; but orthographic has become the more commonly accepted term.

tion. In this case, the orthographic projection may appear as shown in Fig.
235. Since the cube can be placed in an infinite number of positions with the

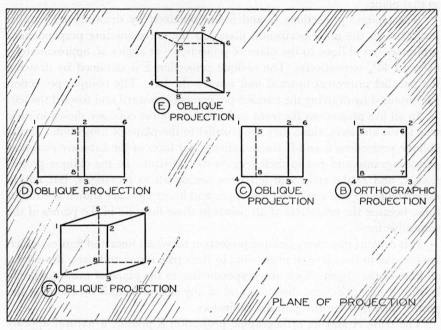

FIG. 233　True Shapes of Projections Shown Pictorially in Fig. 232.

faces inclined to the plane of projection, there can be an infinite number of
axonometric projections of the same object.

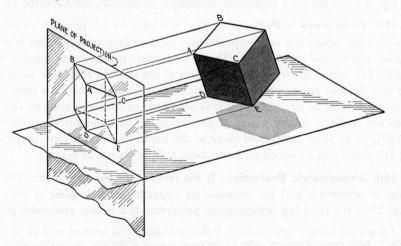

FIG. 234　Normal Axonometric Projection.

In these cases, the edges of the cube are inclined to the plane of projection, and are therefore not shown in their true lengths. The degree of foreshortening of any line depends on its inclination to the plane of projection; the greater the angle, the greater the foreshortening.

If the degree of foreshortening is determined for each of the three edges of the cube which meet at one corner, scales can be constructed by which these edges, as well as all lines parallel to them, can be measured, as shown in Figs. 563 and 566.

It is customary to consider the three edges of the cube meeting at a corner as the *coordinate axes* on which the projections can be measured; hence, this type of projection is known as *normal axonometric projection*.

Since, in normal axonometric projection, the edges of the objects are inclined to the plane of projection, it is obvious that their projections are fore-

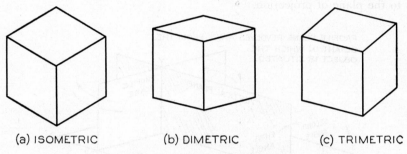

(a) ISOMETRIC   (b) DIMETRIC   (c) TRIMETRIC

FIG. 235   Axonometric Projections.

shortened, and that to represent them as projected, they must be drawn to reduced scales which are calculated from the inclinations of the edges.

As shown in Fig. 235, normal axonometric projections are classified as: (a) Isometric Projection, (b) Dimetric Projection, (c) Trimetric Projection, depending upon the number of scales of reduction required. See also Chapter 11.

If the projectors are *oblique* to the plane of projection, the resulting drawing is an *oblique axonometric projection* (Fig. 568). This usually produces distortion, and for this reason is infrequently used in practice.

181. Isometric Projection. If the cube is situated so that its edges are inclined equally to the plane of projection, all edges are foreshortened equally, as shown in Fig. 235 (a), and the same scale can be used to measure the three axes and all lines parallel to them. This type of projection is known as *isometric projection*, the word *"isometric"* meaning "equal measure."

In this case the angle between the plane of projection and any edge of the cube is 35° 16'. The cosine of this angle, $\sqrt{2/3}$ or 0.8165, is the degree of foreshortening. For example, if the length of the edge of the cube is 10 inches, the length of its projection is 8.165 inches. See also Chapter 11.

182. Dimetric Projection. If the cube is situated so that only two sets of its edges make the same angle with the plane of projection, its projection may be as illustrated in Fig. 235 (b), and two scales are necessary to construct its projection. This type is known as *dimetric projection*, the word *"dimetric"* meaning "two measures." See also §§ 279 to 281.

183. Trimetric Projection. If the cube is situated so that no two sets of its edges make the same angle with the plane of projection, its projection may be as illustrated in Fig. 235 (c), and three scales are necessary to construct its projection. This type is known as *trimetric projection*, the word *"trimetric"* meaning "three measures." See §§ 282-284.

184. Multiview Projection. It is evident from Fig. 233, *B*, that a single orthographic projection of a cube or similar object does not describe the form of that object completely if the cube is situated so that one of its faces is parallel to the plane of projection.

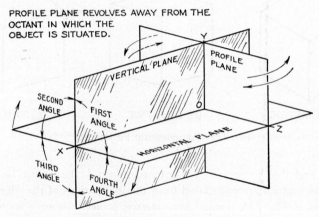

FIG. 236   Planes of Projection.

In order to obtain a complete shape description in such cases, it is necessary to show more than one projection, and hence additional planes of projection are used, as shown in Fig. 236. This method is known as *multiview projection* and is almost universally used in technical drawing as the simplest means of representing objects.

The three principal planes of projection are situated at right angles to each other and are known as the *vertical, horizontal,* and *profile* planes. They are assumed to be indefinite in extent and intersect in straight lines known as the *coordinate axes.* The line of intersection of the vertical and the horizontal plane is the *X-axis;* the line of intersection of the vertical and the profile plane is the *Y-axis;* and the line of intersection of the horizontal and the profile plane is the *Z-axis.*

The three axes intersect in a point known as the *origin of coordinates*. The four dihedral angles formed by the vertical and the horizontal planes are known, respectively, as the *first, second, third, and fourth angles*, and the eight spaces formed by the three planes of projection are called *octants*.

185. First-Angle Projection. If the object (Fig. 237) is situated so that its front and back faces are parallel to the vertical plane of projection, and its top and bottom faces parallel to the horizontal plane of projection, the side

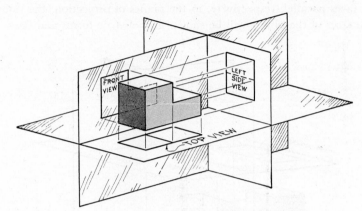

FIG. 237   First-Angle Projection.

faces will be parallel to the profile plane of projection, and the faces will be shown in their true forms and sizes in their respective projections. These projections are known, respectively, in technical drawing as *front, top,* and *side views* of the object.

Having determined the three views of the object on the respective planes situated at right angles to each other, as shown in Fig. 237, the draftsman's next step in the representation of the object is to revolve two of the planes into the third plane so that the three views of the object may be shown on one plane, as is necessary when the views are to be drawn on a blackboard or on a sheet of paper (Fig. 238).

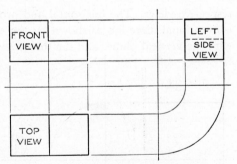

FIG. 238   Revolved Position of Planes in First-Angle Projection.

According to this conventional method of revolution, as shown in Fig. 236, the horizontal plane is revolved about the *X*-axis in the direction of the arrows till it coincides with the vertical plane, and the profile plane is revolved about the *Y*-axis *away from the object* until it coincides with the vertical plane. The three views of the object shown in Fig. 237, before the planes of projection are revolved, will then appear as shown in Fig. 238. It should be noted that the top view is directly below the front view and the left side view is to the right of the front view.

This method of projection is known as *first-angle projection*, and is used in practically all European countries.

186. Third-Angle Projection. If the object is in the third angle (Fig. 239) with its faces parallel, respectively, to the planes of projection, the front, top, and side faces of the object will be shown in their true forms and sizes, in the

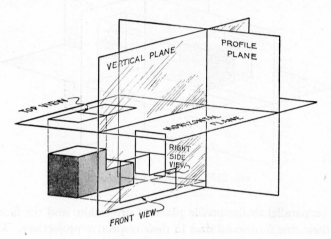

FIG. 239   Third-Angle Projection.

respective views. The horizontal and profile planes are again revolved in the conventional direction as shown by the arrows in Fig. 236, till they coincide with the vertical plane, and the three views of the object will appear as shown in Fig. 240.

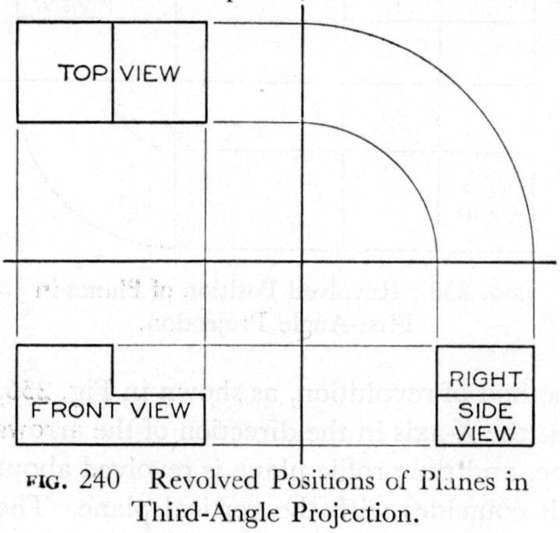

It should be noted that the top view, in this case, is directly above the front view and the right side view is directly to the right of the front view.

This method of projection is known as *third-angle projection* and is universally used for working drawings in the United States and Canada.

FIG. 240   Revolved Positions of Planes in Third-Angle Projection.

187. Second- and Fourth-Angle Projections. If the object is placed in the second or the fourth angle, the front and top views are on the same side of the X-axis after the horizontal plane has been revolved into the vertical plane and may overlap; for this reason, second- and fourth-angle projections are seldom used. Third-angle projection is preferable in technical drawing because the views are in their natural relative positions.

188. Classification of Projections. All drawings are *projections* of one kind or another on one or more planes of projection, as shown in the graphical chart of Fig. 241. The two main branches, *perspective* and *parallel projection*, are classified according to whether the projectors converge toward a point or are

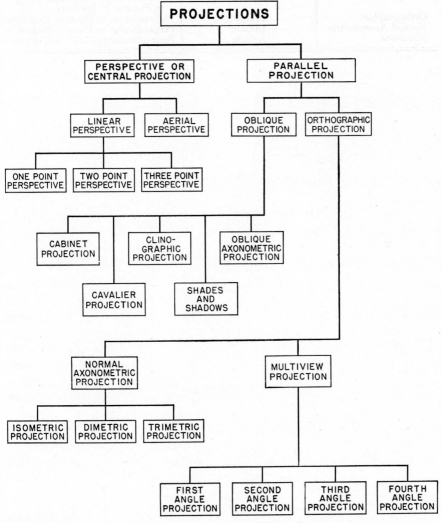

FIG. 241   Classification of Projections.

parallel to each other. These two basic types are then classified according to other differences, as shown in the chart.

A classification of the main types of projection according to their projectors is shown in Table 1 below.

TABLE 1. CLASSIFICATION BY PROJECTORS

CLASSES OF PROJECTION	DISTANCE FROM OBSERVER TO PLANE OF PROJECTION	DIRECTION OF PROJECTORS
Perspective	Finite	Radiating from Station Point
Parallel	Infinite	Parallel to Each Other
Oblique	Infinite	Parallel to Each Other and Oblique to Plane of Projection
Orthographic	Infinite	Perpendicular to Plane of Projection
Normal Axonometric	Infinite	Perpendicular to Plane of Projection
Multiview	Infinite	Perpendicular to Planes of Projection

CHAPTER 7

Multiview Projection

189. Views of Objects. A photograph or a pictorial drawing shows an object as it *appears* to the observer, but not as it *is*. Such a picture cannot describe the object fully, no matter from which direction it is viewed, because it does not show the exact shapes and sizes of the several parts.

In industry, a complete and clear description of the shape and size of an object to be made is necessary to make certain that the object will be manufactured exactly as intended by the designer. In order to provide this informa-

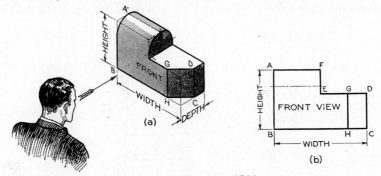

FIG. 242 A View of an Object.

tion clearly and accurately, a number of *views, systematically arranged*, are used. Each view will provide certain definite information, if the view is taken in a direction perpendicular to a principal face or side of the object. For example, as shown in Fig. 242 (a), if the observer looks perpendicularly toward one side of the object, he obtains a true view of the shape and size of that side. This view, as seen by the observer, is shown at (b).*

An object has three principal dimensions, *width, height,* and *depth,* as shown in Fig. 242 (a). In technical drawing, these fixed terms are used for dimensions taken in these directions, regardless of the shape of the object. The terms "length" and "thickness" are not used because they cannot be applied in all cases.

* The observer is theoretically at an infinite distance from the object.

153

In Fig. 242 (b) the front view shows only the width and height of the object, and not the depth. As a matter of fact, *no single view can show more than two of the three principal dimensions in their true sizes.* Also, in (b), the true curvature of the top is not shown, and the angle of the inclined surface does not appear. These features must remain to be described by means of additional views of the object, as will be shown in the following sections.

190. The Six Views. Any object can be viewed from six mutually perpendicular directions, as shown in Fig. 243. Thus, there are six possible views which can be drawn if necessary. These six views may be obtained by shifting the object (or imagining it to be shifted) so that the principal sides may be viewed in turn, as shown in Fig. 244.

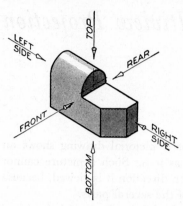

FIG. 243 The Six Directions of Sight.

The view which is seen from the front, as we have seen, is the *front view;* that seen from above is the *top view;* that seen from the right side is the *right*

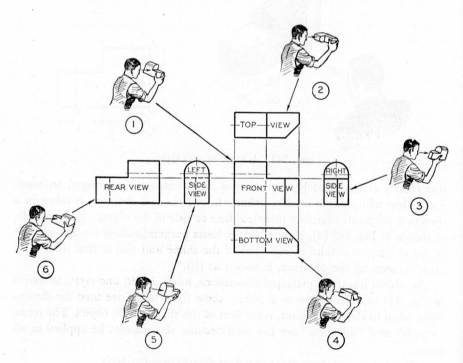

FIG. 244 Six Views of an Object.

side view, and so on. The six possible views are always arranged as shown in Fig. 244, which is the system approved by the American Standards Association.*

The top view is placed directly above the front view; the bottom view directly below the front view; the right side view, directly to the right of the front view; the left side view to the left of the front view; and the rear view to the left of the left side view, or, if necessary, to the right of the right side view. *Each view should be regarded as representing the object itself.*

While some views can be omitted, as will be shown later, *no view should be drawn in any other position* (except in the case discussed in § 199).

Obviously, the six views may be obtained either by shifting the object with respect to the observer, as we have seen (Fig. 244), or by shifting the observer with respect to the object. In the case of a house, for example (Fig. 245), the observer can walk around the house and view its front, sides, and rear,

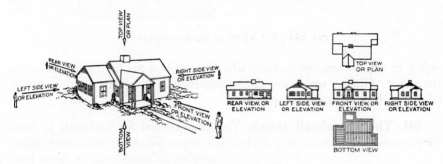

FIG. 245   Six Views of a House.

and he can imagine the top view as seen from an airplane, and the bottom view as seen from underneath.**

Notice, in Fig. 245, the use of the term *plan* for the top view, and *elevation* for all views showing the height of the building. These terms are used principally in architectural drawing, but occasionally they are used with reference to drawings in other fields.

Six views of an automobile are shown in Fig. 246. The view chosen for the front view, in this case, is not the "front" view of the automobile as usually regarded, but is simply a view which is definitely needed to describe the shape of the object. The front of the automobile could have been taken as the front view, but the top and bottom views would then be in a vertical position, and the six views would not space as satisfactorily on the paper.

In general, objects should be drawn in the positions they naturally occupy with respect to the ground, as illustrated in Figs. 245 and 246. A machine

* ASA Z14.1—1946 (See Appendix 2).
** Architects usually draw the views of a building on separate sheets. When two or more views are drawn together, they are usually drawn in the arrangement of first-angle projection (§ 185). See also Chapter 26 on Architectural Drawing.

part would usually be drawn in the position it occupies in the machine. However, in many cases this is not important, and the draftsman may assume the

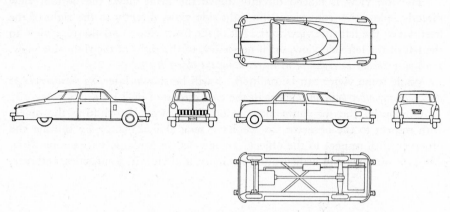

FIG. 246   Six Views of an Automobile.

object in any convenient position which seems best for its representation on the paper. Objects which are always regarded in a certain position should, of course, be drawn in that position.

191. The Thumbnail Sketch. The best method for beginners to learn the fundamentals of this system of views is to secure a series of small wood blocks, varying in complexity of form from the simple rectangular forms to those having inclined surfaces and curved surfaces. The student should make six-view thumbnail sketches of the blocks (Fig. 247), followed possibly by instrumental drawings of the several views. Such a series of blocks is shown in Figs. 300 and 301.

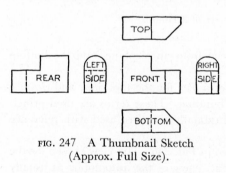

FIG. 247   A Thumbnail Sketch
(Approx. Full Size).

It is suggested that the beginning student make six-view sketches of several of the objects shown in Fig. 300 before proceeding further. For this purpose cross-section paper is recommended (§ 219).

192. Multiview Projection. A view of an object is known, technically, as a *projection* and the system of views discussed above is known as *multiview projection*. A projection is a view of an object drawn on a plane known as the *plane of projection*. Multiview projection is only one of the several types of projection described in Chapter 6.

The method of viewing an object to obtain a projection is illustrated in Fig. 248 (a). Between the observer and the object a transparent plane, or pane of glass, representing a *plane of projection*, is placed parallel to a face of the object. On the pane of glass is shown in outline how the object appears to the observer from that direction. Theoretically, the observer is at an infinite distance from the object, so that the lines of sight are parallel. This view represents all edges and contours of the object seen by the observer. The view obtained from the direction indicated is shown at (b).

In more precise terms this view is obtained by drawing perpendiculars, called *projectors*, from all points in the edges or contours of the object to the plane of projection. The piercing points of these projectors, being infinite in number, form lines on the pane of glass, as shown in Fig. 248. Thus, if from

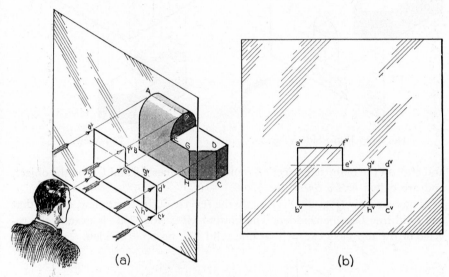

(a)   (b)

FIG. 248   Projection of an Object.

a point D on the object a perpendicular is drawn to the plane of projection, it will pierce that plane at d^v, and d^v will be one view of the point D. The same procedure applies to the point C, and c^v will be one view of the point C. If the projections, or views, of the end-points of the line DC of the object are found, the line d^vc^v on the plane of projection will be the projection or "view" of the line DC. The same procedure can be applied to all lines or edges of the object, and thus a complete view or projection of the object can be obtained.

A similar procedure may be applied to obtain the right side view (Fig. 249). This view is necessary in the shape description because it shows the true curvature of the top of the object. Likewise, the top view (Fig. 250) is needed because it shows the true angle of the inclined surface.

The left side view (Fig. 251) is the same as the right side view of Fig. 249, except for the central dashed lines. In Fig. 251 the lines AB and CD on the object are completely hidden from the observer as he looks through the plane of projection in the direction indicated by the arrow. The dashed lines $a^p b^p$

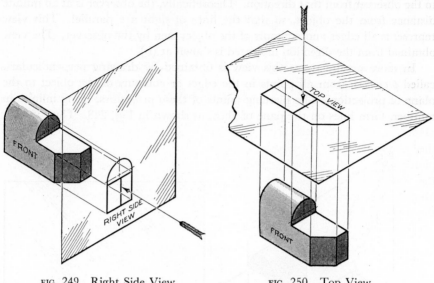

FIG. 249   Right Side View.   FIG. 250   Top View.

and $c^p d^p$ on the plane of projection represent the lines AB and CD on the object, and are called *hidden lines*. See § 200.

The rear view (Fig. 252) is exactly the reverse of the front view, except that one solid line becomes hidden. The bottom view (Fig. 253) is exactly the reverse of the top view except that one solid line becomes hidden.

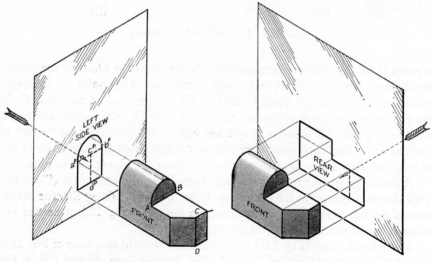

FIG. 251   Left Side View.   FIG. 252   Rear View.

193. The "Glass Box." If planes of projection are placed parallel to the main faces of the object, they may be assumed to form a "glass box," as shown in Fig. 254. Notice that the observer is always *on the outside looking in,* so that he sees the object through the planes of projection.*

Since it is required to show the views of a solid, or three-dimensional object, on a flat sheet of paper, it is obviously necessary to unfold the planes, so that they will all lie in the same plane. For reasons explained in § 184 all planes except the rear plane are assumed to be hinged upon the front plane, and the rear plane is assumed to be

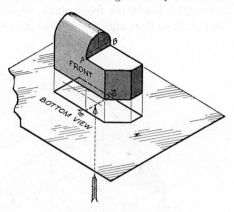

FIG. 253   Bottom View.

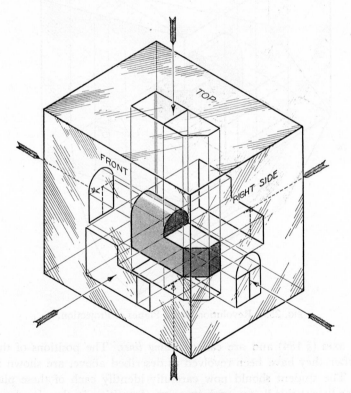

FIG. 254   The "Glass Box."

* This is a distinguishing characteristic of *third-angle projection* (§ 186)

hinged upon the left side plane. The direction of revolution of the planes is shown in Fig. 255. Each plane revolves outwardly from the original box position until it lies in the front plane, which remains stationary, as shown in Fig. 256 (a). The lines about which the planes are revolved correspond to the co-

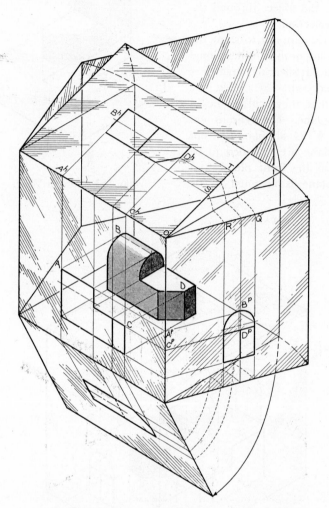

FIG. 255   Revolution of the Planes of Projection.

ordinate axes (§ 184) and are called *folding lines*. The positions of these six planes, after they have been revolved as described above, are shown in Fig. 256 (b). The student should now carefully identify each of these planes as "front" or "right side," etc., with its original position in the glass box. This mental procedure should be repeated until the revolutions are thoroughly understood.

In Fig. 255, observe that lines extend around the glass box from one view to the other upon the surfaces of the planes of projection. These lines are the *projections of the projectors* from points on the object to the planes of projection.

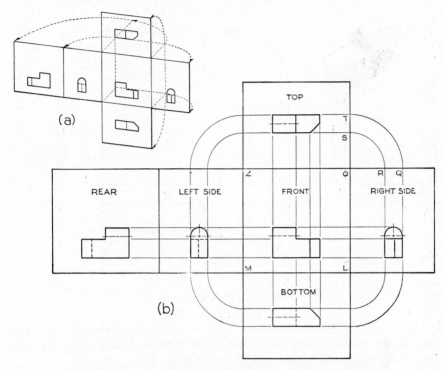

FIG. 256   The Six Views as They Appear on a Sheet of Paper.

In Fig. 256 (b), the equal lines OS and OR, and OT and OQ, are shown as they appear after all planes have been revolved into the front plane. Since OS is equal to OR, the top view is the same distance from the axis OZ as the right end view is from the axis OL. Moreover, it should be apparent that the bottom view and the left side view are the same distance from their respective axes as the right side view and the top view. Thus the depth of all of these views may be found by construction, as shown, after the depth of one has been determined.

194. View Analysis. In Fig. 257, observe the following:

(1) The *height* of the block is shown in the front view, right side view, left side view, and rear view, and these line up horizontally.

(2) The *depth* is shown in the top view, right side view, left side view, and bottom view, and these views are grouped around the front view.

(3) The *width* is shown in the front view, top view, bottom view, and rear view, and the first three line up vertically.

(4) The *front face* is shown as a line, that is *edgewise*, in the top, bottom, and both side views, and faces *inward*, or *toward the front view*.

(5) The *rear face* is shown as a line, that is *edgewise*, in the top, bottom, and both side views, and faces *outward*, or *away from the front view*.

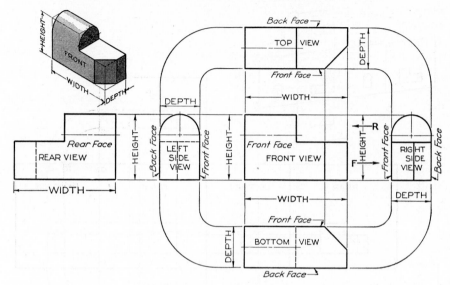

FIG. 257   View Analysis.

(6) Every object line or hidden line on the drawing represents a line of intersection of two surfaces of the object, or a contour (such as the top contour of the cylindrical surface as seen in the front view).

(7) *Adjacent Views Are Reciprocal.*—If the front view is imagined to be the object itself, the right side view is obtained by looking toward the right side of the front view, as shown by the arrow R. Likewise, if the right side view is imagined to be the object itself, the front view is obtained by looking toward the left side of the right side view, as shown by the arrow F. The same relation exists between all adjacent views.

195. Choice of Views. Up to this point we have considered the six possible views, so that any of them may be drawn if needed. However, it should now be apparent that there is a great deal of repetition in the six views. *A multiview drawing, for use in the shop, should contain only those views needed to describe the object completely.*

Examination of the pictorial drawing in Fig. 257 (a), and the thumbnail sketch in Fig. 258, shows that there are three distinctive features of this object which must be described on the drawing:

1. Right-angled notch
2. Rounded top
3. Inclined surface

Both the front and rear views show the right-angled notch, but the front view is preferred, because it has no hidden lines. The rear view is therefore crossed out.

Both the right side and left side views show the curvature of the top, but the right side view is preferred because it has no hidden lines. The left side view is therefore crossed out.

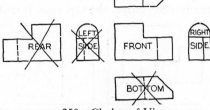
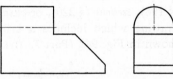

Both the top and bottom views show the angle of the inclined surface, but the top view is preferred because

FIG. 258   Choice of Views.

it has no hidden lines. The bottom view is, therefore, crossed out.

The required views in this problem are the three remaining views: the front, top, and right side. While it is not necessary actually to draw a six-view sketch before making a choice of necessary views, the draftsman must *think through* the six views in the manner described.

This does not mean that a required view *must* be one without hidden lines. In general, however, the chosen views will have a minimum of hidden lines, because in most cases hidden features in one view will appear visible in another, and the latter can be chosen as shown above.

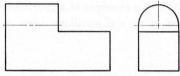

FIG. 259   Two-View Drawing.

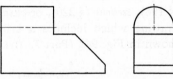

FIG. 260   Two-View Drawing.

If the object does not have the inclined surface (or one of the other features), only two significant features remain, and *two views* are sufficient to describe the shape of the object (Fig. 259). Or, if the inclined surface is situated so that the angle shows in the same view along with one of the other two significant features, only two views are necessary (Fig. 260). There-fore, the number of necessary views depends upon the number and location of the significant features of the object.

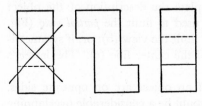

FIG. 261   Choice of Right Side View.

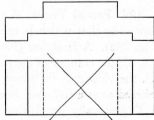

FIG. 262   Choice of Top View.

If the object requires only two views, and the right side and left side views are equally descriptive, the right side view is customarily used (Fig. 261).

If the object requires only two views, and the top and bottom views are equally descriptive, the top view is customarily used (Fig. 262).

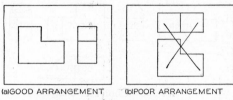

(a)GOOD ARRANGEMENT   (b)POOR ARRANGEMENT

FIG. 263   Arrangement of Views.

If the object requires only two views, and the top and right side views are equally descriptive, the combination chosen is the one which spaces best on the paper (Figs. 263 and 264).

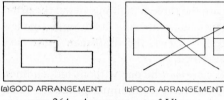

(a)GOOD ARRANGEMENT   (b)POOR ARRANGEMENT

FIG. 264   Arrangement of Views.

Two views are generally considered minimum for the description of even a simple object. However, many cylindrical parts may be represented adequately by only *one view*, provided diameter dimensions are given marked with the letter D (Fig. 265).

A complicated object may require more than three views, and also special views, such as *partial views* (§ 196), *sections* (§ 220), or *auxiliary views* (§ 236). An example of a four-view drawing which includes a broken section and a partial auxiliary view is shown in Fig. 942 (Part 3. CYLINDER BLOCK).

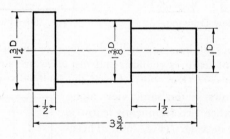

FIG. 265   One-View Drawing.

196. Partial Views. A view need not be a complete projection, but may show only that which is necessary to complete the description of the object (Fig. 266). A *break line* (Fig. 85) may be used to limit the *partial view* (Fig. 266, a); the contour of the part shown may limit the view (b); or, if symmetrical, the view may be drawn on one side of the center line (c). The latter is referred to as a *half view*. See also § 235.

Occasionally the distinctive features of an object are on opposite sides, so that in either complete side view there would be a considerable overlapping of shapes, resulting in an unintelligible view. In such cases two side views

are often the best solution (Fig 267). Observe that the views are partial
views, in both of which certain visible or invisible lines have been omitted
for clearness.

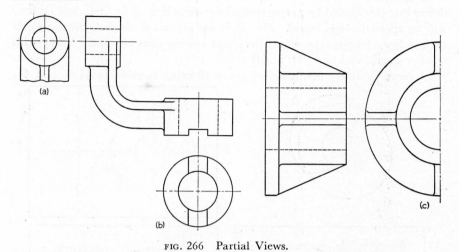

FIG. 266   Partial Views.

197. Laying Out Two-View Drawings. *All instrumental drawings should
first be drawn lightly with construction lines, using a hard pencil* (as 4H to 6H). The

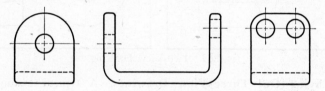

FIG. 267   Two Partial Side Views.

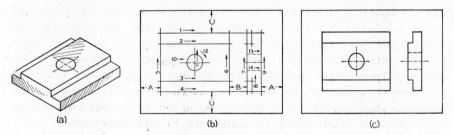

FIG. 268   Two-View Drawing.

views should be constructed simultaneously (Fig. 268), the construction lines
being drawn in the order shown. Distances A should be approximately equal,
with the distance B equal to, or slightly less than either of the distances A.
Distances C should be approximately equal. If dimensions (§§ 357–406) or

notes (§§ 384 and 471) are used, allowances of space for them should be made.

In laying out a two-view drawing of a circular object, the *center lines are drawn first* (Fig. 269, I), distances *A* being approximately equal. The vertical center line (II) should be so spaced that the areas *B–B–B*, *C–C–C*, and *D–D–D* will be approximately equal. The *circles and arcs are drawn first, followed by the straight lines*. Finally, the object lines and hidden lines are made heavy with a softer pencil, such as F, H, or 2H (III).

A more complete discussion of pencil drawing is given in §§ 66 and 67.

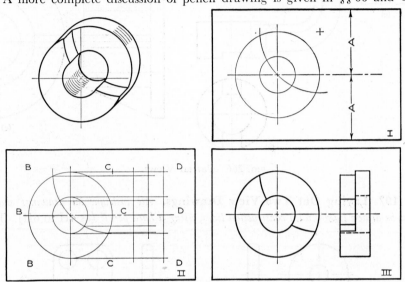

FIG. 269   Two-View Drawing.

198. Laying Out Three-View Drawings. A typical example of an object which requires three views is shown in Fig. 270 (a). When the planes of the glass box have been unfolded, the views appear as shown at (b), which also shows the elimination of three unnecessary views. The three required views, together with the axes, are shown at (c). Note the projection lines between the views, particularly the arcs from the top view to the side view.

The construction may be considerably simplified by omitting the axes and transferring depth dimensions from the top view to the side view, and vice versa, by means of a 45° line *AB*, as shown in Fig. 271. Obviously, the right side view may be moved to the right or left, or the top view may be moved upward or downward, by shifting the 45° line accordingly.

In practice, it is often more convenient to transfer the depth dimensions from the top view to the side view, or vice versa, by using the dividers or the scale. These methods are apt to be faster and more accurate than the 45° line method, and are generally recommended.

In spacing a three-view drawing, spaces *A* (Fig. 272) should be approximately equal, and space *B* should be equal to, or slightly less than, either of

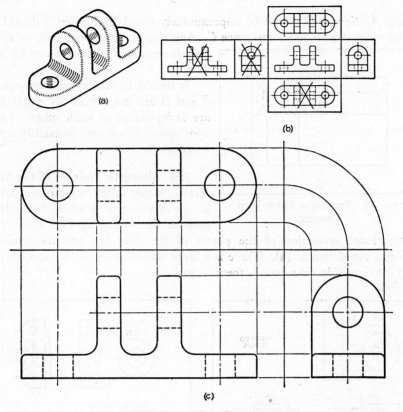

FIG. 270 Three-View Drawing.

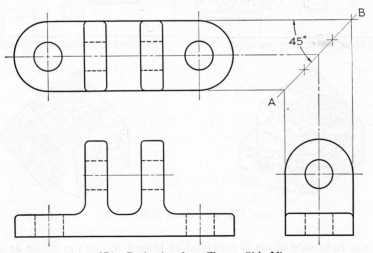

FIG. 271 Projecting from Top to Side View.

167

spaces *A.* Spaces *C* should be approximately equal, and space *D* should be equal to, or slightly less than, space *C.* Adjustments should be made for notes and dimensions (Chapter 16 and §§ 384, 471).

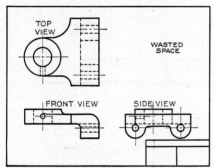

FIG. 272   Spacing a Three-View Drawing.

It should be understood that spaces *B* and *D* are not necessarily equal, but are independent of each other. Likewise, spaces *C* are not necessarily equal to spaces *A.*

199. Alternate Position of the Side View. A special spacing problem arises in the drawing of a wide, flat object, such as the casting in Fig. 273. The conventional revolution of the planes of the glass box and the resulting drawing are shown at (a). There is a large wasted space at the upper right, and the right side view crowds the title box.

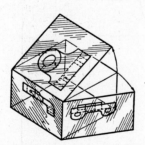

(a) POOR ARRANGEMENT OF VIEWS

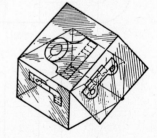

(b) APPROVED ARRANGEMENT OF VIEWS

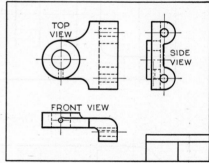

FIG. 273   Position of Side View.

If the right side plane is regarded as hinged to the top plane as shown at (b), instead of to the front plane as shown at (a), the resulting drawing is much more satisfactorily spaced.

200. Hidden Lines. Correct and incorrect practice in the drawing of hidden lines is illustrated in Fig. 274. The examples at (a), (b), and (c) show how to draw the dashes to secure sharp corners. Dashes should not cross an

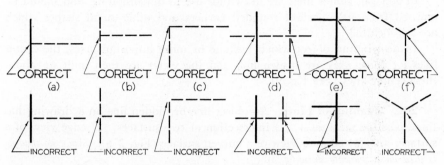

FIG. 274   Intersections of Hidden Lines.

object line (d), as this would make the invisible line appear as near the observer as the object line. Two hidden dashes should not cross (d). If a dash of a hidden line is joined to the visible line as shown in the lower part of (e), the object line would appear to continue; hence a gap should always be left in such cases. Correct and incorrect practices in drawing hidden arcs are illustrated in Fig. 275.

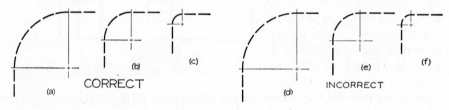

FIG. 275   Hidden Arcs.

The draftsman should choose views which show all features with visible lines so far as this is possible. After this has been done, *hidden lines should be used wherever necessary to make the drawing clear.* Where they are not needed for clearness, hidden lines should be omitted. The beginner, however, would do well to be cautious about leaving out hidden lines until experience shows him when they are not required for clearness.

201. Center Lines. Center lines (§§ 64 and 67) are used to indicate axes of symmetrical objects or parts of objects. They are not only convenient to the draftsman in laying out his views, but are necessary in dimensioning and in laying out in the shop.

Typical applications of center lines are shown in Figs. 259, 265–271, and 290. Note that the center lines cross in the end views (curved views) of cylindrical shapes, and that the small dashes cross at the center where the compass needle point is placed. Only one center line in the longitudinal view is used to denote the axis.

In general, center lines are drawn for use in dimensioning, and should be omitted from unimportant rounded corners and other small shapes which are self-locating.

In drawing an object which has one or more important axes, the center lines for these axes are drawn first and the views are then built up about these center lines. See Fig. 91.

202. Meaning of Lines. An object line or hidden line on a drawing has three possible meanings: (1) intersection of two surfaces; (2) edge view of a surface; and (3) contour view of a curved surface (Fig. 276). Since *no shading is used on a working drawing*, it is necessary to examine all the views to determine the meaning of a given line. For example (Fig. 276), the top line of the front view might be regarded as the edge view of a plane and not as the contour of a curved surface if the side view is not examined. Similarly, the inside vertical line in the front view might be regarded as the edge view of a plane if we look at only the front and side views. The top

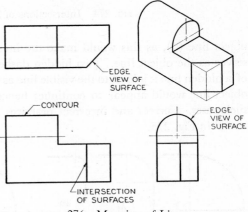

FIG. 276   Meaning of Lines.

view shows that the line stands for the intersection of two surfaces.

203. Precedence of Lines. Object lines, hidden lines, and center lines often coincide on a drawing, and it is necessary to follow a consistent rule as to which takes precedence over the other. As shown in Fig. 277, an object line always "takes precedence over" (covers up) a center line or a hidden line (A and B). A hidden line takes precedence over a center line (C). Note that at A and C the ends of the center line are shown, but are separated from the ends of the object or hidden lines by small gaps.

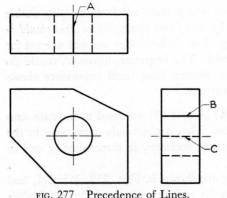

FIG. 277   Precedence of Lines.

204. Points. Three views of single points are shown in Fig. 278. Note that if a point is *visible* in a given view, the numeral is placed *outside* the corner, but if a point is *invisible* the numeral is placed *inside* the corner. In Fig. 278

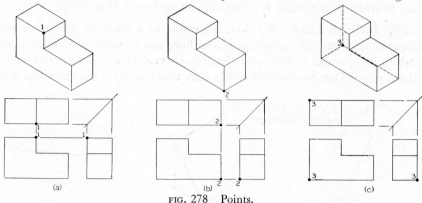

FIG. 278 Points.

(a) point *1* is visible in all three views, and is, therefore, placed outside the corners in each view. At (b) the point is invisible in the top view, and the numeral *2* is placed inside the corner. At (c) point *3* is invisible in all three views, and hence is placed inside the corner in each view.

This numbering system, in which points are identified by the same numbers (or letters *A, B, C* or *a, b, c*, etc.) in the several views, is useful in projecting known points in two views to unknown positions in a third view. Study Fig. 296 carefully, which shows how a third view is projected in this manner, point by point. See also § 219.

This numbering system should not be confused with that discussed in § 217, where a given point has been assigned different numbers in the different views for study purposes.

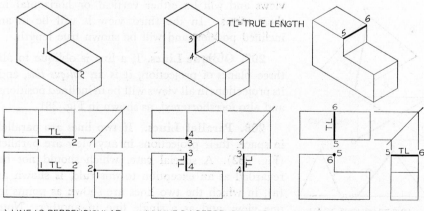

(a) LINE 1,2 PERPENDICULAR TO SIDE PLANE OF PROJECTION

(b) LINE 3,4 PERPENDICULAR TO TOP PLANE OF PROJECTION

(c) LINE 5,6 PERPENDICULAR TO FRONT PLANE OF PROJECTION

FIG. 279 Normal Lines.

205. Normal Lines. If a line is perpendicular to a plane of projection, it will be parallel to adjacent planes of projection, and is called a *normal* line. Its projection on the plane to which it is perpendicular is a point, and on a plane to which it is parallel is a line shown true length (Fig. 279).

206. Inclined Lines. If a line is parallel to a plane of projection and oblique to adjacent planes, it is an *inclined* line, and its projection on the plane to which it is parallel is shown true length. Its projections on planes to which it is not parallel are *foreshortened*, or less than true length, as shown in Fig. 280.

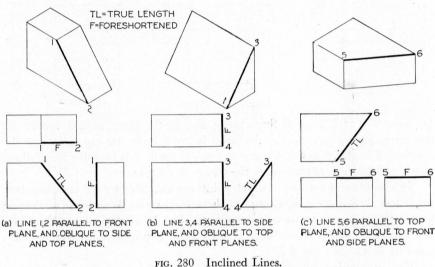

(a) LINE 1,2 PARALLEL TO FRONT PLANE, AND OBLIQUE TO SIDE AND TOP PLANES.

(b) LINE 3,4 PARALLEL TO SIDE PLANE, AND OBLIQUE TO TOP AND FRONT PLANES.

(c) LINE 5,6 PARALLEL TO TOP PLANE, AND OBLIQUE TO FRONT AND SIDE PLANES.

FIG. 280   Inclined Lines.

An inclined line will always be foreshortened in two of the three regular views and will be either vertical or horizontal in those views. In the third view it will be in an inclined position and will be shown true length.

207. Oblique Lines. If a line is oblique to all three planes of projection, it is an *oblique line*, and its projections in all views will be in inclined positions and also foreshortened, as shown in Fig. 281.

208. Parallel Lines. If two lines are parallel in space, their projections in any view are parallel (Fig. 282). A special case, which should not be regarded as an exception to this rule, is shown at (a), in which the two lines are shown as points in one view, and as a single line in another. Note that even in the pictorial drawings, the lines are shown parallel.

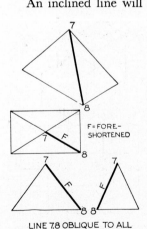

LINE 7,8 OBLIQUE TO ALL PLANES OF PROJECTION.

FIG. 281   Oblique Lines.

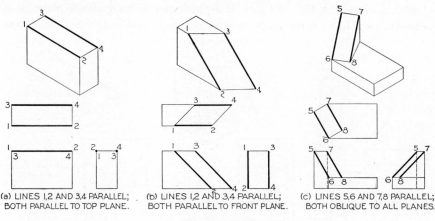

(a) LINES 1,2 AND 3,4 PARALLEL;   (b) LINES 1,2 AND 3,4 PARALLEL;   (c) LINES 5,6 AND 7,8 PARALLEL;
BOTH PARALLEL TO TOP PLANE.   BOTH PARALLEL TO FRONT PLANE.   BOTH OBLIQUE TO ALL PLANES.

FIG. 282   Parallel Lines.

209. Angle Between Lines. If an angle is in a normal plane—that is, parallel to a plane of projection (§ 212)—the angle will be shown true size on the plane of projection to which it is parallel. See Fig. 283 (a).

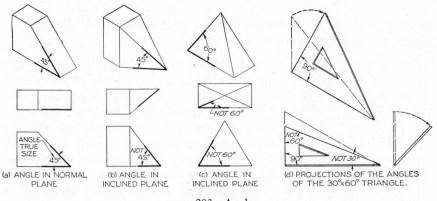

(a) ANGLE IN NORMAL   (b) ANGLE IN   (c) ANGLE IN   (d) PROJECTIONS OF THE ANGLES
PLANE   INCLINED PLANE   INCLINED PLANE   OF THE 30°x60° TRIANGLE.

FIG. 283   Angles.

If the angle is in an inclined plane (§ 213), as shown in Fig. 283 (b) and (c), the angle may be projected either larger or smaller than the true angle, depending upon its position. At (b) the 45° angle is shown *oversize* in the front view, and at (c) the 60° angle is shown *undersize* in both views.

A 90° angle will be projected true size, even though it is in an inclined plane, provided one leg of the angle is a normal line, as shown at (d). In this figure, the 60° angle is projected *oversize* and the 30° angle *undersize*. Study these relations, using your own 30° x 60° triangle as a model.

210. Circles and Curves. If a circle is parallel to a plane of projection, it is projected as a circle, true size, on that plane, and as a line on adjacent planes, as shown in Fig. 284 (a). If a circle lies in an inclined plane, it is projected as a line on the plane to which it is perpendicular, and as ellipses

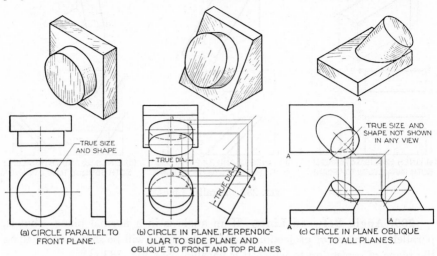

(a) CIRCLE PARALLEL TO FRONT PLANE.

(b) CIRCLE IN PLANE, PERPENDIC- ULAR TO SIDE PLANE, AND OBLIQUE TO FRONT AND TOP PLANES.

(c) CIRCLE IN PLANE OBLIQUE TO ALL PLANES.

FIG. 284   Circles and Ellipses.

on adjacent planes (b). If a circle lies in a plane oblique to all planes of pro- jection, it is projected as ellipses in all views (c).

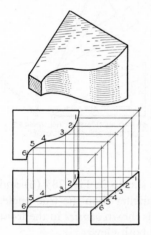

FIG. 285   Space Curve.

211. Space Curves. The views of a *space curve* are established by the projections of points along the curve (Fig. 285). In this figure any points *1, 2, 3,* etc., are selected along the curve in the top view and then projected to the side view (or the reverse) and points are located in the front view by projecting downward from the top view and across from the side view. The resulting curve in the front view is drawn with the aid of the irregular curve (§ 72).

212. Normal Surfaces. If a plane surface is parallel to a plane of projection, it is shown in its true size and shape on that plane, and as a line on each adjacent plane (Fig. 286). Such a surface is called a *normal surface.*

213. Inclined Surfaces. If a plane is perpendicular to one plane of projection and inclined to adjacent planes, it is an *inclined surface* (Fig. 287), and is shown as a *line* on the plane of projection to which it is perpendicular. It will appear foreshortened on the planes to which it is inclined, the degree of foreshortening being proportional to the angle of inclination. For example

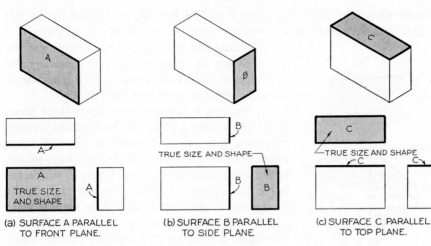

FIG. 286   Normal Surfaces.

in Fig. 287 (a), the plane A is foreshortened more in the side view than in the top view because it makes a greater angle with the side plane of projection.

An inclined plane will not appear true size in any regular view because it is not parallel to any plane of projection. To show the true size, a special

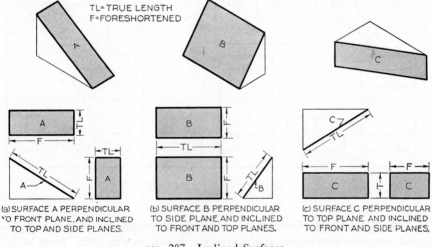

FIG. 287   Inclined Surfaces.

auxiliary view (§§ 236–238) is required, or the surface must be *revolved* until it is parallel to a regular plane of projection (§§ 250–254).

214. Oblique Surfaces. If a plane is oblique to all planes of projection, it is an *oblique surface*, and its true size and shape will not be shown in any regular view (Fig. 288). An oblique surface is easily recognized by the fact that it does not appear as a line in any view, but as a surface in all views.

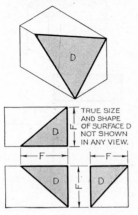

FIG. 288   Oblique Surface.

To obtain the true size of an oblique surface. it is necessary to construct a *secondary auxiliary view* (§ 249), or to revolve the surface until it is parallel to a regular plane of projection (§§ 250–254).

In Fig. 289 it is required to draw three views of the block after a plane has been passed through the points A, B, and C. As shown at (b), only points which lie in the same plane of the object are joined. In the front view, join points A and C which are in the same plane, extending the line to P on the front corner of the block extended. In the side view, join P to B, and in the top view, join B to A. The figure is completed by applying the rule which states that *parallel lines in space will be projected as parallel lines in any view* (§ 208). The remaining lines are thus drawn parallel to the lines AP, PB, and BA.

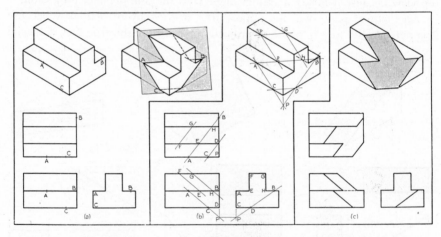

FIG. 289   Oblique Surface.

215. Cylindrical, Conical, and Spherical Surfaces. Views of cylindrical, conical, and spherical surfaces are shown in Fig. 290. Note at (a) the cylindrical surface is shown as a circle in the front view and as rectangles in the top and side views. Note the application of center lines in all views. A combination of these surfaces in a machine part is shown at (d).

Three views are shown in each case in Fig. 290, to illustrate how the surfaces appear in the different views. However, only two views are needed to describe each object, and in a working drawing, one view would be omitted.

These types of surfaces are very common in industry as they can be easily produced by rotary motion on such machine tools as the lathe, drill press, etc. (§§ 451 and 452).

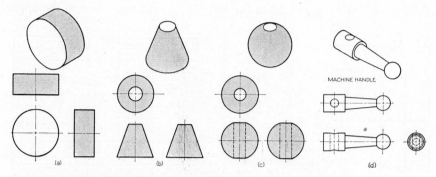

FIG. 290   Cylindrical, Conical, and Spherical Surfaces.

216. Tangent Surfaces. When a cylindrical surface is tangent to a plane surface, as in Fig. 291 (a), there is no line of intersection, and the juncture is not shown in the drawing.

When a cylindrical surface *intersects* a plane surface, the line of intersection must be shown, as in Fig. 291 (b).

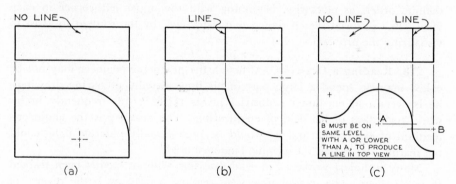

FIG. 291   Tangencies and Intersections.

When two cylindrical surfaces are tangent, a line is necessary to show the juncture only when it becomes a contour line, as in Fig. 291 (c). See also § 194 (6).

217. Identification of Lines and Surfaces. A method of studying multi-view projection by means of numbering points in the views is shown in Fig. 292. All points are numbered at random, each number being used only once. Corresponding points in the three views, therefore, have different numbers. In the table, in one of the three columns, the numbers of a certain line or surface are given. The student finds the line or surface in the two remaining views, and gives the corresponding numbers in the appropriate columns. For example, in the "FRONT VIEW" column, "LINE *15, 16*" is given. The student then examines the drawing and finds the corresponding numbers *10, 11* in the top view and *28* in the side view, and letters these in the appro-

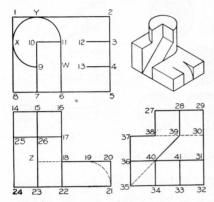

FRONT VIEW	TOP VIEW	SIDE VIEW
LINE 15,16	10,11	28
14,16	LINE 9,X,Y,11	27, 29,28
26,23	LINE 10,7	39,35
SURFACE 26,17,22,23	10,11,6,7	39,35
15,16,17,26	SURFACE 10,11	28,39
SURFACE 19,21	12,3,4,13	40,41,33,34
15,23	SURFACE 10,7	27,28,39,35,37,38
SURFACE 14,15,26,25	9,X	27,28,39,38
LINE 20	5,4,-3,2	36,40-41,31
LINE 21	5,2	35,32
SURFACE 19,20,21	13,4 OR 12,3	40,34 OR 41,33
26,17	10, 11	LINE 39
25,26,23,24	SURFACE 8,7	37, 35
LINE 25,26	8,7	37
SURFACE 18,22	W,6	36,40,35

FIG. 292   Lines and Surfaces.

priate columns, as shown. The numbers should be listed in the table in some definite order, as clockwise, beginning with the upper left corner in each view. The pictorial sketch shown may be drawn by the student to assist in visualizing the problem.

218. Reading a Drawing. Although the practicing engineer may not be called upon to spend a large part of his time actually preparing drawings, he is certain to encounter industrial prints (§§ 611–615) frequently in his work, regardless of his field of engineering. The drawing is the engineer's medium of expression, and he would be professionally illiterate if he could not readily understand the graphic language used.

Many technical workers can read drawings without having been trained to make them. The mental process of reading a drawing is the reverse of that of making a drawing. The draftsman has a knowledge of the shape, and he then makes a drawing describing that shape. The reader of a drawing is unfamiliar with the object represented, and must learn to interpret the meaning of every line in order to understand it (§ 202).

Even the student who has received considerable training in drafting may find it difficult to understand a complicated drawing if he does not approach the task correctly. He must learn not to stare at one view, but to examine and compare all the views simultaneously. First, he should try to get a mental picture of the entire object without regard to small details; then he should examine the details one by one, comparing them in the different views, and finally he must determine the meaning of every line on the drawing.

Excellent practice in reading drawings can be obtained by sketching a third view of an object when two views are given. A large number of these, called *completion problems*, are given in Fig. 302. In each, the student is to sketch the given views on cross-section paper and then add the right side view.

Another type of exercise is the *missing-line problem*, a large number of which are shown in Figs. 303 and 304. In each problem the student is to study the given views and then sketch the missing line or lines.

Another type of problem which is useful in developing the *constructive imagination*, so important to the engineer in design work as well as in reading drawings, is the *possible-view problem*, a number of which are given in Fig. 305. At the top of Fig. 305 at (a), there is given a top view of an object whose shape otherwise is not known. The student is to imagine and sketch front and right side views which "go with" the given top view. Obviously there are an infinite number of solutions. Two of these are shown at (b) and (c). The problems may be sketched on cross-section paper, as shown, or drawn with instruments on blank paper.

219. Visualization. Often the student may have difficulty reading the given views of such problems as those discussed in § 218, and therefore cannot add the required lines or views. A typical "completion problem" is shown in Fig. 293 (a), in which the top and front views are given, and the right side

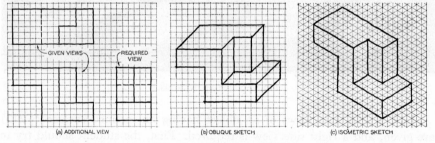

(a) ADDITIONAL VIEW   (b) OBLIQUE SKETCH   (c) ISOMETRIC SKETCH

FIG. 293   Interpretation of Views.

view is to be supplied. To assist in visualizing the object from the two given views, the student may sketch on cross-section paper an *oblique sketch* as shown at (b), or an *isometric sketch* on isometric paper, as shown at (c). For complete information on isometric drawing, see §§ 260–273; and for oblique drawing, see §§ 285–294.

For a complete discussion of multiview and pictorial sketching, see §§ 313–323.

One of the best aids in visualization is the use of an actual model of the object. Such a model need not be made accurately to scale, and may be made of any convenient material, such as children's modeling clay, laundry soap, Irish potatoes, or wood.

A typical example of the use of soap or clay models is shown in Fig. 294, in which three views of an object are given, and the student is to supply a

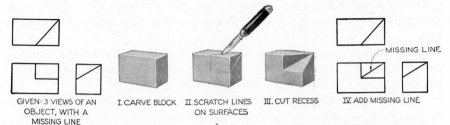

GIVEN: 3 VIEWS OF AN   I. CARVE BLOCK   II. SCRATCH LINES   III. CUT RECESS   IV. ADD MISSING LINE
OBJECT, WITH A   ON SURFACES
MISSING LINE

FIG. 294   Use of Model to Aid Visualization.

missing line. The model is carved as shown in steps I, II, and III, and the "missing" line is added to the drawing as shown in step IV.

Some typical examples of soap models are shown in Fig. 295.

The instrumental drawing of completion problems is excellent for learning to visualize. The mechanics of projecting from view to view can be a considerable aid to the student in visualizing the required view, as shown below.

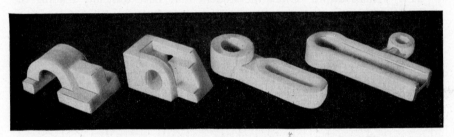

FIG. 295   Soap Models.

In Fig. 296, two views of an object having an inclined surface (§ 213) are given, and a right side view is required. First, the student should try to visualize the right side view as seen in the direction of the arrow; then he should construct, lightly, with a hard pencil, the right side view, point by point. In space I, the side view of point 1 is found by projecting from point 1 in the top view and point 1 in the front view. In space II, points 2, 3, and 4 are similarly projected to complete the vertical end surface (a normal surface) of the object. In space III, points 5 and 6 are projected, to complete the side view of the inclined surface 5, 6, 2, 1. This completes the right side view, since invisible points 9, 10, 8, 7 are directly behind visible corners 5, 6, 4, 3. Note that the numbers of all visible points in any view are lettered outside the corners, and the numbers of all invisible points are lettered within the corners. See § 204.

In Fig. 297, another object having an inclined surface is used, and in addition, a rectangular hole through the object intersects the inclined surface.

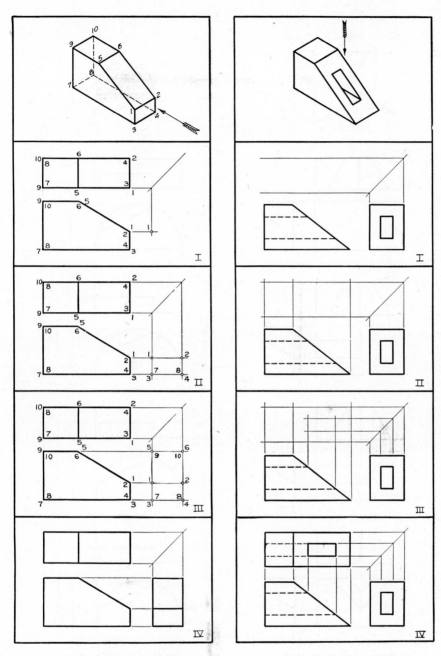

FIG. 296 Use of Numbers in Studying Projections.

FIG. 297 A Study in Projection.

181

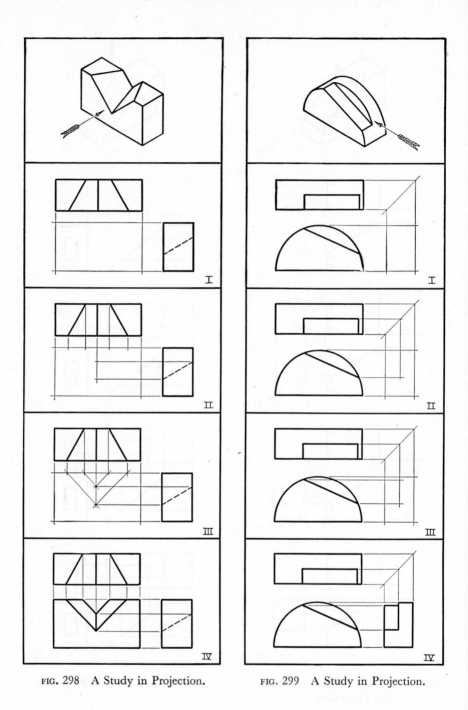

FIG. 298   A Study in Projection.

FIG. 299   A Study in Projection.

Note especially how the opening of the rectangular hole appears in the top view.

In Fig. 298, an object having two oblique surfaces (§ 214) is used. The front view is constructed merely by projecting points down from the top view, and the corresponding points across from the side view. However, in such a problem, if the student does not have a clear mental picture of the object or of the view to be drawn, he may not be sure which points should be connected in the required view. In such case, he must visualize the edges to be projected, and see that the corresponding end points are connected in the required view. *If two points of an object are joined by an edge, those two points will be joined by a line in every view of the object. If two points are joined by a line in two views, those two points will be joined by a line in every other view.* Of course, if a line is perpendicular to a plane of projection, it will be projected as a point on that plane (§ 205).

Another rule which will prove helpful is that applying to parallel lines (§ 208). Try to determine which lines of the object are parallel in space, and then be sure to draw them parallel respectively in all views.

In Fig. 299, an object having a cylindrical surface and an intersecting inclined surface is used. The problem may be varied by assuming the inclined surface in a variety of positions.

Excellent training in visualization, as well as practice in the use of the slide rule, may be obtained by calculating the weights or volumes of the object. A student has correctly visualized an object if the numerical values obtained are correct.

A selected group of multiview problems are given on pages 184–215.*

* Problems in convenient form for solution may be found in *Technical Drawing Problems*, by Giesecke, Mitchell, and Spencer, and in *Technical Drawing Problems—Series 2*, by Spencer and Grant, both designed to accompany this text, and published by The Macmillan Company.

MULTIVIEW PROBLEMS

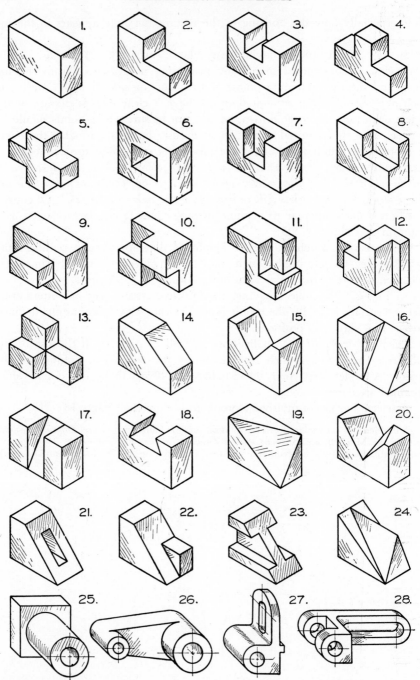

FIG. 300 Sketch necessary views of assigned problems on cross-section paper ($8\frac{1}{2}''$ x $11''$) about four times size shown, two problems per sheet. *Alternate:* Sketch six views of assigned problems, one problem per sheet, and cross out unnecessary views. See § 195.

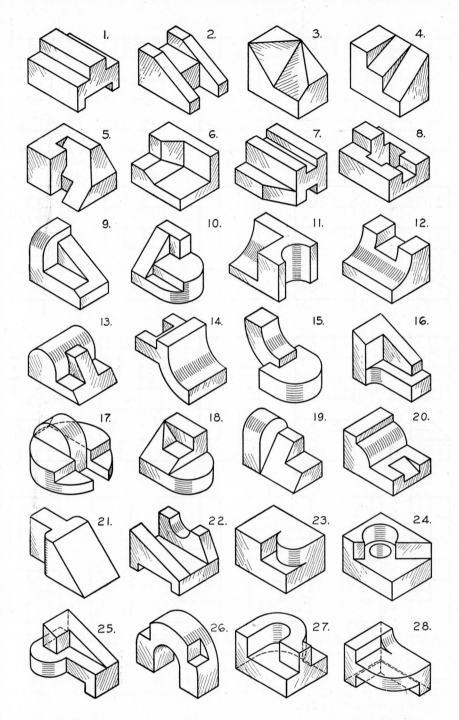

FIG. 301 Sketch necessary views of assigned problems on cross-section paper ($8\frac{1}{2}''$ x $11''$) about four times size shown, two problems per sheet. *Alternate:* Sketch six views of assigned problems, one problem per sheet, and cross out unnecessary views. See § 195.

185

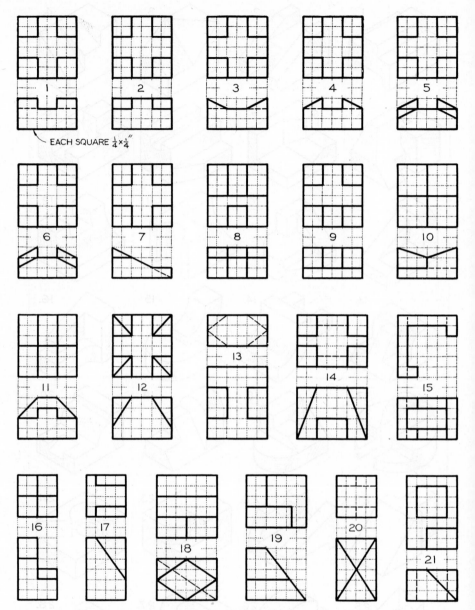

EACH SQUARE ¼×¼″

FIG. 302 (1) Sketch given views of assigned problems and add right side views, using cross-section paper, four problems per sheet. See § 219. (2) Sketch oblique drawings of assigned problems, using cross-section paper, four problems per sheet. See §§ 219 and 287. (3) Sketch isometric drawings of assigned problems, using isometric paper, four problems per sheet. See §§ 219 and 260. (4) Make soap or clay models of assigned problems. See § 219.

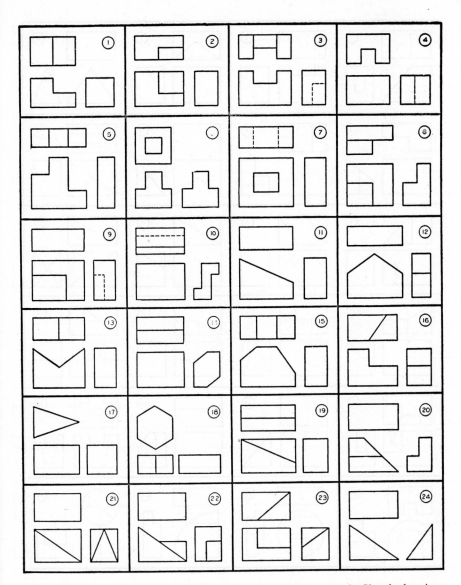

FIG. 303 In each problem one or more lines have been omitted. Sketch the given views, enlarged as required, and add the missing lines.

187

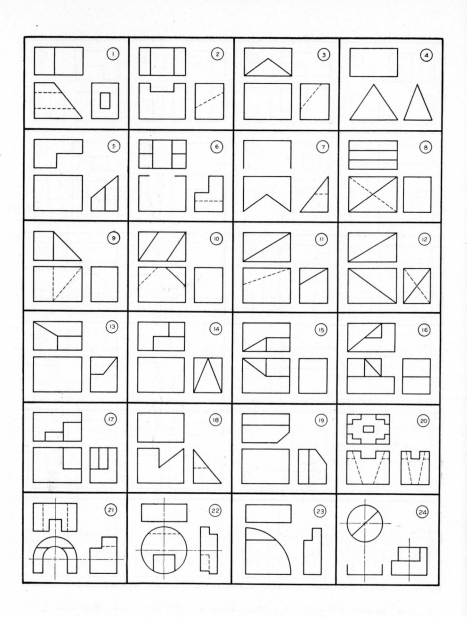

FIG. 304 In each problem one or more lines have been omitted. Sketch the given views, enlarged as required, and add the missing lines.

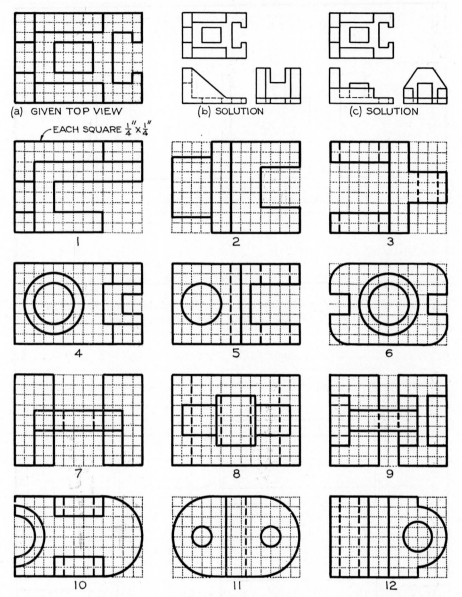

FIG. 305 (1) Sketch given top views of assigned problems, and add front and right side views, using cross-section paper, two problems per sheet. See § 219. (2) Sketch isometric drawings on isometric paper of assigned problems, two problems per sheet. See §§ 219 and 260.

189

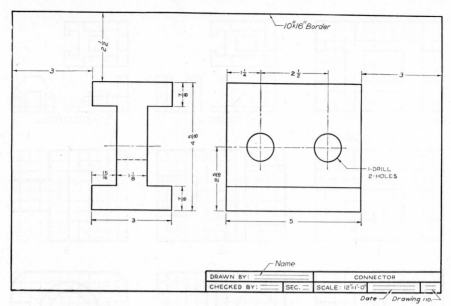

FIG. 306   Draw views with instruments, adding missing lines. Layout B4
(Appendix 1). Omit dimensions unless assigned (§§ 357–386).

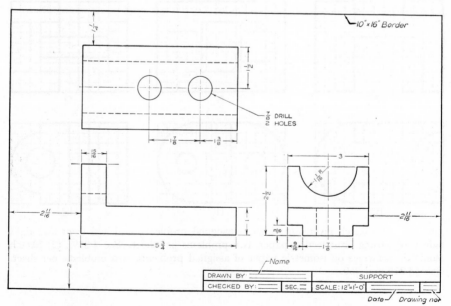

FIG. 307   Draw views with instruments, adding missing lines. Layout B4
(Appendix 1). Omit dimensions unless assigned (§§ 357–386).

190

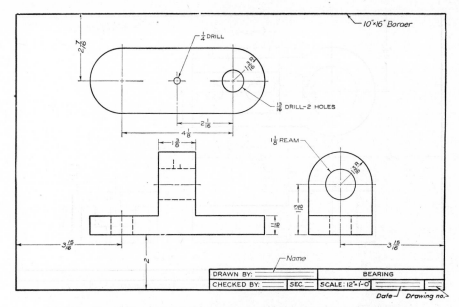

FIG. 308 Draw views with instruments, adding missing lines. Layout B4 (Appendix 1). Omit dimensions unless assigned (§§ 357–386).

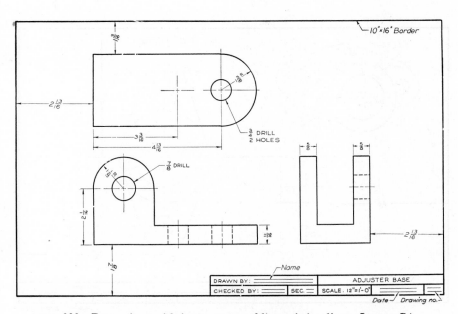

FIG. 309 Draw views with instruments, adding missing lines. Layout B4 (Appendix 1). Omit dimensions unless assigned (§§ 357–386).

191

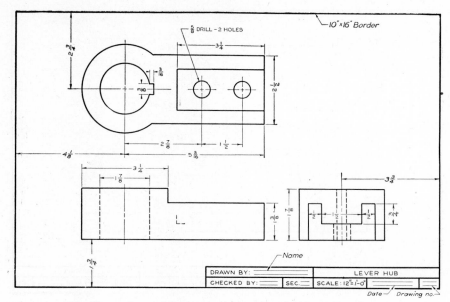

FIG. 310 Draw views with instruments, adding missing lines. Layout B4 (Appendix 1). Omit dimensions unless assigned (§§ 357–386).

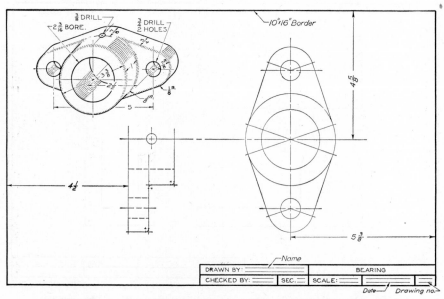

FIG. 311 Draw views with instruments, adding missing lines. Layout B4 (Appendix 1). Omit dimensions unless assigned (§§ 357–386).

192

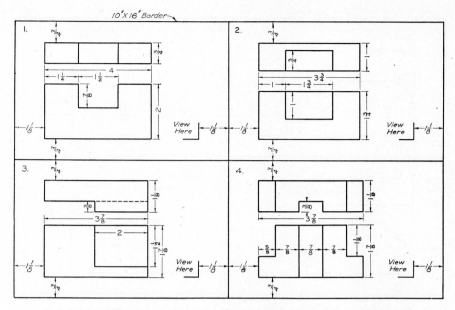

FIG. 312 Draw views with instruments, adding missing views. Layout B3
(Appendix 1). Omit dimensions unless assigned ($\S\S$ 357–386).

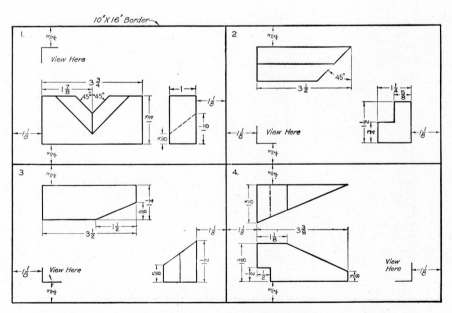

FIG. 313 Draw views with instruments, adding missing views. Layout B3
(Appendix 1). Omit dimensions unless assigned ($\S\S$ 357–386).

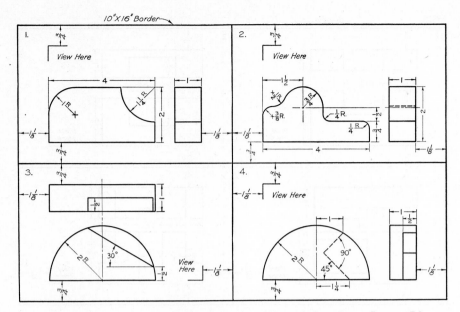

FIG. 314 Draw views with instruments, adding missing views. Layout B3 (Appendix 1). Omit dimensions unless assigned (§§ 357–386).

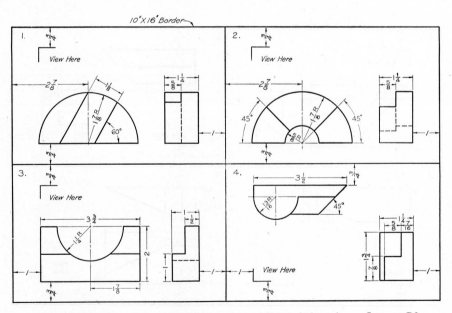

FIG. 315 Draw views with instruments, adding missing views. Layout B3 (Appendix 1). Omit dimensions unless assigned (§§ 357–386).

194

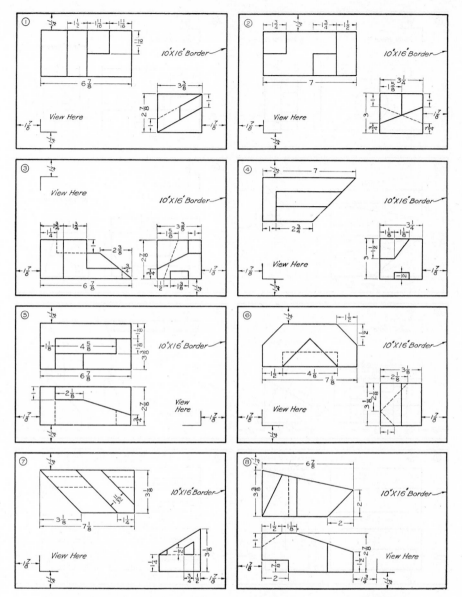

FIG. 316   Draw views with instruments, adding missing views.   Layout B3
(Appendix 1).   Omit dimensions unless assigned (§§ 357–386).

195

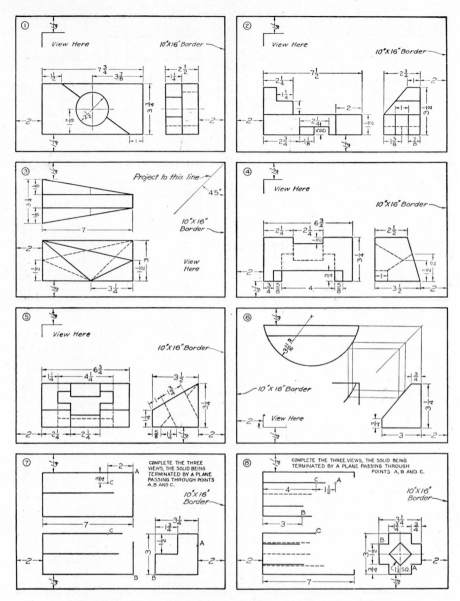

FIG. 317   Draw views with instruments, adding missing views.   Layout B3
(Appendix 1).   Omit dimensions unless assigned (§§ 357–386).

196

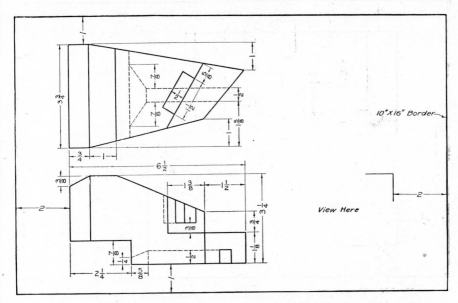

FIG. 318   Draw views with instruments, adding right side view.   Layout B3
(Appendix 1).   Omit dimensions unless assigned (§§ 357–386).

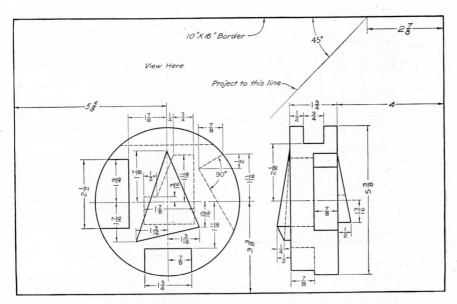

FIG. 319   Draw views with instruments, adding top view.   Layout B3
(Appendix 1).   Omit dimensions unless assigned (§§ 357–386).

197

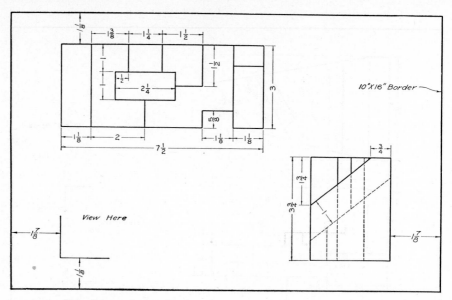

FIG. 320 Draw views with instruments, adding front view. Layout B3 (Appendix 1). Omit dimensions unless assigned (§§ 357–386).

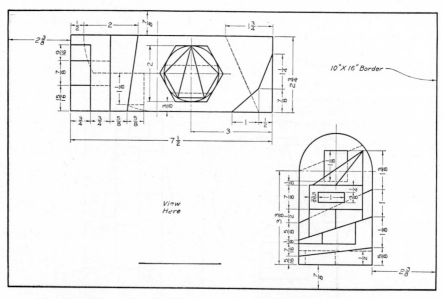

FIG. 321 Draw views with instruments, adding front view. Layout B3 (Appendix 1). Omit dimensions unless assigned (§§ 357–386).

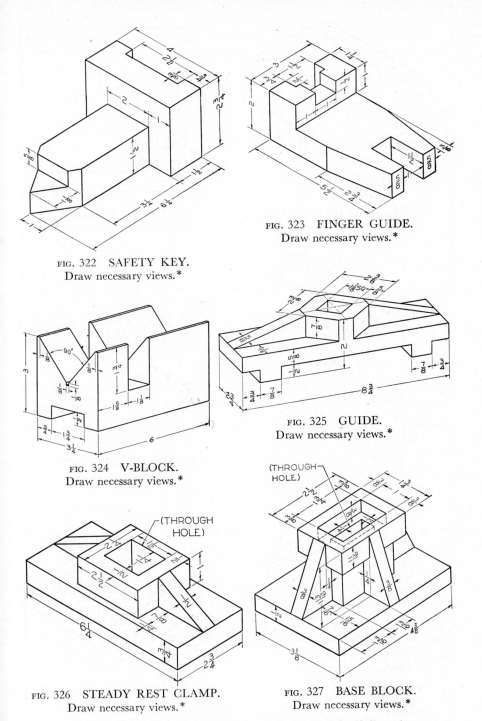

FIG. 322   SAFETY KEY.
Draw necessary views.*

FIG. 323   FINGER GUIDE.
Draw necessary views.*

FIG. 324   V-BLOCK.
Draw necessary views.*

FIG. 325   GUIDE.
Draw necessary views.*

FIG. 326   STEADY REST CLAMP.
Draw necessary views.*

FIG. 327   BASE BLOCK.
Draw necessary views.*

* Make freehand sketch or instrumental drawing, as assigned. If dimensions are required, study §§ 357–386, and if tracing is required, study § 68 or § 70.

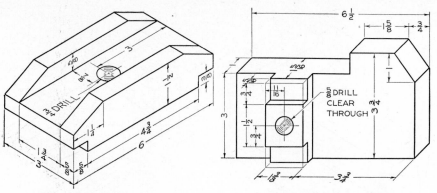

FIG. 328 TAILSTOCK CLAMP.
Draw necessary views.*

FIG. 329 STOP BLOCK.
Draw necessary views.*

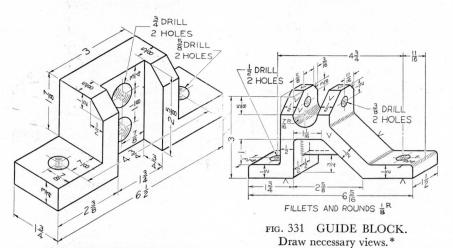

FILLETS AND ROUNDS $\frac{1}{8}$ R

FIG. 330 SUPPORT BRACKET.
Draw necessary views.*

FIG. 331 GUIDE BLOCK.
Draw necessary views.*

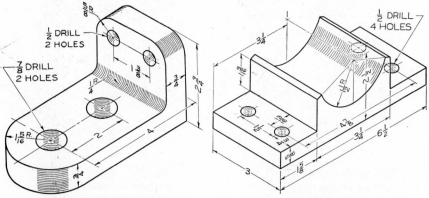

FIG. 332 ANGLE BRACKET.
Draw necessary views.*

333 TRUNNION BLOCK.
Draw necessary views.*

* Make freehand sketch or instrumental drawing, as assigned. If dimensions are required, study §§ 357–386, and if tracing is required, study § 68 or § 70.

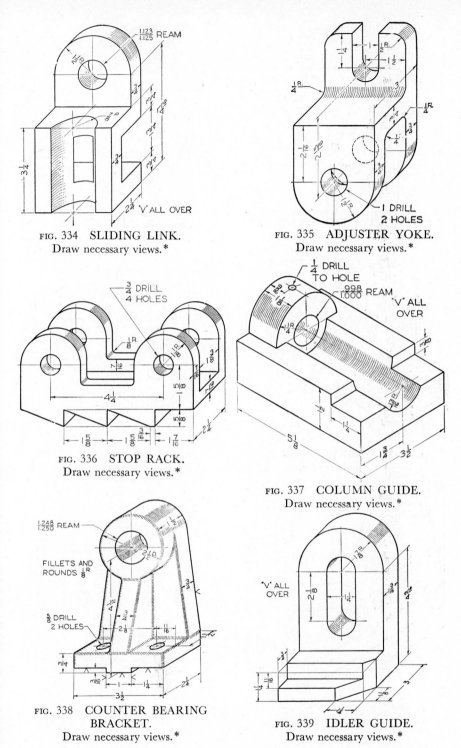

FIG. 334   SLIDING LINK.
Draw necessary views.*

FIG. 335   ADJUSTER YOKE.
Draw necessary views.*

FIG. 336   STOP RACK.
Draw necessary views.*

FIG. 337   COLUMN GUIDE.
Draw necessary views.*

FIG. 338   COUNTER BEARING
BRACKET.
Draw necessary views.*

FIG. 339   IDLER GUIDE.
Draw necessary views.*

* Make freehand sketch or instrumental drawing, as assigned. If dimensions are required, study §§ 357–386, and if tracing is required, study § 68 or § 70.

201

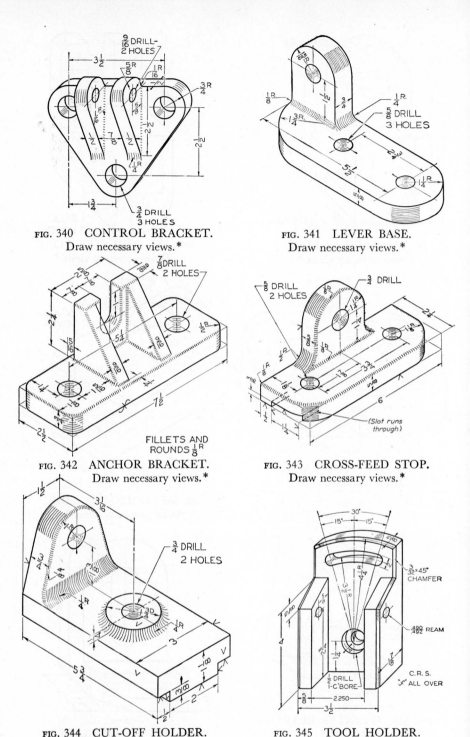

FIG. 340 CONTROL BRACKET.
Draw necessary views.*

FIG. 341 LEVER BASE.
Draw necessary views.*

FIG. 342 ANCHOR BRACKET.
Draw necessary views.*

FIG. 343 CROSS-FEED STOP.
Draw necessary views.*

FIG. 344 CUT-OFF HOLDER.
Draw necessary views.*

FIG. 345 TOOL HOLDER.
Draw necessary views.*

* Make freehand sketch or instrumental drawing, as assigned. If dimensions are required, study §§ 357–386, and if tracing is required, study § 68 or § 70.

202

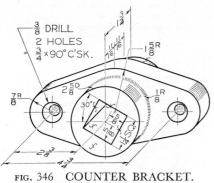

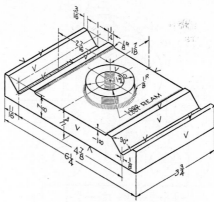

FIG. 346 COUNTER BRACKET.
Draw necessary views. *

FIG. 347 CLAMP PLATE.
Draw necessary views. *

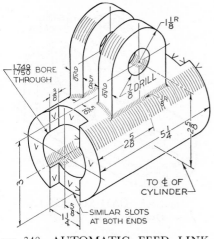

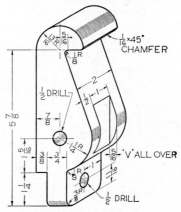

FIG. 348 AUTOMATIC FEED LINK
Draw necessary views. *

FIG. 349 CROSS-FEED PAWL.
Draw necessary views. *

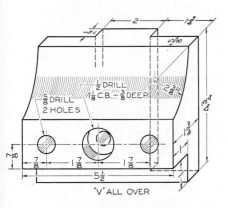

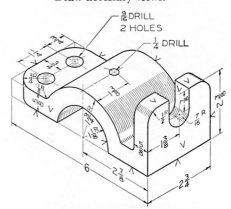

FIG. 350 CAP GUIDE.
Draw necessary views. *

FIG. 351 FRAME GUIDE.
Draw necessary views. *

* Make freehand sketch or instrumental drawing, as assigned. If dimensions are required, study §§ 357–386, and if tracing is required, study § 68 or § 70.

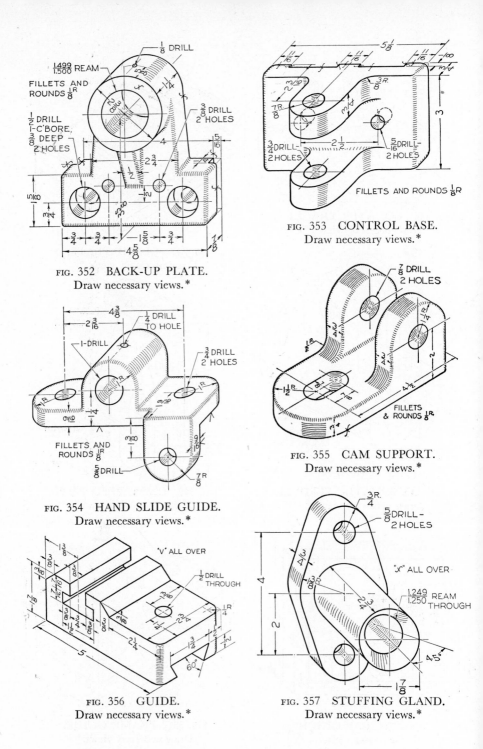

FIG. 352 BACK-UP PLATE.
Draw necessary views.*

FIG. 353 CONTROL BASE.
Draw necessary views.*

FIG. 354 HAND SLIDE GUIDE.
Draw necessary views.*

FIG. 355 CAM SUPPORT.
Draw necessary views.*

FIG. 356 GUIDE.
Draw necessary views.*

FIG. 357 STUFFING GLAND.
Draw necessary views.*

* Make freehand sketch or instrumental drawing, as assigned. If dimensions are required, study §§ 357–386, and if tracing is required, study § 68 or § 70.

204

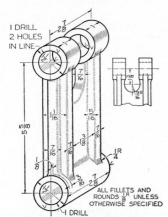

FIG. 358   BRACKET.
Draw necessary views.*

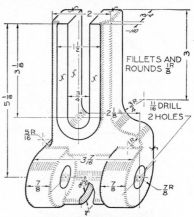

FIG. 359   FEEDER FINGER.
Draw necessary views.*

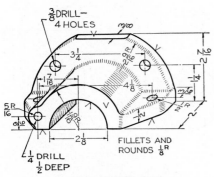

FIG. 360   DUST CAP.
Draw necessary views.*

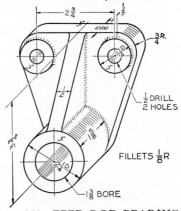

FIG. 361   FEED ROD BEARING.
Draw necessary views.*

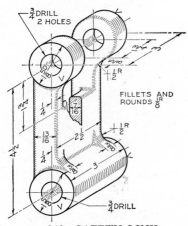

FIG. 362   SAFETY LINK.
Draw necessary views.*

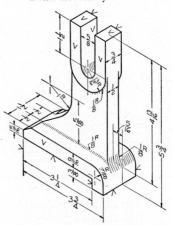

FIG. 363   CAM SUPPORT.
Draw necessary views.*

* Make freehand sketch or instrumental drawing, as assigned. If dimensions are required, study §§ 357–386, and if tracing is required, study § 68 or § 70.

205

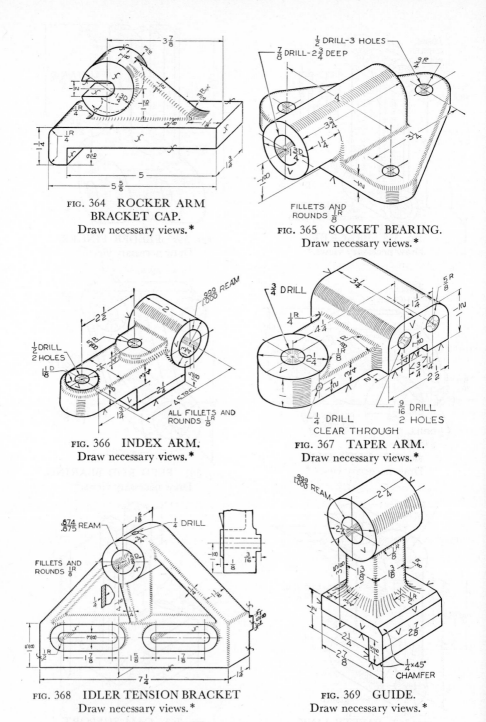

FIG. 364 ROCKER ARM
BRACKET CAP.
Draw necessary views.*

FIG. 365 SOCKET BEARING.
Draw necessary views.*

FIG. 366 INDEX ARM.
Draw necessary views.*

FIG. 367 TAPER ARM.
Draw necessary views.*

FIG. 368 IDLER TENSION BRACKET
Draw necessary views.*

FIG. 369 GUIDE.
Draw necessary views.*

* Make freehand sketch or instrumental drawing, as assigned. If dimensions are required, study §§ 357–386, and if tracing is required, study § 68 or § 70.

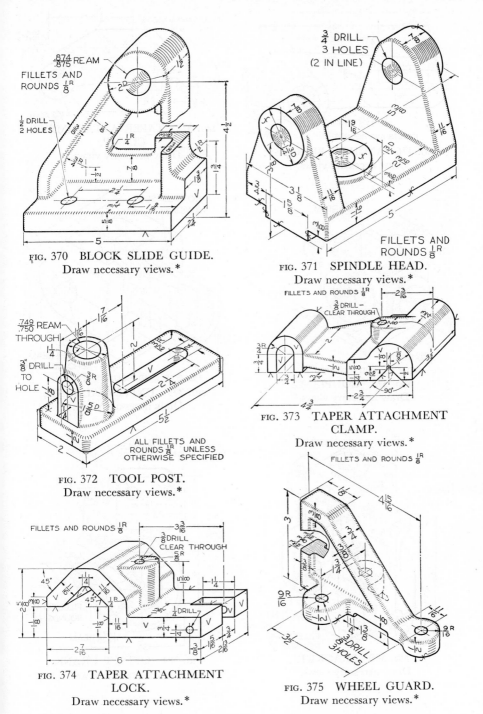

FIG. 370   BLOCK SLIDE GUIDE.
Draw necessary views.*

FIG. 371   SPINDLE HEAD.
Draw necessary views.*

FIG. 372   TOOL POST.
Draw necessary views.*

FIG. 373   TAPER ATTACHMENT
CLAMP.
Draw necessary views.*

FIG. 374   TAPER ATTACHMENT
LOCK.
Draw necessary views.*

FIG. 375   WHEEL GUARD.
Draw necessary views.*

* Make freehand sketch or instrumental drawing, as assigned. If dimensions are required, study §§ 357–386, and if tracing is required, study § 68 or § 70.

207

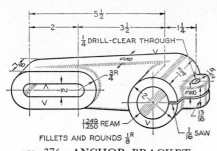

FIG. 376 ANCHOR BRACKET.
Draw necessary views.*

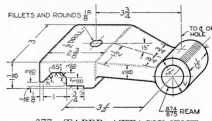

FIG. 377 TAPER ATTACHMENT
CLAMP.
Draw necessary views.*

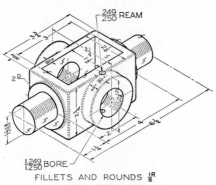

FIG. 378 COUPLING.
Draw necessary views.*

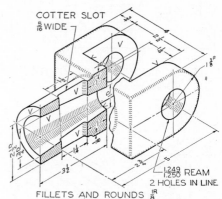

FIG. 379 UNIVERSAL LINK.
Draw necessary views.*

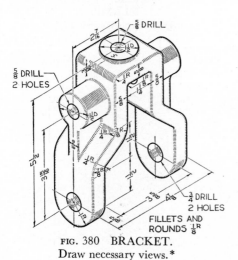

FIG. 380 BRACKET.
Draw necessary views.*

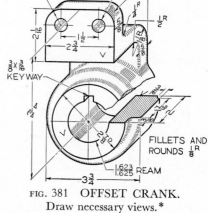

FIG. 381 OFFSET CRANK.
Draw necessary views.*

* Make freehand sketch or instrumental drawing, as assigned. If dimensions are required, study §§ 357–386, and if tracing is required, study § 68 or § 70.

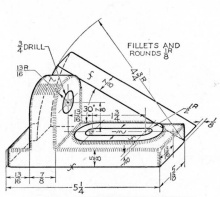

FILLETS AND ROUNDS $\frac{1}{8}$R

FIG. 382 CENTERING WEDGE.
Draw necessary views.*

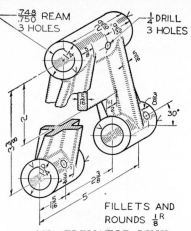

$\frac{.748}{.750}$ REAM 3 HOLES

$\frac{1}{4}$ DRILL 3 HOLES

FILLETS AND ROUNDS $\frac{1}{8}$R

FIG. 383 ELEVATOR LINK.
Draw necessary views.*

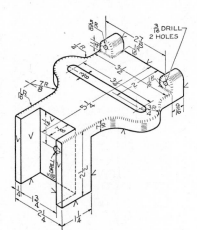

$\frac{3}{16}$ DRILL 2 HOLES

FIG. 384 OFFSET GUIDE.
Draw necessary views.*

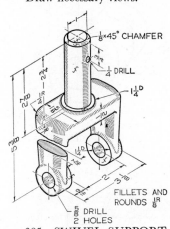

$\frac{1}{8}$×45° CHAMFER

$\frac{1}{4}$ DRILL

$1\frac{1}{4}$D

FILLETS AND ROUNDS $\frac{1}{8}$R

$\frac{5}{8}$ DRILL 2 HOLES

FIG. 385 SWIVEL SUPPORT.
Draw necessary views.*

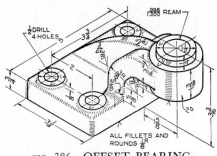

$\frac{1}{4}$ DRILL 4 HOLES

$\frac{.998}{1.000}$ REAM

ALL FILLETS AND ROUNDS $\frac{1}{8}$R

FIG. 386 OFFSET BEARING.
Draw necessary views.*

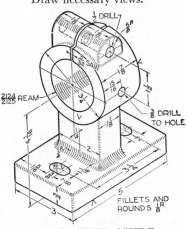

$\frac{1}{2}$ DRILL

$\frac{2.124}{2.125}$ REAM

$\frac{3}{8}$ DRILL TO HOLE

FILLETS AND ROUNDS $\frac{1}{8}$R

FIG. 387 FEED GUIDE.
Draw necessary views.*

* Make freehand sketch or instrumental drawing, as assigned. If dimensions are required, study §§ 357–386, and if tracing is required, study § 68 or § 70.

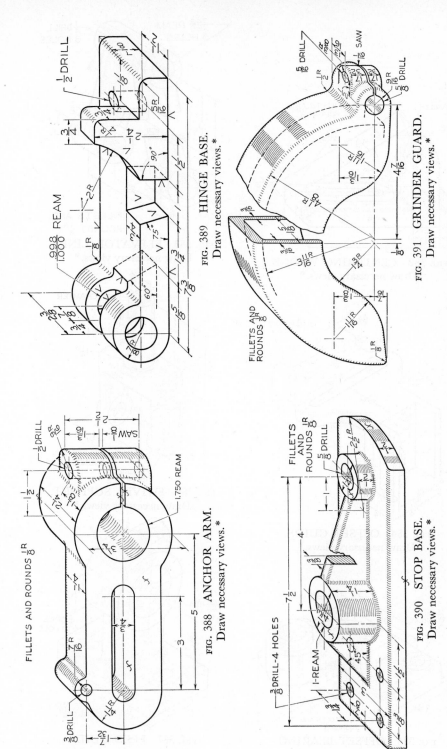

FIG. 388 ANCHOR ARM.
Draw necessary views.*

FIG. 389 HINGE BASE.
Draw necessary views.*

FIG. 390 STOP BASE.
Draw necessary views.*

FIG. 391 GRINDER GUARD.
Draw necessary views.*

* Make assigned freehand sketch or instrumental drawing. If dimensions are required, study §§ 357–386; if tracing is required, study § 68 or § 70.

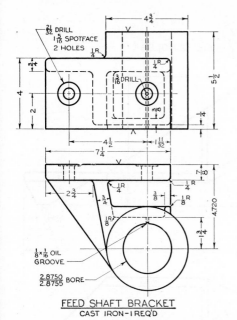

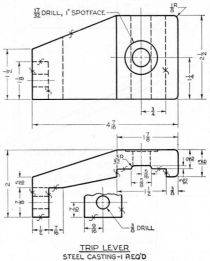

FEED SHAFT BRACKET
CAST IRON-1 REQ'D

FIG. 392 FEED SHAFT BRACKET.
Given: Front and top views.
Required: Front, top, and right side views; half size, on Layout B2.*

TRIP LEVER
STEEL CASTING-1 REQ'D

FIG. 393 TRIP LEVER.
Given: Front, top, and partial side view.
Required: Front, bottom and left side views (complete); full size, on Layout B2.*

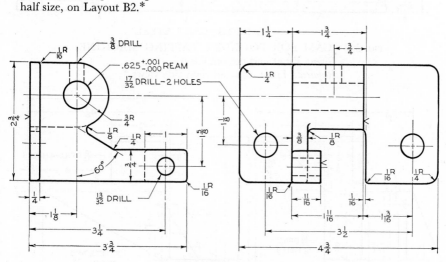

KNURL BRACKET BEARING
CAST IRON - 1 REQ'D

FIG. 394 KNURL BRACKET BEARING.
Given: Front and left side views.
Required: Take front as top view on new drawing, and add front and right side views. Layout B2.*

*Draw with instruments. If dimensions are required, study §§ 357-386. If tracing is required, study § 68 or 70.

211

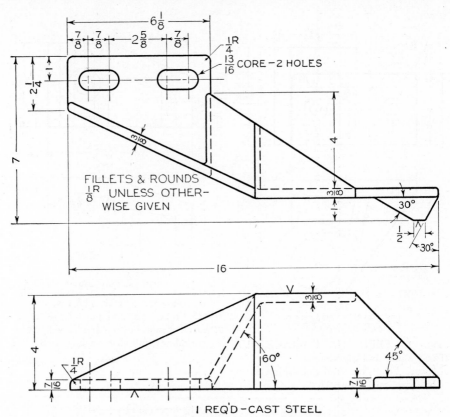

FILLETS & ROUNDS $\frac{1}{8}$R UNLESS OTHER-WISE GIVEN

$\frac{1}{4}$R

$\frac{13}{16}$ CORE – 2 HOLES

30°

30°

60°

45°

1 REQ'D – CAST STEEL

FIG. 395 CAM FOR FOUNDRY TAPPING MACHINE.

Given: Front and bottom views.

Required: Front, top and right side views.*

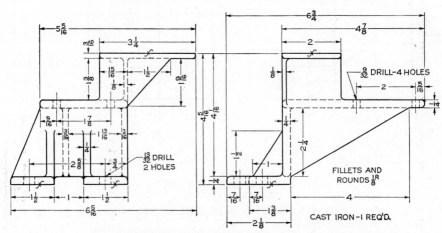

$\frac{9}{32}$ DRILL – 4 HOLES

$\frac{13}{32}$ DRILL 2 HOLES

FILLETS AND ROUNDS $\frac{1}{8}$R

CAST IRON – 1 REQ'D.

FIG. 396 LIMIT SWITCH BRACKET FOR FREON COMPRESSOR.

Given: Front and left side views.

Required: Front, top and right side views.*

* Draw with instruments. If dimensions are required, study §§ 357–386. If tracing is required, study § 68 or § 70.

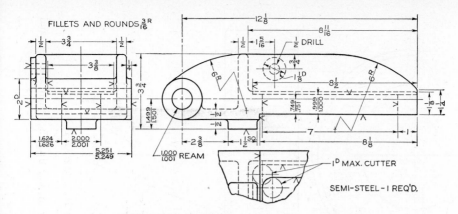

FIG. 397   LOCATING PENDULUM FOR 25-TON PRESS.
Given: Front, left side, and partial bottom views.
Required: Front, right side and top views.*

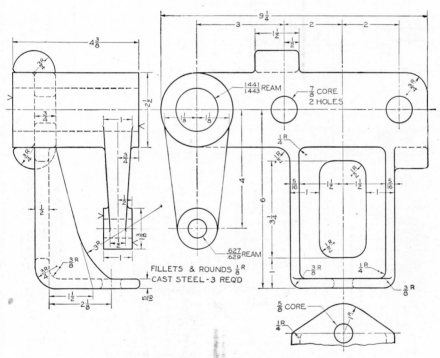

FIG. 398   BRAKE PEDAL HUB FOR POWER SHOVEL.
Given: Front, left side and partial bottom views.
Required: Front, right side and top views.*

* Draw with instruments.   If dimensions are required, study §§ 357–386.   If tracing is required, study § 68 or § 70.

213

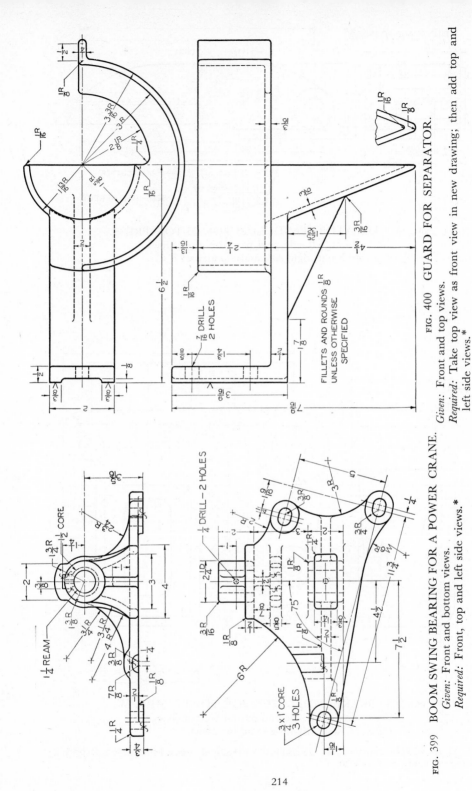

FIG. 400 GUARD FOR SEPARATOR.

Given: Front and top views.

Required: Take top view as front view in new drawing; then add top and left side views.*

FIG. 399 BOOM SWING BEARING FOR A POWER CRANE.

Given: Front and bottom views.

Required: Front, top and left side views.*

* Draw with instruments. If dimensions are required, study §§ 357–386. If tracing is required, study § 68 or § 70.

214

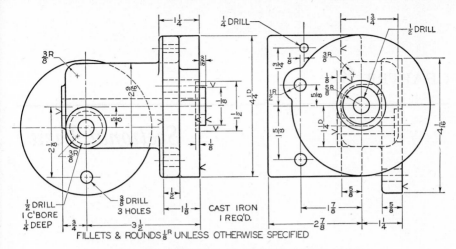

FIG. 401 HEADSTOCK BRACKET FOR LATHE.

Given: Front and right side views.

Required: Take present front view as top view in new drawing; then add front and left side views.*

* Draw with instruments. If dimensions are required, study §§ 357–386. If tracing is required, study § 68 or § 70.

CHAPTER 8

Sectional Views

220. Sections. The basic idea of representing an object by its projections, or views, was explained in Chapter 7. By means of a limited number of carefully chosen views, the external features of the most complicated objects can be thus fully described.

However, if an object has interior features which are hidden from view by other parts of the object, many hidden lines might be needed to describe those interior shapes. As illustrated in Fig. 402, which shows two exterior views of a step-cone pulley, the interior features of even a comparatively simple object are not very clearly described by means of hidden lines. If the part to be represented is complicated, or if the object is an assembly of few or many parts, hidden-line representation is extremely confusing and entirely inadequate.

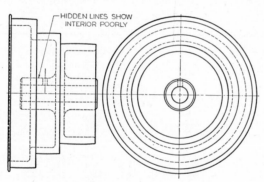

FIG. 402   Hidden-Line Representation.

In order to represent interior features, draftsmen imagine an object to be sliced in two, much as one would cut through an apple or a watermelon. A cutaway view of the object is then drawn; it is called a *sectional view*, or simply a *section*. If the cut is assumed lengthwise of an object, the resulting section is sometimes called a *longitudinal section;* if it is crosswise, a *cross section*.

221. Full Section. More exactly, a *cutting plane* (§ 225) is assumed to be passed through the object, as shown in Fig. 403 (a). Then, the portion of the object in front of the plane (the part between the plane and the observer) is assumed to be removed, exposing the back portion showing the interior construction of the object, as shown at (b). The cutting plane is then removed, as shown at (c), and the observer views the object as shown by the arrow.

The observer sees not only the cut surface, but many other visible edges of the object as well. The resulting sectional view is shown at (d). Such a sectional view is called a *full section*, because the cutting plane passes "fully" through the object.

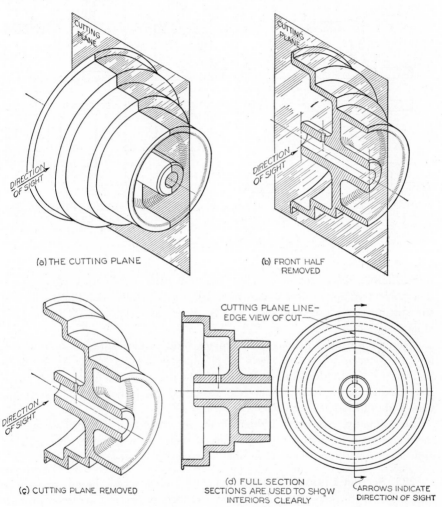

(a) THE CUTTING PLANE

(b) FRONT HALF REMOVED

(c) CUTTING PLANE REMOVED

CUTTING PLANE LINE—
EDGE VIEW OF CUT—

(d) FULL SECTION
SECTIONS ARE USED TO SHOW
INTERIORS CLEARLY

ARROWS INDICATE
DIRECTION OF SIGHT

FIG. 403   Full Section.

In Fig. 403 (d), the *cutting-plane line* (§ 225) in the circular view represents the *edge view of the cutting plane*. The arrows indicate the direction the cut is observed to obtain the section shown at the left. Notice also at (d) that in order to obtain the sectional view, the left half of the circular view is *imagined* to be removed, but not actually shown removed anywhere except in the sectional view itself.

222. Visible and Hidden Lines. In general, *all visible edges and contours of the object behind the cutting plane must be shown.* As shown in Fig. 404 (a), an

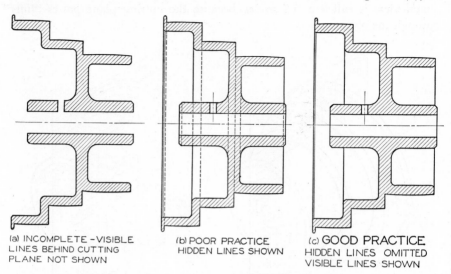

(a) INCOMPLETE – VISIBLE LINES BEHIND CUTTING PLANE NOT SHOWN

(b) POOR PRACTICE HIDDEN LINES SHOWN

(c) GOOD PRACTICE HIDDEN LINES OMITTED VISIBLE LINES SHOWN

FIG. 404   Visible and Hidden Lines.

unintelligible, disconnected drawing results if such visible lines are omitted. The correct sectional view is shown at (c). Occasionally, visible lines behind the cutting plane are confusing, and in those cases they should be omitted (Fig. 420, Sec. A–A).

Sections are used primarily to replace hidden-line representation; therefore, in general, *hidden lines should not be drawn in sectional views.* As shown in Fig. 404 (b), the hidden lines do not clarify the drawing, but only tend to make it confusing—not to mention the time wasted by the draftsman! The sectional view without hidden lines is shown at (c).

Occasionally, however, hidden lines are necessary for clearness, and should be used in such cases; especially if their use will make it possible to omit a view of the object that would otherwise be necessary (Fig. 425).

223. Section Lining. The parallel lines drawn across the cut surface in Fig. 403 (b), (c), and (d), called *section lines* or *crosshatching*, are used for two purposes: (1) to define clearly the cut surface or surfaces produced by the cutting plane, in order to differentiate these surfaces from other features back of that plane, and (2) to indicate the kind of material (a general indication—not an official specification) of which the object is made.

The American Standard symbols for section lining are shown in Fig. 405; the symbols for outside views, in Fig. 406.

The symbol for cast iron (No. 1, Fig. 405) is actually an all-purpose symbol used to represent a section through any material (except concrete, water, etc.). The various symbols are used only when it is desired to call special attention to the material or to identify the material.

On detail drawings (single parts), it is necessary to give exact specifications of material. For example, it is necessary to specify exactly which steel is required, since there are hundreds of different kinds of steel. Obviously, the symbol for steel (No. 2, Fig. 405) gives only a general indication of the class of material, and cannot be depended upon for material specification. For this reason, on detail drawings, it is recommended that *the all-purpose symbol (No. 1, Fig. 405) be used for all materials*, and that the exact specification be given in a note on the drawing either near the views (Fig. 841), or, preferably,

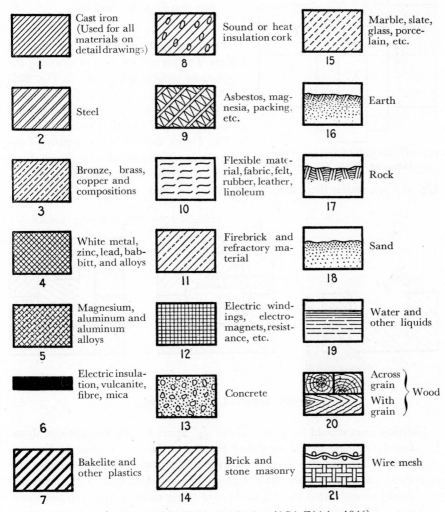

1	Cast iron (Used for all materials on detail drawings)
2	Steel
3	Bronze, brass, copper and compositions
4	White metal, zinc, lead, babbitt, and alloys
5	Magnesium, aluminum and aluminum alloys
6	Electric insulation, vulcanite, fibre, mica
7	Bakelite and other plastics
8	Sound or heat insulation cork
9	Asbestos, magnesia, packing, etc.
10	Flexible material, fabric, felt, rubber, leather, linoleum
11	Firebrick and refractory material
12	Electric windings, electromagnets, resistance, etc.
13	Concrete
14	Brick and stone masonry
15	Marble, slate, glass, porcelain, etc.
16	Earth
17	Rock
18	Sand
19	Water and other liquids
20	Across grain / With grain } Wood
21	Wire mesh

FIG. 405 Symbols for Section Lining (ASA Z14.1—1946).

Brick

Uncoursed
and coursed
rubble

Ashlar

Transparent
materials,
glass, etc.

Marble

FIG. 406   Symbols for Outside Views (ASA Z14.1—1946).

in the title strip (Figs. 845 and 846), or in a parts list (Fig. 847).

On assembly drawings, where only a general indication of materials is needed, it is customary to use the various section lining symbols, as illustrated in Fig. 407. See also Figs. 859 and 861.

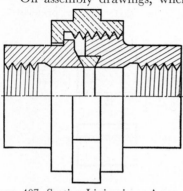

FIG. 407 Section Lining in an Assembly Drawing (ASA Z14.1—1946).

224. Correct Execution of Section Lines. The correct method of drawing the all-purpose section lining (No. 1, Fig. 405) is shown in Fig. 408 (a). Section lines should be drawn with a very sharp medium-grade pencil with a conical point, as shown in Fig. 61 (c), or with a fine setting of the ruling pen. They are drawn at an angle of 45° with the horizontal, as shown in Fig. 408 (a), unless there is some advantage in using a different angle.

CLOSER TOGETHER IN SMALL AREAS

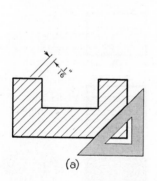

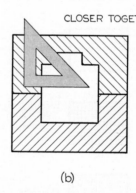

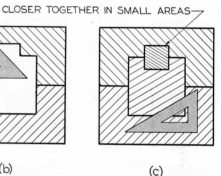

(a)   (b)   (c)

FIG. 408   Section Lining (Full Size).

Section lines should be drawn about $\frac{1}{16}''$ apart for the average-size drawing, but the spacing should vary with the size of the area sectioned. For very small areas, the distance may be as little as $\frac{1}{32}''$; for very large areas, a distance of $\frac{1}{8}''$, or slightly more, may be used. The spacing should not be measured but should be estimated by eye, great care being exercised to keep the spaces uniform. After the first few lines have been drawn, the draftsman should

look back repeatedly at the original spacing in order to avoid gradually increasing or decreasing the spacing. Special care should be taken to avoid
unconsciously crowding the lines together as the sectioning approaches a
corner or other restricted area.

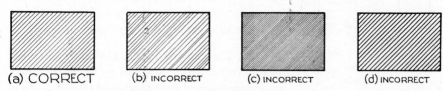

(a) CORRECT   (b) INCORRECT   (c) INCORRECT   (d) INCORRECT

FIG. 409   Section Lining Technique.

As shown in Fig. 409, the three most common faults in drawing section
lines are (b) lack of uniform spacing, (c) spacing section lines too close together,
and (d) drawing section lines too heavy (especially the use of a dull pencil).

If two adjacent parts are sectioned (assembly drawing), as shown in Fig.
408 (b), the section lines should slope in opposite directions, in order to provide contrast. If additional parts, adjacent to the first two, are added as
shown at (c), the lines should slope at 30° or 60° with the horizontal, or an odd
angle may be used if necessary. Notice, at (c), that for very small areas the
lines are drawn more closely together. As shown at (b) and (c), section lines
in adjacent areas should not meet at the common boundaries. A typical
assembly in section is shown in Fig. 407.

All sectioned areas of a single part or object must be sectioned in the
same direction and at the same inclination, because the use of section lines
in different directions is a definite *indication of different parts* (as in assembly
drawing). This means that if a single object has three views, and there are
sections in all three views, the section lines must all be parallel. It also means
that in a given sectional view, all the section lines must be parallel whether
the sectioned areas are close together or considerably separated.

As indicated in Fig. 408 (c), there should be
strong contrast between the heavy object lines
and the enclosed *sharp* section lines. See also
Fig. 90 (a).

It is necessary to change the direction of section lines in some cases other than in sections of
adjacent parts, as illustrated in Fig. 410. A
grooved appearance results when the 45° section
lines happen to be parallel to the bounding object lines, as shown at (a). A representation
similar to that of a spur gear occurs at (b). In
such cases, the direction of the section lines
should be changed to 30°, 60°, or some odd angle,

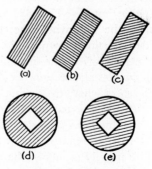

FIG. 410   Examples of Sectioning at Various Angles.

as indicated at (c). Another illustration of a similar case is shown at (d) and (e).

Sometimes sections are too narrow for section lining, especially in drawings of structural shapes, sheet metal, packing, gaskets, etc. In such cases, the sectioned parts may be shown solid, as in Fig. 411, with white spaces left to separate the sections, as at (a), in order to maintain the identity of the parts.

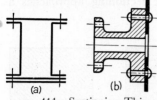

FIG. 411 Sectioning Thin Materials.

225. The Cutting Plane. The *cutting plane* employed in sectioning is indicated on the drawing in a view adjacent to the sectional view, as shown in Fig. 403 (d). In this view, the plane appears as a line, called the *cutting-plane line*. This line (Fig. 85) is about as thick as an object line, but composed of long and short dashes, as shown in Fig. 412 (a). Arrowheads indicate the

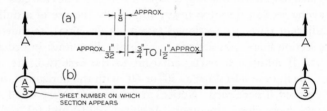

FIG. 412 Cutting Plane Lines (Full-Size).

direction the cutaway object is viewed; that is, in the "direction of sight," as shown in Fig. 403 (b) and (c). At (d) this direction of sight is shown in the right side view by arrows at the ends of the cutting-plane line. Notice that the arrows always point *away* from the view showing the section. Observe, also, that the part of the object imagined to be removed is the part *opposite* to the direction of the arrows.

As shown in Fig. 412 (a), at the ends of the cutting-plane line, capital letters are often needed to identify the cutting-plane line with the corresponding section. See Figs. 420 and 426. If the sectional view is on a different sheet from the view where the cutting-plane line is shown (§ 229), the method of identification shown in Fig. 412 (b) is used. A small circle, with its center at the "elbow" of the cutting-plane line, contains a fraction whose numerator designates the section, as *A–A*, *B–B*, etc., and whose denominator indicates the sheet where the section will be found.

When the cutting-plane line coincides with a center line, the cutting-plane line takes precedence.

It is customary to omit the cutting-plane line when its position is obvious. This usually occurs in the case of symmetrical objects, in which the plane is understood to pass through the axis of symmetry. In short, the cutting-plane line is omitted unless needed for clearness.

226. Half Sections. If the cutting plane passes halfway through the object, the result is a *half section* (Fig. 413). A half section has the advantage of exposing the interior of one-half of the object and retaining the exterior of

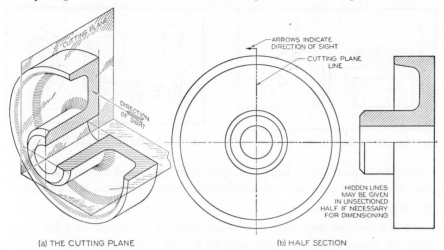

(a) THE CUTTING PLANE   (b) HALF SECTION

FIG. 413   Half Section.

the other half. Its usefulness is, therefore, largely limited to symmetrical objects. It is not widely used in detail drawings (single parts) because of this limitation of symmetry and also because of difficulties in dimensioning internal shapes, part of which are shown in the sectioned half and part in the unsectioned half.

In general, hidden lines should be omitted from both halves of a half section. However, they may be used in the unsectioned half if necessary for dimensioning.

The greatest usefulness of the half section is in assembly drawing (Fig. 407) where it is often necessary to show both internal and external construction on the same view, but without the necessity of dimensioning and the attendant undesirable hidden lines.

As shown in Fig. 413 (b), a center line is used to separate the two halves of a half section. The center line is preferred, instead of an object line, because the "removed" quarter of the object is only imagined to be removed, and not actually to be cut out in the shop. The center line, therefore, denotes a theoretical edge, whereas an object line would indicate an actual edge.

Nevertheless, many have objected to the use of a center line here, and insist on using an object line. The American Standard (ASA Z14.1—1946) gives definite preference for the center line, but mentions in a footnote that an object line *may be* used, if desired.

227. Broken-Out Sections. It often happens that only a partial section of a view is needed to expose interior construction. Such a section, limited by a *break line* (Fig. 85) is called a *broken-out section*. In Fig. 414, a full or half section is not necessary, a small broken-out section being sufficient to explain the construction. In Fig. 415, a half section would have caused the removal

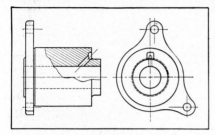

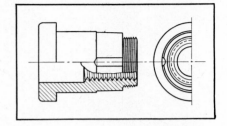

FIG. 414   Broken-out Section.   FIG. 415   Break Around Keyway.

of half the keyway. The keyway is preserved by "breaking-out" around it. Note that in this case the section is limited partly by a break line and partly by a center line.

228. Revolved Sections. The shape of the cross section of a bar, arm, spoke, or other elongated object may be shown in the longitudinal view by means of a *revolved section* (Fig. 416). Such sections are made by assuming a

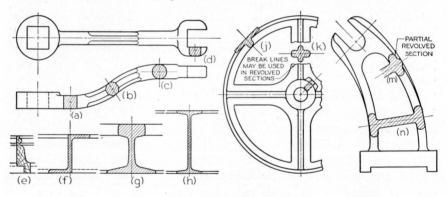

FIG. 416   Revolved Sections.

plane perpendicular to the center line or axis of the bar or other object, as shown in Fig. 417 (a), then revolving the plane through 90° about a center line at right angles to the axis, as in Fig. 417 (b) and (c).

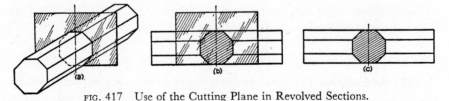

FIG. 417   Use of the Cutting Plane in Revolved Sections.

The object lines adjacent to a revolved section may be "broken-out" if desired, as shown in Figs. 416 (k), and 838.

The superimposition of the revolved section requires the removal of all original lines covered by it (Fig. 418). The true shape of a revolved section

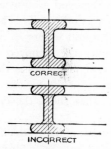

FIG. 418   A Common Error in
Drawing Revolved Sections.

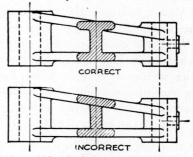

FIG. 419   A Common Error in
Drawing Revolved Sections.

should be retained during and after the revolution of the cutting plane, regardless of the direction of the lines in the view (Fig. 419).

229. Removed Sections. It is often desirable to show a section detached from any regular view of the drawing. Such a section is called a *removed section*, and is used in a variety of ways. It may be a full section through the object, as shown in Fig. 420, or a partial section, as shown in Fig. 421. The advantage

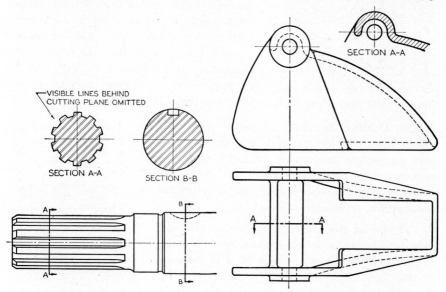

FIG. 420   Removed Sections.   FIG. 421   Partial Removed Section.

of a removed section is that it takes the section away from the views, leaving the views intact; in addition, the removed section can be drawn to a larger scale, if desired. Thus, some small detail of the object can be magnified and dimensioned clearly by means of such a section, as shown in Fig. 880.

Since the removed section may be placed in any convenient position on the sheet or even on a different sheet (not obeying the regular arrangement of views), it is essential to identify carefully the removed section as well as the cutting-plane line, showing where the section was taken. This is done by labeling the cutting-plane line at each end with capital letters A, B, C, etc., as shown in Fig. 412 (a), and then lettering under the removed section a note, such as SECTION A–A. See Figs. 420 and 421. The arrows at the ends of the cutting-plane line show clearly the direction of sight for the removed section. If the removed section is drawn on another sheet, the circles and symbols shown in Fig. 412 (b) should be used.

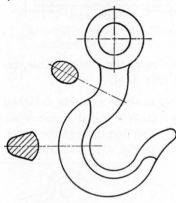

FIG. 422   Removed Sections
(ASA Z14.1—1946).

Removed sections of parts which are symmetrical may be placed on extended center lines, as shown in Fig. 422. In this case the center lines act as cutting-plane lines in showing where the sections are taken.

230. Phantom Sections. A *phantom section* is a section in which all lines are made with small, thin dashes to give the appearance of a hidden section or one having a semireal existence. This type of section is occasionally useful in showing the interior construction of an object without cutting away the exterior features in front of the cutting plane, as shown in Fig. 423 (a). The phantom section is also sometimes used to show adjacent parts in connection with the part being represented, as in Fig. 423 (b).

231. Outline Sections. When a very large area is shown in section, it is not necessary to draw the section lines across the entire area, but to draw section lines adjacent to the outline, as shown in Fig. 424. Such a section is called an *outline section*, or *herringbone section*.

232. Offset Sections. In sectioning through irregular objects, it is often convenient to show several features which are not in a continuous straight line, by "offsetting," or bending the plane. Such a section is called an *offset section*. For example, in Fig. 425 (a), the cutting plane is offset in several places in order to include the hole at the left end, one of the slots, the rec-

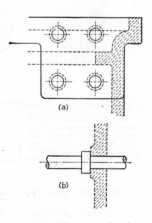

FIG. 423   Phantom Sections.

tangular recess, and one of the holes at the right end. The portion of the object in front of the cutting plane is then removed, as shown at (b). The path of the cutting plane is clearly shown by the cutting-plane line in the top view at (c), and the resulting offset section is shown in the front view. Observe that the *offsets are not shown in the sectional view*, but only in the view showing the cutting-plane line.

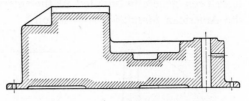

FIG. 424　Outline Section.

The offset section in Fig. 425 (c) also illustrates an example where hidden lines are correctly used in a section. In this case, an extra view would be needed

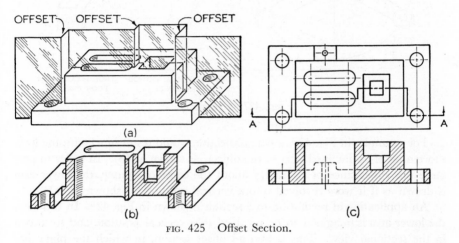

OFFSET　　OFFSET　　　　　OFFSET

(a)

(b)

FIG. 425　Offset Section.

to show the boss on the back of the object if the hidden lines were not shown.

An example in which three different offset sections are used is shown in Fig. 426.

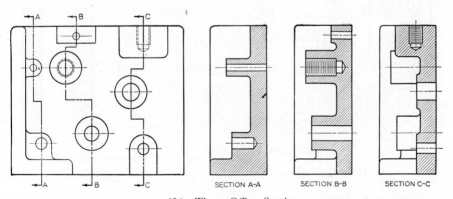

SECTION A-A　　SECTION B-B　　SECTION C-C

FIG. 426　Three Offset Sections.

233. Conventional Violations. In some cases, *true projections* are either awkward or actually confusing. Conventional methods of treating such cases have been generally adopted in the interest of clearness, and approved by the American Standards Association.*

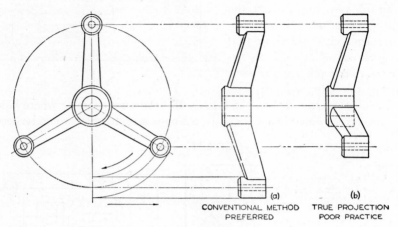

FIG. 427   Symmetry.

For example, in Fig. 427, a true projection would result in a confusing foreshortening of an inclined part of the object, as shown at (b). In order to preserve the appearance of symmetry about the common center, the lower arm is drawn as if it were revolved into a vertical position, as shown at (a).

An application of revolution to a section is shown in Fig. 428. In this case, the lower arm is imagined to be revolved to a vertical position, and so drawn in the sectional view. This is also an offset section, in which the plane has one right-angled offset and one acute-angled offset.

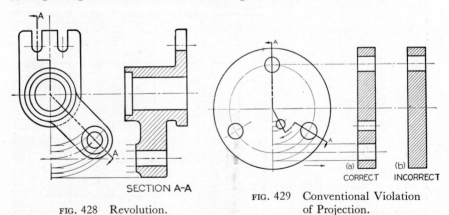

SECTION A-A

FIG. 428   Revolution.

FIG. 429   Conventional Violation of Projection.

* ASA Z14.1—1946.

Another application of revolution in sectioning is shown in Fig. 429, in which two holes are revolved until they line up vertically with the top hole and are included in the section in their true relationship with the rim of the flange.

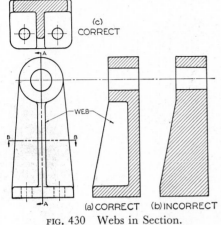

The conventional treatment of webs and similar shapes in section is illustrated in Fig. 430 (a). The cutting plane passes longitudinally through the web, as shown by the cutting-plane line A–A in the front view.

If the web is section-lined, as shown in (b), the object appears to have great thickness or bulk. Such a *thin feature should not be section-lined*, even though the cutting plane actually passes through the part.

However, if the cutting plane passes crosswise through the web, the feature would be section-lined as usual, as shown in (c).

FIG. 430   Webs in Section.

Another example involving webs and also revolution is shown in Fig. 431. In the circular view, the cutting plane is offset to include the lower hole, the lower web, the keyway, an upper web, and the upper hole. These features are

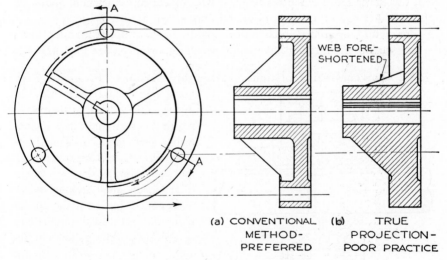

FIG. 431   Symmetry of Webs.

then considered to be revolved so that they line up vertically, and are shown correctly at (a). Note that the webs are not sectioned. If a regular full section were drawn in true projection, the resulting section, as shown at (b), is both incomplete and confusing.

In sectioning a pulley or a spoked wheel, it is standard practice to revolve the spokes where necessary, and not to section the spokes, as shown in Fig. 432 (a). If a spoke is sectioned, as shown at (b), the section gives the appearance of a wheel having a solid web instead of spokes.

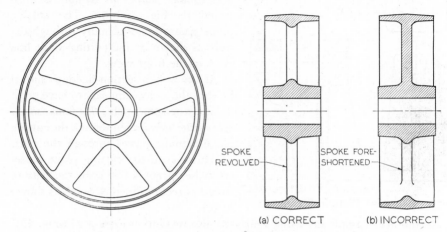

FIG. 432   Spokes in Section.

If the lower spoke is not revolved, it will appear foreshortened, giving the appearance of having been "amputated," as shown at (b).

Intersections are represented conventionally in the simplest manner, unless the intersections are large or have some special importance. See Figs. 827–829.

234. Conventional Violations in Assembly Sections. In assembly sections, many solid parts may fall in the section which in themselves require no section. These include webs, gear teeth, spokes, bolts, nuts, screws, ball or roller bearings, and similar shapes. Where these occur, they should be left unsectioned, just as if the cutting plane did not pass through them. A typical example is shown in Fig. 433. See also Figs. 859, 861, and 863.

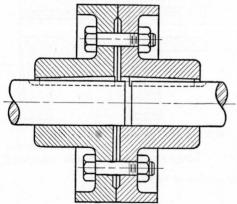

FIG. 433 Assembly Section (ASA Z14.1—1946).

235. Half Views. If space is limited, it may be convenient to draw a *half view* of a symmetrical object, as shown in Fig. 434. If the adjacent view is an exterior view, the near half of the symmetrical view should be drawn, as shown at (a). If the adjacent view is a full or half section, the far half of the symmetrical view should be drawn, as shown at (b) and (c). Refer also to § 196.

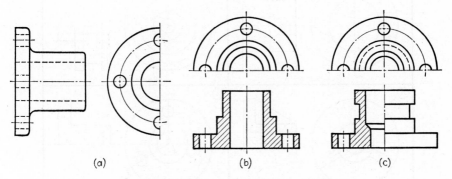

(a)   (b)   (c)

FIG. 434   Half Views (ASA Z14.1—1946).

SECTIONING PROBLEMS*

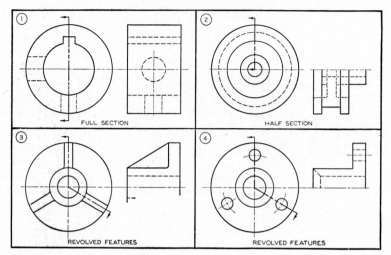

FIG. 435 Using Layout B3 (Appendix 1), divide sheet into four equal spaces, as shown above, and draw with instruments the views and sections indicated. Transfer all measurements with dividers, making your drawings four times the size shown above.

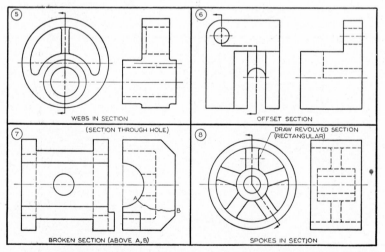

FIG. 436 Using Layout B3 (Appendix 1), divide sheet into four equal spaces, as shown above, and draw with instruments the views and sections indicated. Transfer all measurements with dividers, making drawing four times the size shown above.

* Sectioning problems in convenient form for solution may be found in *Technical Drawing Problems*, by Giesecke, Mitchell, and Spencer, and in *Technical Drawing Problems—Series 2*, by Spencer and Grant, both designed to accompany this text, and published by The Macmillan Company.

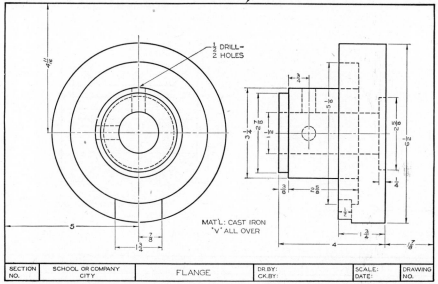

FIG. 437 Draw views with instruments, changing right side view into full section or half section, as assigned. Layout B5 (Appendix 1). Omit dimensions, unless assigned (§§ 357–386).

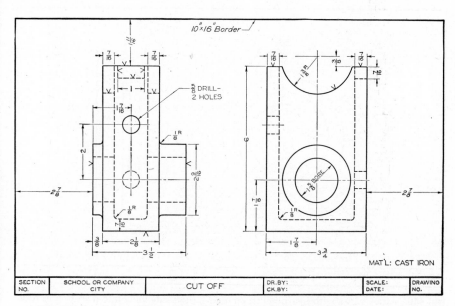

FIG. 438 Draw views with instruments, changing left side view into a full section. Layout B5 (Appendix 1). Omit dimensions, unless assigned (§§ 357–386).

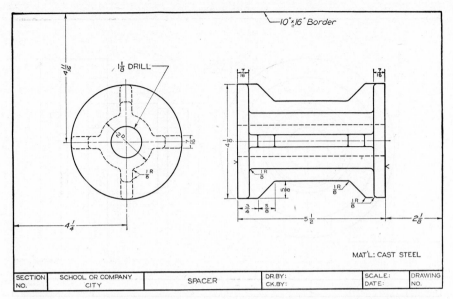

FIG. 439 Draw views with instruments, changing right side view into a full section. Layout B5 (Appendix 1). Omit dimensions, unless assigned (§§ 357–386).

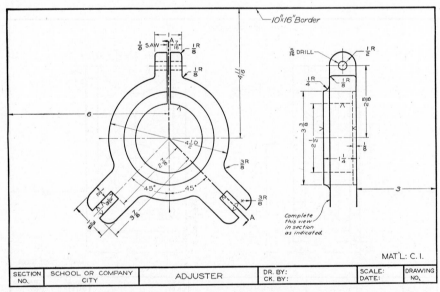

FIG. 440 Draw views with instruments, changing right side view into a section as indicated. Layout B5 (Appendix 1). Omit dimensions, unless assigned (§§ 357–386).

234

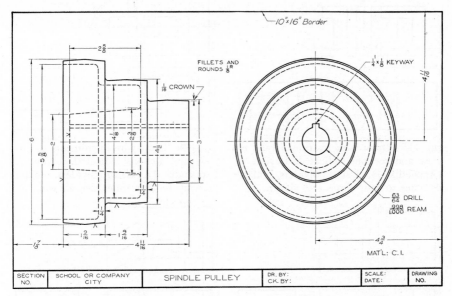

FIG. 441 Draw views with instruments, changing longitudinal view into a full or half section, as assigned. Layout B5 (Appendix 1). Omit dimensions unless assigned (§§ 357–386).

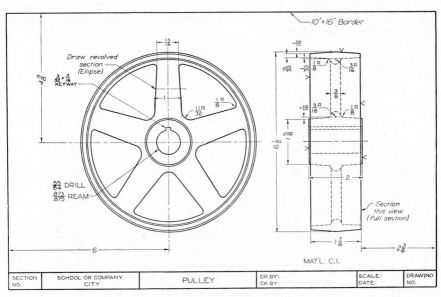

FIG. 442 Draw views with instruments, changing right side view into a full section and adding revolved section, as indicated. See Fig. 153 (c). Layout B5 (Appendix 1). Omit dimensions unless assigned (§§ 357–386).

235

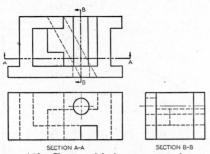

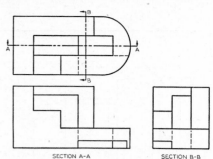

SECTION A-A   SECTION B-B

FIG. 443 Draw with instruments the top view and sections indicated. Layout A3 (Appendix 1). Using dividers, enlarge drawing to four times size shown.

SECTION A-A   SECTION B-B

FIG. 444 Draw with instruments the top view and sections indicated. Layout A3 (Appendix 1). Using dividers, enlarge drawing to four times size shown.

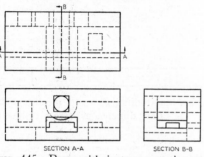

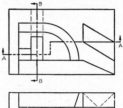

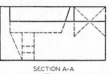

SECTION A-A   SECTION B-B

FIG. 445 Draw with instruments the top view and sections indicated. Layout A3 (Appendix 1). Using dividers, enlarge drawing to four times size shown.

SECTION A-A   SECTION B-B

FIG. 446 Draw with instruments the top view and sections indicated. Layout A3 (Appendix 1). Using dividers, enlarge drawing to four times size shown.

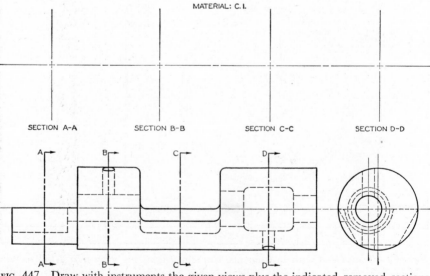

MATERIAL: C. I.

SECTION A-A   SECTION B-B   SECTION C-C   SECTION D-D

FIG. 447 Draw with instruments the given views plus the indicated removed sections. Layout A2 (Appendix 1). Using dividers, enlarge to twice the size shown.

236

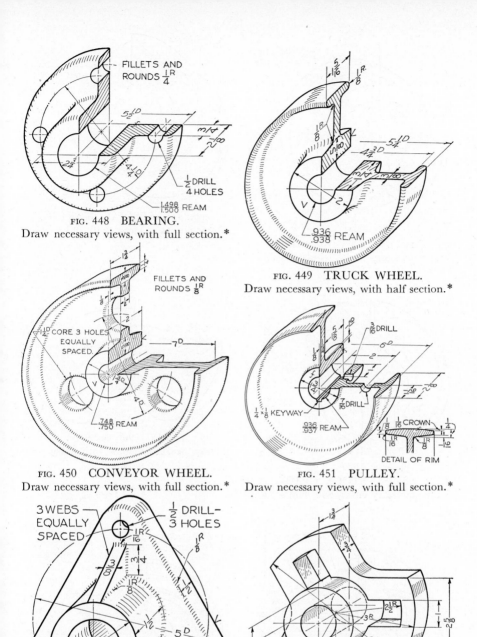

FIG. 448 BEARING.
Draw necessary views, with full section.*

FIG. 449 TRUCK WHEEL.
Draw necessary views, with half section.*

FIG. 450 CONVEYOR WHEEL.
Draw necessary views, with full section.*

FIG. 451 PULLEY.
Draw necessary views, with full section.*

FIG. 452 COLUMN SUPPORT.
Draw necessary views, with full section.*

FIG. 453 ROTARY STOP.
Draw necessary views, with full section.*

* Make freehand sketch or instrumental drawing, as assigned. If dimensions are required, study §§ 357–386, and if tracing is required, study § 68 or § 70.

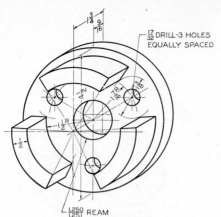

FIG. 454   CUP WASHER.
Draw necessary views, with full section.*

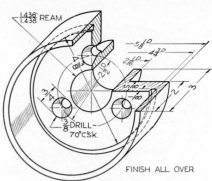

FIG. 455   SPECIAL BEARING.
Draw necessary views, with full section.*

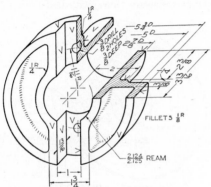

FIG. 456   STOCK GUIDE.
Draw necessary views, with half section.*

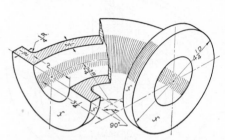

FIG. 457   90° ELBOW.
Draw necessary views, with broken-out
section.*

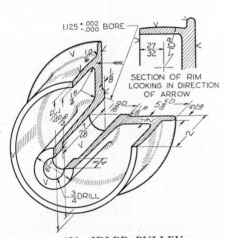

FIG. 458   IDLER PULLEY.
Draw necessary views, with full section.*

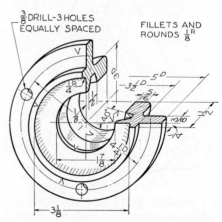

FIG. 459   FIXED BEARING CUP.
Draw necessary views, with full section.*

* Make freehand sketch or instrumental drawing, as assigned. If dimensions are required, study §§ 357–386, and if tracing is required, study § 68 or § 70.

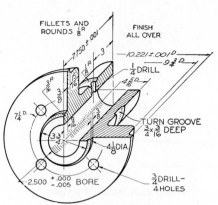

FIG. 460 BEARING.
Draw necessary views, with half section.*

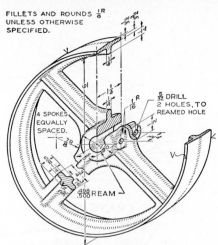

FIG. 461 PULLEY.
Draw necessary views, with full section, revolved section of spoke, and partial auxiliary view of two bosses (§ 244).*

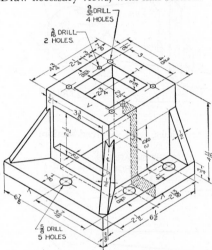

FIG. 462 MOTOR BASE.
Draw necessary views, including a full section. Add $\frac{1}{8}^R$ fillets and rounds at all rough corners.*

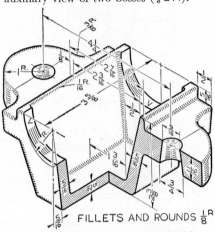

FILLETS AND ROUNDS $\frac{1}{8}^R$

FIG. 463 BEARING HOUSING.
Draw necessary views, with half sections in front and side views.*

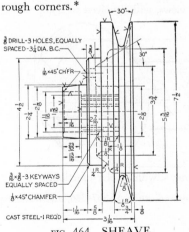

FIG. 464 SHEAVE.
Draw two views, including half section.*

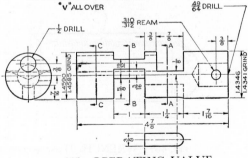

FIG. 465 OPERATING VALVE.
Draw present front view and add right side view, bottom view, and indicated removed sections. Omit present left side view and partial bottom view.*

* Make freehand sketch or instrumental drawing, as assigned. If dimensions are required, study §§ 357–386, and if tracing is required, study § 68 or § 70.

239

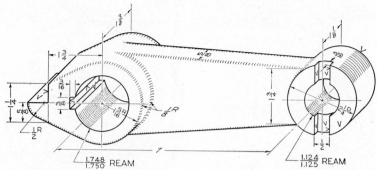

FIG. 466   CRANK ARM. Draw necessary views, with revolved section.*

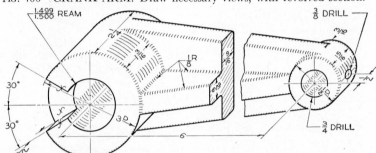

FIG. 467   CRANK ARM. Draw necessary views, with revolved section.*

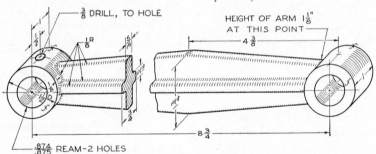

FIG. 468   CAM LINK. Draw necessary views, with revolved section.*

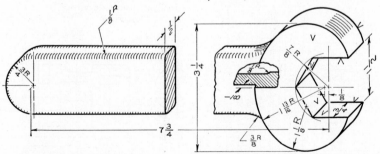

FIG. 469   WRENCH. Draw necessary views, with revolved section.*

* Draw with instruments. If dimensions are required, study §§ 357–386, and if tracing is required, study § 68 or § 70.

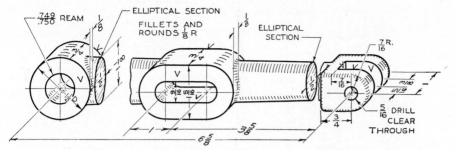

FIG. 470   ADJUSTABLE ARM. Draw necessary views, with removed sections.*

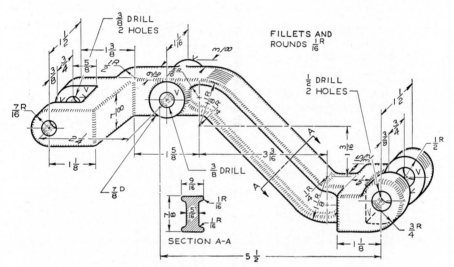

FIG. 471   DASH POT LIFTER. Draw necessary views, with removed section.*

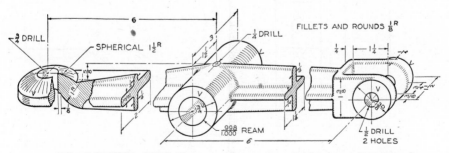

FIG. 472   ROCKER ARM. Draw necessary views, with removed sections.*

   * Draw with instruments. If dimensions are required, study §§ 357–386, and if tracing is required, study § 68 or § 70.

241

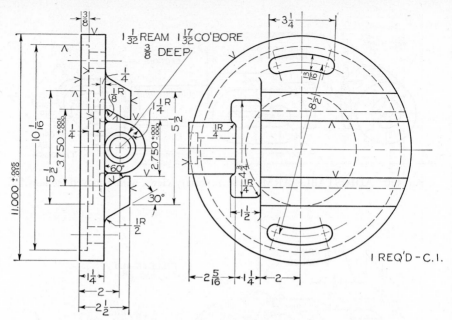

FIG. 473 SLOTTED DISC FOR THREADING MACHINE.
Given: Front and left side views.
Required: Front and right side views and top full-section view.*

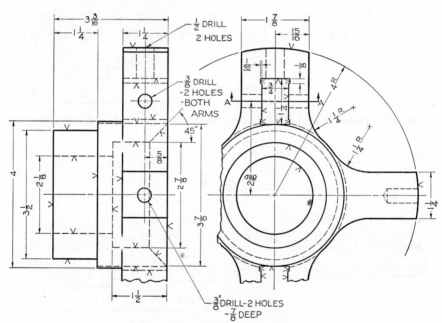

FIG. 474 WEB FOR LATHE CLUTCH.
Given: Partial front and left side views.
Required: Complete front view, and right side view in full section, and removed section A-A.*

* Draw with instruments. If dimensions are required, study §§ 357–386, and if tracing is required, study § 68 or § 70.

242

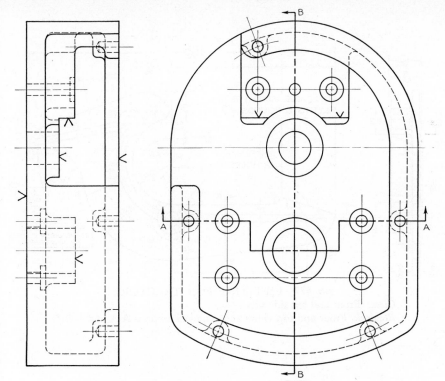

FIG. 475   COLUMN BASE HOUSING.

Given: Front and left side views.

Required: Draw front view and sections indicated. Using dividers, enlarge drawing to twice size shown.*

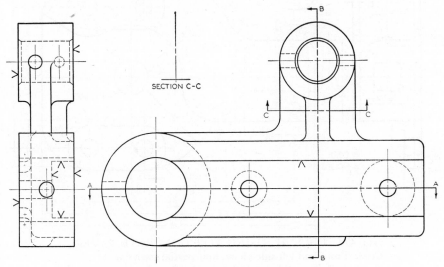

SECTION C-C

FIG. 476   PIVOT ARM.

Given: Front and left side views.

Required: Draw front view and sections indicated. Using dividers, enlarge drawing to twice size shown.*

* Draw with instruments, unless otherwise assigned. If dimensions are required, study §§ 357–386, and if tracing is required, study § 68 or § 70.

243

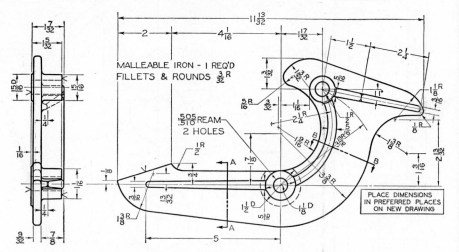

FIG. 477 LIFT TRIP FOR TRACTOR.

Given: Front and left side views.

Required: Front and top views and removed sections A-A and B-B.*

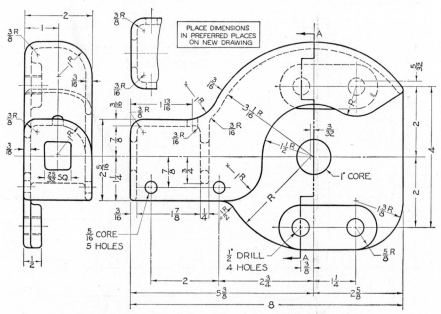

FIG. 478 LOCK HOUSING FOR CONCRETE PAVER.

Given: Front and left side views, and partial top view.

Required: Front and bottom views and right side offset section.*

* Draw with instruments. If dimensions are required, study §§ 357–386, and if tracing is required, study § 68 or § 70.

CHAPTER 9

Auxiliary Views

236. Auxiliary Views. Many objects are of such shape that their principal faces cannot always be assumed parallel to the regular planes of projection. For example, in Fig. 479 (a), the base of the bearing is shown in its true size and shape, but the rounded upper portion is situated at an angle with the planes of projection and does not appear in its true size and shape in any of the three regular views.

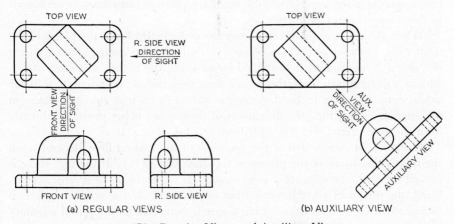

FIG. 479 Regular Views and Auxiliary Views.

In order to show the true circular shapes, it is necessary to assume a direction of sight which is perpendicular to the plane of those curves, as shown in Fig. 479 (b). The resulting view is called an *auxiliary view*. This view, together with the top view, completely describes the object, and the front and right side views are not necessary.

237. The Auxiliary Plane. A view projected on any plane other than one of the six regular planes of projection (§ 193) is an auxiliary view. In Fig. 480 (a), for example, the object has an inclined surface which does not show in its true size and shape in the top view, nor does it show in any other regular view. The auxiliary plane is assumed parallel to the inclined surface;

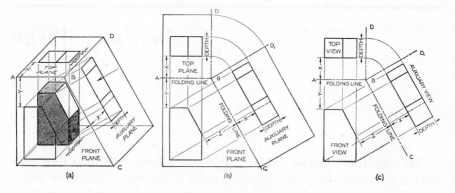

FIG. 480   An Auxiliary View.

that is, perpendicular to the line of sight which is at right angles to that surface. The auxiliary plane will then be perpendicular to the front plane of projection (as is the top plane); the auxiliary plane is considered to be hinged to the front plane of projection.

When the top and auxiliary planes are unfolded to lie in the plane of the front view, as shown at (b), the *folding lines* represent the "hinge" lines between the views. The drawing is simplified by omitting the planes, as shown at (c), and, as will be shown later, the folding lines may themselves be omitted in the actual drawing. The inclined surface is shown in its true size and shape in the auxiliary view, the long dimension of the surface being projected directly from the front view, and the *depth* from the top view.

It should be observed that the positions of the folding lines depend upon the relative positions of the planes in the glass box at (a). If the top plane is moved upward, the distance *y* is increased. If the front plane is brought forward, the distances *x* are increased but *remain equal*. If the auxiliary plane is moved to the right, the distance *z* is increased. Note that both top and auxiliary views show the *depth* of the object.

238. To Draw an Auxiliary View. The object shown in Fig. 481 (I) is numbered as explained in § 204.

STEP I. Draw two views of the object and of an arrow indicating the direction in which the auxiliary view is to be taken.

STEP II. Assume a *reference plane*, from which measurements are to be made, either coinciding with the front plane of projection or parallel to it. This reference plane will be shown as a line in the top view and in the auxiliary view. In Fig. 481, the reference plane was placed so as to contain the back face of the object.

STEP III. Draw auxiliary view of the reference plane (a line) at any desired distance from the front view, and perpendicular to the front view of the arrow. The *reference line* represents the auxiliary view of the reference plane.

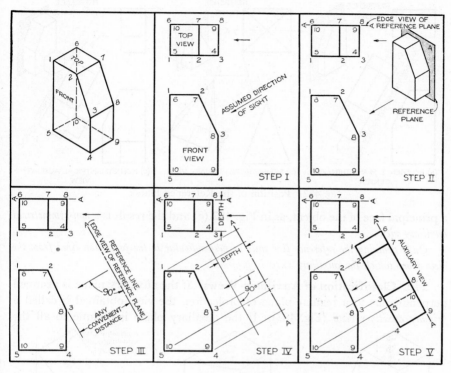

FIG. 481   To Draw an Auxiliary View.

The reference line is also the line of intersection of the auxiliary plane (§ 237) and the reference plane.

STEP IV. Draw projection lines from the front view perpendicular to the reference line, as shown. Transfer, with dividers, the *depth* of the object from the top view to the auxiliary view, as shown.

STEP V. Complete the auxiliary view, noting visibility of lines, which is determined by the direction of the lines of sight represented by the assumed arrow. Observe that each numbered point in the auxiliary view lies on its corresponding projection line from the front view, and is the same distance from the reference line *A–A* as it is in the top view.

239. Position of the Reference Plane. The reference plane may coincide with the back face of the object, as in Fig. 481 (II), or the front face of the object, or it may be assumed cutting through the object, as in Fig. 482 (a). In practice, *the plane is assumed in that position which best facilitates the construction* *of the auxiliary view.* If the object is symmetrical, the plane should be assumed through the center, as in Fig. 482 (b), and the result is a *symmetrical auxiliary view;* if the object is non-symmetrical, the plane is assumed to coincide with

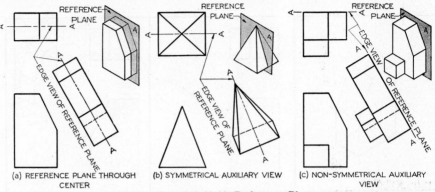

(a) REFERENCE PLANE THROUGH CENTER   (b) SYMMETRICAL AUXILIARY VIEW   (c) NON-SYMMETRICAL AUXILIARY VIEW

FIG. 482   Position of the Reference Plane.

a principal face of the object, as in Fig. 482 (c) and the result is a *non-symmetrical auxiliary view.*

On a drawing the reference line will be perpendicular to the projection lines from the view from which the auxiliary view is projected.

240. Classification of Auxiliary Views. If the auxiliary plane is assumed perpendicular to a regular plane of projection, the view obtained is called a *primary auxiliary view* (Fig. 483). If the auxiliary plane is oblique to all the

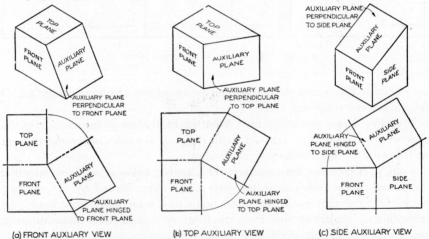

(a) FRONT AUXILIARY VIEW   (b) TOP AUXILIARY VIEW   (c) SIDE AUXILIARY VIEW

FIG. 483   Primary Auxiliary Views.

regular planes of projection, it must be hinged to some primary auxiliary plane to which it is perpendicular. Such a view is called a *secondary auxiliary view* (§ 249).

Primary auxiliary views are classified according to the plane of projection to which the auxiliary plane is hinged, as follows: (see Fig. 483)

(a) *Front auxiliary view,*
(b) *Top auxiliary view,*
(c) *Side auxiliary view.*

241. Front Auxiliary Views. An infinite number of auxiliary planes can be assumed perpendicular to, and, therefore, *hinged to* the front plane of projection. Five such auxiliary planes are shown in Fig. 484 (a), and the aux-

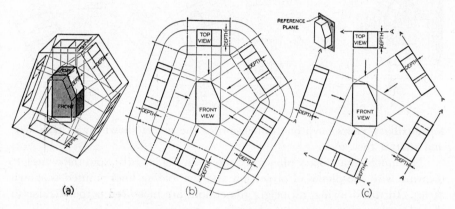

FIG. 484   Front Auxiliary Views.

iliary views projected to them are front auxiliary views. Note that the top view and all front auxiliary views have one dimension of the object shown in its true size, and that is the *depth*.

The unfolded auxiliary planes are shown in Fig. 484 (b), where also is seen how the depth dimension may be projected from the top view to all auxiliary views. The arrows indicate the directions of sight for the several views, and the projection lines are respectively parallel to these arrows. The arrows may be assumed but need not be actually drawn, since the projection lines determine the direction of sight. The folding lines are perpendicular to the arrows and to the corresponding projection lines. Since the auxiliary planes can be assumed at any distance from the object, it follows that the folding lines may be any distance from the front view.

The complete drawing with the planes of projection and folding lines omitted is shown in Fig. 484 (c). This shows the drawing as it would be drawn on paper, in which use is made of the reference plane as described in § 239, all depth dimensions being measured perpendicular to the edge view of the reference plane in each view.

242. Top Auxiliary Views. An infinite number of auxiliary planes can be assumed perpendicular to, and therefore *hinged to* the top plane of projec-

tion, several of which are shown in Fig. 485 (a). All of the auxiliary views
projected to them are top auxiliary views. Note that the front view and all

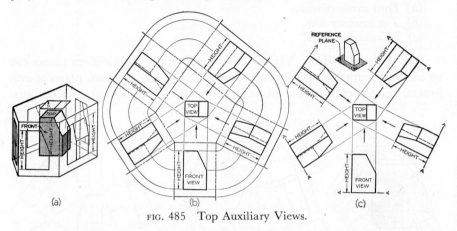

FIG. 485   Top Auxiliary Views.

top auxiliary views have one dimension of the object shown in its true size,
and that is the *height*.

The unfolded auxiliary planes are shown in Fig. 485 (b), and the complete
drawing with the planes of projection and the folding lines omitted is shown
at (c). In this drawing, all height dimensions are measured perpendicular to
the edge view of the reference plane in each view.

243. Side Auxiliary Views. An infinite number of auxiliary planes can
be assumed perpendicular to, and, therefore, *hinged to* the side plane of projection, several of which are shown in Fig. 486 (a). All of the auxiliary views

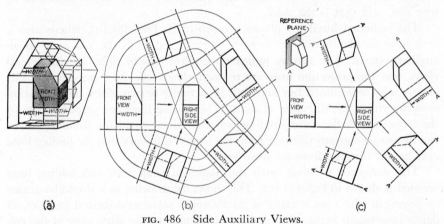

FIG. 486   Side Auxiliary Views.

projected to them are side auxiliary views. Note that the front view and all
side auxiliary views have one dimension of the object shown in its true size,
and that is the *width*.

The unfolded auxiliary planes are shown in Fig. 486 (b), and the complete drawing with the planes of projection and the folding lines omitted is shown at (c). In this drawing, all width dimensions are measured perpendicular to the edge view of the reference plane in each view.

244. Partial Auxiliary Views. As shown in Fig. 479, the use of an auxiliary view makes it possible to eliminate certain regular views which are no longer needed. In this case a *complete* auxiliary view is used not only to

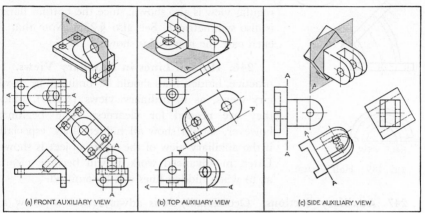

| (a) FRONT AUXILIARY VIEW | (b) TOP AUXILIARY VIEW | (c) SIDE AUXILIARY VIEW |

FIG. 487   Primary Auxiliary Views.

describe the shape of the semicircular raised portion of the object, but also the height of the base.

Other examples, showing the application of auxiliary views in drawings of machine parts, are shown in Fig. 487. It should be evident, however, that

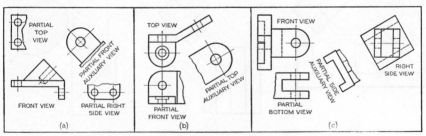

FIG. 488   Partial Views.

in each of these cases the auxiliary view plus the view from which it is projected is insufficient for a complete description. Moreover, it is equally clear that complete auxiliary views and complete regular views are not necessary.

As shown in § 196, *partial views* are often sufficient, and the resulting drawings are considerably simplified, and thus easier to draw and to read. Similarly, as shown in Fig. 488, partial regular views and *partial auxiliary views* are used with the same result. Usually a break line (Fig. 85) is used to indicate the imaginary "break" in the partial views. See also Fig. 496.

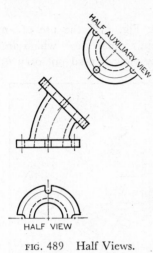

245. Half Auxiliary Views. If an auxiliary view is symmetrical, and if it is desirable to save space on the drawing or to save time in drafting, only a half of the auxiliary view may be drawn, as shown in Fig. 489. In this case, a half of a regular view is also shown, since the bottom flange is also symmetrical. See also § 235. Note that in each case the *near half* is shown.

246. Hidden Lines in Auxiliary Views. In practice, hidden lines should be omitted in auxiliary views, as in ordinary views (§ 200), unless they are needed for clearness. The beginner, however, should show all hidden lines, especially if the auxiliary view of the entire object is shown. Later, in advanced work, it will become clearer as to when hidden lines can be omitted.

HALF VIEW

FIG. 489   Half Views.

247. Auxiliary Sections. Occasionally it is advantageous to show an *auxiliary section*, as shown in Figs. 490-492. In Fig. 490 note the cutting-plane

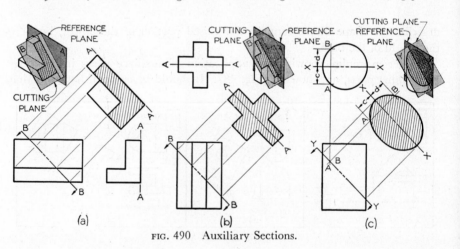

(a)   (b)   (c)

FIG. 490   Auxiliary Sections.

line (§ 225) and the terminating arrows which indicate the direction in which the cut surface is viewed. Note also in Fig. 490 the use of section lining to indicate the cut surfaces (§§ 223 and 224).

In drawing an auxiliary section, the entire part of the object behind the cutting plane may be shown, as in Fig. 490 (a), or the cut surface alone, as

in (b). The general method of showing curves in auxiliary views is shown at
(c). The reference plane is assumed through the axis of the cylinder and at
right angles to the cutting plane. In the top view, the points A and B are
equidistant from the reference plane, and are set off identically in the auxiliary
view.

An auxiliary section through a cone is shown in Fig. 491. This is one of
the conic sections (§ 118), in this case a *parabola*. The parabola may be drawn
by other methods (§§ 118 and 120), but the method shown here is by pro-

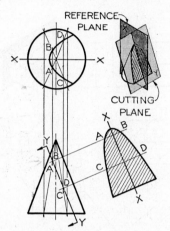

FIG. 491   Auxiliary Section.

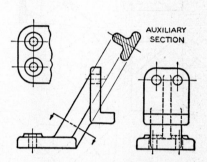

FIG. 492   Auxiliary Section.

jection. In Fig. 491, elements of the cone are drawn in the front and top views
which intersect the cutting plane at points A, B, C, and so on. These points
are established in the top view by projecting upward to the top views of the
corresponding elements. In the auxiliary section, all points on the parabola
are the same distance from the reference line as they are in the top view.

A typical example of an auxiliary section in machine drawing is shown in
Fig. 492. Here, there is not sufficient space for a *revolved section* (§ 228), although
a *removed section* (§ 229) could have been used instead of an auxiliary section.

248. True Length of Line. In
Fig. 493 (a), let it be required to find
the true length of the hip rafter AB by
means of a front auxiliary view.

1. Draw an arrow perpendicular to
AB (front view) indicating the direction
of sight, and place the reference plane
through the center of the roof, as shown.

2. Draw the reference line X–X perpendicular to the arrow and at any con-

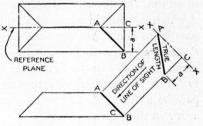

FIG. 493   True Length of a Line by
Means of an Auxiliary View.

venient distance from AB (front view) and project the points A and B toward it.

3. Set off the points A and B in the auxiliary view at the same distance from the reference line as they are in the top view. The triangle ABC in the auxiliary view shows the true size and shape of the roof section ABC, and the distance AB in the auxiliary view is the true length of the hip rafter AB.

249. Secondary Auxiliary Views. If it is necessary to place the auxiliary plane oblique to all the planes of projection, two distinct operations are necessary to draw the auxiliary view. First, a primary auxiliary view must

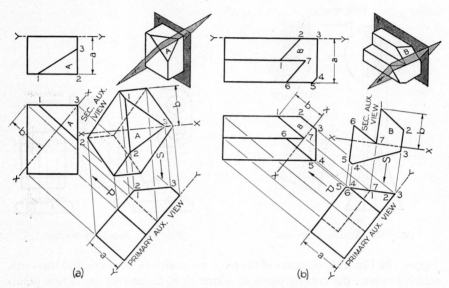

FIG. 494   Secondary Auxiliary Views.

be drawn, and, second, from it a *secondary auxiliary view* can be drawn. For example, in Fig. 494 (a), it is required to show an auxiliary view in which surface A will be shown in its true size and shape. Proceed as follows:

1. *Draw primary auxiliary view* which will show surface A as a line. In order to do this, the direction of sight, arrow P, must be parallel to a line in surface A which is shown in true length in the front view. Arrow P is, therefore, drawn parallel to line $1,2$ of the front view. Draw projection lines parallel to arrow P, and draw reference plane line Y–Y perpendicular to them. All depth measurements, such as a in the figure, are transferred from the top view with respect to Y–Y, to the auxiliary view to complete the latter. Since arrow P was assumed parallel to line $1,2$, the line appears as a point and the surface A appears as a line in the auxiliary view.

2. *Draw secondary auxiliary view* which will show surface A as a surface in true size and shape. In order to do this, the direction of sight, arrow S, must be perpendicular to the edge view $1,2,3$ of surface A in the primary auxiliary view. Draw projection lines upward, parallel to arrow S, and draw reference

plane line *X–X* perpendicular to them. In the front view, draw reference plane line *X–X* perpendicular to the projection lines between the front views and the primary auxiliary views. All measurements, such as *b* in the figure, with respect to the reference plane line, will correspond in the front and secondary auxiliary views.

In Fig. 494 (b), it is required to find the true size and shape of the surface *B*. The method is similar to that described above.

In Fig. 495, two views of a block are given, with two views of an arrow indicating the direction in which it is desired to look at the object to obtain a view. Proceed as follows:

1. *Draw primary auxiliary view of both the object and the assumed arrow*, which will show the true length *of the arrow*. In order to do this, assume a vertical

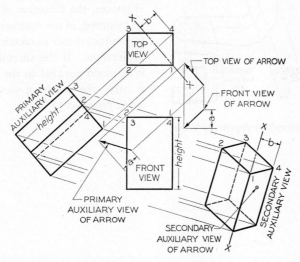

FIG. 495   Secondary Auxiliary View with Direction of Sight Given.

reference plane *X–X* parallel to the arrow (top view), and assume a direction of sight perpendicular to this plane. In the front view the butt end of the arrow is a distance *a* higher than the arrow point, and this distance is transferred to the primary auxiliary view as shown. All *height* measurements in the auxiliary view correspond to those in the front view.

2. *Draw secondary auxiliary view* which will show the arrow as a point. This can be done because the arrow shows in true length in the primary auxiliary view, and projection lines for the secondary auxiliary view are drawn parallel to it. Draw reference plane line *X–X*, for the secondary auxiliary view, perpendicular to these projection lines.

All measurements, such as *b*, with respect to *X–X*, correspond in the secondary auxiliary view and the top view.

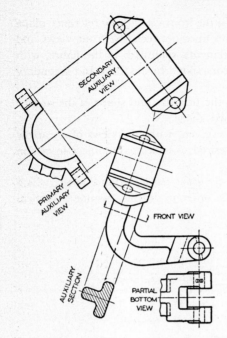

FIG. 496   Secondary Auxiliary View.

A typical application of a secondary auxiliary view in machine drawing is shown in Fig. 496. All views are partial views, except the front view. The partial secondary auxiliary view illustrates a case where break lines are not needed. Note the use of an auxiliary section to show the true shape of the arm.

It will be observed that the secondary auxiliary views of Figs. 494 and 495 have considerable pictorial value. These are trimetric projections (§ 282). However, the direction of sight could be assumed, in the manner of Fig. 495, to produce either isometric or dimetric projections. If the direction of sight is assumed parallel to the diagonal of a cube, the resulting view is an *isometric projection* (§ 260).

AUXILIARY VIEW PROBLEMS*

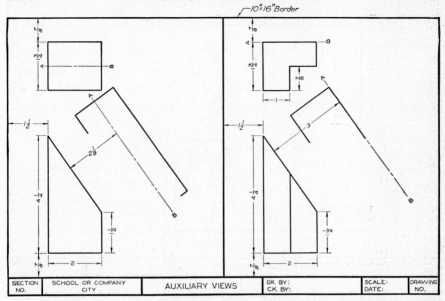

FIG. 497 Using Layout B5 (Appendix 1), draw views as shown, and complete auxiliary views showing the entire object, including all hidden lines. Omit spacing dimensions.

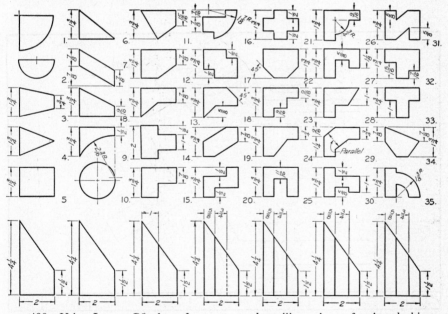

FIG. 498 Using Layout B5, draw front, top, and auxiliary views of assigned objects.

* Auxiliary view problems in convenient form for solution may be found in *Technical Drawing Problems*, by Giesecke, Mitchell, and Spencer, and in *Technical Drawing Problems— Series 2*, by Spencer and Grant, both designed to accompany this text, and published by The Macmillan Company.

257

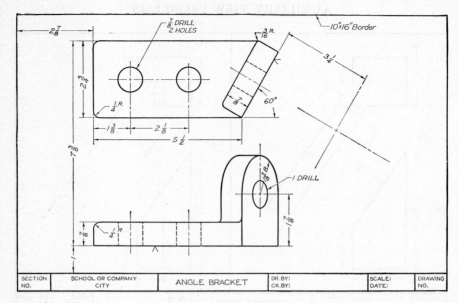

FIG. 499   Using Layout B5 (Appendix 1), draw given views and add auxiliary view.*

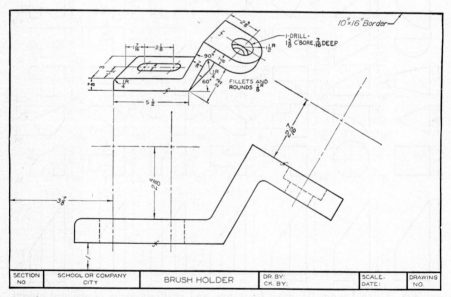

FIG. 500   Using Layout B5, draw given front view; add partial top and auxiliary views.*

* If dimensions are required, study §§ 357–386, and if tracing is required, study § 68 or § 70. Omit spacing dimensions.

258

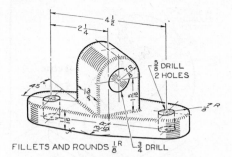

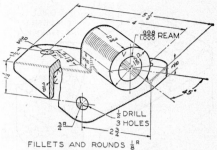

FILLETS AND ROUNDS $\frac{1}{8}$R $\frac{3}{4}$ DRILL

FIG. 501   ROD GUIDE.

Draw necessary views, including complete auxiliary view showing true shape of upper rounded portion.*

FILLETS AND ROUNDS $\frac{1}{8}$R

FIG. 502   BRACE ANCHOR.

Draw necessary views, including partial auxiliary view showing true shape of cylindrical portion.*

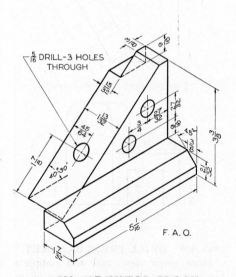

$\frac{5}{16}$ DRILL-3 HOLES THROUGH

F. A. O.

FIG. 503   ADJUSTOR BLOCK.

Draw necessary views, including complete auxiliary view showing true shape of inclined surface.*

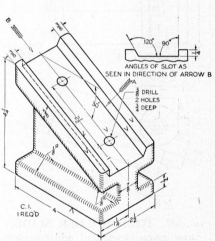

ANGLES OF SLOT AS SEEN IN DIRECTION OF ARROW B

$\frac{3}{4}$ DRILL
2 HOLES
$\frac{3}{4}$ DEEP

C. I.
1 REQ'D

FIG. 504   ANGLE BRACKET.

Draw necessary views, including complete auxiliary views taken in directions of arrows A and B.*

* Make freehand sketch or instrumental drawing, as assigned. If dimensions are required, study §§ 357–386, and if tracing is required, study § 68 or § 70.

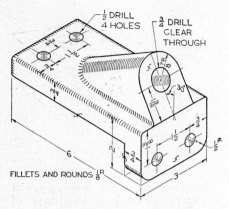

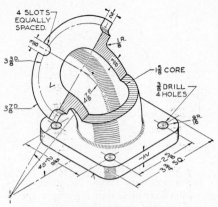

FIG. 505 ANCHOR SUPPORT.

Draw necessary views, including partial auxiliary view showing true shape of upper rounded portion, and partial views showing upper left end and lower right end.*

FIG. 506 45° ELBOW.

Draw necessary views, including a broken section and two half views of flanges.*

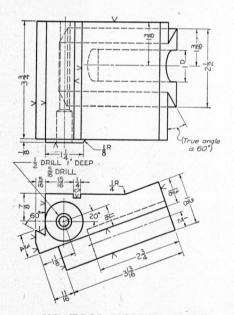

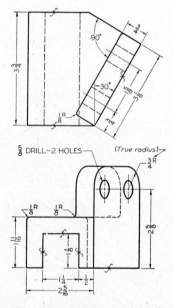

FIG. 507 TOOL HOLDER SLIDE.

Draw given views, and add complete auxiliary view showing true curvature of slot on bottom.**

FIG. 508 DRILL PRESS BRACKET.

Draw given views and add complete auxiliary view showing true shape of inclined face.**

* Make freehand sketch or instrumental drawing, as assigned. If dimensions are required, study §§ 357–386, and if tracing is required, study § 68 or § 70.

** If dimensions are required, study §§ 357–386, and if tracing is required, study § 68 or § 70.

260

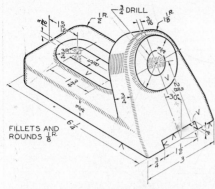

FIG. 509   SLIDE GUIDE.

Draw necessary views, including partial top view showing true shape of slot, and a partial auxiliary view showing true shape of inclined portion.*

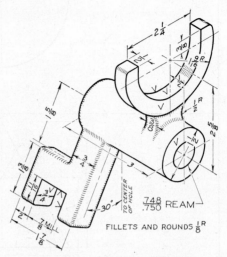

FIG. 510   SHIFTER FORK.

Draw necessary views, including partial auxiliary view showing true shape of inclined arm.*

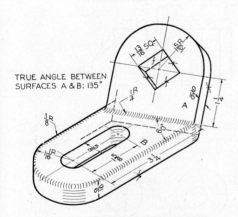

FIG. 511   CONTROL BRACKET.

Draw given views and primary and secondary auxiliary views so that the latter shows true shape of oblique surface.*

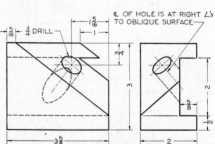

FIG. 512   HOLDER BLOCK.

Draw given views and primary and secondary auxiliary views so that the latter shows true shape of oblique surface.*

---

* If dimensions are required, study §§ 357–386, and if tracing is required, study § 68 or § 70.

261

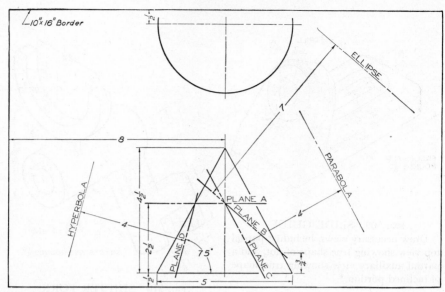

FIG. 513 Using Layout B3 (Appendix 1), draw front view and half top view as shown. Then draw conic sections (§§ 118 and 354) which will be auxiliary views of cuts produced by planes A, B, C, and D. Omit dimensions.

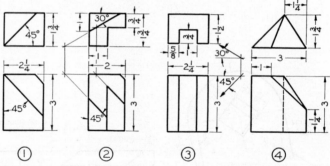

① ② ③ ④

FIG. 514 Using Layout B3, draw secondary auxiliary views which in problems 1, 2, and 4 will show true shapes of inclined surfaces. In problem 3, draw secondary auxiliary view as seen in direction of arrow. See § 249.

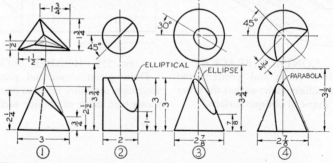

① ② ③ ④

FIG. 515 Using Layout B3, draw secondary auxiliary views showing true shapes of inclined surfaces. For Problem 2, study Fig. 490 (c), and for problems 3 and 4, study Fig. 491.

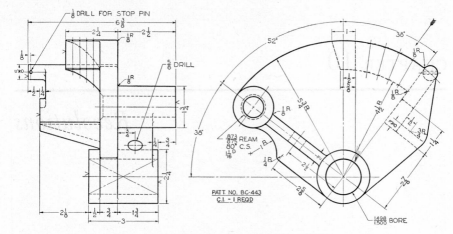

FIG. 516 UNLOADER SLIDE LEVER.

Given: Front and left side views.
Required: Front, right side, and complete auxiliary view as indicated by arrow.*

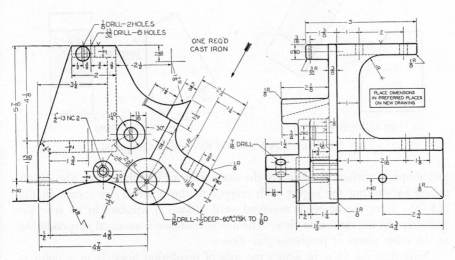

FIG. 517 GRADER BRACKET.

Given: Front and right side views.
Required: Front, left side, and complete auxiliary view as indicated by arrow.*

* If dimensions are required, study §§ 357–386, and if tracing is required, study § 68 or § 70.

CHAPTER 10

Revolutions

250. Revolutions Compared with Auxiliary Views. To obtain an auxiliary view, the observer shifts his position with respect to the object, as shown by the arrow in Fig. 518 (a). The auxiliary view shows the true size

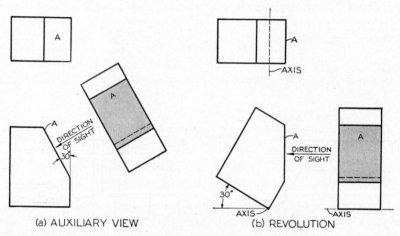

(a) AUXILIARY VIEW　　　　　(b) REVOLUTION

FIG. 518　Auxiliary View and Revolution Compared.

and shape of surface *A*. Exactly the same view of the object can also be obtained by shifting the object with respect to the observer, as shown in Fig. 518 (b). Here the object is revolved until surface *A* appears in its true size and shape in the right side view. The *axis of revolution* is assumed perpendicular to the front plane of projection, as shown.

Note that the view in which the axis of revolution appears as a point *revolves but does not change shape*, and that in the views where the axis is shown in true length the *dimensions of the object parallel to the axis do not change*.

To make a revolution drawing, the view on the plane of projection which is perpendicular to the axis of revolution is drawn first, since it is the only view which remains unchanged in size and shape. This view is drawn revolved

either *clockwise* (as the hands of a clock move) or *counterclockwise* about a point
which is thought of as the end view of the axis of revolution. This point may be
assumed at any convenient point on or outside the view. The other views are
then projected from this view.

The axis of revolution is usually considered perpendicular to one of the
three principal planes of projection. Thus an object may be revolved about an
axis perpendicular to the top, front, or side planes of projection, and the views
drawn in the new positions. Such a process is called a *simple revolution*. If this
drawing is then used as a basis for another revolution, the operation is called
a *successive revolution*. Obviously, this process may be continued indefinitely.

251. Revolution about an Axis Perpendicular to the Front Plane.
A simple revolution is illustrated in Fig. 519. An imaginary axis *XY* is assumed,

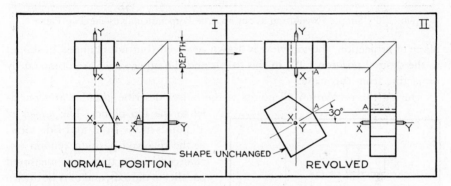

FIG. 519   Simple Revolution about an Axis Perpendicular to the Front Plane.

about which the object is to revolve to the desired position. In this case, the
axis is selected perpendicular to the front plane of projection, and, during the
revolution all points of the object describe circular arcs parallel to that plane.
The axis may pierce the object at any point or may be exterior to it. The
front view, in space II, is drawn *revolved* (but not changed in shape) through
the angle desired (30°, in this case), and the top and side views are obtained by projecting from the front view. The *depth* of the top view and the
side view is found by projecting from the top view of the first unrevolved
position (space I), *because the depth, since it is parallel to the axis, remains unchanged.*
If the front view of the revolved position is drawn directly without first drawing
the normal unrevolved position, the depth of the object, as shown in the revolved top and side views, may be drawn to known dimensions. No difficulty
should be encountered by the student who understands how to obtain projections of points and lines (§§ 204 to 208).

Note the similarity between the top and side views in Fig. 519 (II), and
some of the auxiliary views of Fig. 484 (c).

252. Revolution about an Axis Perpendicular to the Top Plane.
A revolution about an axis perpendicular to the top plane of projection is
shown in Fig. 520. An imaginary axis XY is assumed perpendicular to the top

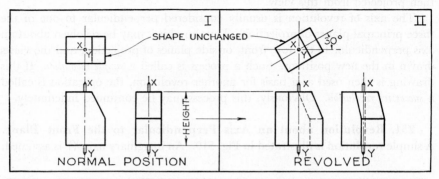

FIG. 520   Simple Revolution about an Axis Perpendicular to the Top Plane.

plane of projection, the top view is drawn revolved (but not changed in shape)
to the desired position (30°, in this case), and the other views are obtained by
projecting from this view.

During the revolution all points of the object describe circular arcs paral-

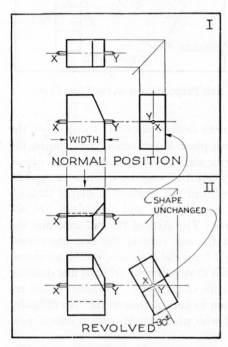

FIG. 521   Simple Revolution about an
Axis Perpendicular to the Side Plane.

lel to the top plane. The *heights* of
all points in the front and side views
in the revolved position remain unchanged, since they are measured
parallel to the axis, and may be drawn
by projecting from the initial front
and side views of Space I.

Note the similarity between the
front and side views in Fig. 520 (II)
and some of the auxiliary views of
Fig. 485 (c).

**253. Revolution about an Axis
Perpendicular to the Side Plane.**
A revolution about an axis XY perpendicular to the side plane of projection is illustrated in Fig. 521.
During the revolution, all points of
the object describe circular arcs parallel to the side plane of projection.
The *widths* of the top and front
views in the revolved position remain
unchanged, since they are measured
parallel to the axis, and may be

obtained by projection from the top and front views of Space I, or may be set off by direct measurement.

Note the similarity between the top and front views in Fig. 521 (II) and some of the auxiliary views of Fig. 486 (c).

254. Successive Revolutions. It is possible to draw an object in an infinite number of oblique positions by making successive revolutions. Such a procedure (Fig. 522) limited to three or four stages, offers excellent practice

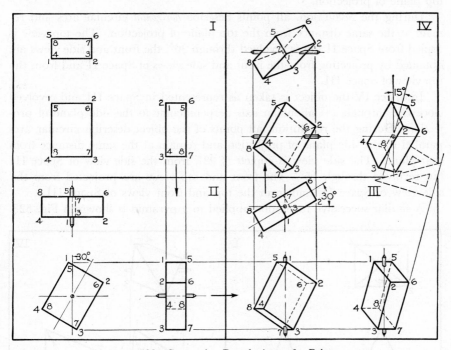

FIG. 522   Successive Revolutions of a Prism.

in orthographic projection. While it is possible to make several revolutions of a simple object without the aid of a system of numbers, it is *absolutely necessary* in complex revolutions to assign a number or a letter to every corner of the object.

The numbering or lettering must be consistent in the various views of the several stages of revolution. Figure 522 shows four sets of multiview projections, or four drawings numbered, respectively, I, II, III, and IV. These represent the same object in different positions with reference to the planes of projection.

In Space I, the object is represented in its normal position, with its faces parallel to the planes of projection. In Space II, the object is represented after it has been revolved clockwise through an angle of 30° about an axis perpendicular to the front plane.

During the revolution, all points of the object describe circular arcs parallel to the front plane of projection and remain at the same distance from that plane. The side view, therefore, may be projected from the side view of Space I and the front view of Space II. The top view may be projected from the front view and side view of Space II.

In Space III, the object is taken as represented in Space II and is revolved counterclockwise through an angle of 30° about an axis perpendicular to the top plane of projection.

During the revolution, all points describe *horizontal* circular arcs and remain at the same distance from the top plane of projection. The top view is copied from Space II but is revolved through 30°; the front and side views are obtained by projecting from the front and side views of Space II and from the top view of Space III.

In Space IV the object is taken as represented in Space III and revolved clockwise through 15° about an axis perpendicular to the side plane of projection. During the revolution, all points of the object describe circular arcs parallel to the side plane of projection and remain at the same distance from that plane. The side view is copied (§ 98), from the side view of Space III but revolved through 15°. The front and top views are projected from the side view of Space IV and from the top and front views of Space III.

A similar successive revolution applied to a pyramid is shown in Fig. 523.

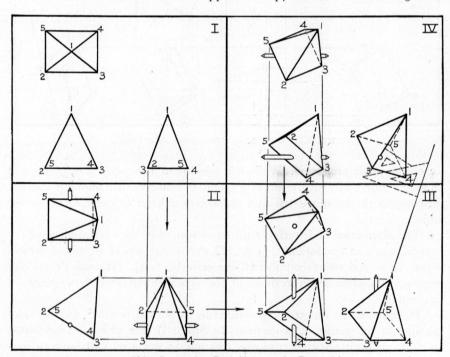

FIG. 523   Successive Revolutions of a Pyramid.

In Spaces III and IV of Figs. 522 and 523, each view is an axonometric projection (§§ 180 and 258). An isometric projection can be obtained by revolution, as shown in Fig. 531, and a dimetric projection (§ 279) can be constructed in a similar manner. If neither an isometric nor a dimetric projection is deliberately sought, the successive revolution will produce a trimetric projection (§ 282) as shown in Figs. 522 and 523.

255. Counterrevolution. The reverse procedure to revolution is *counterrevolution*. For example, if the three views of Space II in Fig. 519 are given, the object can be drawn in the unrevolved position of Space I by counterrevolution. The front view is simply counterrevolved back to its normal upright position, and the top and side views are drawn, as shown. Similarly, in Fig. 522, the object may be counterrevolved from its position of Space IV to its unrevolved position of Space I by simply reversing the process.

In practice, it sometimes becomes necessary to draw the views of an object located on or parallel to a given oblique surface. In such an oblique position, it is very difficult to draw the views of the object, because of the foreshortening of lines. The work is greatly simplified by counterrevolving the oblique surface to a simple position, completing the drawing, and then revolving to the original given position.

An example is shown in Fig. 524. Assume that the oblique surface *8, 4, 3, 7* (three views in Space I) is given, and that it is required to draw the three views of a prism which is $\frac{1}{2}''$ high having the given oblique surface as its base. Revolve the surface about any horizontal axis *X–X*, perpendicular to the side view, until the edges *8, 4* and *3, 7* are horizontal, as shown in Space II. Then revolve the surface about any vertical axis *Y–Y* until the edges *8, 7* and *4, 3* are parallel to the front plane, as shown in Space III. In this position the given surface is perpendicular to the front plane, and the front and top views of the required prism can be drawn, as shown by

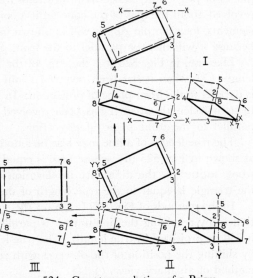

FIG. 524   Counterrevolution of a Prism.

dashed lines in the figure, because the edges *4, 1* and *3, 2*, etc., are parallel to the front plane and are, therefore, shown in their true lengths (§ 256), one-half inch. Having drawn the two views in Space III, counterrevolve the

object from III to II and then from II to I to find the required views of the
given object in Space I.

256. To Find the True Length of a Line.—Fig. 525. *If a line is parallel*

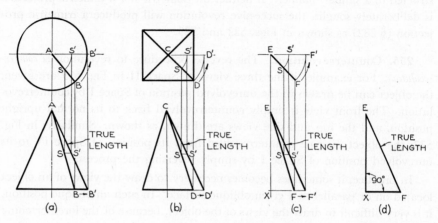

FIG. 525   True Length of a Line.

to one of the planes of projection, its projection on that plane is equal in length to the line.
See §§ 205–207. In Fig. 525 (a), the element *AB* of the cone is oblique to the
planes of projection; hence its projections are foreshortened (§ 207). If *AB* is
revolved about the axis of the cone until it coincides with either of the contour
elements, for example *AB′*, it will be shown in its true length in the front view
because it will then be parallel to the front plane of projection.

Likewise, in Fig. 525 (b), the edge of the pyramid *CD* is shown in its true
length *CD′* when it has been revolved about the axis of the pyramid until it
is parallel to the front plane of projection. In Fig. 525 (c), the line *EF* is shown
in its true length when it has been revolved about a vertical axis until it is
parallel to the front plane of projection.

The true length of a line may also be found by constructing a right triangle,
as shown in Fig. 525 (d), whose base is equal to the top view of the line, and
whose altitude is the difference in elevation of the ends. The hypotenuse of
the triangle is equal to the true length of the line.

In the methods of Fig. 525 (a) to (c) the true length is found by revolution;
that is, by revolving the line until it is parallel to a plane of projection where
it will be projected in true length. The true length of a line may also be found
by shifting the position of the observer with respect to the line; that is, by the
method of auxiliary views (§ 248).

REVOLUTION PROBLEMS*

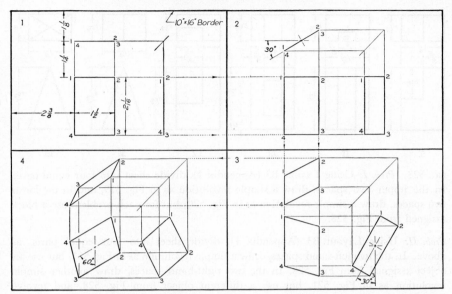

FIG. 526   Using Layout B3, divide sheet into four equal parts, as shown.   Draw given views of rectangle, and then the simple revolution in Space 2, followed by successive revolutions in Spaces 3 and 4.   Number points as shown.   Omit dimensions.

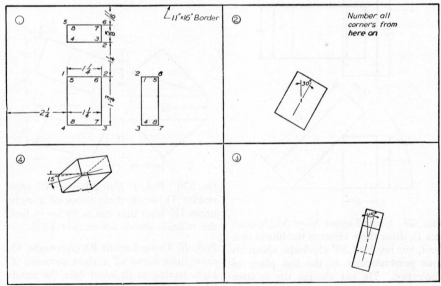

FIG. 527   Using Layout B3 (Appendix 1), divide sheet into four equal parts, as shown. Draw given views of prism as shown in Space 1; then draw three views of the revolved prism in each succeeding space, as indicated.   Number all corners.   Omit dimensions.

* Revolution problems in convenient form for solution may be found in *Technical Drawing Problems*, by Giesecke, Mitchell and Spencer, and in *Technical Drawing Problems—Series 2*, by Spencer and Grant, both designed to accompany this text, and published by The Macmillan Company.

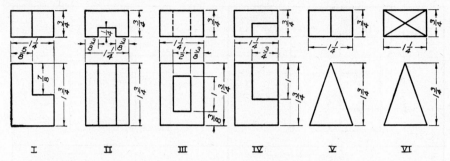

I   II   III   IV   V   VI

FIG. 528   *Prob. I:* Using Layout B3 (Appendix 1), divide sheet into four equal parts. In the upper two spaces, draw a simple revolution as in Fig. 519, and in the lower two spaces, draw a simple revolution as in Fig. 520; but for each problem use a block assigned from Fig. 528.

Prob. II: Using Layout B3 (Appendix 1), divide sheet into four equal parts, as above. In the two left-hand spaces, draw a simple revolution as in Fig. 521, but use an object assigned from Fig. 528. In the two right-hand spaces, draw another simple revolution as in Fig. 521, but use a different object from Fig. 528, and revolve through 45° instead of 30°.

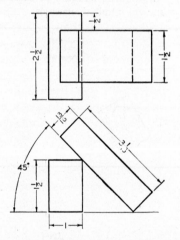

FIG. 529   Using Layout A3 or A4 (Appendix 1), draw three views of the blocks as a unit, but revolved 30° clockwise about an axis perpendicular to the top plane of projection. Do not change the relative positions of the blocks.

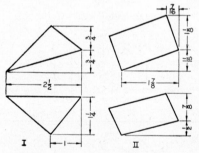

I   II

FIG. 530   *Prob. I:* Using Layout B3 (Appendix 1), draw three views of a right prism $1\frac{1}{2}''$ high that has as its lower base the triangle shown above. See § 255.

Prob. II: Using Layout B3 (Appendix 1), draw three views of a right pyramid $2''$ high, having as its lower base the parallelogram shown above. See § 255.

272

CHAPTER 11

Axonometric Projection*

257. Pictorial Drawing. By means of multiview drawing, it is possible to represent accurately the most complex forms by showing a series of exterior views and sections. This type of representation has, however, two limitations: its execution requires a thorough understanding of the principles of projection, and its reading requires a definite exercise of the constructive imagination.

Frequently it is necessary to prepare drawings which are accurate and scientifically correct, and which can be easily understood by persons without technical training. Such drawings show several faces of an object at once, approximately as they appear to the observer. This type of drawing is called *pictorial drawing*, to distinguish it from multiview drawing discussed in Chapter 7. Since pictorial drawing shows only the appearances of objects, it is not satisfactory for completely describing complex or detailed forms.

Various types of pictorial drawing are used extensively in catalogs and in general sales literature, and also in technical work, † to supplement and amplify multiview drawings; for example, in Patent Office drawings, in piping diagrams, and in machine, structural, and architectural drawings, and in furniture design.

Pictorial drawing enables the person without technical training to visualize the object represented. It also enables the trained designer to visualize the successive stages of the design, and to develop it in a satisfactory manner.

258. Methods of Projection. Pictorial drawings are projected on a single plane of projection by the methods of (1) *axonometric projection*, (2) *oblique projection* (Chapter 12), and (3) *central projection*, or *perspective* (Chapter 13), as distinguished from multiview drawings, which are projected on two or more planes of projection.

In axonometric projection the object, a cube, for example, is placed so that its faces are inclined to the plane of projection, in order that three faces may be represented in one view. If the projectors are perpendicular to the

---

* See §§ 180–183.

† Most of the illustrations in this book were drawn by the methods described in Chapters 11, 12, and 13. See especially Figs. 322–391.

plane of projection (as is usually the case), the resulting projection is a *normal axonometric projection;* otherwise, it is an *oblique axonometric projection.* Since the latter is not used in actual practice, the term "axonometric projection" is generally understood to refer to normal axonometric projection, which is a branch of orthographic projection (§§ 179, 180, 188).

259. Types of Axonometric Projection. The distinguishing feature of axonometric projection is the inclined position of the object with respect to the plane of projection. Since the principal edges, or axes, of the object are inclined to the plane of projection, the lengths of the lines, the sizes of the angles, and the general proportions of the projection of the object vary with the infinite number of possible positions in which the object may be placed with respect to the plane of projection.

Axonometric projection is classified as: (1) *isometric projection,* (2) *dimetric projection,* and (3) *trimetric projection.* Before proceeding with the study of axonometric projection, the student should review carefully §§ 179–183, in Chapter 6, in which the theoretical background for this subject is explained.

ISOMETRIC PROJECTION

260. Method of Projection. To produce an isometric projection ("isometric" means "equal measure"), it is necessary to place the object so that its principal axes, or edges, make equal angles with the plane of projection, and are, therefore, foreshortened equally.

The proper relative positions of the plane of projection and the object may be secured by revolving the object (§§ 250–254) until it occupies the desired position (Fig. 531, c).

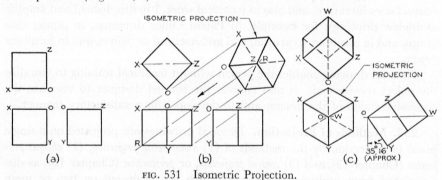

FIG. 531   Isometric Projection.

In Fig. 531 (a) is shown a multiview drawing of a cube. At (b), the cube is shown revolved through 45° about an imaginary vertical axis. Now, an auxiliary view in the direction of the arrow will show the cube diagonal *ZR* as a point, and the cube will show as a true isometric projection. However, instead of the auxiliary view at (b) being drawn, the cube may be further revolved as shown at (c), this time the cube being tilted forward about an imaginary horizontal axis until the three edges, or axes, *OY*, *OX*, and *OZ*, make equal angles with the plane of projection and are, therefore, foreshortened equally. Here again, a diagonal of the cube, in this case *OW*, appears as a point in the isometric view. The front view thus obtained is a true isometric projection. In this projection, the twelve edges of the cube make angles of about 35° 16′ with the front plane of projection. The lengths of their projections are equal to the lengths of the edges multiplied by $\sqrt{2/3}$, or by 0.816, approximately. Thus, the projected lengths are about 80 per cent of the true lengths, or, still more roughly, about three-fourths of the true lengths. The projections of the axes *OX*, *OY*, and *OZ* make angles of 120° with each other, and are called the *isometric axes*. Any line which is par-

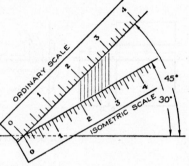

allel to one of these is called an *isometric line;* a line which is not parallel is called a *non-isometric line*. It should be noted that the angles in the isometric projection of the cube are either 120° or 60° and that all are projections of 90° angles. In an isometric projection of a cube, the faces of the cube, or any planes parallel to them, are called *isometric planes*.

FIG. 532   Isometric Scale.

261. The Isometric Scale. A correct isometric projection may be drawn with the use of an *isometric scale*, prepared on a strip of paper or cardboard (Fig. 532). All distances in the isometric scale are $\sqrt{2/3}$ times true size, or approximately 80 per cent of true size. The use of the isometric scale is illustrated in Fig. 533 (a). A scale of $9'' = 1'\text{-}0''$, or $\frac{3}{4}$-size scale may be used to approximate the isometric scale.

262. Isometric Drawing. When a drawing is prepared with an isometric scale, or otherwise as the object is actually *projected* on a plane of projection, it is an *isometric projection*, as illustrated in Fig. 533 (a). When it is prepared

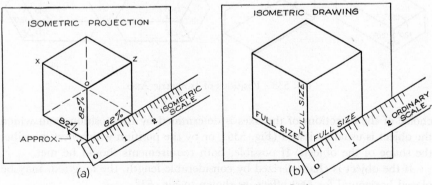

FIG. 533   Isometric and Ordinary Scales.

with an ordinary scale, it is an *isometric drawing*, illustrated in (b). The isometric drawing (b) is about $22\frac{1}{2}$ per cent larger than the isometric projection (a), but the pictorial value is obviously the same in both.

Since the isometric projection is foreshortened and an isometric drawing is full size, it is customary to make an isometric drawing rather than an isometric projection, because it is so much easier to execute, and, for all practical purposes, is just as satisfactory as the isometric projection.

263. Rectangular Construction. The steps in preparing an isometric drawing of a simple rectangular object are illustrated in Fig. 534. The axes

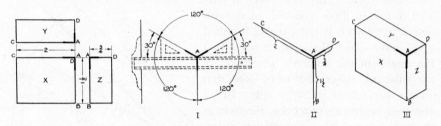

FIG. 534   Steps in Isometric Drawing.

are first drawn at angles of 120° with each other (**I**); the measurements are made actual size along the axes, and the remaining lines drawn parallel to the respective axes (§ 208). The object may be drawn in the same position by beginning at the corner *B* instead of at the corner *A*.

264. Other Positions of the Isometric Axes. The isometric axes may be placed in any desired position according to the requirements of the problem, as shown in Fig. 535, but the angle between the axes must remain 120°. The

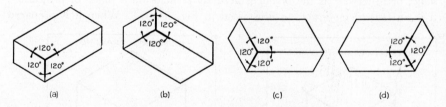

FIG. 535   Positions of Isometric Axes.

choice of the directions of the axes is determined by the position from which the object is usually viewed (Fig. 536), or by the position which best describes the shape of the object. If possible, both requirements should be met.

If the object is characterized by considerable length, the long axis may be placed horizontal for best effect, as shown in Fig. 537.

265. Offset Location Measurements. The method of locating one part with respect to another is illustrated in Figs. 538 and 539. In each case, after the main block has been drawn, the offset lines *CA* and *BA*, in the multiview drawing are drawn full size in the isometric drawing, thus locating corner *A*

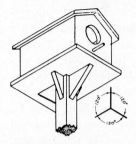

FIG. 536   An Object
Naturally Viewed
from Below.

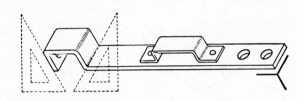

FIG. 537   Long Axes Hroizontal.

of the small block or rectangular recess. These measurements are called *offset measurements*, and since they are parallel to certain edges of the main block in the multiview drawings, they will be parallel respectively to the same edges in the isometric drawings (§ 208). Hence, the rule: *If two lines are parallel on the object (in space), they will be parallel in the isometric drawing.*

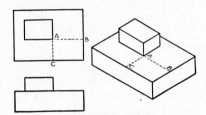

FIG. 538   Offset Location
Measurements.

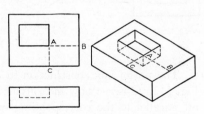

FIG. 539   Offset Location
Measurements.

266. Hidden Lines. The use of hidden lines in isometric drawing is governed by the same rules as in all other types of projection: *Hidden lines are omitted unless they are needed to make the drawing clear.* A case where hidden lines are needed is illustrated in Fig. 540, in which a projecting part cannot be clearly shown without the use of hidden lines.

267. Center Lines. The use of center lines in isometric drawing is governed by the same rules as in multiview drawing: *Center lines are drawn if they are needed to indicate symmetry, or if they are needed for dimensioning* (Fig. 540). In general, center lines should be used sparingly, and omitted in cases of doubt. The use of too many center lines may produce a confusion of lines which diminishes the clearness of the drawing. An example in which center lines

are not needed is shown in Fig. 536. Examples where they are needed are
seen in Figs. 562 (a), 870, 871, etc.

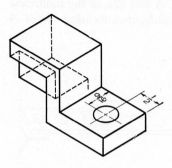

FIG. 540   Use of Hidden Lines.

268. Box Construction. Objects of irregular
shape may be more easily drawn by means of
box construction, which consists simply in imagining the object to be enclosed in a rectangular
box whose sides coincide with the main faces of
the object. For example, in Fig. 541, the object shown in two views is imagined to be enclosed in a construction box. This box is then
drawn lightly with construction lines (Step I),
the irregular features are then constructed
(Step II), and finally (Step III) the required
lines are made heavy.

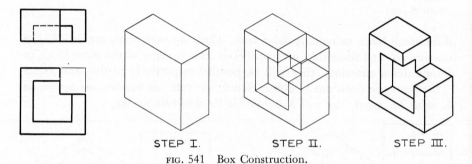

STEP I.   STEP II.   STEP III.

FIG. 541   Box Construction.

The use of box construction in drawing a different object is illustrated in
Fig. 542. Observe how measurements *a* to *f* in the multiview drawing are set
off parallel to the corresponding edges in Step II of the isometric.

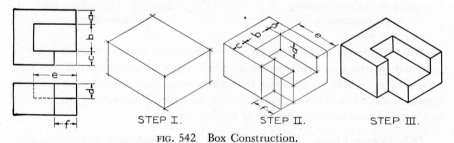

STEP I.   STEP II.   STEP III.

FIG. 542   Box Construction.

269. Non-Isometric Lines. Since the only lines of an object which are likely
to be true length* in an isometric drawing are the isometric axes or lines parallel
to them, *non-isometric lines* cannot be set off directly according to length. For

* A line which is parallel to the plane of projection (unusual) would project true length.

example, in the given views of Fig. 543, the inclined lines *CA* and *BA* (§ 206) are shown in their true length (top view); but, since they are not parallel to the isometric axes, they will not be true length in the isometric. Such lines are drawn in isometric by means of box construction and offset measurements

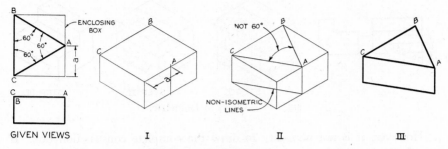

GIVEN VIEWS   I   II   III

FIG. 543   Non-Isometric Lines.

in which the *end points of the lines are located*. Point *A* is located (Step I), by means of offset measurement *a*, and construction lines are then drawn between points *C* and *A*, and *B* and *A*, as shown in Step II. The final lines are then made heavy to complete the drawing, as shown in Step III.

To realize the fact that non-isometric lines will not be true length in the isometric drawing, set your dividers on *BA* of Step III and then compare with *BA* on the given top view. Do the same for line *CA*. It will be seen that *BA* is shorter and *CA* is longer in the isometric than the corresponding lines in the given views.

270. Angles in Isometric. Since the only angles of an object which will be true size in an isometric drawing are those which lie in planes parallel to the plane of projection (§ 209), it follows that angles generally will not be projected in true size. For example, in the multiview drawing of Fig. 543, none of the three 60° angles will be 60° in the isometric drawing.

To realize this fact, measure each angle in the isometric of Step III with your protractor and note the number of degrees compared to the true 60°. No two angles are the same; two are smaller and one larger than 60°.

Since angles cannot be set off directly in isometric drawing, it is necessary to locate the end points of the lines which subtend the angles. For example, in Fig. 543, the three 60° angles are drawn in isometric simply by locating the end point *A*, as shown. Points *B* and *C* were already located, since they coincide with corners of the construction box.

Another example of the construction of angles is shown in Fig. 544. *Angles cannot be set off directly in isometric; they must first be translated to linear measurements along or parallel to the isometric axes.*

271. Irregular Objects. If the general shape of an object does not conform somewhat to a rectangular pattern, it may be drawn, as shown in

Fig. 545 (a), by using the box construction discussed previously. Various points of the triangular base are located by means of offsets *a* and *b* along the edges of the bottom of the construction box. The vertex is located by means of offsets *OA* and *OB* on the top of the construction box.

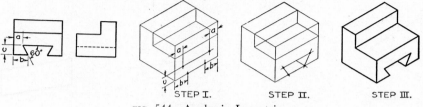

STEP I.   STEP II.   STEP III.

FIG. 544   Angles in Isometric.

However, it is not necessary to draw the complete construction box. If only the bottom of the box is drawn, as shown in Fig. 545 (b), the triangular base can be constructed as before. The orthographic projection of the vertex

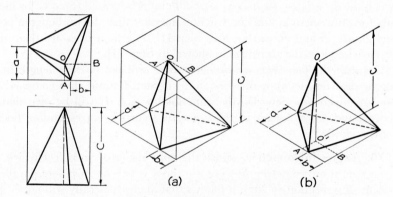

(a)   (b)

FIG. 545   Irregular Object in Isometric.

O' on the base can then be located by offsets *O'A* and *O'B*, as shown, and from this point the vertical center line *O'O* can be erected, using measurement *C*.

Another example showing the use of a combination of partial box construction and offset measurements is shown in Fig. 546.

Sometimes an irregular object may be drawn by means of a series of sections, as illustrated in Fig. 547. The edge views of a series of imaginary cutting planes are shown in the top and front views of the multiview drawing at (a). At (b) the various sections are constructed in isometric and at (c) the object is completed by drawing lines through the corners of the sections. In the isometric at (b), all height dimensions are taken from the front view at (a), and all depth dimensions from the top view at (a).

272. Curves in Isometric Drawing. A curve is drawn in isometric by means of a series of offset measurements similar to those discussed in § 265.

In Fig. 548, any desired number of points, as A, B, C, and so on, are selected at random along the curve in the top view of the multiview drawing. Enough

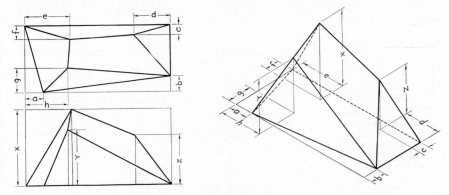

FIG. 546   Offset Space Measurements.

points should be chosen to fix accurately the path of the curve; the more points used, the greater the accuracy. Offset grid lines are then drawn from each point parallel to the edges of the enclosing construction box, as shown.

As shown in Step 1, offset measurements a and b are laid off in the isometric to locate point A on the curve. Points B, C, and D are located in a similar manner, as shown in Step 2. A light freehand curve is sketched smoothly

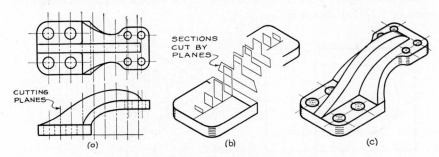

FIG. 547   Use of Sections in Isometric.

through the points, as shown in Step 3. Points A', B', C', and D' are located directly under points A, B, C, and D, as shown in Step 4, by drawing vertical lines downward, using measurement C. Each of these vertical lines is equal in length to the height of the block. A light freehand curve is then sketched through these points. The final curve is produced with the aid of the irregular curve (§ 72), and all required lines made heavy, as shown in Step 5.

273. Circles in Isometric ("True" Methods). As shown in § 210, if a circle lies in a plane which is not parallel to the plane of projection, the circle is projected as an ellipse. This ellipse can be drawn by any of the methods of §§ 112 to 117, but since the major and minor axes are not usually known, the methods of § 116 (based on the given conjugate axes) will be most convenient.

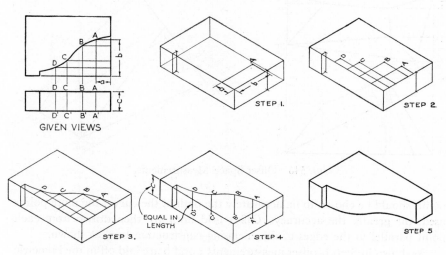

FIG. 548   Curves in Isometric.

The true ellipse can, however, be constructed by the method of offsets discussed in § 272, as shown in Fig. 549:

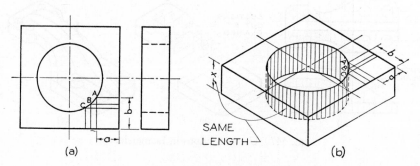

FIG. 549   Ellipse Drawn by Means of Offsets.

As shown at (a), points *A*, *B*, *C*, and so on, are selected at random on the circle. Point *A* is located in the isometric by means of offset measurements *a* and *b*, and points *B* and *C* are located in a similar manner. When enough points have been constructed to determine accurately the ellipse, as shown at (b), the corresponding points on the lower ellipse can be constructed by dropping vertical lines downward as shown. The final curves are drawn with the aid of the irregular curve (§ 72).

If the curve lies in a non-isometric plane, all offset measurements cannot be applied directly. For example, in Fig. 550 (a), the elliptical face shown in the auxiliary view lies in a non-isometric plane. The cylinder is enclosed in a construction box, and the box is then drawn in isometric, as shown at (b). The

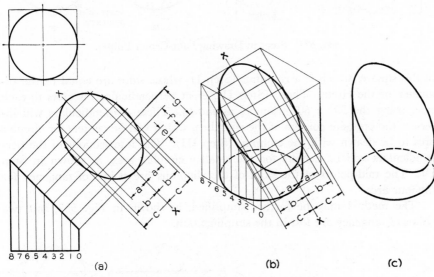

FIG. 550   Ellipse in Non-Isometric Plane.

base is drawn by the method of offsets, as shown in Fig. 549. The inclined ellipse is constructed by locating a number of points on the ellipse in the isometric and drawing the final curve by means of the irregular curve (§ 72).

Measurements a, b, c, and so on, are parallel to an isometric axis and can be set off in the isometric at (b) on each side of the center line X–X, as shown. Measurements e, f, g, and so on are not parallel to any isometric axis, and cannot be set off directly in isometric. However, when these measurements are projected to the front view and down to the base, as shown at (a), they can then be set off along the lower edge of the construction box, as shown at (b). The completed isometric is shown at (c).

The true ellipse is seldom used in isometric drawing because its construction requires a great deal of time, and in most cases approximate methods (§ 274) are sufficient. However, in cases where an accurate ellipse is needed, the above methods are necessary.

274. Approximate Four-Center Ellipse. An approximate ellipse is sufficiently accurate for nearly all isometric drawing. The method commonly used, called the *four-center ellipse*, is illustrated in Figs. 551, 552, and 553. It can be used only for ellipses in isometric planes.

To apply this method (Fig. 551), draw, or conceive to be drawn, a square around the given circle in the multiview drawing. Then draw the isometric

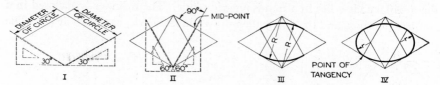

FIG. 551   Steps in Drawing Four-Center Ellipse.

of this square, which is a rhombus (Step I), whose sides are equal to the diameter of the circle. Then, (Step II), erect perpendicular bisectors to each side, using the 30° x 60° triangle, as shown. These perpendiculars will intersect the opposite corners of the rhombus, which will be centers for circular arcs to be drawn with the compass (Step III). The intersections of the perpendiculars will be centers for the smaller circular arcs, as shown in Step IV. The mid-points of the sides of the rhombus are points of tangency for the four arcs.

The method may be further simplified, as shown in Fig. 552, but two points of tangency are lost in the simplification.

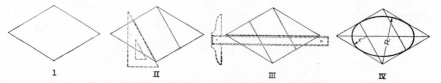

FIG. 552   Steps in Drawing Four-Center Ellipse.

The construction of the four-center ellipse upon the three visible faces of a cube is shown in Fig. 553, a study of which shows that all diagonals are horizontal or inclined 60° to the horizontal; hence, the entire construction can be made with the T-square and the 30° x 60° triangle.

The disadvantage of the four-center ellipse is its inaccuracy. In Fig. 554 is shown a comparison of a true ellipse (shown solid) with the corresponding four-center ellipse (shown dotted). The major axis of the true ellipse is longer and the minor axis somewhat shorter than the corresponding axes of the four-center ellipse. In cases where accuracy is required in the areas where the four-center ellipse deviates from the true ellipse, as when a line is tangent to the ellipse, the true ellipse methods of § 116 should be used.

For ellipses in non-isometric planes, see § 273.

The four-center ellipse construction may also be used in drawing circular arcs in isometric, as shown in Fig. 555. At (a), in the upper right portion of the figure, the complete construction is shown. However, it is not necessary to make the complete construction for circular arcs, as is illustrated at (b) and (c). In each case, from the intersection of the tangent lines, extended, the radius R is set off, as shown. At each point, perpendiculars to the lines are erected, their intersection being the center of the required arc.　Notice

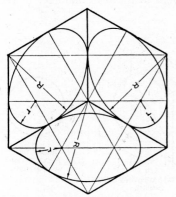

FIG. 553　Four-Center Ellipse.

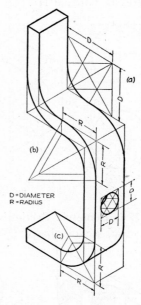

FIG. 555　Arcs in Isometric.

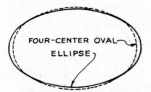

FIG. 554　Comparison of Four-Center Ellipse and the True Ellipse.

that the R distances are equal in both cases (b) and (c), but the radii of the required arcs are quite different.

If a true elliptic arc is necessary, the offset method of Fig. 549 or Fig. 550 is recommended.

275. The Sphere in Isometric. The isometric drawing of any curved surface is evidently the envelope of all lines which can be drawn on that surface. For the sphere, the great circles* may be selected as the lines on the surface. Since all great circles, except those which are perpendicular or parallel to the plane of projection, are shown as ellipses having equal major axes, it follows that their envelope is a circle whose diameter is the major axis of the ellipses.

In Fig. 556 two views of a sphere enclosed in a construction cube are shown at the left. The cube is drawn at I, together with the isometric of a great circle which lies in a plane parallel to one face of the cube. Actually, the ellipse need not be drawn, for only the points on the diagonal located by measurements a are needed. These points establish the ends of the major

* Circles cut by any plane through the center.

axis from which the radius R of the sphere is determined. The resulting drawing, shown at II, is an *isometric drawing* and its diameter is, therefore,
$\sqrt{3}/2$ times the actual diameter of the sphere. The *isometric projection* of the
sphere is simply a circle whose diameter is equal to the true diameter of the
sphere, as shown at III.

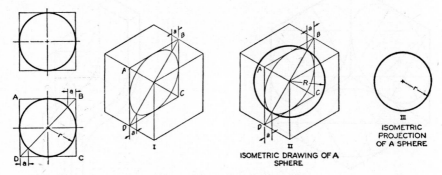

FIG. 556   Isometric of a Sphere.

276. Isometric Sectioning. In the representation of simple objects in
isometric, sections based upon the principles explained for multiview draw-

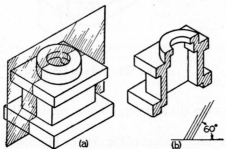

FIG. 557   Isometric Full Section.

ing may be used to show interior
shapes. An *isometric full section* is illustrated in Fig. 557. In such cases,
it is advisable to draw the isometric
of the cut face first, and then to
draw the portion of the object which
lies behind the cutting plane. Other
examples of isometric full sections
are shown in Figs. 379, 391, and
403. Isometric full sections are not
extensively used because the removal
of an entire half of the object usually leaves an insufficient description of
the exterior.

An *isometric half section* is illustrated in Fig. 558. The simplest procedure in

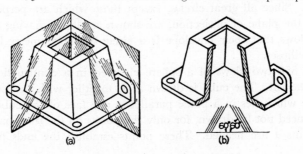

FIG. 558   Isometric Half Section.

this case is to make an isometric drawing of the complete object and then of the cut surfaces. Since only a quarter of the object is removed in a half section, the resulting pictorial drawing is quite useful in describing both the interior and exterior shapes. A number of typical isometric half sections are shown in Figs. 413, 463, 885, 926, and 927.

Isometric half sections are also used extensively in representing assemblies. Typical examples are shown in Figs. 898 and 931.

Isometric broken-out sections are also widely used, as shown in Figs. 375, 381, 457, 866, and 891.

Section lining in isometric drawing is similar to that in multiview drawing. Section lining at an angle of 60° with horizontal (Figs. 557 and 558) is recommended, but the direction should be changed if at this angle the lines would be parallel to a prominent object line bounding the cut surface, or to other lines of the drawing. In Fig. 559 (a) is shown a correct representation of isometric section lining for ordinary conditions.

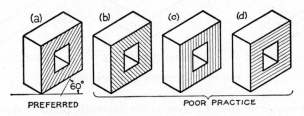

FIG. 559   Section Lining in Isometric.

If the lines are drawn as shown at (b), they are almost parallel to one of the systems of isometric lines of the object, and the effect is not as satisfactory as that shown at (a). Other objectionable effects resulting from drawing the section lines parallel to object lines are shown at (c) and (d).

277. Isometric Dimensioning. Isometric dimensioning follows the general principles of ordinary dimensioning, as discussed in Chapter 16. The dimensions given should be those required to make the object in the shop, should be without duplication, and should above all be legible.

The methods of dimensioning a simple prism are illustrated in Fig. 560. The form shown at (a) is preferred because of its compactness, but the forms at (b) and (c) are sometimes necessary for maximum clarity. As in ordinary dimensioning, the dimensions should be placed outside the boundaries of the drawing, if possible. Sometimes, however, it will not be possible to do this, and in such cases the forms shown at (d) and (e) are permissible. Isometric dimension lines and extension lines must never be given as shown at (f), but should always be drawn in the isometric planes to which they apply. Dimension lines must always be parallel to the direction of measurement, and should apply, if possible, to visible surfaces.

The method of drawing numerals and arrowheads in isometric is shown in Fig. 561 (a). For the $2\frac{1}{2}''$ dimension, the two extension lines, the dimension

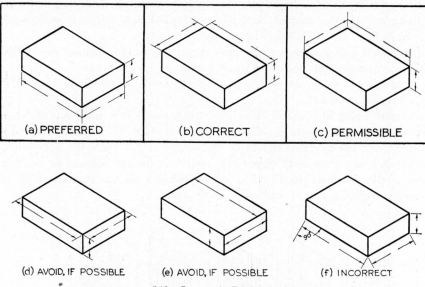

(a) PREFERRED   (b) CORRECT   (c) PERMISSIBLE

(d) AVOID, IF POSSIBLE   (e) AVOID, IF POSSIBLE   (f) INCORRECT

FIG. 560   Isometric Dimensioning.

line, and the numerals are all drawn in the isometric plane of one face of the object. The "horizontal" guide lines for the numerals are drawn parallel to

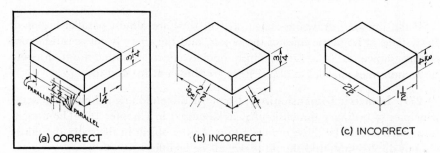

(a) CORRECT   (b) INCORRECT   (c) INCORRECT

FIG. 561   Numerals and Arrowheads in Isometric.

the dimension line, and the vertical guide lines are drawn parallel to the extension lines. The rear ends of the arrowheads should line up parallel to the extension lines.

As shown at (b), the guide lines used to keep the letters vertical should not be perpendicular to the dimension lines. The example at (c) is incorrect because the $2\frac{1}{2}''$ and $1\frac{1}{2}''$ dimensions are not lettered in the same plane with the corresponding extension lines and dimension lines, and the $\frac{3}{4}''$ dimension is turned to read from the left.

Correct and incorrect practices in isometric dimensioning are illustrated in Fig. 562. At (b) the $3\frac{1}{8}''$ dimension runs to a wrong extension line at the top, and, consequently, the dimension does not lie in an isometric plane. Near the bottom, a number of lines cross one another unnecessarily, and terminate on the wrong lines. The lower $\frac{1}{2}''$ drill hole is located from the edge of the cylinder when it should be dimensioned from its center line. Study these two drawings carefully and discover other mistakes at (b) besides those mentioned.

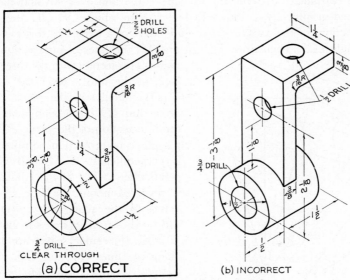

FIG. 562   Isometric Dimensioning.

Many examples of isometric dimensioning are given in the problems at the ends of Chapters 7, 8, 9, and 19, and the student should study these to find examples of almost any special case which he may encounter. See especially Figs. 870, 885, and 893.

278. Piping Diagrams. Isometric and oblique drawings are well adapted for representation of piping layouts, as illustrated in Figs. 992 and 997, as well as for all other structural work which is to be represented pictorially.

DIMETRIC PROJECTION

279. Method of Projection. A *dimetric projection* is an axonometric projection of an object so placed that two of its axes make equal angles with the plane of projection, and the third axis makes either a smaller or a greater angle. Hence, the two axes making equal angles with the plane of projection are foreshortened equally, while the third axis is foreshortened in a different ratio.

Generally, the object is so placed that one axis will be projected in a vertical position. However, if the relative positions of the axes have been determined, the projection may be drawn in any desired position, as in isometric drawing. See § 264, Figs. 535, 536, and 537.

The angles between the *projections of the axes* must not be confused with the angles which the *axes themselves* make with the plane of projection.

280. Dimetric Scales. The positions of the axes may be assumed such that any two angles between the axes are equal and over 90° and the scales determined graphically as shown in Fig. 563, in which OP, OL, and OS are the projections of the axes or converging edges of a cube. In this case, angle $POS =$ angle LOS. Then draw PL, LS, and SP, the lines of intersection of the

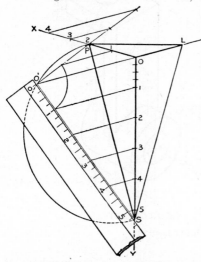

FIG. 563 Dimetric Scales.

plane of projection with the three visible faces of the cube. Since the line LO is perpendicular to the plane POS, its projection LO is perpendicular to PS, the intersection of the plane POS with the plane of projection. Similarly, OP is perpendicular to SL and OS perpendicular to PL. If the triangle POS is revolved about the line PS as an axis into the plane of projection, it will be shown in its true size and shape as $PO'S$. If regular scales are marked along the lines $O'P$ and $O'S$, and the triangle is counterrevolved to its original position, the dimetric scales are found on the lines OP and OS, as shown in Fig. 563.

If the scales are assumed, the positions of the axes may be determined by calculation.*

However, it will be found that one of the three positions shown in the upper row of Fig. 564 will be suitable for almost any practical drawing, and the use of one of the three would simplify the work considerably. The scales of reduction, indicated in the circles attached to the axes, are readily obtained from the architects scale. The inclinations of the axes can be determined with the aid of the protractor (§ 36). True dimetric projections result from the use of these scales and angles.

---

* The following formula may be used:

$$\cos a = -\frac{\sqrt{2h^2v^2 - v^4}}{2hv},$$

where a is one of the two equal angles between the projections of the axes, h is one of the two equal scales, and v is the third scale.

The positions shown at I, II, and III in Fig. 564 can be further varied by sloping the inclined lines downward at the same angles with horizontal. The position at III can also be reversed from left to right; that is, the 41° 25′ angle can be placed on the left, and the 7° 10′ angle on the right.

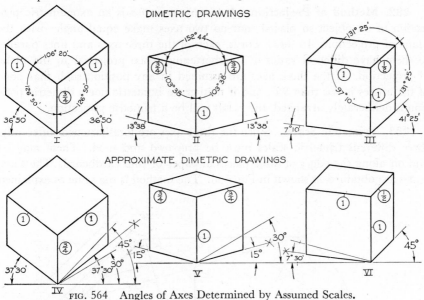

FIG. 564   Angles of Axes Determined by Assumed Scales.

281. Approximate Dimetric Drawing. If a special triangle having an angle of 36° 50′, or a protractor, is available, an accurate dimetric drawing can be made as indicated in Fig. 564, I. An approximate dimetric drawing can be constructed by substituting for the angle 36° 50′ one of 37° 30′ which can be obtained with the use of the ordinary triangles and compass, as shown in Fig. 564, IV. The resulting drawing will be sufficiently accurate for all practical purposes. Similar approximations may be made for the other two cases, as shown in Fig. 564, V and VI.

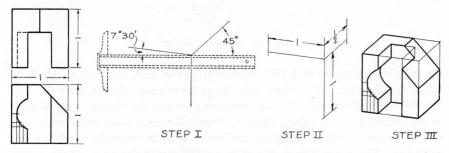

FIG. 565   Steps in Dimetric Drawing.

The procedure of preparing an approximate dimetric drawing is illustrated in Fig. 565. The position adopted is that of Fig. 564, VI.

TRIMETRIC PROJECTION

282. Method of Projection. A *trimetric projection* is an axonometric projection of an object so placed that no two axes make equal angles with the
plane of projection. In other words, each of the three axes and lines parallel
to them have different ratios of foreshortening when projected to the plane
of projection. If the three axes are assumed in any position such that none
of the angles is less than 90°, and if neither an isometric nor a dimetric position is deliberately arranged, the result will be a trimetric projection.

283. Trimetric Scales. Since the three axes are foreshortened differently,
three different trimetric scales must be prepared and used. These may be
laid off along the edges of three pieces of paper or thin cardboard. The three
scales are obtained as shown in Fig. 566. The method is the same as explained

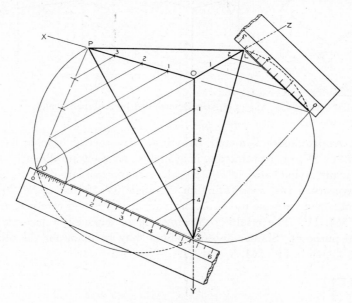

FIG. 566   Trimetric Scales.

for the dimetric scales in § 280. As shown in Fig. 566, any two of the three
triangular faces can be revolved into the plane of projection to show the true
lengths of the three axes. In the revolved position, the regular scale is used
to set off inches or fractions thereof. When the axes have been counterrevolved to their original positions, the scales will be correctly foreshortened,
as shown. These dimensions should be transferred to the edges of three thin
cards and marked *OX*, *OZ*, or *OY* for easy reference. The trimetric drawing

is made in a manner similar to isometric, but separate scales must be used for measurements parallel to the three axes.

284. Axonometric Projection by the Method of Intersections. Instead of constructing axonometric projections as explained in the preceding paragraphs, an axonometric projection of an object can be obtained directly by projection from two orthographic views of the object. This method is called the *method of intersections;* it was developed by Prof. L. Eckhart of the Vienna College of Engineering and published by him in 1937.

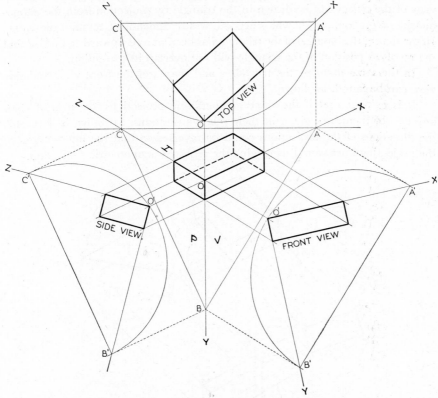

FIG. 567   Views from the Axonometric Projection.

To understand this method, let us assume (Fig. 567) that the axonometric projection of a rectangular object is given and it is required to find its three orthographic projections: the top view, front view, and side view.

Assume that the object is placed so that its principal edges coincide with the coordinate axes and assume that the plane of projection (the plane upon which the axonometric projection is drawn) intersects the three coordinate planes in the triangle *ABC*. From descriptive geometry we know that lines *BC, CA,* and *AB* will be perpendicular, respectively, to axes *OX, OY,* and

OZ. Any one of the three points *A*, *B*, or *C* may be assumed at pleasure on one of the axes, and the triangle *ABC* drawn.

To find the true size and shape of the top view it is only necessary to re-volve the triangular portion of the horizontal plane *AOC*, which is in front of the plane of projection, about its base *CA*, into the plane of projection. In this case, the triangle is revolved *inward* to the plane of projection through the smallest angle made with it, while in Figs. 563 and 566, the triangles were revolved *outward* through the largest angle made with the plane of pro-jection. The triangle will then be shown in its true size and shape, and the top view of the object can be drawn in the triangle by projection from the axono-metric projection, as shown, since all width dimensions remain the same. In the figure, the base *CA* of the triangle has been moved upward to *C'A'* so that the revolved position of the triangle will not overlap its projection.

In the same manner, the true sizes and shapes of the front view and side view can be found, as shown.

It is evident that if the three orthographic projections, or in most cases any two of them, are given in their relative positions, as shown in Fig. 567, the directions of the projections could be reversed so that the intersections of the projecting lines would determine the required axonometric projection.

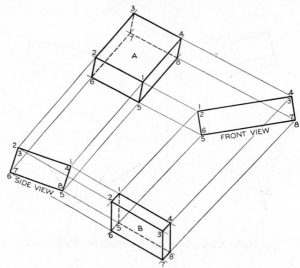

FIG. 568   Oblique Axonometric Projections.

In Fig. 568, the front view and the side view of the object shown in Fig. 567 are drawn at random, and two sets of intersecting projecting lines drawn at random from the two views, producing the axonometric projection at *A*. Two different sets of projecting lines, with directions at random, intersect to produce the axonometric projection at *B*. In the same manner, an infinite number of *oblique axonometric projections* (§ 258) can be obtained from the two views by changing their positions or changing the directions of the projecting lines, or both.

Unless an oblique axonometric projection differs only slightly from a normal axonometric projection, it appears distorted because the projection is viewed by the observer in a direction inclined to the direction in which

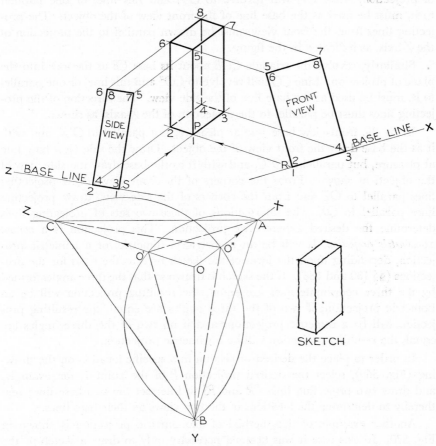

FIG. 569 Normal Axonometric Projection.

the object was projected toward the plane of projection. A *normal axonometric projection* presents a natural appearance because the projection is viewed by the observer in the direction in which the object was projected, namely perpendicularly to the plane of projection.

In order to secure a normal axonometric projection by the method of intersections, it is well to make a sketch (Fig. 569) of the desired general appearance of the projection. If the object is a complicated one, this sketch need not be complete but may be only a sketch of an enclosing box. Having made the sketch, draw the projections of the coordinate axes OX, OY, and OZ, parallel to the principal edges of the object as shown in the sketch, and the triangle ABC to represent the intersection of the three coordinate planes with the plane of projection.

Revolve the triangle ABO about its base AB as the axis into the plane of projection. Line OA will revolve to $O'A$ and this line, or one parallel to it, must be used as the base line of the front view of the object. The projecting lines from the front view must be drawn parallel to the projection of the Z-axis, as indicated in the figure.

Similarly, revolve the triangle COB about its base CB as the axis into the plane of projection. Line CO will revolve to CO'' and this line, or one parallel to it, must be used as the base line of the side view. The direction of the projecting lines must be parallel to the projection of the X-axis, as shown.

Draw the front-view base line at pleasure, but parallel to $O'X$, and with it as the base draw the front view of the object. Draw the side-view base line at pleasure, but parallel to $O''C$, and with it as the base draw the side view of the object, as shown. From the corners of the front view, draw projecting lines parallel to OZ and from the corners of the side view, draw projecting lines parallel to OX. The intersections of these two sets of projecting lines determine the desired axonometric projection. This projection is a *normal axonometric projection*. It will be an isometric, a dimetric, or a trimetric projection, depending upon the form of the sketch used as the basis for the projections (§§ 180 and 188). If the sketch is drawn so that the three angles formed by the three coordinate axes are equal, the resulting projection will be an isometric projection; if two of the three angles are equal, the resulting projection will be a dimetric projection; and if no two of the three angles are equal, the resulting projection will be a trimetric projection.

In order to place the desired projection in a specific location on the drawing (Fig. 569), select the desired projection P of the point 1, for example, and draw two projecting lines PR and PS to intersect the two base lines and thereby to determine the locations of the two views on their base lines.

Another example of this method of axonometric projection is shown in Fig. 570. In this case it was deemed necessary only to draw a sketch of the plan or base of the object in the desired position, as shown. The axes are then drawn with OX and OZ parallel respectively to the sides of the sketch plan, and the remaining axis OY is assumed in a vertical position. The triangles COB and AOB are revolved, and the two base lines drawn parallel to $O''C$ and $O'A$ as shown. Point P, the lower front corner of the axonometric drawing, was then chosen at pleasure, and projecting lines drawn toward the base lines parallel to axes OX and OZ to locate the positions of the views on the base lines. The views are drawn upon the base lines or cut apart from another drawing and fastened in place with drafting tape or thumbtacks.

To draw the elliptical projection of the circle, assume any points, as A

for example, on the circle in both front and side views. Note that point A is the same altitude d above the base line in both views. The axonometric projection of point A is found simply by drawing the projecting lines from the two views. In order to draw the ellipse approximately, with the compass, find the lengths of the major and minor axes by projection in the same way, and apply the method of Fig. 153 (c).

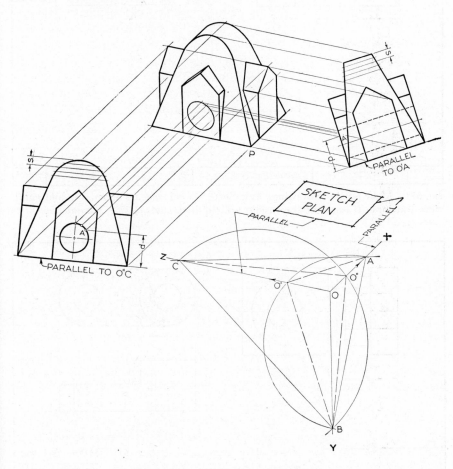

FIG. 570   Normal Axonometric Projection.

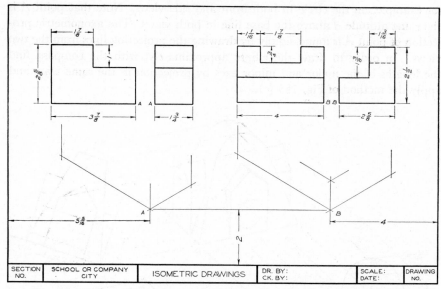

FIG. 571 Make isometric drawings, as indicated. Omit spacing dimensions and multiview drawings. If isometric dimensions are required, study § 277. Layout B5.

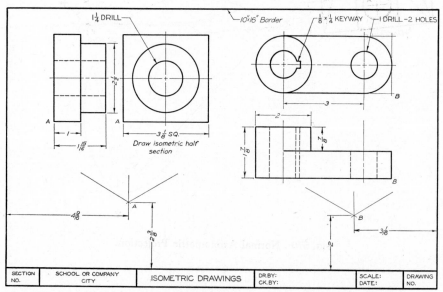

FIG. 572 Make isometric drawings, as indicated. Omit spacing dimensions and multiview drawings. If isometric dimensions are required, study § 277. Layout B5.

* Axonometric problems in convenient form for solution may be found in *Technical Drawing Problems*, by Giesecke, Mitchell, and Spencer, and in *Technical Drawing Problems— Series 2*, by Spencer and Grant, both designed to accompany this text, and published by The Macmillan Company.

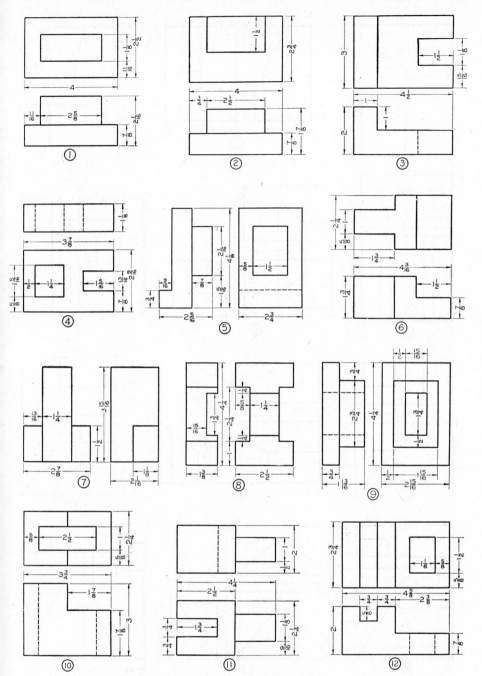

FIG. 573 (1) Make freehand isometric sketches. (2) Make isometric drawings with instruments on Layout B5 similar to Fig. 571. (3) Make dimetric drawings with instruments, using Layout B5 and position assigned from Fig. 564. (4) Make trimetric drawings, using instruments, with axes chosen to show the objects to best advantage. Use method of intersections (§ 284). If dimensions are required, study § 277.

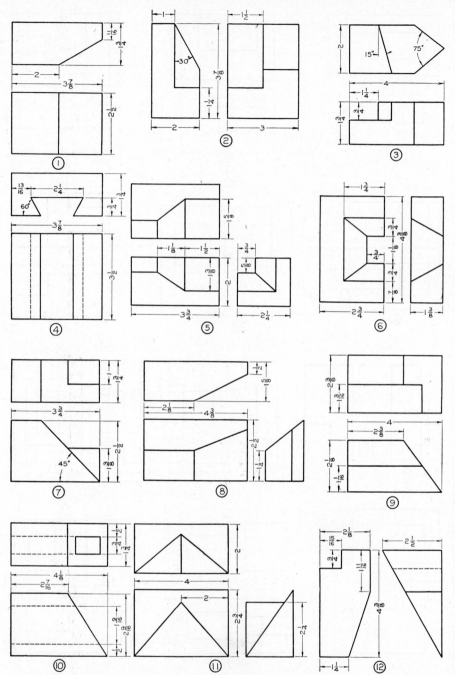

FIG. 574 (1) Make freehand isometric sketches. (2) Make isometric drawings with instruments on Layout B5 similar to Fig. 571. (3) Make dimetric drawings with instruments, using Layout B5 and position assigned from Fig. 564. (4) Make trimetric drawings, using instruments, with axes chosen to show the objects to best advantage. Use method of intersections (§ 284). If dimensions are required, study § 277.

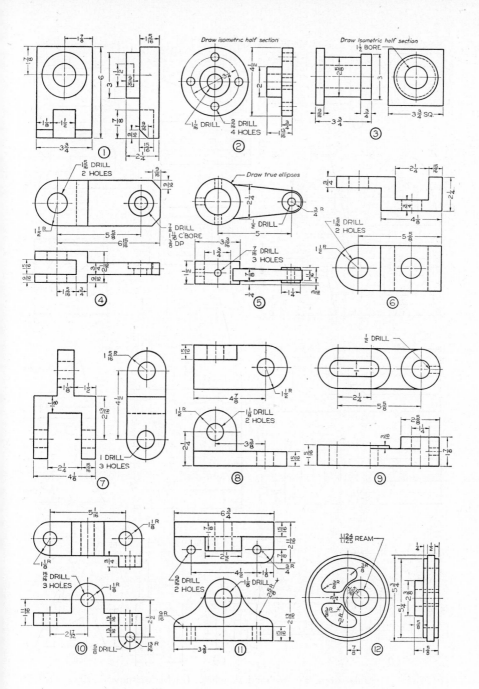

FIG. 575 (1) Make isometric freehand sketches. (2) Make isometric drawings with instruments, using Size A or Size B sheet, as assigned. (3) Make dimetric drawings with instruments, using Size A or Size B sheet, as assigned, and position assigned from Fig. 564. (4) Make trimetric drawings, using instruments, with axes chosen to show the objects to best advantage. If dimensions are required, study § 277.

301

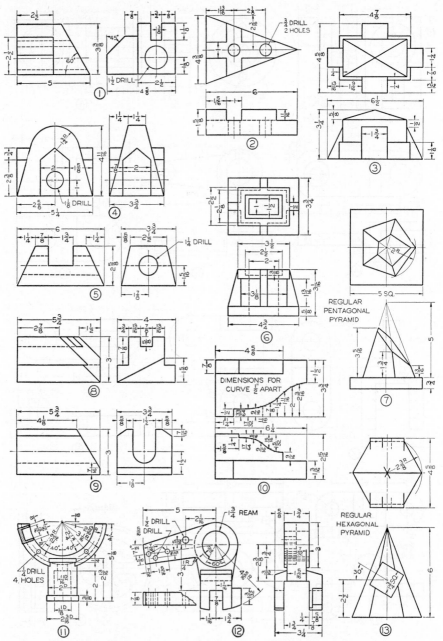

FIG. 576* (1) Make isometric freehand sketches. (2) Make isometric drawings with instruments, using Size A or Size B sheet, as assigned. (3) Make dimetric drawings with instruments, using Size A or Size B sheet, as assigned, and position assigned from Fig. 564. (4) Make trimetric drawings, using instruments, with axes chosen to show the objects to best advantage. If dimensions are required, study § 277.

* For additional problems, assignments may be made from any of the problems in Figs. 598–600.

CHAPTER 12

Oblique Projection*

285. Pictorial Drawing. Oblique projection is a form of pictorial drawing similar to normal axonometric projection, but differing from it in the direction of the projectors and generally also in the position of the object with reference to the plane of projection.

In normal axonometric projection, the projectors are perpendicular to the plane of projection and the principal faces of the object oblique to it.

In oblique projection, the projectors are oblique to the plane of projection but parallel to each other, and one of the principal faces of the object is generally parallel to the plane of projection.

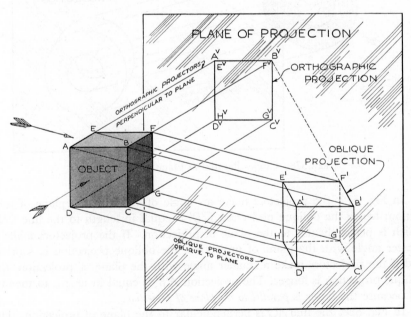

FIG. 577   Comparison of Oblique and Orthographic Projections.

* See § 178.

286. Method of Projection. A comparison of oblique projection and orthographic projection is shown in Fig. 577. It should be observed that the front face $A'B'C'D'$ of the oblique projection is identical with the front view $A^vB^vC^vD^v$ of the orthographic projection. An advantage of oblique projection over isometric projection is that, in most cases, the oblique projections of circles are circles. Figure 578 shows the oblique and the orthographic projections of a cylindrical object. In isometric projection, circles are generally projected as ellipses, because the circles are not parallel to the plane of projection.*

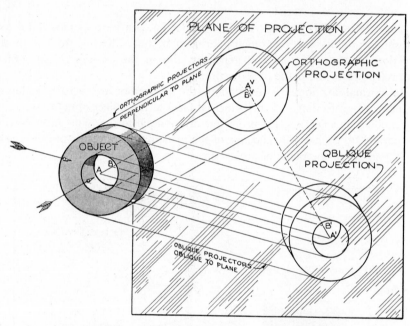

FIG. 578　Circles Parallel to Plane of Projection.

In Fig. 579, the projectors make an angle of 45° with the plane of projection; hence the oblique projection $C'D'$ is equal in length to the line CD', which is perpendicular to the plane of projection. If the projectors make a greater angle with the plane of projection, the oblique projection is shorter, and if the projectors make a smaller angle with the plane of projection, the oblique projection is longer. The projection $A'B'$ is equal in length to the line AB because the latter is *parallel to the plane of projection.*

In Fig. 580, the line AO is perpendicular to the plane of projection. The projectors make angles of 45° with the plane of projection, and the projections BO, CO, DO, EO, etc., are therefore equal in length to the line AO. It

* A circle in a plane parallel to the plane of projection would be projected as a circle, in its true size, in either isometric or oblique projection.

will be seen from this figure that the projectors may be selected in any one of an infinite number of directions and yet maintain any desired angle with the plane of projection. It is also evident that the directions of the projec-

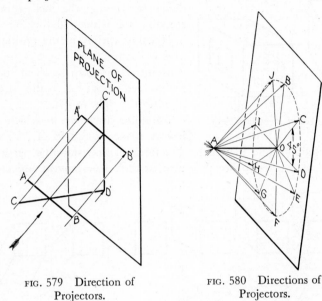

FIG. 579   Direction of
Projectors.

FIG. 580   Directions of
Projectors.

tions *BO, CO, DO, EO*, etc., are independent of the angles the projectors make with the plane of projection. Ordinarily this inclination of the projection is 45° (see the line *CO* in the figure), 30°, or 60° with the horizontal, since these angles may be easily drawn with the triangles.

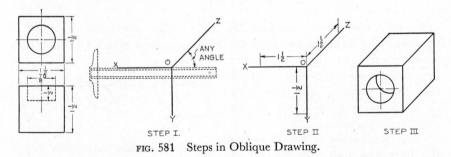

STEP I.   STEP II   STEP III

FIG. 581   Steps in Oblique Drawing.

287. Oblique Drawing. The procedure in constructing an oblique drawing is illustrated in Fig. 581. The axes *OX* and *OY* are perpendicular to each other, since the front face of the block is assumed parallel to the plane of projection. The receding axis *OZ may be drawn at any angle*, depending upon the character of the object represented. For example, in Fig. 582 at (a), a large angle was used in order to show the hole in the top to better advantage, while at (b) a small angle was desirable to show a similar feature on the side.

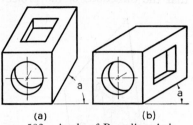

(a)   (b)

FIG. 582   Angle of Receding Axis.

The infinite range of projections produced by varying the inclination of the receding axis is suggested in Fig. 583.

Further variety in the positions of the axes is illustrated in Fig. 584, in which a constant relationship between the axes is maintained, but the entire drawing is tilted to the right or left.

Oblique drawings in which the projectors make an angle of 45° with the plane of projection, and in which, therefore, all lines standing perpendicular to the plane of projection are projected in their true lengths are commonly

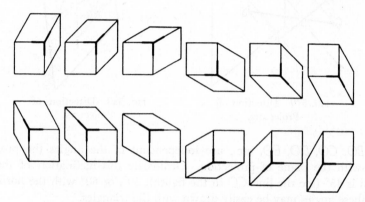

FIG. 583   Variation in Direction of Receding Axis.

called *cavalier projections*. See Fig. 585 (a). Cavalier projection originated in the drawing of medieval fortifications; these projections were made upon horizontal planes. In these fortifications the central portion was higher than the remaining portions, and was called *cavalier* because of its dominating and commanding position.

288. Reduction of the Length of the Receding Axis. Because the eye

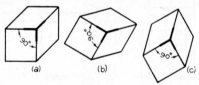

(a)   (b)   (c)

FIG. 584   Inclined Positions of Axes.

is accustomed to seeing objects with all receding parallel lines appearing to converge, an oblique projection presents an unnatural appearance. For example, in the oblique drawings of *cubes* in Fig. 583, the receding lines appear to be too long and to diverge. In Fig. 586 is shown a striking example of the *unnatural* appearance of an *oblique drawing* when compared with the *natural* appearance of the *perspective* representation.

This appearance of distortion may be materially lessened by decreasing the length of the receding lines. As suggested in § 286, this may be accomplished by increasing the angle which the projectors make with the plane of projection.

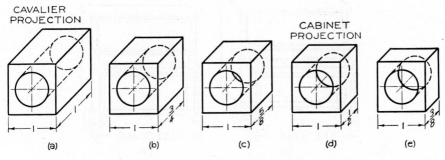

FIG. 585　Foreshortening of Receding Lines.

In Fig. 585, a cube is shown in five oblique drawings with varying degrees of foreshortening of the receding lines. The range of scales chosen is sufficient for almost all problems, and some of the scales are available on the architects scale.

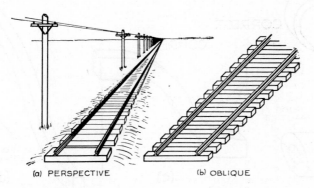

(a) PERSPECTIVE　　　　　(b) OBLIQUE

FIG. 586　Unnatural Appearance of Oblique Drawing.

When the receding lines are drawn to a scale of $6'' = 1'\text{-}0''$ (half size), as shown in Fig. 585 (d), the drawing is commonly called a *cabinet projection*. The term cabinet projection is attributed to the early use of this type of oblique drawing in the furniture industries. A comparison of cavalier projection and cabinet projection is shown in Fig. 587.

289. Choice of Position. That face of an object showing the essential contours of the object should generally be placed parallel to the plane of projection (Fig. 588).

By this practice distortion is kept at a minimum and labor is reduced. For example, in Fig. 588 (a) and (c) the circles and circular arcs are shown

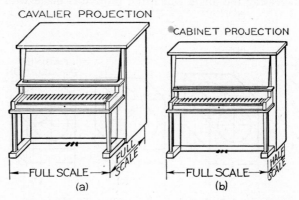

FIG. 587   Comparison of Cavalier and Cabinet Projections.

in their true sizes and shapes, and may be drawn with the compass, while in (b) and (d) these curves are not shown in their true sizes and shapes, and

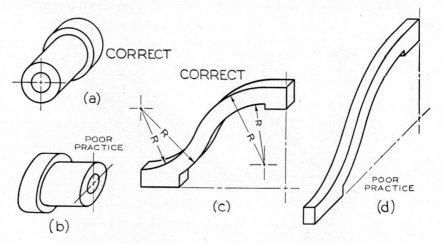

FIG. 588   Essential Contours Parallel to Plane of Projection.

must be constructed with irregular curves, except in those cases where the four-center ellipse may be used (§ 291).

The longest dimension of an object should generally be placed parallel to the plane of projection, as illustrated in Fig. 589.

290. Center-Line Skeleton Construction. The steps in making a typical oblique drawing are illustrated in Fig. 590. The object shown in the multi-view drawing is particularly appropriate for oblique representation, since all curves lie in planes which are parallel. In isometric, a great many ellipses would be required.

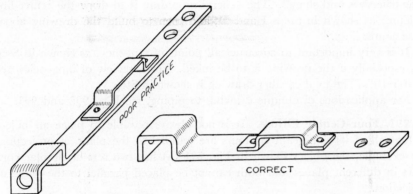

FIG. 589   Long Axis Parallel to Plane of Projection.

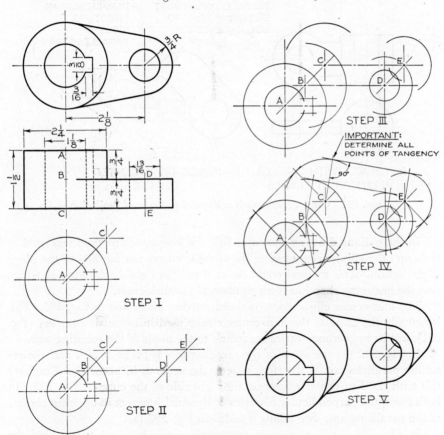

FIG. 590   Steps in Oblique Drawing.

The object is imagined to be turned so that the circles as shown in the top view are parallel to the plane of projection, and would therefore be drawn in their true sizes and shapes. The general procedure is to draw the center-line skeleton, as shown in Steps I and II, and then to build the drawing about these center lines.

It is very important to construct all points of tangency, as shown in Step IV, especially if the drawing is to be inked. For a review of tangencies, see §§ 105–107. The final cavalier drawing is shown in Step V.

For applications of oblique drawing to piping, see Figs. 992 and 993.

291. Four-Center Ellipse. It is not always possible to place an object so that all of its significant contours are parallel to the plane of projection. For example, the object shown in Fig. 591 (a) has two sets of circular contours in different planes and both cannot be placed parallel to the plane of projection.

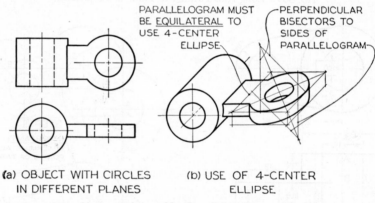

PARALLELOGRAM MUST BE EQUILATERAL TO USE 4-CENTER ELLIPSE

PERPENDICULAR BISECTORS TO SIDES OF PARALLELOGRAM

(a) OBJECT WITH CIRCLES IN DIFFERENT PLANES

(b) USE OF 4-CENTER ELLIPSE

FIG. 591   Circles and Arcs Not Parallel to Plane of Projection.

In the oblique drawing shown at (b), the four-center method was used to construct the ellipses representing the circular curves not parallel to the plane of projection. This method could be used only in cavalier drawing in which case the enclosing rhombus is an equilateral parallelogram.

The four-center ellipse construction is further illustrated in Fig. 592. This is actually the same as the four-center ellipse used in isometric drawing (Fig. 551), but its appearance varies according to the angle of the receding axis.

In Fig. 592 (a) the angle of the receding axis is taken at 30°, and the resulting parallelogram is therefore exactly the same as in isometric. Compare this with the four-center ellipse on the right side of the cube in Fig. 553. In both cases, the perpendicular bisectors of the sides intersect in opposite corners of the parallelogram. See points B and D in Fig. 592 (a).

In Fig. 592 (b), the angle of the receding axis is taken at 45°, and the resulting parallelogram is "flatter" than in isometric. The perpendicular bisectors do not intersect in corners *B* and *D*, but *outside* the parallelogram at points *J* and *K*.

In Fig. 592 (c), the angle of the receding axis is taken at 15°, and the resulting parallelogram is "fatter" than in isometric. The perpendicular bisectors do not intersect at corners *B* and *D*, but *inside* the parallelogram at points *J* and *K*.

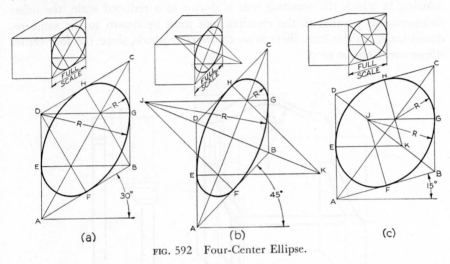

FIG. 592   Four-Center Ellipse.

However, it must be remembered that the four-center ellipse can be inscribed only in an *equilateral* parallelogram and hence cannot be used in any oblique drawing in which the receding axis is foreshortened. Its use is limited, therefore, to cavalier drawing.

292. Offset Measurements. Circles, circular arcs, and other curved or irregular lines may be drawn by means of offset measurements, as shown in Fig. 593. The offsets are first drawn on the multiview drawing of the curve,

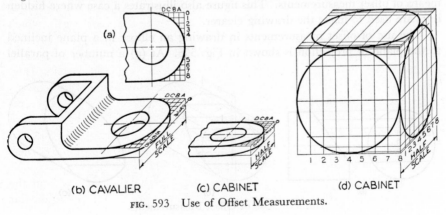

FIG. 593   Use of Offset Measurements.

as shown at (a), and these are transferred to the oblique drawing, as shown
at (b). In this case, the receding axis is full scale and therefore all offsets can
be drawn full scale. The four-center ellipse could be used, but the method
here is more accurate. The final curve is drawn with the aid of the irregular
curve (§ 72).

If the oblique drawing is a cabinet drawing, as shown at (c), or any oblique
drawing in which the receding axis is drawn to a reduced scale, the offset
measurements parallel to the receding axis must be drawn to the same reduced scale. In this case, there is no choice of methods, since the four-center
ellipse could not be used.

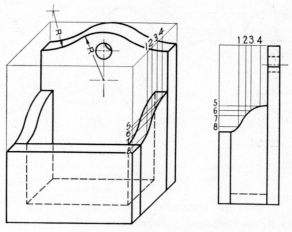

FIG. 594   Use of Offset Measurements.

A method of drawing ellipses in a cabinet drawing of a cube is shown in
Fig. 593 (d).

As shown in Fig. 594, an irregular curve may be drawn in oblique by
means of offset measurements. This figure also illustrates a case where hidden
lines are used to make the drawing clearer.

The use of offset measurements in drawing an ellipse in a plane inclined
to the plane of projection is shown in Fig. 595. At (a) a number of parallel

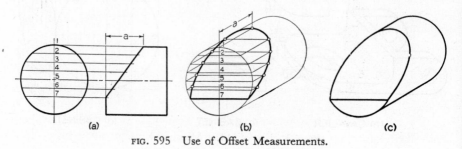

FIG. 595   Use of Offset Measurements.

lines are drawn to represent imaginary slicing planes. Each plane will cut a rectangular surface between the front end of the cylinder and the inclined surface. These rectangles are drawn in oblique, as shown at (b), and the curve is drawn through the corner points, as indicated. The final cavalier drawing is shown at (c).

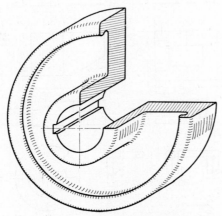

FIG. 596　　Oblique Half Section.

293. Oblique Sections. Sections are often useful in oblique drawing. They are especially useful for showing interior shapes. An *oblique half section* is shown in Fig. 596. Other examples are shown in Figs. 448 to 451 and following figures. *Oblique full sections*, in which the plane passes completely through the object, are seldom used, because they do not show enough of the exterior shapes. In general, all the sections discussed in § 276 for isometric drawing may be applied equally to oblique drawing.

294. Oblique Dimensioning. An oblique drawing may be dimensioned in a manner similar to that described in § 277 for isometric drawing, as illustrated in Fig. 597. The general principles of dimensioning, as outlined in Chapter 16, must be followed.

As shown in Fig. 597, all dimensions must lie in the planes of the object

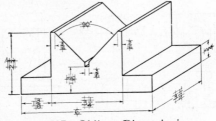

FIG. 597　　Oblique Dimensioning.

to which they apply, and must be perfectly legible. Whenever possible, the dimensions are placed outside the boundaries of the drawing, but if greater clearness would result, they are placed directly on the drawing. For many other examples of dimensioning in oblique drawings, see problems at the ends of Chapters 7, 8, and 19. See especially Figs. 934–939.

OBLIQUE PROJECTION PROBLEMS*

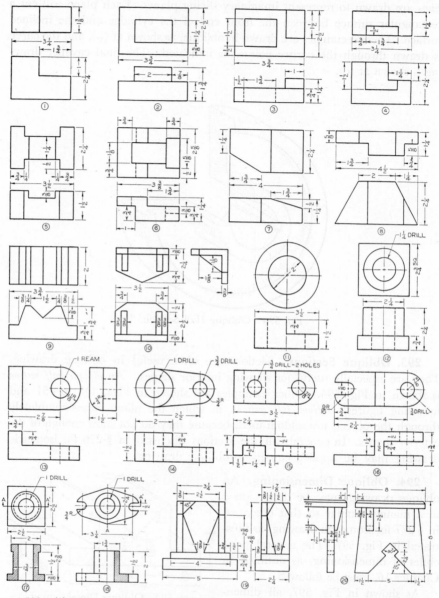

FIG. 598   (1) Make freehand oblique sketches.   (2) Make oblique drawings with instruments, using Size A or Size B sheet, as assigned.   If dimensions are required, study § 294.

* For additional problems, see Figs. 573 to 576. Oblique problems in convenient form for solution may be found in *Technical Drawing Problems*, by Giesecke, Mitchell, and Spencer, and in *Technical Drawing Problems—Series 2*, by Spencer and Grant, both designed to accompany this text, and published by The Macmillan Company.

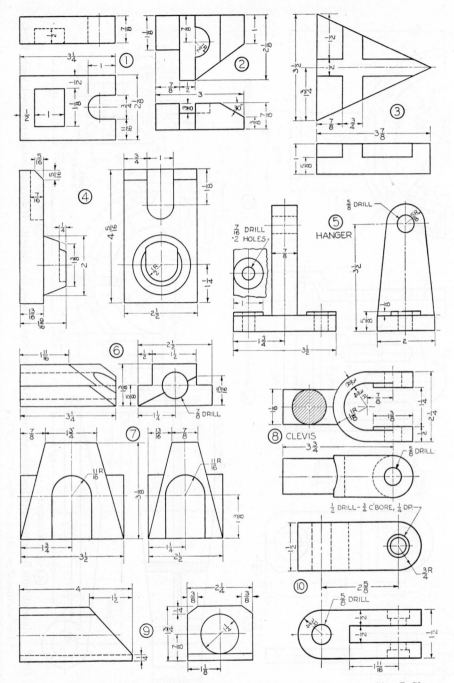

FIG. 599* Make oblique drawings with instruments, using Size A or Size B Sheet, as assigned. If dimensions are required, study § 294.

* For additional problems, see Figs. 573 to 576.

315

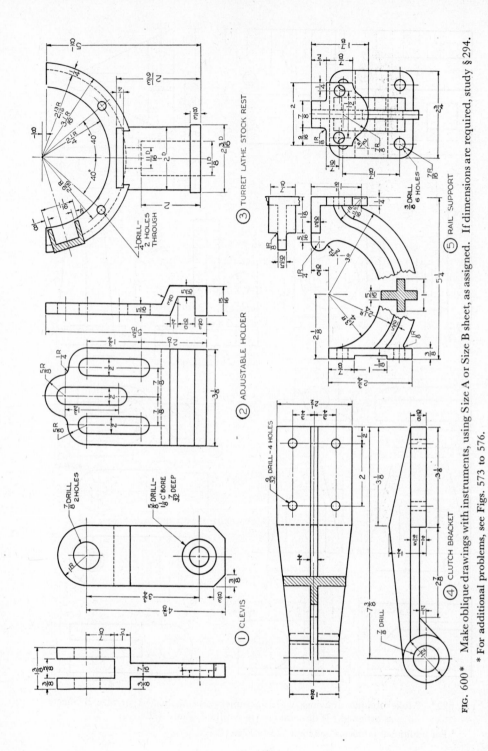

③ TURRET LATHE STOCK REST

② ADJUSTABLE HOLDER

⑤ RAIL SUPPORT

① CLEVIS

④ CLUTCH BRACKET

FIG. 600* Make oblique drawings with instruments, using Size A or Size B sheet, as assigned. If dimensions are required, study §294.

* For additional problems, see Figs. 573 to 576.

316

CHAPTER 13

Perspective

295. General Principles. *Perspective*, or *central projection*,* excels all other types of projection in the pictorial representation of objects because it more nearly approximates the results obtained by the human eye. Geometrically, an ordinary photograph is a perspective. While perspective is of major importance to the architect or illustrator, every engineer will at one time or another be concerned with the pictorial representation of objects, and should understand the basic principles.

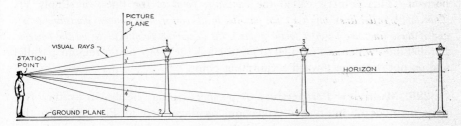

FIG. 601   Looking through the Picture Plane.

In Fig. 601, the observer is shown looking through an imaginary plane of projection, along a boulevard. This plane is called the *picture plane*, or simply *PP*. The position of the observer's eye is called the *station point*, or simply *SP*. The lines leading from *SP* to the various points in the scene are called *projectors*, *lines of sight*, or (more commonly, in perspective) *visual rays*. The points where the visual rays pierce *PP* are the *perspectives* of the respective points. Collectively, these piercing points form the perspective of the object or the

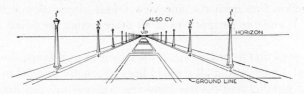

* See § 176.   FIG. 602   A Perspective.

317

scene as viewed by the observer. The perspective as obtained in Fig. 601 is shown in Fig. 602.

In Fig. 601, the perspective of lamp post *1,2* is shown at *1',2'* on the picture plane; the perspective of lamp post *3,4* is shown at *3',4'*, and so on. Each succeeding lamp post, as it attains greater distance from the observer, will be projected smaller than the one preceding. A lamp post at an infinite distance from the observer would appear as a point on the picture plane. A lamp post in front of the picture plane would be projected longer than it is, and a lamp post in the picture plane would be projected in its true length.

In Fig. 601, the line representing the *horizon* is the edge view of the *horizon plane*, which is parallel to the ground and passes through *SP*. In Fig. 602, the *horizon* is the line of intersection of this plane with the picture plane, and represents the eye level of the observer.

In Fig. 601, the *ground plane* is the edge view of the ground upon which the object usually rests. In Fig. 602, the *ground line* is the intersection of the ground plane with the picture plane.

In Fig. 602, it will be seen that parallel lines which are not parallel to the picture plane, such as the curb lines, sidewalk lines, and lines through the tops and bottoms of the lamp posts, all converge toward a single point on the horizon. This point is called the *vanishing point* of the lines, or simply *VP*. *Thus, all parallel lines which are not parallel to PP vanish at a common vanishing point, and if these lines are parallel to the ground, the vanishing point will be on the horizon.* Parallel lines which are parallel to *PP* (such as the lamp posts) remain parallel and do not converge toward a vanishing point.

296. Multiview Perspective. A perspective may be drawn by the ordinary methods of multiview projection, as illustrated in Fig. 603. In this example, four cubes are placed with faces parallel to the picture plane, and the observer is stationed in front of the picture plane. The top and right side views of the cubes, the picture plane, the station point, and the visual rays are shown. In the front view, the picture plane coincides with the plane of the paper, and the perspectives are drawn upon it (the regular orthographic front view of the cubes is omitted).

In Fig. 603, only the visual rays to the upper right cube are shown. To obtain the perspective of point *1*, a visual ray is drawn in the top view from SP_T to point *1* on the top view of the cube. From the intersection *1* of this ray with the picture plane, a projection line is drawn downward till it meets a similar projection line from the side view. This intersection is the perspective of point *1*, and the perspectives of all other points are found in a similar manner.

It will be seen that front face *1,2,3,4* is shown in true shape, but is smaller than true size. Observe that all parallel lines which are parallel to the picture plane remain parallel and do not converge, whereas parallel lines *1–5, 2–6, 3–7,* and *4–8,* which are not parallel to the picture plane, converge toward a common vanishing point. Since these lines are horizontal lines, this vanishing point is on the horizon. Notice that the horizon line is on a level with the eye level *SP* of the side view.

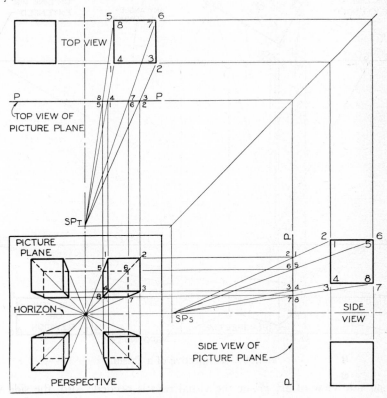

FIG. 603   Multiview Method of Drawing a Perspective.

The perspective of any object may be drawn in this way, but the method is cumbersome if the object is not placed parallel to the picture plane, in which case the given views would have to be shown revolved.

297. The Setup for a Simple Perspective. The construction of a perspective of a simple prism is shown in Fig. 604. The upper portion of the drawing, as was the case in Fig. 603, shows the top view of the station point, of the picture plane, and of the object. In this case, however, the object has been revolved to a more suitable position so that its view from *SP* will show three surfaces and have more pictorial effectiveness. *PP* is the top view of the picture plane, *SP* is the top view of the station point, and *1,2,3,4,* is the top view of the object. The lines *SP–1*, *SP–2*, *SP–3*, and *SP–4* are the top views of the visual rays from *SP* to the corners of the object.

In the side view position, a departure from Fig. 603 is made. In the method of Fig. 604, the side view is used only to provide elevation measurements,

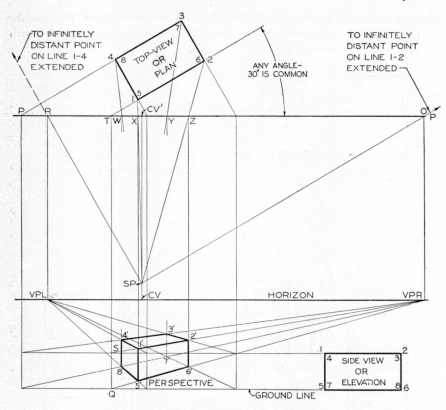

FIG. 604   Perspective of a Prism.

and no side view of *SP*, *PP*, or the visual rays is needed. Also, the side view need not be revolved in conformity with the revolved top view. If elevation measurements are known, the side view of the object is not needed.

The perspective itself is drawn in the place where the front view of the object would be drawn in multiview projection, the picture plane being considered as the plane of the paper upon which the drawing is made. The ground line is the edge view of the ground plane or the intersection of the ground plane with the picture plane.

The *horizon* is a horizontal line in the picture plane which is the intersection of the horizon plane with the picture plane. Since the horizon plane passes through the observer's eye or *SP*, the horizon is drawn at the level of the eye: that is, at the distance above the ground line representing the altitude of the eye above the ground.

The *center of vision*, *CV*, is the orthographic projection (or front view) of *SP* on the picture plane, and since the horizon is at eye level, *CV* will always be on the horizon.* In Fig. 604, the top view of *CV* is *CV'*, found by dropping

* Except in three-point perspective (§ 305).

a perpendicular from SP to PP; the front view CV is found by projecting downward from CV' to the horizon.

298. To Draw an Angular Perspective. Since objects are defined principally by edges which are straight lines, the drawing of a perspective resolves itself into drawing the *perspective of a line*. If a draftsman can draw the perspective of a line, he can draw the perspective of any object, no matter how complex.

To draw the perspective of any horizontal straight line not parallel to PP, for example, the line 1,2 in Fig. 604, proceed as follows:

Step 1. *Find the piercing point in PP of the line.* In the top view, extend line 1,2 until it pierces PP at T; then project downward to the level of line 1,2 projected horizontally from the side view. The point S is the piercing point of the line.

Step 2. *Find the vanishing point of the line.* The vanishing point of a line is the piercing point in PP of a line drawn through SP parallel to that line. Hence, the vanishing point VPR of the line 1,2 is found by drawing a line from SP parallel to that line and finding the top view of its piercing point O, and then projecting downward to the horizon. The line $SP-O$ is actually a visual ray drawn toward the infinitely distant point on line 1,2 of the object, extended, and the vanishing point is the intersection of this visual ray with the picture plane. The vanishing point is, then, the perspective of the infinitely distant point on the line extended.

Step 3. Join the piercing point and the vanishing point with a straight line. The line $S-VPR$ is the line joining these two points, and it is the perspective of a line of infinite length containing the required perspective of the line 1,2.

Step 4. *Locate the end points of the perspective of the line.* The end points 1' and 2' can be found by the *method of intercepts*, or by simply drawing the perspectives of the remaining horizontal edges of the prism. In practice, it is quite helpful to use both methods as a check on the accuracy of the construction. To locate the end points by means of intercepts, draw visual rays from SP to the points 1 and 2 in the top view. The top view of the resulting intercept is shown at XZ. Since the perspectives of points 1 and 2 are on the line $S-VPR$, project downward from intercept XZ to locate the points 1' and 2'.

After the perspectives of the horizontal edges have been drawn, the vertical edges can be drawn, as shown, to complete the perspective of the prism. It should be observed that vertical heights can be measured only in the picture plane. If the front vertical edge 1,5 of the object is actually in PP—that is, if the object is situated with the front edge in PP—the vertical height can be set off directly full size. If the vertical edge is behind PP, a plane of the object, such as surface 1,2,5,6, can be extended forward until it intersects PP in line TQ. The line TQ is called a *measuring line*, and the true height SQ of line 1,5 can be set off with a scale or projected from the side view as shown.

If a large drawing board is not available, one vanishing point, such as *VPR* in Fig. 604, may fall off the board. By using one vanishing point *VPL* and the method of intercepts, vanishing point *VPR* may be eliminated. However, a valuable means of checking the accuracy of the construction will be lost.

299. Position of the Station Point. The center line of the cone of visual rays should be directed toward the approximate center or center of interest of the object. In a perspective of the type shown in Fig. 604,* the location of *SP* in the plan view should be slightly to the left and not directly in front of

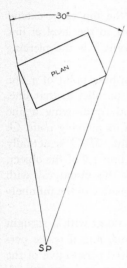

FIG. 605   Distance from *SP* to Object.

the center of the object and at such a distance from it that the object can be viewed at a glance without turning the head. This is accomplished if a cone of rays with its vertex at *SP* and a vertical angle of about 30° entirely encloses the object, as shown in Fig. 605.

In the perspective portion of Fig. 604, *SP* does not appear, as *SP* is in front of the picture plane. However, the orthographic projection *CV* of *SP* in the picture plane does show the height of *SP* with respect to the ground plane. Since the horizon is at eye level, it also shows the altitude of *SP*. Therefore in the perspective portion of the drawing, the horizon is drawn a distance above the ground line at which it is desired to assume *SP*. For most small and medium-size objects, such as machine parts or furniture, *SP* is best assumed slightly above the top of the object. Large objects, such as buildings, are usually viewed from a station point about the altitude of the eye above the ground, or about 5′ 6″.

In viewing a perspective drawing, the observer should place his eye at or near the *SP* used in the drawing.

300. Location of the Picture Plane. In general, the picture plane is placed in front of the object, as in Fig. 606 (b) and (c). However, it may be placed behind the object, as shown at (a), and it may even be placed behind *SP*, as shown at (d), in which event the perspective is reversed as is the case with a camera. Of course, the usual position of the picture plane is between *SP* and the object. It should be observed that the perspectives in Fig. 606 differ in size but not in proportion.

As shown in Fig. 606 (b) and (c), the farther the picture plane is from the object, the smaller the perspective will be. This distance may be assumed, therefore, with the thought of controlling the scale of the perspective. In

* Two-point perspective (§ 304).

practice, however, the object is usually assumed with the front corner in the
picture plane to facilitate vertical meaurements. See Fig. 610.

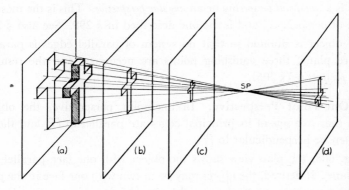

FIG. 606   Location of *PP*.

301. Position of the Object with Respect to the Horizon. To compare
the elevation of the object with that of the horizon is equivalent to referring
it to the level of the eye or *SP*, because the horizon is on a level with the eye.*

The differences in effects produced by placing the object on,
above, or below the horizon
are shown in Fig. 607.

If the object is placed above
the horizon, it is above the
level of the eye, or above *SP*,
and is seen from below. Likewise, if the object is below the
horizon, it is seen from above.

**302. The Three Types of
Perspectives.** Perspectives are
classified according to the
number of vanishing points required, which in turn depends
upon the position of the object
with respect to the picture plane.

If the object is situated
with one face parallel to the
plane of projection, only one
vanishing point is required, and
the result is a *one-point perspective*
or *parallel perspective* (§ 303).

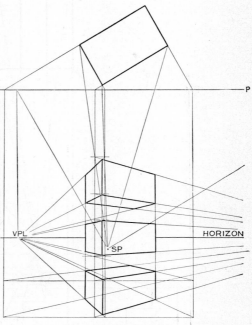

FIG. 607   Position of Object Relative
to the Horizon.

* Except in three-point perspective (§ 305).

If the object is situated at an angle with the picture plane but with vertical edges parallel to the picture plane, two vanishing points are required, and the result is a *two-point perspective* or an *angular perspective*. This is the most common type of perspective, and is the one described in § 298. See also § 304.

If the object is situated so that no system of parallel edges is parallel to the picture plane, three vanishing points are necessary, and the result is a *three-point perspective* (§ 305).

303. One-Point Perspective. In one-point perspective, the object is placed so that two sets of its principal edges are parallel to *PP*, and the third set will then be perpendicular to *PP*.

In Fig. 608, the plan view shows the object with one face parallel to the picture plane. If desired, the object may be drawn with one face in the picture plane. The piercing points of the eight edges of the object perpendicular to *PP* are found by extending them to *PP* and then projecting downward to the level of the lines as projected across from the orthographic view.

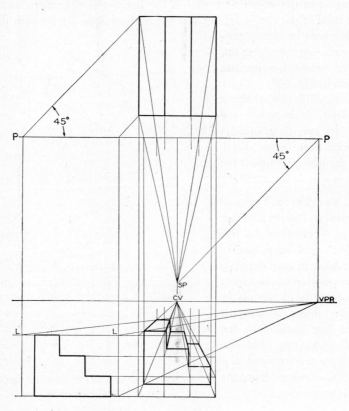

FIG. 608   One-Point Perspective.

To find the *VP* of these lines, a visual ray is drawn from *SP* parallel to them and it is found that *the vanishing point of all lines perpendicular to PP is in CV*.

By connecting the eight piercing points with the vanishing point *CV* the indefinite perspectives of the eight edges are obtained.

To cut off on these lines the definite lengths of the edges of the object, horizontal lines are drawn from the ends of one of the edges in the top view and at any desired angle with *PP*, 45° for example, as shown. The piercing points, and the vanishing point *VPR* of these lines are found and the perspectives of the lines drawn. The intersections of these with the perspectives of the corresponding edges of the object determine the lengths of the receding edges. The perspective of the object may then be completed as shown.

One of the most common uses of parallel perspective is in the representation of interiors of buildings, as illustrated in Fig. 609.

FIG. 609   One-Point Perspective of an Interior.

304. Two-Point Perspective. In two-point perspective, the object is placed so that one set of parallel edges is vertical and has no vanishing point, while the two other sets each have vanishing points. This is the most common type and is the method discussed in § 298. It is suitable especially for representing buildings in architectural drawing or large structures in civil engineering such as dams or bridges.

The perspective of a small building is shown in Fig. 610. It is common practice (1) to assume a vertical edge of an object in *PP* so that direct measurements may be made on it, and (2) to place the object so that its faces make unequal angles with *PP*; for example, one angle may be 30° and the other 60°.

In practical work, complete drawings are usually available, and the plan and elevation may be thumbtacked in position, used in the construction of the perspective, and later removed.

Since the front corner *AB* (Fig. 610) lies in *PP*, its perspective *A'B'* may be

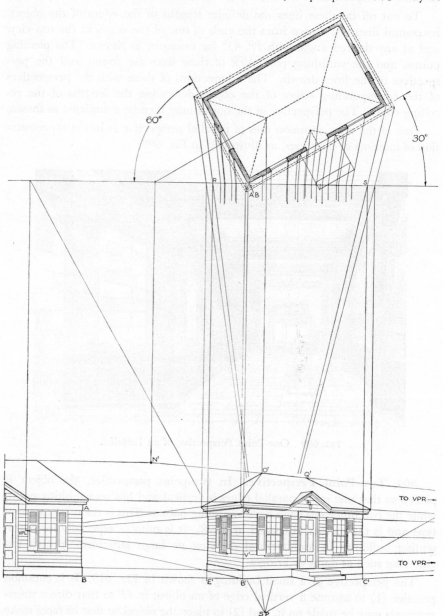

FIG. 610   Perspective of a Small Building.

drawn full size by projecting downward from the plan and across from the elevation. The lengths of the receding lines from this corner are cut off by vertical lines SC' and RE' drawn from the intersections S and R, respectively, of the visual rays to these points of the object. The perspectives of the tops of the windows and the door are determined by the lines $A'–VPR$ and $A'–VPL$, and their widths and lateral spacings are determined by projecting downward from the intersections with PP of the respective visual rays. The bottom lines of the windows are determined by the lines $V'–VPR$ and $V'–VPL$.

The perspective of the line containing the ridge of the roof is found by joining N', the point where the ridge line pierces the picture plane, and VPR. The ridge ends O' and Q' are found by projecting downward from the sections of the visual rays with PP, or by drawing the perspectives of any two lines intersecting at the points. The perspective of the roof is completed by joining the points O' and Q' to the ends of the eaves.

305. Three-Point Perspective. In drawing a perspective of a building, it is customary to make a two-point perspective (Fig. 610) by choosing PP parallel to the vertical edges of the building and inclined to the sides of the building, and selecting SP, as nearly as practicable, opposite the center of the building so that the person viewing the perspective will naturally place his eye at or near SP, the only point from which the perspective presents a correct appearance.

If the perspective is to represent a building as it would appear from a point above the building—from an airplane, for example—a two-point perspective may be drawn. However, such a drawing will not present a natural appearance if viewed from a point directly in front of the picture, as would generally be the case.

To secure a natural appearance, it is necessary to select PP perpendicular to the visual ray of a point near the center of the building so that CV will be at or near the center of the perspective. In this case, PP will be inclined to the three sets of principal edges, and there will be three principal vanishing points. The resulting drawing is a *three-point perspective*. It may be constructed as follows:

Let the building be a tall structure, given by its plan (top view) and elevation (front view) as shown in Fig. 611 (a). Select SP (shown in top view and front view) at any desired distance in front of the building and at any desired elevation above that of the roof, and then draw the principal line of sight or visual ray, $SP–C$, from SP toward a point approximately in the center of the building. Draw PP perpendicular to the principal visual ray and at any convenient location with reference to the building. Pass a horizontal plane through SP and find its intersection with PP; the line of intersection XX is the horizon of the perspective. Draw visual rays from SP parallel to the three principal edges of the building and determine the three principal vanishing points VPL,

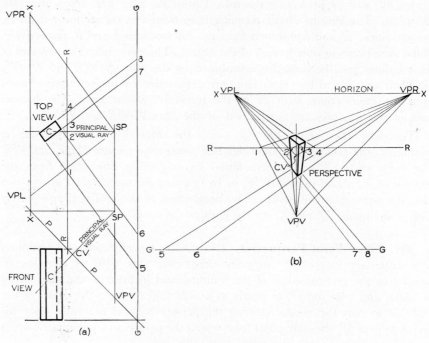

FIG. 611   Three-Point Perspective.

VPR, and VPV. Pass horizontal planes containing the roof of the building and the base of the building and find their intersections RR and GG with PP.

Draw the three-point perspective shown in Fig. 611 (b), by transferring the station point SP (or CV), the horizon XX, and the three principal vanishing points VPL, VPR, and VPV from (a) to (b), as shown. The distance CV–VPV is shown in its true size in the elevation at (a). Draw lines from CV and from VPV to VPL and VPR, as shown. As a check upon the accuracy of the drawing, CV–VPL must be perpendicular to VPV–VPR, and CV–VPR to VPV–VPL. Transfer the lines RR and GG to the new position, as shown. Produce the horizontal roof lines in the top view to find their piercing points 1, 2, 3, and 4. Transfer these points to the perspective, along the line RR, and draw the perspectives of the horizontal roof lines as shown.

Find the perspectives of the horizontal base lines in the same manner. Draw the vertical edges of the building by connecting corresponding corners of the roof and the base. As a check upon the accuracy of the drawing, these lines must intersect at VPV.

To secure details of the elevations, windows, doors, and so on, pass horizontal planes through them, and proceed as for the roof and base lines of the building.

306. The Perspective Linead and Template.

(1) *Perspective Linead.*—The *perspective linead* (Fig. 612, b) consists of three straight-edged blades which can be clamped to each other at any desired angles. This instrument is convenient in drawing lines toward a vanishing point outside the limits of the drawing.

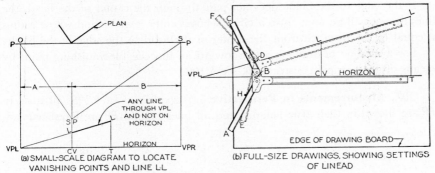

(a) SMALL-SCALE DIAGRAM TO LOCATE
VANISHING POINTS AND LINE LL

(b) FULL-SIZE DRAWINGS, SHOWING SETTINGS
OF LINEAD

FIG. 612   Perspective Linead.

Before starting such a drawing, a small-scale diagram should be made, as indicated in Fig. 612 (a), in which the relative positions of the object, *PP*, and *SP* are assumed, and the distances of the vanishing points from *CV* determined. Then draw any line *LL* through a vanishing point as shown. Then, on the full-size drawing, assume *CV* and locate *LL*, as shown at (b).

To set the linead, clamp the blades in any convenient position; set the edge of the long blade along the horizon and draw the lines *BA* and *BC* along the short blades. Then set the edge of the long blade along the line *LL* and draw the lines *DE* and *DF* to intersect the lines first drawn at points *G* and *H*. Set pins at these points. If the linead is moved so that the short blades touch the pins, all lines drawn along the edge of the long blade will pass through *VPL*. This method is based on the principle that *an angle inscribed in a circle is measured by half the arc it subtends.*

(2) *Templates.*—Fig. 613. A *template* of thin wood or heavy cardboard

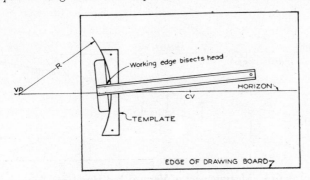

FIG. 613   Perspective Template.

having a circular arc may be used instead of a perspective linead. If the template is attached to the drawing board so that the inaccessible *VP* is at the center of the circular arc, and the T-square is moved so that the head remains in contact with the template, lines drawn along the edge of the blade will, if extended, pass through the inaccessible *VP*.

If the edge of the blade does not pass through the center of the head, the lines drawn will be tangent to a circle whose center is at *VP* and whose radius is equal to the distance from the center of the head to the edge of the blade.

For a method of drawing a line toward an inaccessible vanishing point by means of geometrical construction, see § 100.

307. Measurements in Perspective. As explained in § 295, all lines in *PP* are shown in their true lengths, and all lines behind *PP* are foreshortened.

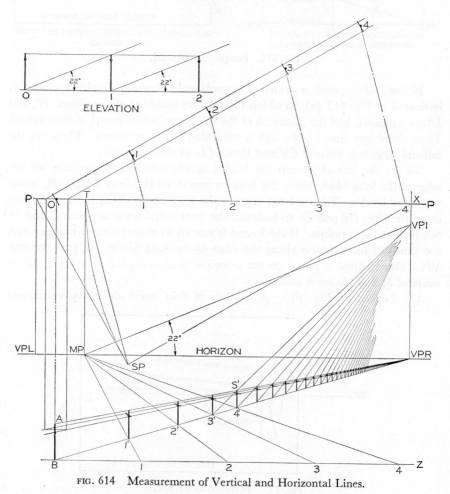

FIG. 614   Measurement of Vertical and Horizontal Lines.

Let it be required to draw the perspective of a line of telephone poles (Fig. 614). Let *OB* be the line of intersection of *PP* with the vertical plane containing the poles. In this line, the height *AB* of a pole is set off directly to the scale desired and the heights of the perspectives of all poles are determined by drawing lines from *A* and *B* to *VPR*.

To locate the bottoms of the poles along the line *B–VPR*, set off along *PP* the distances *O–1*, *1–2*, *2–3*, etc., equal to the distance from pole to pole; draw the lines *1–1*, *2–2*, *3–3*, etc., forming a series of isosceles triangles *O–1–1*, *O–2–2*, *O–3–3*, etc. The lines *1–1*, *2–2*, *3–3*, etc., are parallel to each other, and therefore have a common vanishing point *MP*, which is found in the usual manner by drawing from *SP* a line *SP–T* parallel to the lines *1–1*, *2–2*, *3–3*, etc., and finding its piercing point *MP* (*measuring point*) in *PP*.

Since the line *SP–X* is parallel to the line of poles, *1–2–3*, etc., the triangle *SP–X–T* is an isosceles triangle, and *T* is the top view of *MP*. The point *T* may be determined by setting off the distance *X–T* equal to *SP–X* or simply by drawing the arc *SP–T* with center at *X* and radius *SP–X*.

Having the measuring point *MP*, find the piercing points in *PP* of the lines *1–1*, *2–2*, *3–3*, etc., and draw their perspectives as shown. Since these lines are horizontal lines, their piercing points fall in a horizontal line *BZ* in *PP*. Therefore, along the line *BZ*, the true distances between the poles are set off. The line *BZ*, in *PP*, along which the measurements are set off, is a *measuring line*. The intersections *1'*, *2'*, *3'*, etc., of the perspectives of the lines *1–1*, *2–2*, *3–3*, etc., with the line *B–VPR* determine the spacing of the poles. It will be seen that only a few measurements may be made along the measuring line *BZ*, within the limits of the drawing. For additional measurements, the *diagonal method* of spacing may be employed, as shown. Since all diagonals from the bottom of one pole to the top of the succeeding pole are parallel, they have a common vanishing point *VPI*, which may be found as explained in § 308. Evidently, the diagonal method may be used exclusively in the solution of this problem.

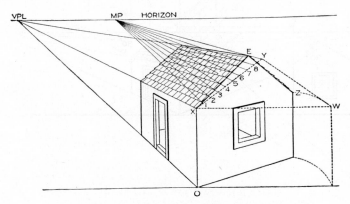

FIG. 615   Measurement of Inclined Lines.

The method of direct measurements may be applied also to lines inclined to PP and to the ground plane, as illustrated in Fig. 615 for the line XE, which pierces PP at X.

If the end of the house in Fig. 615 is conceived to be revolved about a

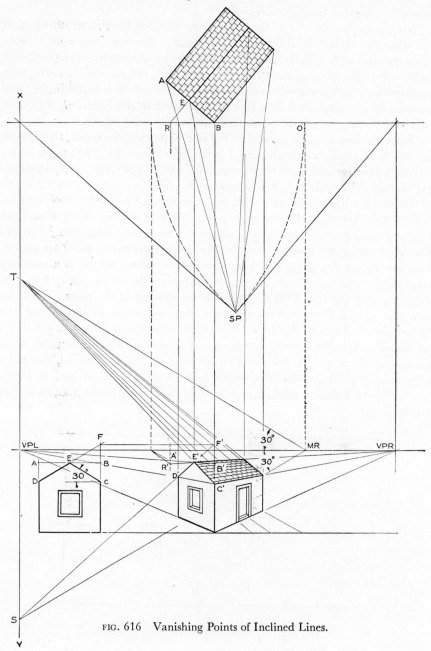

FIG. 616   Vanishing Points of Inclined Lines.

vertical axis *XO* into *PP*, the line *XE* would be shown in its true length and inclination at *XY*. This line may be used as the measuring line for *XE*; it remains only to find the corresponding measuring point *MP*. The line *YE* is the horizontal base of an isosceles triangle having its vertex at *X*, and a line drawn parallel to it through *SP* will determine *MP*, as described for Fig. 614.

308. Vanishing Points of Inclined Lines. The vanishing point of an inclined line is determined, as for all other lines, by finding the piercing point in *PP* of a line drawn from *SP* parallel to the given line.

In Fig. 616 is shown the perspective of a small building. The vanishing point of the inclined roof line *C'E'* can be determined as follows: If a plane is conceived to be passed through the station point and parallel to the end of the house, it would intersect *PP* in the line *XY*, through *VPL*, and perpendicular to the horizon. Since the line drawn from *SP* parallel to *C'E'* is in the plane *SP–X–Y*, it will pierce *PP* at some point *T* in *XY*. To find the point *T*, conceive the plane *SP–X–Y* revolved about the line *XY* as an axis into *PP*. The point *SP* will then fall into the horizon at a point shown by *O* in the top view, and by *MR* in the front view. From the point *MR* draw the revolved position of the line *SP–T* (now *MR–T*) making an angle of 30° with the horizon and thus determining the point *T*, which is the vanishing point of the line *C'E'* and of all lines parallel to that line. The vanishing point *S* of the line *D'E'* is evidently

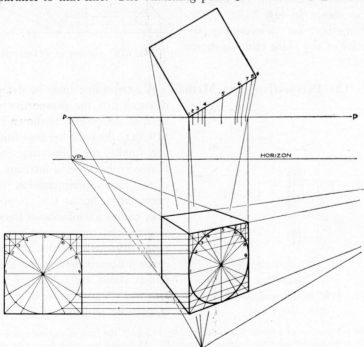

FIG. 617   Circles in Perspective.

in the line *XY* because *D'E'* is in the same vertical plane as the line *C'E'*. The vanishing point *S* is as far below the horizon as *T* is above the horizon, because the line *E'D'* slopes downward at the same angle at which the line *C'E'* slopes upward.

The perspectives of inclined lines can generally be found without finding the vanishing points, by finding the perspectives of the end points, and joining them. *The perspective of any point may be determined by finding the perspectives of any two lines intersecting at the point.* Obviously, it would be best to use horizontal lines, parallel, respectively, to systems of lines whose vanishing points are already available.

For example, in Fig. 616, to find the perspective of the inclined line *EC*, the point *E'* is the intersection of the horizontal lines *R'–VPR* and *B'–VBL*. The point *C'* is already established, since it is in *PP*; but if it were not in *PP* it could be easily found in the same manner. The perspective of the inclined line *EC* is, therefore, the line joining the perspectives of the end points, *E'* and *C'*.

309. Curves and Circles in Perspective. If a circle is parallel to *PP*, its perspective is a circle. If the circle is inclined to *PP*, its perspective may be any one of the conic sections,* but usually an ellipse. The ellipse may be constructed by the method of § 116, or by means of lines intersecting the circle, as shown in Fig. 617. A convenient method for determining the perspective of any plane curve is shown in Fig. 618.

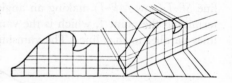

FIG. 618   Curves in Perspective.

310. The Perspective Plan Method. A perspective may be drawn by drawing first the perspective of the plan of the object, as shown in Fig. 619 (a), then the vertical lines (b), and finally, the connecting lines (c). However, in drawing intricate structures, the superimposition of the perspective upon the perspective plan causes a confusion of lines. For this reason, the perspective of the plan from which the location of vertical lines is determined is drawn either above or below its normal location. A suggestion of the range of possible positions of the perspec-

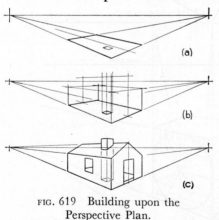

(a)

(b)

(c)

FIG. 619   Building upon the Perspective Plan.

---

* The perspective of a circle is a conic section, in which the base of the cone is the given circle, the vertex is *SP*, and the cutting plane is *PP*. However, since *SP* should be assumed in such position that the center line of the cone of rays is approximately perpendicular to *PP*, the perspective will generally be an ellipse.

tive plan is given in Fig. 620. The use of the perspective plan below the perspective is illustrated in Fig. 621.

The chief advantages of the perspective plan method over the ordinary plan method are that the vertical lines of the perspective can be spaced more accurately and that a considerable portion of the construction can be made above or below the principal drawing, so that a confusion of lines on the required perspective is avoided.

When the perspective plan method is used, the ordinary plan can be dispensed with and measuring points used to determine distances along horizontal lines.

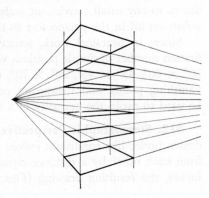

FIG. 620   Positions of Perspective Plan.

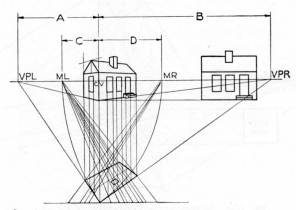

FIG. 621   Perspective Plan Method.

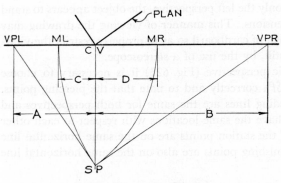

FIG. 622   Perspective Diagram.

311. Perspective Diagram. The spacing of vanishing points and measuring points may be determined graphically, or may be calculated. In Fig. 622 is shown a simple diagram of the plan layout showing the position of the object, the picture plane, the station point, and the construction for

finding the vanishing points and measuring points for the problem in Fig. 621.
As shown, the complete plan need not be drawn. The diagram should be
drawn to any small convenient scale, and the vanishing points and measuring
points set off in the perspective to the scale used.

Since, in practical work, structures are usually considered in one of a
limited number of simple positions with reference to the picture plane, such as
30° × 60°, 45° × 45°, 20° × 70°, etc., a table of measurements for locating
vanishing points and measuring points may be easily prepared, and may
be used to avoid the necessity of a special construction for each drawing.

312. Stereographic Perspective. When two perspectives of an object are
drawn under like conditions except that the two station points are separated
from each other by a distance equal to that between human eyes, about $2\frac{3}{4}$
inches, the resulting drawing (Figs. 623 and 624) is a stereographic perspec-

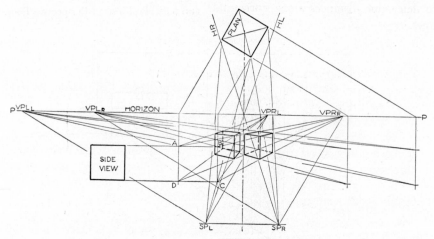

FIG. 623   Stereographic Perspective of a Cube.

tive. When such a drawing is viewed so that the right eye sees only the right
perspective and the left eye only the left perspective, the object appears to stand
out clearly in its three dimensions. This manner of viewing the drawing may
be attained by holding a sheet of cardboard so as to properly restrict the views
of the two eyes, or, better still, by the use of a stereoscope.*

To draw a stereographic perspective (Fig. 623) it is necessary to choose
the station points SP_L and SP_R correctly and to note that the piercing points,
A, B, C, and D of the receding lines are the same for both perspectives and
that their vanishing points have the same locations with respect to each other
as the station points; i.e., if the station points are on the same horizontal line
and $2\frac{3}{4}$ inches apart, the vanishing points are also on the same horizontal line
and $2\frac{3}{4}$ inches apart.

* Keystone View Co., Meadville, Penna.

It is necessary to place the object at a sufficient distance behind *PP* so that the two perspectives will not overlap. This is accomplished if the object is placed within the dihedral angle formed by the planes whose top views are shown by *HR* and *HL* in Fig. 623.

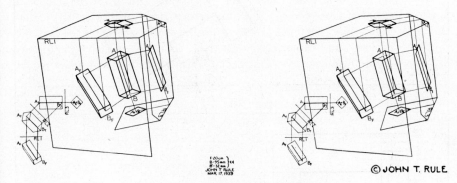

FIG. 624　Stereographic Perspective.*

If the two perspectives overlap, a clear picture may be obtained by drawing one perspective with red lines and the other with green lines, and viewing the drawing through glasses having one green and one red lens.

The construction shown in Fig. 623 is similar to that shown in Fig. 604 except that the lines representing the picture plane and the horizon coincide.

If the resulting perspectives are to be viewed through a stereoscope, they must be redrawn to a size to fit the stereoscope and placed so that the distance between centers is practically equal to the distance between the centers of the lenses of the stereoscope.

* Courtesy of Prof. John T. Rule, Mass. Institute of Technology. For a more detailed explanation of stereographic perspective, see *Descriptive Geometry*, by Watts and Rule (Prentice-Hall, 1946).

PERSPECTIVE PROBLEMS

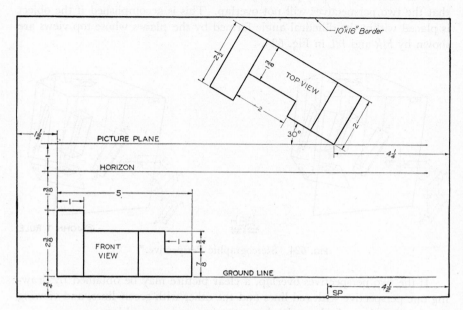

FIG. 625 Draw views and perspective. Omit dimensions. Layout B3.

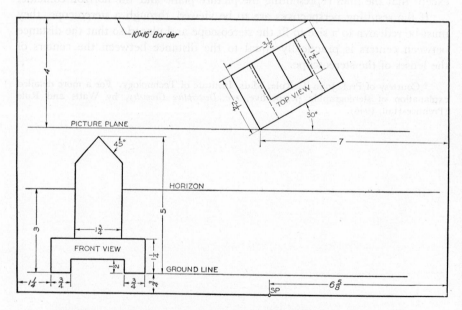

FIG. 626 Draw views and perspective. Omit dimensions. Layout B3.

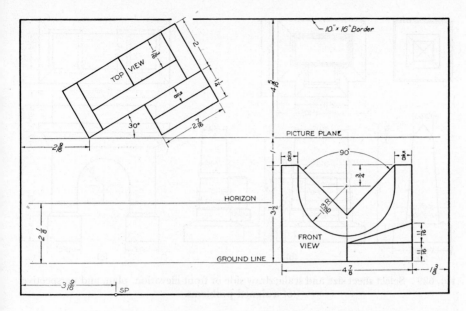

FIG. 627 Draw views and perspective. Omit dimensions. Layout B3.

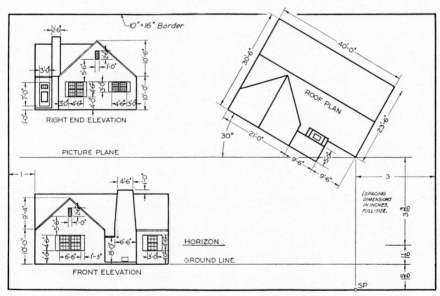

Courtesy of Professors F. R. Hughes, J. N. Eckle, and D. F. Grant ,Yale Universit

FIG. 628 Draw front elevation, plan, and perspective. Omit dimensions.
Scale: $\frac{1}{8}'' = 1'-0''$. Layout B3.

339

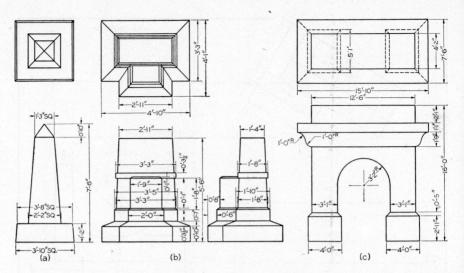

FIG. 629   Select sheet size and scale; draw side or front elevation, plan, and perspective of assigned problems.

CHAPTER 14

Technical Sketching

313. Importance of Technical Sketching. The importance to the engineer of freehand sketching cannot be overestimated. To the person who possesses a complete knowledge of drawing as a language, the ability to execute quick, accurate, and clear sketches constitutes a valuable means of expression. There is an old saying that "a picture is worth a thousand words."

Most original mechanical ideas find their first expression through the medium of a freehand sketch (§ 462). It is a valuable means of amplifying and clarifying, as well as recording, verbal explanations. Executives resort to it daily to explain their ideas to subordinates. Engineers usually prepare their designs and turn them over to their detailers or draftsmen in this convenient form. Information concerning changes in design, or covering replacement of broken parts or lost drawings, is usually conveyed through sketches. Many engineers consider the ability to render serviceable sketches of even greater value to them than skill in mechanical drawing. The draftsman will find daily use for this valuable means of formulating, expressing, and recording ideas in his work.

The degree of perfection required in a given sketch depends upon its use. Sketches which are hurriedly made to supplement oral description may be rough and incomplete. On the other hand, if a sketch is the medium of conveying important and precise information to engineers or to workers, it should be executed as carefully as possible under the circumstances.

314. Sketching Materials. One of the advantages of freehand sketching is that it requires only pencil, paper, and eraser—items which anyone has for ready use.

When sketches are made in the field, where an accurate record is required, a small notebook is frequently used. Oftentimes clip boards holding manila or bond paper are used.

Cross-section paper is helpful to the person who cannot sketch reasonably well without guide lines. This paper is available in rolls, sheets, and in tablet form. Ordinarily, the ruled lines form squares of various sizes. For isometric sketching, a specially-ruled paper is available. Cross-section paper is of real

341

practical value in sketching to scale, as values can be assigned to squares, and the squares counted to secure proportional distances, as illustrated in Fig. 630. Examples of sketching on cross-section paper are shown in Fig. 293.

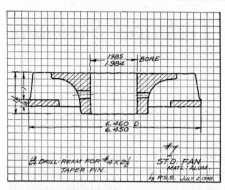

An ideal paper for use in free-hand sketching is "ledger paper," a smooth white paper which may be procured at low cost from a stationer or printing establishment.

Soft pencils, such as an HB, or F, should be used for freehand sketching. For carefully made sketches, two erasers are desirable, an art-gum and an ordinary soft pencil eraser (§ 9).

FIG. 630   Sketch on Cross-Section Paper.

315. Types of Sketches. Technical sketches are made of three-dimensional objects, and therefore the form of the sketch conforms approximately to one of the standard types of projection. There are four general types of projection, as shown in Fig. 631. In making a sketch, the draftsman must be familiar with the methods of mechanical projection discussed in previous chapters, and he should keep in mind the rules of projection in the particular type being used.

In a multiview sketch, as shown in Fig. 631 (a), the views must be drawn in approximately correct proportion, and should be arranged as shown in

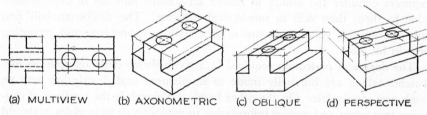

(a) MULTIVIEW   (b) AXONOMETRIC   (c) OBLIQUE   (d) PERSPECTIVE

FIG. 631   Types of Projection.

Chapter 7. In an axonometric sketch, the rules of axonometric projection, discussed in Chapter 11, must be kept in mind. If the sketch is an isometric, as in Fig. 631 (b), the receding lines should slope upward at an angle of about 30° with horizontal, and should be drawn approximately full length. In an oblique sketch, as shown in Fig. 631 (c), the receding lines are drawn at any convenient angle, and the sketch in general conforms to the rules of oblique projection, as discussed in Chapter 12. In a perspective sketch, as in Fig. 631 (d), the receding lines slope toward vanishing points which are simply estimated by eye, and the sketch in general conforms to the rules of perspective, as discussed in Chapter 13.

316. Scale. *Sketches are not usually made to any scale.* Objects should be sketched in their true proportions as accurately as it is possible for the eye to estimate. *Distances should not be set off with a scale or ruler on a freehand sketch.* The size of the sketch is purely optional, depending upon the shape of the object and the requirements of the sketch.

In sketching from an existing object, reasonably accurate estimates of relative sizes may be made as shown in Fig. 632. If this method is used, the sketcher

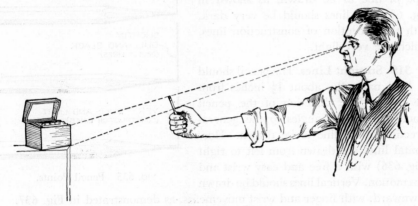

FIG. 632   Estimating Distances.

must remain at a practically constant distance from the object and he should hold the pencil at arm's length, as shown in the figure.

317. Quality of Lines. The chief difference between a mechanical drawing and a freehand sketch lies in the *technique* of the lines. In this respect, they differ from each other materially. A good freehand line, unlike a mechanical line, is not rigidly straight, nor is it uniform in strength.

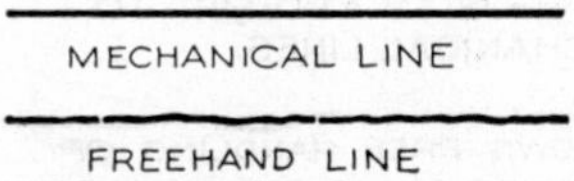

—————— MECHANICAL LINE ——————

~~~~~~ FREEHAND LINE ~~~~~~

FIG. 633   Comparison of Lines.

The effectiveness of a mechanical line lies in its *exacting uniformity;* the attractiveness of a freehand line lies in its *freedom and variety.* See Fig. 633.

A freehand interpretation of the conventional lines used in technical drawing (Fig. 85) is shown in Fig. 634. The widths of the lines are determined more by the size of the pencil point than by the pressure on the pencil.

Freehand lines, like mechanical lines, should have "color," or *blackness*, and should contrast sharply in size. See Figs. 89 and 90.

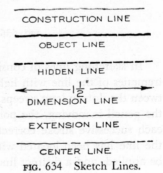

CONSTRUCTION LINE

OBJECT LINE

HIDDEN LINE

$1\frac{1}{2}''$
DIMENSION LINE

EXTENSION LINE

CENTER LINE

FIG. 634   Sketch Lines.

318. Sharpening Sketching Pencils.
Lines of the same relative widths are used in sketching as in instrumental pencil drawing. The pencil should be sharpened to a conical point as shown in Fig. 61 (c), and then slightly rounded to varying degrees of dullness, depending upon the type of line to be drawn, as shown in Fig. 635. All lines should be very dark, with the exception of construction lines, which are very light.

319. Straight Lines. The pencil should be held naturally, about $1\frac{1}{2}$ inches from the point. The direction of the pencil should be at right angles to the general direction of the line to be drawn. Horizontal lines are drawn from left to right (Fig. 636) with a free and easy wrist and arm motion. Vertical lines should be drawn

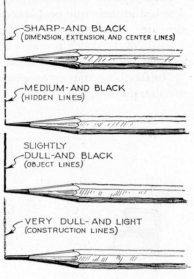

SHARP-AND BLACK
(DIMENSION, EXTENSION, AND CENTER LINES)

MEDIUM- AND BLACK
(HIDDEN LINES)

SLIGHTLY
DULL-AND BLACK
(OBJECT LINES)

VERY DULL- AND LIGHT
(CONSTRUCTION LINES)

FIG. 635   Pencil Points.

downward, with finger and wrist movements, as demonstrated in Fig. 637.

Inclined lines may be made to conform in direction to horizontal or vertical lines by turning the paper slightly or by the draftsman's shifting his position; hence they may be drawn with the same general movements (Fig. 638).

(a) POOR–SHOWS TIGHT GRIP ON PENCIL–DOES NOT CONTINUE ALONG STRAIGHT PATH – IS AN ATTEMPT TO IMITATE MECHANICAL LINES.

(b) BETTER–SHOWS FREE HANDLING OF PENCIL–CONTINUES ALONG STRAIGHT PATH– SLIGHT WIGGLES DO NOT DETRACT

(c) BEST–HAS EFFECTIVENESS OF (b), PLUS SNAP ADDED BY OCCASIONAL GAPS – EASIER TO DRAW STRAIGHT.

FIG. 636   Drawing Horizontal Lines.

In sketching lines of considerable length, the student should mark the extremeties of the line with light dots, then move the pencil back and forth between the dots in long sweeps, keeping the eye always on the dot toward which the pencil is moving, the point of the pencil touching the paper lightly, and each successive stroke correcting the defects of the preceding strokes. When the line has been located with sufficient accuracy, a little more pressure may be applied, and a distinct line drawn to replace the trial series. Then the line may be dimmed with the eraser and the final line finished with the desired strength, keeping the eye now on the point of the pencil.

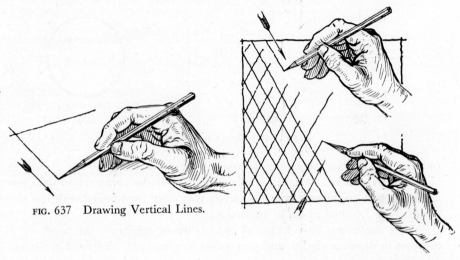

FIG. 637   Drawing Vertical Lines.

FIG. 638   Drawing Inclined Lines.

By "technique" of a line is meant the *freedom, snap, and confidence* expressed by the line, but the beginner is cautioned against overemphasis of technique.

In drawing horizontal or vertical lines, reference should be constantly made to the edges of the paper or of the sketch pad to see that the lines are parallel to them. A long horizontal or vertical line can be "roughed in" parallel to the edges by holding the pencil rigidly and allowing the little finger to glide along the edge as a definite guide. Such a line should be made lightly and then heavied in afterwards without using the edge as a guide.

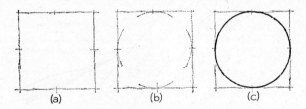

FIG. 639   Sketching a Circle.

320. Circles and Arcs. A circle may be easily sketched by first drawing an enclosing square with light construction lines, and marking the approximate mid-points of the sides, as shown in Fig. 639 (a). Tangent arcs are then sketched, as shown at (b), and the full circle is then completed lightly and finally heavied in, as shown at (c).

Another method is to draw radial construction lines lightly, as shown in Fig. 640 (a) and (b); then to sketch short arcs across the lines at the estimated

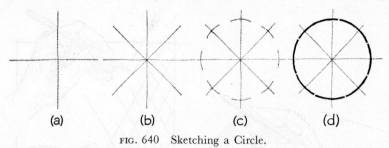

(a)   (b)   (c)   (d)

FIG. 640   Sketching a Circle.

radius distance from the center, as shown at (c); and finally to sketch the full circle lightly and heavy it in, as shown at (d). If the construction lines are heavy enough to detract from the circle, they may be dimmed with the art-gum before the final circle is heavied in.

Many draftsmen have acquired the ability to substitute the hand for a compass in drawing circles, and they attain a remarkable degree of accuracy. The little finger is used as a pivot. When the pivot finger and pencil point have been adjusted to the desired radius, the hand is held in a rigid position, while the sheet of paper is carefully turned with the other hand. This is a trick that requires skill, and is not to be thought of as a mechanical aid.

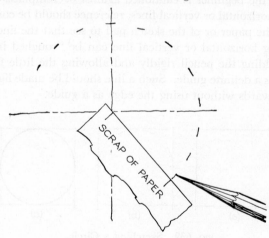

FIG. 641   Drawing Circles.

Another simple aid in the drawing of large circles is illustrated in Fig. 641, in which a piece of paper is used as a trammel.

Methods of sketching arcs are adaptations of those used in sketching circles, as shown in Fig. 642. Curves should usually be drawn with the pencil on the concave side of the curve. Points of tangency should be carefully approximated.

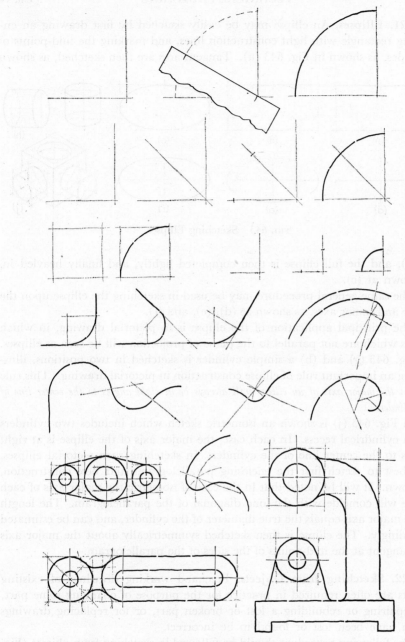

FIG. 642 Sketching Arcs.

347

321. Ellipses. An ellipse may be easily sketched by first drawing an enclosing rectangle with light construction lines, and marking the mid-points of the sides, as shown in Fig. 643 (a). Tangent arcs are then sketched, as shown

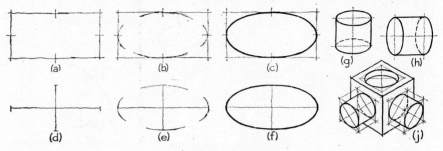

FIG. 643   Sketching Ellipses.

at (b), and the full ellipse is then completed lightly, and finally heavied in, as shown at (c).

The same general procedure may be used in sketching the ellipse upon the major and minor axes, as shown at (d), (e), and (f).

The principal application of the ellipse is in pictorial drawing, in which circles which are not parallel to the plane of projection will be seen as ellipses. In Fig. 643 (g) and (h) a simple cylinder is sketched in two positions, illustrating an important rule of ellipse construction in pictorial drawing. This rule is that *the major axis of an ellipse will always be at right angles to the center line of the cylinder.*

In Fig. 643 (j) is shown an isometric sketch which includes two cylinders and a cylindrical recess. In each case, the major axis of the ellipse is at right angles to the center line of the cylinder. In sketching such pictorial ellipses, it is best to sketch first the enclosing parallelograms and box construction, as shown. It will be noted that in the case of isometric the major axis of each ellipse will coincide with the long diagonal of the parallelogram. The length of the major axis equals the true diameter of the cylinder, and can be estimated accordingly. The ellipse is then sketched symmetrically about the major axis and tangent at the mid-points of the sides of the parallelogram.

322. Sketching from Objects. Freehand working drawings of existing objects are often required in practice for the purpose of changing some part, for repairing or rebuilding a lost or broken part, or for replacing drawings which have been lost or found to be incorrect.

The following procedure should be followed in sketching from objects (Fig. 644):

1. Study the object until its function is understood.
2. Determine the views which describe the shape of the object best. Make a thumbnail sketch (§ 191) of these views, if necessary.

3. Block in the views very lightly with freehand construction lines. At this stage the main proportions of the object should be carefully considered together with the spacing of the views on the sheet.

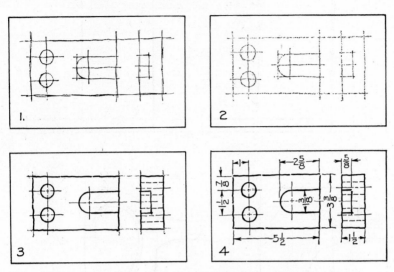

FIG. 644   Steps in Freehand Sketching.

4. Dim the construction lines with an eraser (preferably artgum).

5. Sketch object lines, hidden lines, and center lines as in Fig. 634. These should all be dark.

6. Sketch extension lines, dimension lines, and arrowheads as in Fig. 634.

7. Measure the object (§ 323), lettering each dimension on the sketch as it is taken.

8. Letter notes, title, date, and name of sketcher.

The steps in blocking in and completing a view of a machine part are illustrated in Fig. 645. The general proportions of the object are first considered carefully and blocked in, and the details are added afterwards. Just before darkening the final lines, all construction lines may be dimmed with the eraser, leaving them just dark enough to follow.

323. Measuring Objects. The measuring devices required when sketches are drawn from existing structures depend upon the degree of accuracy *originally required* to produce the objects, and the purpose for which the sketch is made. If the sketch is to be a freehand working drawing, it must carry all dimensions required to build the part, and measuring devices of the type used in its production must be employed by the sketcher. Whereas a wooden structure, such as a tool house, a table, or a bench, may be measured accurately enough with a 2-foot folding rule or a steel framing square, an automobile piston or a gear wheel would require the use of a micrometer (Fig. 863) for certain measurements. A typical example of the use of the micrometer is shown in Fig. 801.

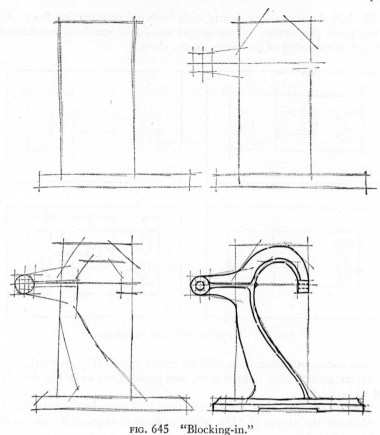

FIG. 645   "Blocking-in."

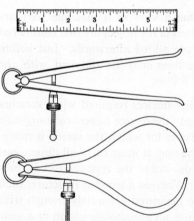

FIG. 646   Measuring Instruments.

For sketches of ordinary machine parts, a steel scale and a set of outside and inside spring calipers are sufficient. See Fig. 646 and Fig. 812.

Frequently, the radii of large arcs may be found with sufficient accuracy by tracing the curve from the model on a sheet of paper, and following later with the compass after the radius has been found by trial.

Sometimes irregular shapes may be transferred to sheets of paper by pressing the paper along the edges, so that a dented impression is left.

To secure some dimensions, a surface plate and surface gage, or other precision measuring devices, may be required.

PROBLEMS*

324. Technical Sketching. Problems in technical sketching are given in Figs. 300, 301 and 305. In addition, any of the problems following the chapters on Multiview Drawing, Sectioning, Auxiliary Views, Axonometric Drawing, Oblique Drawing, Perspective, and Working Drawings may be assigned as sketching problems.

* Technical sketching problems in convenient form for solution may be found in *Technical Drawing Problems*, by Giesecke, Mitchell, and Spencer, and in *Technical Drawing Problems— Series 2*, by Spencer and Grant, both designed to accompany this text and published by The Macmillan Company.

CHAPTER 15

Intersections and Developments

325. Introduction. A comprehensive treatment of lines, surfaces, intersections, and developments belongs to the province of descriptive geometry. However, some of the basic principles are included here in order to explain the more common applications with regard to intersections and developments. Some of the more common terms related to lines, circles, arcs, angles, and plane figures are illustrated and explained in §§ 77 and 78.

326. Lines. A *geometric line* is one generated by a point moving according to a law which may be expressed by a geometric description or by an algebraic equation. The following diagram illustrates the classification of geometric lines.

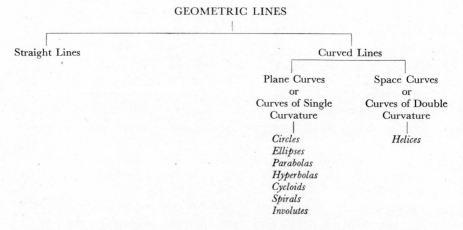

GEOMETRIC LINES

Straight Lines   Curved Lines

Plane Curves or Curves of Single Curvature   Space Curves or Curves of Double Curvature

Circles
Ellipses
Parabolas
Hyperbolas
Cycloids
Spirals
Involutes

Helices

327. Surfaces. A *surface* is a geometric magnitude having two dimensions. The boundary of a solid is a surface. A *geometric surface* may be generated by the motion of a geometric line, which is then called the *generatrix*. Any position of the generatrix is called an *element* of the surface.

A *ruled surface* is one which may be generated by a straight line. A ruled surface may be a *plane*, a *single curved surface*, or a *warped surface*.

A *plane* is a ruled surface which may be generated by a straight line of which one point moves along another straight line, while the generating line remains parallel to its original position. In Fig. 648, solids *1* to *5*, and *12* and *13*, are bounded by plane surfaces.

A *single curved surface* is a ruled surface which is developable, i.e., which may be unrolled to coincide with a plane. If two adjacent positions of the generating line lie in the same plane, the surface is a single curved surface. In Fig. 648, solids *7* and *8* are bounded by single curved surfaces.

A *warped surface* is a ruled surface that is not developable. No two adjacent positions of the generating line lie in the same plane. See Fig. 647.

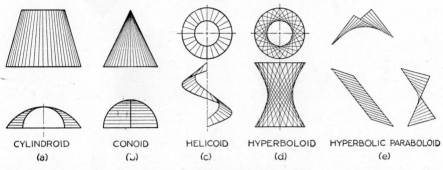

| CYLINDROID | CONOID | HELICOID | HYPERBOLOID | HYPERBOLIC PARABOLOID |
| (a) | (b) | (c) | (d) | (e) |

FIG. 647 Warped Surfaces.

A *double curved surface* is one which may be generated only by a curved line. It has no straight line elements. If such a surface can be generated by revolving a curved line about a straight line in·the plane of the curve, it is a *double curved surface of revolution*. In Fig. 648, solids *6*, *9*, *10*, and *11* are bounded by double curved surfaces.

A hyperboloid of one nappe may be generated either by revolving a hyperbola about its conjugate axis or by revolving a straight line about another straight line located so that the two lines are not in the same plane. Such a surface may be classified either as a surface of revolution or as a warped surface. It is classified, in this text, as a warped surface in accordance with the definitions given above. A similar statement applies to the hyperbolic paraboloid. See Fig. 647.

A *developable surface* is one which may be unfolded or unrolled so as to coincide with a plane (§ 331). Surfaces composed of single curved surfaces, or of planes, or of combinations of these types, are developable. Warped surfaces and double curved surfaces are not developable. They may be developed approximately by dividing them into sections and substituting for each section a developable surface, that is, a plane or a single curved surface. If the material used is sufficiently pliable, the flat sheets may be stretched, pressed, stamped, spun, or otherwise forced to assume the desired shape. Non-developable surfaces are often produced by a combination of developable surfaces which are then formed slightly to produce the required shapes.

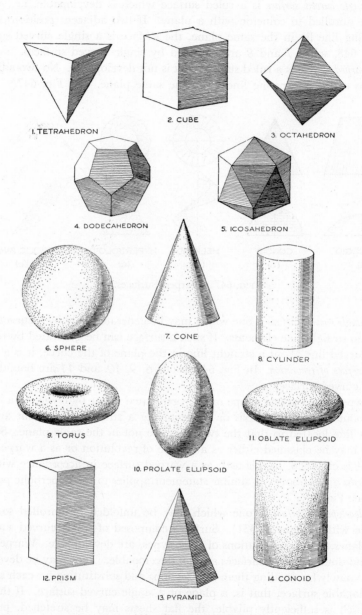

FIG. 648   Geometric Solids.

The following diagram illustrates the classification of geometric surfaces:

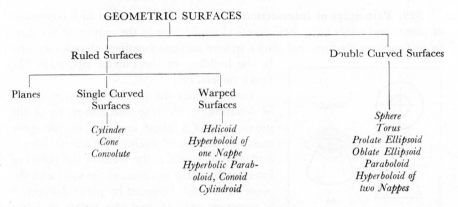

GEOMETRIC SURFACES

Ruled Surfaces — Double Curved Surfaces

Planes | Single Curved Surfaces | Warped Surfaces

Cylinder
Cone
Convolute

Helicoid
Hyperboloid of one Nappe
Hyperbolic Paraboloid, Conoid
Cylindroid

Sphere
Torus
Prolate Ellipsoid
Oblate Ellipsoid
Paraboloid
Hyperboloid of two Nappes

328. Solids.—Fig. 648. Solids which are bounded by geometric surfaces are *geometric solids*. Solids bounded by plane surfaces are *polyhedra*, the most common of which are the pyramid and prism. Convex solids whose faces are all equal regular polygons are *regular polyhedra*. The simple regular polyhedra are the *tetrahedron, cube, octahedron, dodecahedron,* and *icosahedron,* known as the five *Platonic* solids.

Plane surfaces which bound polyhedra are *faces* of the solids. Lines of intersection of faces are *edges* of the solids.

A solid generated by revolving a plane figure about an axis in the plane of the figure is a *solid of revolution*.

Solids bounded by warped surfaces have no group name. The most common example of such solids is the screw thread.

The following diagram illustrates the classification of geometric solids:

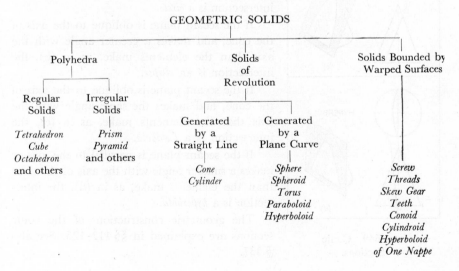

GEOMETRIC SOLIDS

Polyhedra | Solids of Revolution | Solids Bounded by Warped Surfaces

Regular Solids | Irregular Solids

Generated by a Straight Line | Generated by a Plane Curve

Tetrahedron
Cube
Octahedron
and others

Prism
Pyramid
and others

Cone
Cylinder

Sphere
Spheroid
Torus
Paraboloid
Hyperboloid

Screw Threads
Skew Gear Teeth
Conoid
Cylindroid
Hyperboloid of One Nappe

INTERSECTIONS OF PLANES AND SOLIDS

329. Principles of Intersections. The principles involved in intersections of planes and solids have their practical application in the cutting of openings in roof surfaces for flues and stacks, in wall surfaces for pipes, chutes, etc., and in the building of sheet-metal structures like tanks, boilers, etc.

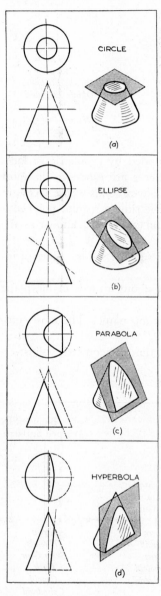

FIG. 649 Conic Sections.

In such cases the problem is generally one of determining the true size and shape of the intersection of a plane and one of the more common geometric solids. The intersection of a plane and a solid is the locus of the points of intersection of the elements of the solid with the plane. For solids bounded by plane surfaces, it is necessary only to find the points of intersection of the edges of the solid with the plane, and to join these points, in consecutive order, with straight lines. For solids bounded by curved surfaces, it is necessary to find the points of intersection of several elements of the solid with the plane and to trace a smooth curve through these points.

330. Conic Sections.—Fig. 649. The curve of intersection of a plane and a circular cone is a *conic section*.

If the secant plane is perpendicular to the axis of the cone, as in Fig. 649 (a), the curve of intersection is a *circle*.

If the secant plane is oblique to the axis of the cone, and makes a greater angle with the axis than the elements make, as in (b), the intersection is an *ellipse*.

If the secant plane is oblique to the axis of the cone, and makes the same angle with the axis that the elements make, as in (c), the intersection is a *parabola*.

If the secant plane is parallel to the axis or makes a smaller angle with the axis of the cone than the elements make, as in (d), the intersection is a *hyperbola*.

The geometric constructions of the conic sections are explained in §§ 112–123. See also § 337.

331. Developments. The development of a surface is that surface laid out on a plane (Fig. 650). Practical applications of developments occur in sheet-metal work, stone cutting, and pattern making.

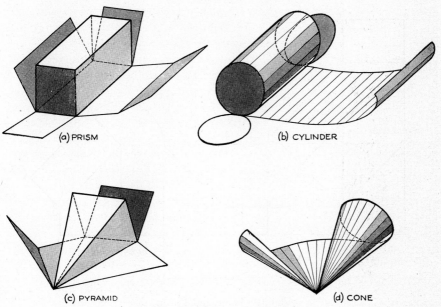

(a) PRISM   (b) CYLINDER

(c) PYRAMID   (d) CONE

FIG; 650   Development of Surfaces.

Single curved surfaces and the surfaces of polyhedra can be developed. Warped surfaces and double curved surfaces can be developed only approximately. See § 327.

In sheet-metal layout, extra material must be provided for laps or seams. If the material is heavy, the thickness may be a factor and the crowding of metal in bends must be considered. The draftsman must also take stock sizes into account and should make his layouts so as to economize in the use of material and of labor.

It is common practice to draw development layouts with the inside surfaces up. In this way, all fold lines and other markings are related directly to inside measurements which are the important dimensions in all ducts, pipes, tanks, and other vessels.

332. To Find the Intersection of a Plane and a Prism and the Development of the Prism.—Fig. 651.

(a) *Intersection.*—The true size and shape of the intersection is shown in the auxiliary view. See §§ 236–244. The length *AB* is the same as *AB* in the front view and the width *AD* is the same as *AD* in the top view.

(b) *Development.*—On the straight line *1–1*, called the *stretch-out line*, set off the widths of the faces *1–2*, *2–3*, etc., taken from the top view. At the division points, erect perpendiculars to *1–1*, and set off on each the length of the respective edge, taken from the front view. The lengths can also be projected across from the front view, as shown. Join the points thus found by straight lines to

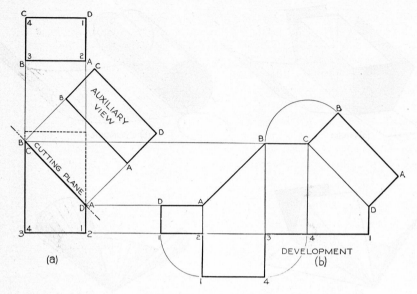

FIG. 651   Plane and Prism.

complete the development of the lateral surface. Attach to this development the lower base and the upper base or auxiliary view, to obtain the development of the entire surface of the frustum of the prism.

In practical work, it is best to put the seam at the shortest edge and to attach the bases at edges where they match, so as to economize in soldering, welding, or riveting seams. In sheet-metal patterns, allowance must be made for lapping at seams where required.

333. To Find the Intersection of a Plane and a Cylinder and the Development of the Cylinder.—Fig. 652.

(a) *Intersection.*—The intersection is an ellipse whose points are the piercing points in the secant plane of the elements of the cylinder. In spacing the elements, it is best, though not necessary, to divide the circumference of the base into *equal* parts, and to draw an element at each division point. In the auxiliary view, the widths *BC, DE*, etc., are taken from the top view at *2–16*, *3–15*, etc., respectively, and the curve is traced through the points thus determined, with the aid of the irregular curve (§ 72).

The major axis *AH* and the minor axis *JK* are shown true length in the front view and the top view, respectively; therefore, the ellipse may also be constructed as explained in §§ 112–118.

(b) *Development.*—The base of the cylinder develops into a straight line *1–1*, the stretch-out line, equal to the circumference of the base, whose length may be determined by calculation (πd), by setting off with the bow dividers, or by rectifying the arcs of the base *1–2*, *2–3*, etc. (§ 111). Divide the stretch-out line into the same number of equal parts as the circumference of the base and draw an element through each division perpendicular to the line. Set off on each element its length, taken from the front view, as shown; then trace a smooth curve through the points *A, B, D*, etc. (§ 72) and attach the bases.

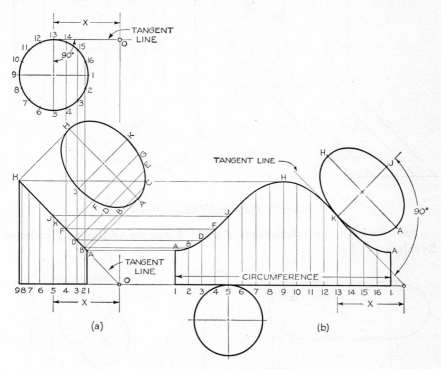

FIG. 652   Plane and Cylinder.

334. To Find the Intersection of a Plane and an Oblique Prism and the Development of the Prism.—Fig. 653.

(a) *Intersection.*—The right section cut by the plane *WX* is a regular hexagon, as shown in the auxiliary view; the oblique section, cut by the horizontal plane *YZ*, is shown in the top view.

(b) *Development.*—The right section *WX* develops into the straight line *WX*, the stretch-out line. Set off, on the stretch-out line, the widths of the faces *1–2*, *2–3*, etc., taken from the auxiliary view, and draw a line through each division perpendicular to the line. Set off, from the stretch-out line, the lengths of the respective edges measured from *WX* in the front view. Join the points A, B, C, etc., with straight lines and attach the bases, which are shown in their true sizes in the top view.

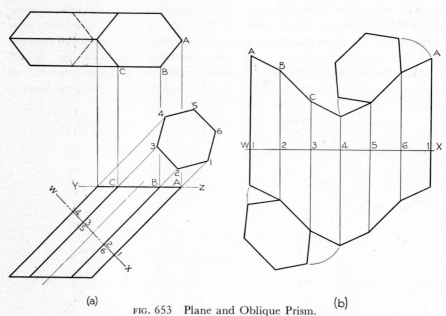

(a)   (b)

FIG. 653   Plane and Oblique Prism.

335. To Find the Intersection of a Plane and an Oblique Cylinder of Revolution.—Fig. 654.

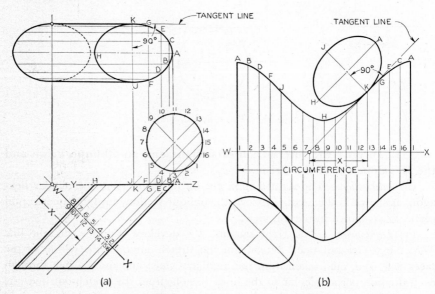

(a)   (b)

FIG. 654   Plane and Oblique Circular Cylinder.

(a) *Intersection.*—The right section cut by the plane *WX* is a circle, shown in the auxiliary view. The intersection of the horizontal plane *YZ* with the cylinder is an ellipse shown in the top view, whose points are found as explained for the auxiliary view in § 333 (a). The major axis *AH* is shown true length in the top view, and the minor axis *JK* is equal to the diameter of the cylinder; therefore the ellipse may be constructed as explained in §§ 112–118.

(b) *Development.*—The cylinder may be considered as a prism having an infinite number of edges; therefore the development is found in a manner similar to that of the oblique prism shown in Fig. 653.

The circle of the right section cut by plane *WX* develops into a straight line *1–1*, the stretch-out line, equal in length to the circumference of the circle. Divide the stretch-out line into the same number of equal parts as the circumference of the circle as shown in the auxiliary view, and draw elements through these points perpendicular to the line. Set off on each element its length, taken from the front view, as shown; then trace a smooth curve through the points *A*, *B*, *D*, etc. (§ 72), and attach the bases.

336. To Find the Intersection of a Plane and a Pyramid and the Development of the Resulting Truncated Pyramid.—Fig. 655.

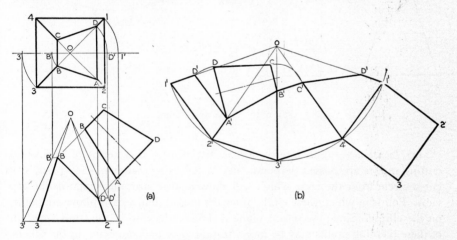

FIG. 655   Plane and Pyramid.

(a) *Intersection.*—The intersection is a trapezoid whose vertices are the points in which the edges of the pyramid pierce the secant plane. In the auxiliary view the altitude of the trapezoid is projected from the front view, and the widths *AD* and *BC* are transferred from the top view.

(b) *Development.*—With *O* in the development as center and *O–1′* in the front view (the true length of one of the edges) as radius, draw the arc *1′*, *2′*, *3′*, etc. Inscribe the chords *1′–2′*, *2′–3′*, etc., equal, respectively, to the sides of the base, as shown in the top view. Draw the lines *1′–O*, *2′–O*, etc., and set off the true lengths of the lines OD', OA', OB', etc., respectively, taken from the true lengths in the front view (§ 256).

To complete the development, join the points D', A', B', etc., by straight lines, and attach the bases to their corresponding edges. To transfer an irregular figure, such as the trapezoid shown here, refer to § 98.

337. To Find the Intersection of a Plane and a Cone and the Development of the Lateral Surface of the Cone.—Fig. 656.

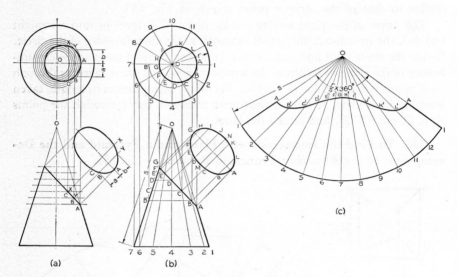

FIG. 656   Plane and Cone.

(a) *Intersection.*—The intersection is an ellipse. If a series of horizontal cutting planes are passed perpendicular to the axis, as shown, each plane will cut a circle from the cone which will show in true size and shape in the top view. Points in which these circles intersect the original secant plane are points on the ellipse. Since the secant plane is shown edgewise in the front view, all of these piercing points may be found in that view and projected to the others, as shown.

(b) *Intersection.*—This method is most suitable where a development also is required, since it utilizes elements which are also needed in the development. The piercing points of these elements in the secant plane are points on the intersection. Divide the base into any number of equal parts, and draw an element at each division point. These elements pierce the secant plane in points A, B, C, etc. The top views of these points are found by projecting upward from the front view, as shown. In the auxiliary view, the widths BL, CK, etc., are taken from the top view. The ellipse is then drawn with the of the irregular curve (§ 72).

The major axis of the ellipse, shown in the auxiliary view, is equal to *AG* in the front view. The minor axis *MN* bisects the major axis, and is equal to the minor axis of the ellipse in the top view. With these axes, the ellipse may also be constructed as explained in §§ 112–118.

(c) *Development.*—The cone may be considered as a pyramid having an infinite number of edges; hence the development is found in a manner similar to that explained for the pyramid in § 336. The base of the cone develops into a circular arc with the slant height of the cone as its radius, and the circumference of the base as its length (§ 111). The lengths of the elements in the development are taken from the element *O–7* or *O–1* in the front view (b). Instead of finding the true circumference of the base, the vertical angle *1–O–1*, in the development, can be set off equal to $(\frac{r}{s})$ 360° (where *r* is the radius of the base, and *s* the slant height of the cone).

338. To Find the Development of a Hood and Flue.—Fig. 657. Since the hood is a conical surface, it may be developed as described in § 337. The

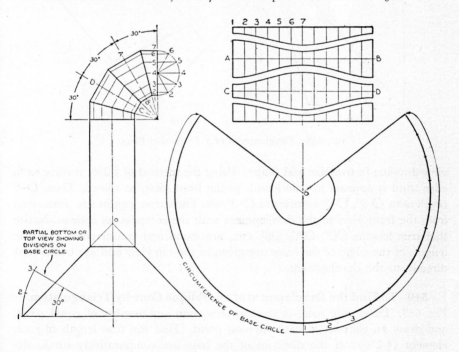

FIG. 657   A Hood and Flue.

two end sections of the elbow are cylindrical surfaces, and may be developed as described in § 333. The two middle sections of the elbow are cylindrical surfaces, but since their bases are not perpendicular to the axes, they will not develop into straight lines. If the auxiliary planes *AB* and *DC* are passed perpendicular to the axes, they will cut right sections from the cylinders, which will develop into the straight lines AB and CD.

If the developments are arranged as shown, the elbow can be constructed from a rectangular sheet of metal without wasting material.

339. To Find the Development of a Truncated Oblique Rectangular Pyramid.—Fig. 658. None of the four lateral surfaces is shown in the multi-

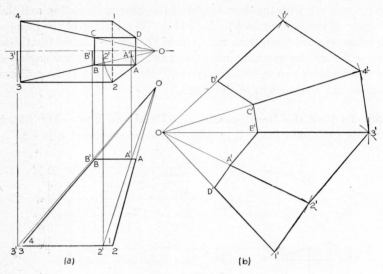

FIG. 658   Development of a Transition Piece.

view drawing in true size and shape. Using the method of § 256, revolve each edge until it appears in true length in the front view, as shown. Thus, O–2 revolves to O–$2'$, O–3 revolves to O–$3'$, etc. These true lengths are transferred from the front view to the development with the compass, as shown. Notice that true lengths OD', OA', OB', etc., are found and transferred. The true lengths of the edges of the bases are given in the top view and are transferred directly to the development.

340. To Find the Development of an Oblique Cone by Triangulation.— Fig. 659. Divide the base, in the top view, into any number of equal parts, and draw an element at each division point. Find the true length of each element (§ 256). If the divisions of the base are comparatively small, the lengths of the chords may be set off in the development as representing the lengths of the respective subtending arcs. In the development, set off O–$1'$ equal to O–$1'$ in the "true-length diagram," which is the true length of the shortest element. With $1'$ in the development as center, and the chord 1–2, taken from the top view, as radius, strike an arc at $2'$. With O as center, and O–$2'$, the true length of the element O–2, as radius, draw the arc at $2'$.

The intersection of these arcs is a point in the development of the base of the cone. The points *3'*, *4'*, etc., in the curve may be found in a similar manner, and the curve may be traced through these points with the aid of the irregular curve (§ 72).

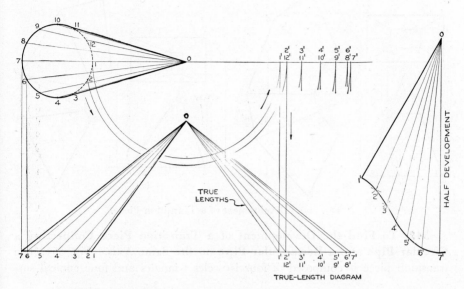

FIG. 659   Development of an Oblique Cone by Triangulation.

Since the development is symmetrical about element *O–7'*, it is necessary only to lay out half the development, as shown.

The term *triangulation* simply means development by laying out triangles individually, such as *O–1'–2'*, *O–2'–3'*, etc., in Fig. 659.

341. To Find the Development of a Transition Piece* Connecting Rectangular Pipes on the Same Axis.—Fig. 660 (a). The transition piece is a frustum of a pyramid. Find the vertex *O* of the pyramid by extending its edges to their intersection. Find the true lengths of the edges by any one of the methods explained in § 256. The development can then be found as explained in § 336.

If the transition piece is not a frustum of a pyramid, as in Fig. 660 (b), it can best be developed by triangulation (§ 340), i.e., by dividing the faces into triangles, as shown for the faces *1–5–8–4* and *2–6–7–3*, or by extending the sides to form triangles, as shown for faces *1–2–6–5* and *3–4–8–7*, and then finding the true lengths of the sides of the triangles (§ 256) and setting them off as shown.

* A transition piece is one which connects openings of different shapes or sizes, or connects pipes, flues, stacks, etc., of different cross sections.

As a check on the development, lines which are parallel on the surface must also be parallel on the development; for example, $8'-5'$ must be parallel to $4'-1'$ on the development.

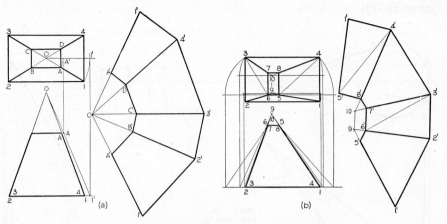

FIG. 660   Development of a Transition Piece.

342. To Find the Development of a Transition Piece Connecting a Circular Pipe and a Rectangular Pipe on the Same Axis.—Fig. 661. The transition piece is composed of four isosceles triangles and four conical sur-

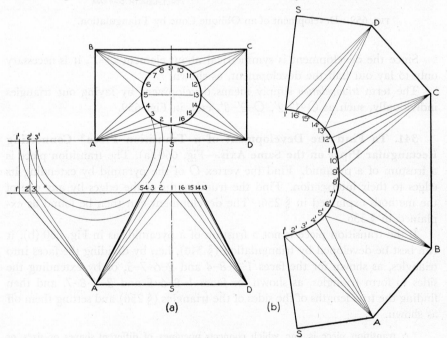

FIG. 661   Development of a Transition Piece.

faces. Begin the development on the line *1'–S*, and draw the right triangle *1'–S–A*, whose base *SA* is equal to half the side *AD* and whose hypotenuse *A–1'* is equal to the true length of the side *A–1*.

The conical surfaces are developed by triangulation as explained in § 340.

343. To Find the Development of a Transition Piece Connecting Two Cylindrical Pipes on Different Axes.—Fig. 662. The transition piece is a frustum of a cone the vertex of which may be found by extending the contour elements to their interesection *A*.

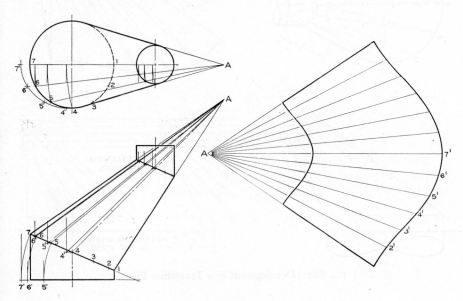

FIG. 662   Development of a Transition Piece.

The development can be found by triangulation as explained in § 340. The sides of each triangle are the true lengths of two adjacent elements of the cone and the base is the true length of the curve of the base of the cone between the two elements. This curve is not shown in its true length in either view and the plane of the base of the frustum must, therefore, be revolved until it is horizontal in order to find the distance from the foot of one element to the foot of the next. When the plane of the base is thus revolved, the foot of any element, as 7, revolves to 7', and the curve 6'–7' (top view) is the true length of the curve of the base between the elements 6 and 7. In practice, the chord distances between these points are generally used to approximate the curved distances.

After the conical surface has been developed, the true lengths of the elements on the truncated section of the cone are set off from the vertex *A* of the development to secure points on the upper curve of the development.

If the transition piece is not a frustum of a cone, its development is found by another variation of triangulation, as shown in Fig. 663. The circular intersection with the large vertical pipe is shown true size in the top view, and the circular intersection with the small inclined pipe is shown true size in the

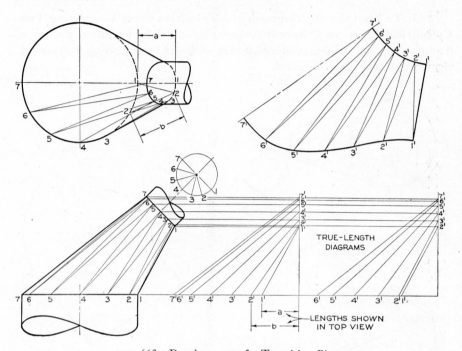

FIG. 663   Development of a Transition Piece.

auxiliary view. Since both intersections are true circles, and the planes containing them are not parallel, the lateral surface of the transition piece is a warped surface and not conical (single curved). It is theoretically non-developable, but may be approximately developed by considering it to be made up of plane triangles, every other one of which is inverted, as shown in the development. The true lengths of the sides of the triangles are found by the method of Fig. 525 (d), but in a systematic manner so as to form "true-length diagrams," as shown in Fig. 663.

344. To Find the Development of a Transition Piece Connecting a Square Pipe and a Cylindrical Pipe on Different Axes.—Fig. 664. The development of the transition piece is made up of four plane triangular surfaces and four triangular conical surfaces. The development is made in a similar manner to those described in §§ 340 and 342.

345. To Find the Intersection of a Plane and a Sphere, and to Find the Approximate Development of the Sphere.—Figs. 665 and 666.

(a) *Intersection.*—The intersection of a plane and a sphere is a circle, as shown in the top views of Figs. 665 and 666; the diameter of the circle depend-

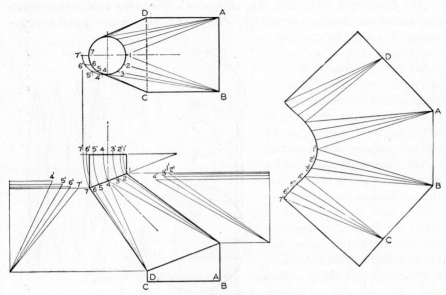

FIG. 664   Development of a Transition Piece.

ing upon where the plane is passed. Any circle cut by a plane through the center of the sphere is called a *great circle*. If a plane passes through the center,

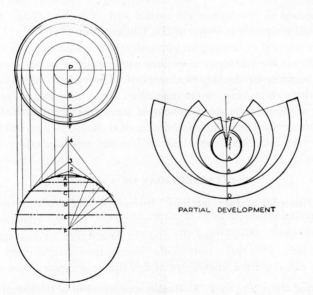

PARTIAL DEVELOPMENT

FIG. 665   Approximate Development of a Sphere by the Polyconic Method.

and perpendicular to the axis, the resulting great circle is called the *equator*. If a plane contains the axis, it will cut a great circle called a *meridian*.

(b) *Development*.—Fig. 665. The surface of a sphere is a double curved surface and is not developable (§ 327). The surface may be developed approximately (Fig. 665) by dividing it into a series of zones and substituting for each zone a frustum of a right circular cone. The development of the conical surfaces is an approximate development of the spherical surface. If the conical surfaces are inscribed within the sphere, the resulting development will be smaller than the spherical surface. If the conical surfaces are circumscribed about the sphere, the resulting development will be larger than the spherical surface. If the conical surfaces are partly within and partly without the sphere, as indicated in the figure, the resulting development very closely approximates the spherical surface.

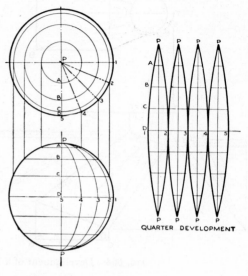

FIG. 666 Approximate Development of a Sphere by the Polycylindric Method.

This method of developing a spherical surface is the *polyconic* method. It is used on all government maps of the United States.*

Another method of making an approximate development of a sphere (Fig. 666) is to divide the surface into sections with meridian planes, and substitute cylindrical surfaces for the spherical sections. The cylindrical surfaces may be inscribed within the sphere, or circumscribed about it, or located partly within and partly without. The development of the series of cylindrical surfaces is an approximate development of the spherical surface. This method is the *polycylindric* method, sometimes designated as the *gore* method.

INTERSECTIONS OF SOLIDS

346. Principles of Intersections. Intersections of solids are generally regarded as in the province of descriptive geometry, and for information on the more complicated intersections the student is referred to any standard text on that subject. However, most of the intersections encountered in drafting practice do not require a knowledge of descriptive geometry, and some of the

* Developed about 1815 by F. R. Hassler, superintendent of the United States Coast Survey.

more common solutions may be found in the paragraphs that follow.

An intersection of two solids is referred to as a *figure of intersection*. Two plane surfaces intersect in a straight line; hence if two solids which are composed of plane surfaces intersect, the figure of intersection will be composed of straight lines, as shown in Figs. 667–670. The method generally consists in finding the piercing points of the edges of one solid with the surfaces of the other solid, and joining these points with straight lines.

If curved surfaces intersect, or if curved surfaces and plane surfaces intersect, the figure of intersection will be composed of curves, as shown in Figs. 652, 656, 671–676. The method generally consists in finding the piercing points of *elements* of one solid with the surfaces of the other. A smooth curve is then traced through these points, with the aid of the irregular curve (§ 72).

347. To Find the Intersection and the Developments of Two Prisms.— Fig. 667.

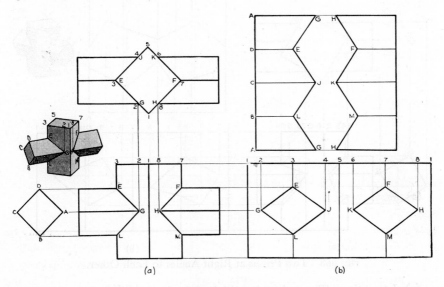

FIG. 667   Two Prisms at Right Angles to Each Other.

(a) *Intersection.*—The points in which the edges *A*, *B*, *C*, and *D* of the horizontal prism pierce the vertical prism are vertices of the intersection. The edges *D* and *B* of the horizontal prism intersect the edges *3* and *7* of the vertical prism at the points *E*, *F*, *L*, and *M*. The edges *A* and *C* of the horizontal prism intersect the faces of the vertical prism at the points *G*, *H*, *J*, and *K*. The intersection is completed by joining these points in order by straight lines.

(b) *Developments.*—To develop the lateral surface of the horizontal prism, set off on the stretch-out line *A–A* the widths of the faces *AB*, *BC*, etc., taken from the end view, and draw the edges through these points, as shown. Set off, from the stretch-out line, the lengths of the edges *AG, BL,* etc., taken from the front view or from the top view, and join the points *G, L, J,* etc., by straight lines.

To develop the lateral surface of the vertical prism, set off on the stretch-out line *1–1* the widths of the faces *1–3, 3–5,* etc., taken from the top view, and draw the edges through these points, as shown. Set off on the stretch-out line, the distances *1–2, 5–4, 5–6,* and *1–8,* taken from the top view, and draw the intermediate elements parallel to the principal edges. Take the lengths of the principal edges and of the intermediate elements from the front view, and join the points *E, G, L,* etc., in order with straight lines, to complete the development.

348. To Find the Intersection and the Developments of Two Prisms.— Fig. 668.

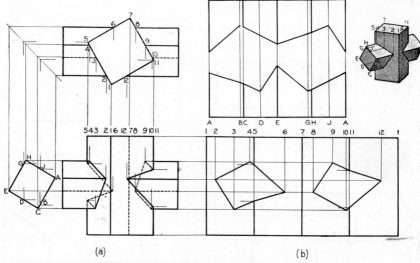

(a)   (b)
FIG. 668   Two Prisms at Right Angles to Each Other.

(a) *Intersection.*—The points in which the edges *ACEH* of the horizontal prism pierce the surfaces of the vertical prism are found in the top view and are projected downward to the corresponding edges *ACEH* in the front view. The points in which the edges *5* and *11* of the vertical prism pierce the surfaces of the horizontal prism are found in the left side view at *G, D, J,* and *B,* and are projected horizontally to the front view, intersecting the corresponding edges as shown. The intersection is completed by joining these points in order by straight lines.

(b) *Developments.*—The lateral surfaces of the two prisms are developed as explained in § 347. True lengths of all lateral edges and lines parallel to them are shown in the front view of Fig. 668 (a).

349. To Find the Intersection and the Developments of Two Prisms.—
Fig. 669.

(a) *Intersection.* — The points in which edges *1–2–3–4* of the inclined
prism pierce the surfaces of the vertical prism are vertices of the intersection. These points, found in the top view, are projected downward to the

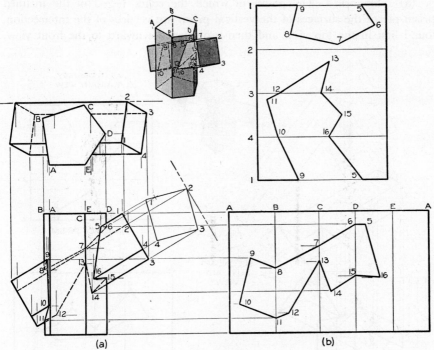

FIG. 669   Two Prisms Oblique to Each Other.

corresponding edges *1–2–3–4* in the front view, as shown. The intersection
is completed by joining these points in order by straight lines.

(b) *Developments.* — The lateral surfaces of the two prisms are developed
as explained in § 347. True lengths of all edges of both prisms are shown in
the front view of Fig. 669 (a).

350. To Find the Intersection and the Developments of Two Prisms.—
Fig. 670. In this case the edges of the inclined prism are oblique to the planes
of projection, and in the front and top views none of the edges is shown true
length (§ 207), and none of the faces is shown true size (§ 214). Furthermore,
none of the angles, including the angle of inclination, is shown true size (§ 209).
Therefore, it is necessary to draw a secondary auxiliary view (§ 249) to obtain
the true size and shape of the right section of the inclined prism.

The direction of sight, indicated by arrow *A*, is assumed perpendicular
to the end face *1–2–3*, that is, parallel to the principal edges of the prism.

The primary auxiliary view, taken in the direction of arrow *B*, shows the true lengths of the edges, the true inclination of the prism with respect to the horizontal and, incidentally, the true length and inclination of arrow *A*. In the secondary auxiliary view, arrow *A* is shown as a point and the end face *1–2–3* is shown in its true size.

(a) *Intersection.* — The points in which the edges *1–2–3* of the inclined prism pierce the surfaces of the vertical prism are vertices of the intersection, found first in the top view and then projected downward to the front view.

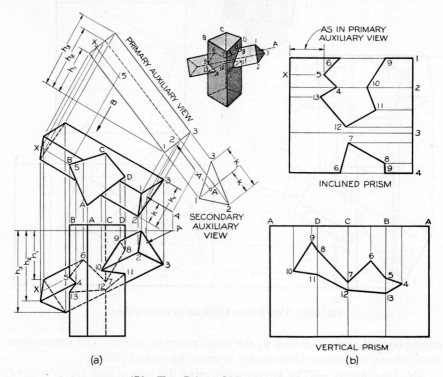

FIG. 670 Two Prisms Oblique to Each Other.

(b) *Developments.* — The lateral surfaces of the two prisms are developed as explained in § 347. True lengths of the edges of the vertical prism are shown in the front view. True lengths of the edges of the inclined prism are shown in the primary auxiliary view; true lengths to the vertices of the intersection may be found in this view, as shown for line *X–5*.

351. To Find the Intersection and the Developments of Two Cylinders.—Fig. 671.

(a) *Intersection.* — Assume a series of elements (preferably equally spaced) on the horizontal cylinder, numbered *1–2–3*, etc., in the side view, and draw their top and front views. Their points of intersection with the surface of the vertical cylinder are shown in the top view at *A, B, C*, etc., and may be found in the front view by projecting downward to their intersections with the corresponding elements *1–2–3*, etc., in the front view. When a sufficient number

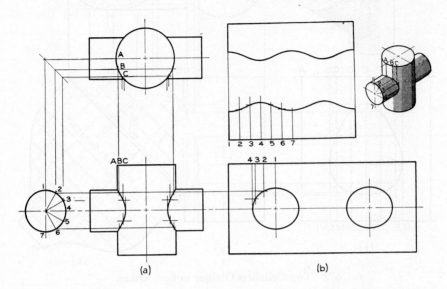

FIG. 671   Two Cylinders at Right Angles to Each Other.

of points have been found to determine the intersection, the curve is traced through the points, with the aid of the irregular curve (§ 72).

(b) *Developments.* — The lateral surfaces of the two cylinders are developed as explained in § 333. True lengths of all elements of both cylinders are shown in the front view.

352. To Find the Intersections and the Developments of Two Cylinders.—Fig. 672.

(a) *Intersections.* — A revolved right section of the inclined cylinder is divided into a number of equal parts *1–2–3*, etc., and an element is drawn at each of the division points. The points of intersection of these elements with the surface of the vertical cylinder are shown in the top view at *B, C, D*, etc., and are found in the front view by projecting downward to intersect the corresponding elements *1–2–3*, etc. The curve is traced through these points, with the aid of the irregular curve (§ 72).

(b) *Developments.* — The lateral surfaces of the two cylinders are developed as explained in §§ 333 and 335. True lengths of all elements of both cylinders are shown in the front view.

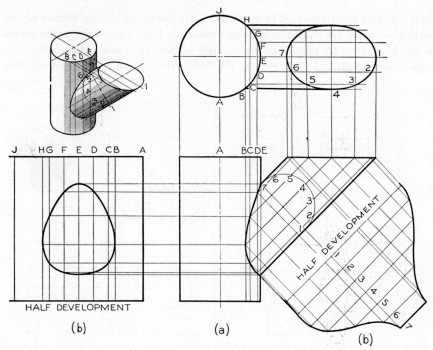

FIG. 672   Two Cylinders Oblique to Each Other.

353. To Find the Intersection and the Developments of a Prism and a Cone.—Fig. 673.

(a) *Intersection.* — Points in which the edges of the prism intersect the surface of the cone are shown in the side view at A, C, and F. Intermediate points such as B, D, E, and G are piercing points of any lines along the prism parallel to the edges. Through all of the piercing points in the side view, elements of the cone are drawn and then drawn in the top and front views. The intersections of the elements of the cone with the edges of the prism (and lines along the prism drawn parallel thereto) are points of the intersections. The figures of intersection are traced through these points, with the aid of the irregular curve (§ 72).

(b) *Developments.* — The lateral surface of the prism is developed as explained in § 347. True lengths of all edges and lines parallel thereto are shown in both the front and top views. The lateral surface of the cone is developed as explained in § 337. True lengths of elements from the vertex to points on the intersections are found as shown in Fig. 525 (a), p. 270.

354. To Find the Intersection of a Prism and a Cone with Edges of Prism Parallel to Axis of Cone.—Fig. 674 (a).

Since the lateral surfaces of the prism are parallel to the axis of the cone, the figure of intersection will be composed of a series of hyperbolas (§§ 118 and 330). If a series of planes are assumed containing the axis of the cone, each plane will contain edges of the prism or will cut lines parallel to them along the prism, and will cut elements in the cone that intersect these at points of the figure of intersection.

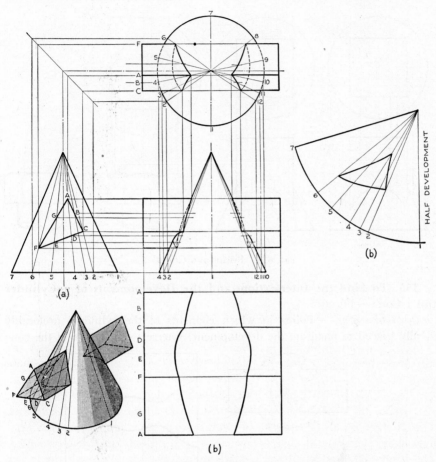

FIG. 673   Prism and Cone.

Fig. 674 (b). — The intersection is the same as at (a), but found in a different manner. Here, a series of parallel planes, perpendicular to the axis of the cone, cut circles of varying diameters on the cone. These circles are shown true size in the top view, where also are shown the piercing points of these circles in the vertical plane surfaces of the prism. The front views of these piercing points are found by projecting downward to the corresponding cutting plane lines.

Fig. 674 (c). — The chamfer on an ordinary hexagon bolt head or hexagon nut (§ 427) is actually a conical surface which intersects the six vertical sides of a hexagonal prism to form hyperbolas. In the figure, the methods of both (a) and (b) are shown to illustrate how points may be found by either method.

In machine drawings of bolts and nuts, these hyperbolic curves are approximated by means of circular arcs, as shown in Fig. 776, p. 453.

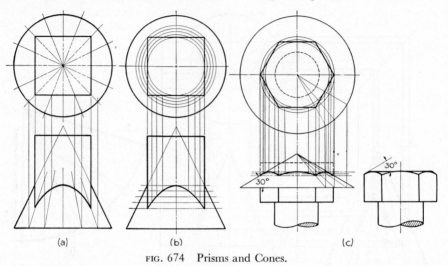

FIG. 674   Prisms and Cones.

355. To Find the Intersections and the Developments of a Cylinder and a Cone.—Fig. 675.

(a) *Intersections.* — Points in which elements of the cylinder (preferably equally spaced to facilitate the development) intersect the surface of the cone

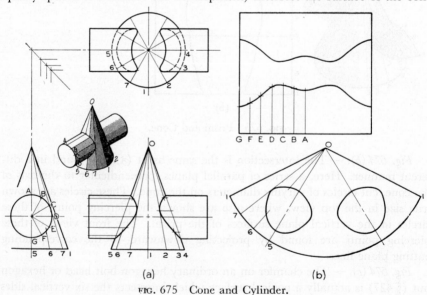

FIG. 675   Cone and Cylinder.

are shown in the side view at A, B, C, etc. The elements of the cylinder are here shown as points. Elements of the cone are then drawn from the vertex through each of these points. These elements are drawn in their correct locations in the top and front views. The intersections of these elements with the elements A, B, C, etc., of the cylinder are points on the figures of intersection. The curves are then traced through these points, with the aid of the irregular curve (§ 72).

(b) *Developments.* — The lateral surface of the cylinder is developed as explained in § 351. True lengths of all elements are shown in both the front and top views. The lateral surface of the cone is developed as explained in § 337. True lengths of elements from the vertex to points on the intersections are found as shown in Fig. 525, p. 270.

356. To Find the Intersection of a Cylinder and a Sphere.—Fig. 676. Horizontal planes 1, 2, 3, etc., which appear edgewise in the front and side

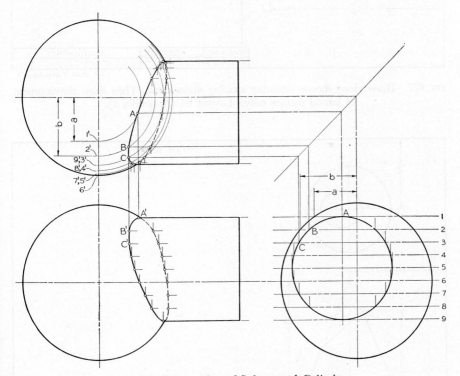

FIG. 676   Intersection of Sphere and Cylinder.

views, cut elements A, B, C, etc., from the cylinder and circular arcs $1'$, $2'$, $3'$, etc., from the sphere. The intersections of the elements with the arcs produced by the corresponding planes are points on the figure of intersection. Joint the points with a smooth curve (§ 72).

INTERSECTION AND DEVELOPMENT PROBLEMS

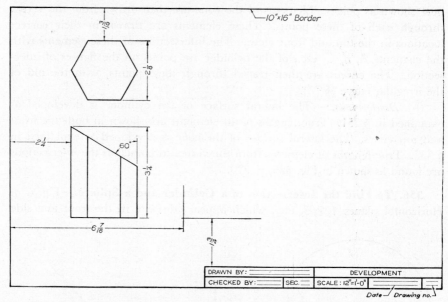

FIG. 677 Draw views shown, omitting spacing dimensions. Then draw development of lateral surface only. Layout B4 (Appendix 1).

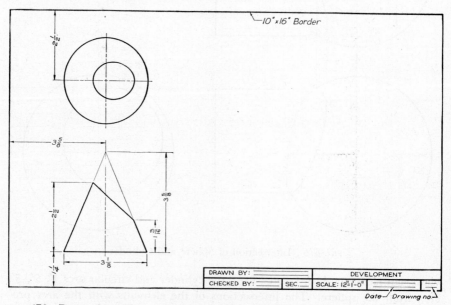

FIG. 678 Draw views shown, omitting spacing dimensions. Then draw development of lateral surface only. Layout B4 (Appendix 1).

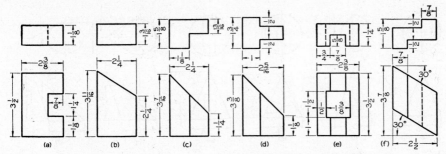

FIG. 679 Draw given views; develop lateral surface. Layout B4.*

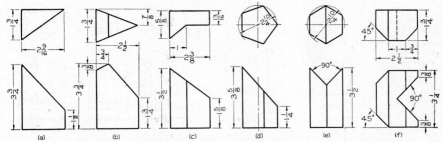

FIG. 680 Draw given views; develop lateral surface. Layout B4.*

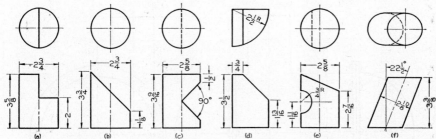

FIG. 681 Draw given views; develop lateral surface. Layout B4.*

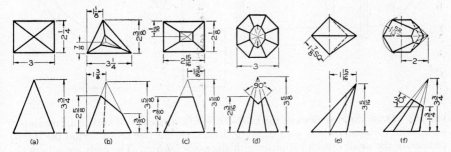

FIG. 682 Draw given views; develop lateral surface. Layout B4.*

* Arrangement similar to Fig. 677, p. 380.

381

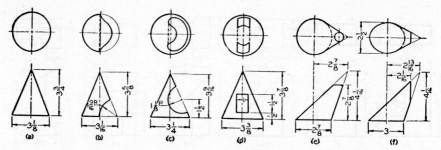

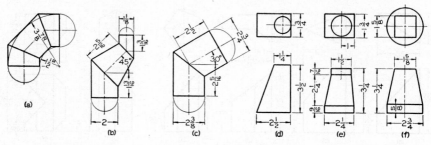

FIG. 683 Draw given views; develop lateral surface. Layout B4.*

FIG. 684 Draw given views; develop lateral surface. Layout B4.*

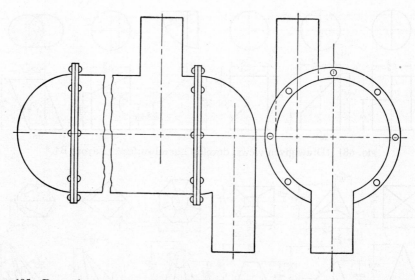

FIG. 685 Draw the two views of the CONDENSER, as shown. Transfer all measurements with dividers, making your drawing three times the size shown. Find the intersections of the small cylindrical pipes with the main portion. The ends are spherical. Layout B4 (Appendix 1).

* Arrangement similar to Fig. 678, p. 380.

382

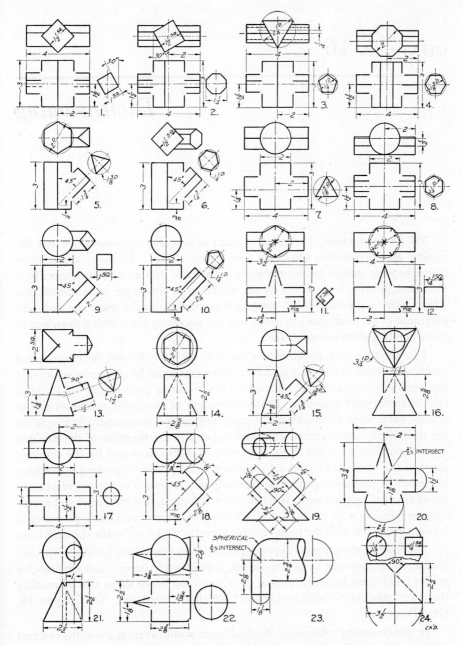

FIG. 686 Draw the given views of assigned object, and complete the intersection. Then develop lateral surfaces. Layout B4 (Appendix 1).

383

CHAPTER 16

Dimensioning

357. Introduction. In the early years of machine manufacturing the designing and production functions were closely allied. In many cases, these processes were carried out by the same individual. Design drawings, usually of the assembly type, were scaled by the workmen to obtain the basic dimensions. The proper functioning of the product depended primarily upon the skill and judgment of the workman; hence it was not necessary for working drawings to carry detailed descriptions of sizes.

The need for *interchangeability* of parts is the basis for the development of modern methods of size specification. Drawings must be dimensioned so that workmen in widely separated places can make mating parts which will fit properly when brought together. The development of automatic machines and of devices for precision-measuring has made size control comparatively simple for the machinist, and accuracy control has become the function of the drafting department instead of the shop. Size control is now exercised by the engineer through the medium of working drawings. The workman no longer exercises judgment in engineering matters, but only in the proper execution of instructions conveyed by drawings. It is necessary, therefore, that engineers and draftsmen be familiar with methods and materials of construction, with processes of manufacture, and with the requirements of workers who are to use the drawings.

The student should seize every opportunity to familiarize himself with such fundamental processes as *pattern making*, *foundry work*, *forging*, and *machine-shop practice*. This may be accomplished by observation in the shops and by reading the many good books and periodicals* which are available. See Chapter 18, Shop Processes.

In dimensioning a drawing, the draftsman should keep in mind the finished piece and its function in the assembly. The dimensions given should be those which will assure that the part will be made only in one way, and exactly as intended by the designer or draftsman. In addition, he should keep in mind the manufacturing methods employed and the facilities available in the shop, and

* See Technical Bibliography in Appendix 44.

should, wherever possible, give dimensions which are convenient for the workman. The dimensions should be so given that it will never be necessary for the workman to calculate, scale, or assume any dimension in order to make the part as intended by the designer. Dimensions should never be duplicated on a drawing and no dimensions should be given except those needed to produce or inspect the part.

Dimensions should be given between points or surfaces which have a functional relation to each other or which control the location of other mating parts.

Dimensions should be given to finished surfaces in preference to rough surfaces wherever possible.

The student often makes the mistake of giving the dimensions *he used to make the drawing*. In many cases, these dimensions will not be the same as the dimensions needed in the shop, or in the function of the parts.

358. Learning to Dimension. First, the student must learn the *technique of dimensioning*: the character of the lines, the spacing of dimensions, the correct way to make arrowheads, and other items which come under the heading of

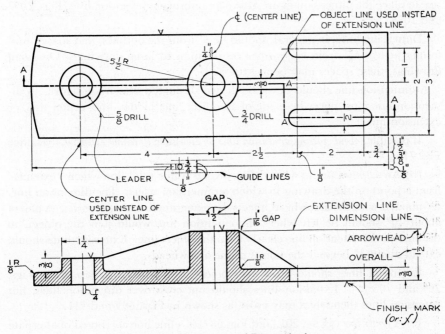

FIG. 687   Technique of Dimensioning.

technique. A model dimensioned drawing is shown in Fig. 687. This drawing illustrates the strong *contrast* between object lines and the secondary lines used for dimensioning. The center lines, dimension lines, and extension lines should all be extremely fine, while the object lines should be heavy. The dimensions should not detract from the views of the object, which should stand out clearly from everything else on the drawing.

Second, the student must learn *what dimensions* to give. This involves the function of the part in the assembly, and the production facilities in the shop. A geometric shape analysis (§ 367) will aid materially in determining the dimensions needed to make the object, but is not sufficient by itself.

Third, the student must develop judgment in regard to *placement of dimensions* (§§ 366–383) on the drawing.

359. Lines.

(a) A *dimension line* (§ 64 and Fig. 687) is a fine solid line, terminated by arrowheads, which bears the numeral denoting the dimension indicated. The distance between the arrowhead points shows the extent of the dimension, and the numeral denotes the amount. The dimension lines should be fine enough to contrast distinctly with the object lines, as shown in Fig. 687. In machine drawing, the dimension line is broken near its middle to permit the insertion of the numeral. In structural drawing and architectural drawing, it is common practice to place the dimension figure above an unbroken dimension line (Figs. 1057 and 1088).

Dimension lines, in general, should be $\frac{1}{2}''$ from the outlines, and spaced uniformly at least $\frac{3}{8}''$ from each other on medium to large drawings. On small drawings, these spaces may be as little as $\frac{1}{4}''$.

A dimension line should never be drawn through a dimension figure. A dimension line must never be made of an object line, hidden line, center line, or extension line.

If possible, *avoid crossing dimension lines or dimension lines and extension lines.* See Fig. 711.

(b) An *extension line* (§ 64 and Fig. 687) is a fine solid line which "extends" from a point on the drawing to which a dimension refers. The dimension line, terminated with the arrowhead, meets the extension line *at right angles.* A gap of about $\frac{1}{16}''$ should be left where the extension line would join the object, to distinguish the extension line clearly from the object line. Extension lines should extend about $\frac{1}{8}''$ beyond the points of the arrowheads.

Extension lines should cross over object lines without a gap, as in Figs. 704 and 705 (a). Extension lines should not cross over dimension lines, but extension lines themselves may cross, as shown in Figs. 699 and 711.

(c) A *center line* (§§ 64, 201, and Fig. 687) is a fine line composed of alternate $\frac{1}{8}''$ dashes and $\frac{3}{4}''$ to $1\frac{1}{2}''$ dashes with spaces of about $\frac{1}{16}''$ between them. It is used to represent the axis of symmetrical parts and also serves as an extension line in the location of holes and other symmetrical features. When the center line is so used, it is extended as necessary without changing into a solid line and without a gap where it crosses an object line (Fig. 687). Center lines should extend about $\frac{1}{4}''$ beyond the feature for which they are drawn, as in the circular and rectangular views of a hole (Fig. 687). Center lines should generally not be extended to connect views except when used for dimensioning.

In structural drafting, the lines along which the rivet holes are punched are thin solid lines, and are called *gage lines*. See Fig. 1084.

360. Arrowheads. *Arrowheads* (Figs. 687 and 688) terminate dimension lines, aiding the eye to determine the extent of the dimensions. *They should be uniform in size throughout the drawing* and not graded according to the size of the drawing or amount of the dimension.

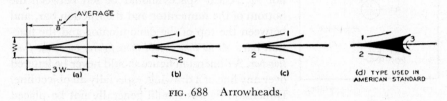

FIG. 688 Arrowheads.

The arrowhead should be approximately $\frac{1}{8}''$ in length, and *narrow:* about one-third as wide as it is long, as shown in Fig. 688 (a). It is made in two strokes, as shown at (b) or (c), the method at (b) being easier if the strokes are drawn toward the draftsman. The arrowhead used in the American Standard* is solid, as shown at (d). It is made with three strokes, and when done in ink will fill in solidly if made sufficiently narrow. This arrowhead is recommended for high-grade drafting.

The Gillott's 303 pen point, or equivalent, is recommended for making arrowheads in ink.

361. Leaders. A *leader* (Figs. 687, 689, and 725) is a fine solid line which "leads" from a note or dimension, and which is terminated by an arrowhead touching the part to which attention is directed. For mechanical drawings (except architectural), the leader lines should be *straight*, as shown in Fig. 689 (a). Curved leader lines are used in architectural drawings, as shown at (j), (k), and (l). A drawing presents a more pleasing appearance if all leaders near each other on a sheet are inclined at the same angle. *Leaders should never cross.*

Leaders are usually drawn, for convenience, at an angle of 30°, 45°, or 60° to horizontal, as shown in Fig. 689 (a) to (c), which shows the approved forms, but may be drawn at any desired angle if necessary *except vertical or horizontal*.

The leader should terminate in a short horizontal "shoulder" at the mid-height of the lettering at the beginning or end of a note, as in Fig. 689 (a) to (c).

362. Lettering. The importance of good lettering of dimension figures and notes cannot be overstated. The shop produces according to the dimen-

* ASA Z14.1—1946. See Appendix 2.

sions on the drawing, and to save time and prevent costly mistakes, all lettering must be perfectly legible. A complete discussion of vertical and inclined numerals and fractions is given in §§ 156, 157, 162, and 163.

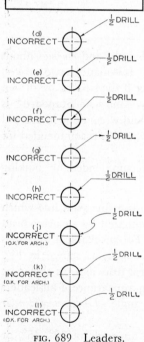

FIG. 689 Leaders.

As shown in Figs. 192, 194, and 687, the standard height for dimension whole numbers is $\frac{1}{8}''$ and for fractions $\frac{1}{4}''$. Beginners should use guide lines until they are able to letter uniformly and well. The fraction bar should always be horizontal, thus: $\frac{1}{4}''$, not ¼″. Clear spaces should be left between the bottom of the numerator and the fraction bar, and between the top of the denominator and the fraction bar. *At no time should these figures touch the fraction bar.* A dimension figure should never be lettered over any line of a drawing, especially an object line. Dimension figures should generally not be placed on sectioned areas, but when this is necessary, the section lines should be omitted where the dimension figure is placed, as in Fig. 904.

Notes should always be lettered horizontally on the sheet.

When there is a "stack" of parallel dimension lines, the dimension figures should be *staggered*, as shown in Figs. 690 (a) and 699, to provide ample space for the figures.

Dimension figures should generally be lettered half way between the two arrowheads, except when some other lines interfere, as for example, a center line or when the figures are staggered.

363. Direction of Dimension Figures. Two systems of alignment of dimension figures are approved by the American Standards Association.* The system in long use is the *aligned system*, and the newer is called the *unidirectional system*.

(a) *Aligned System.*—Fig. 691 (a). According to this system, all dimension lines and the corresponding lettering are placed so as to be read from the bottom or right-hand edge of the sheet, the dimension figures being placed so as to read in the direction of the dimension line. Dimension lines should not run in directions included in the shaded area of Fig. 692, if avoidable. A few examples of correct and incorrect applications of inclined dimension lines are shown in Fig. 693.

Notes should always be lettered horizontally on the sheet.

(b) *Unidirectional System.* — Fig. 691 (b). According to this system, all dimension figures are placed to read from the bottom of the sheet. In the

* ASA Z14.1—1946. See Appendix 2.

automotive, aircraft, and in other industries where drawings are often very
large and therefore difficult to read from the side, the unidirectional system

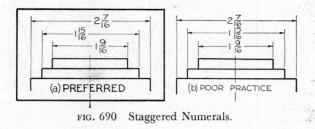

FIG. 690   Staggered Numerals.

has become widely accepted. Its use seems to be increasing, and is recommended along with the older method.

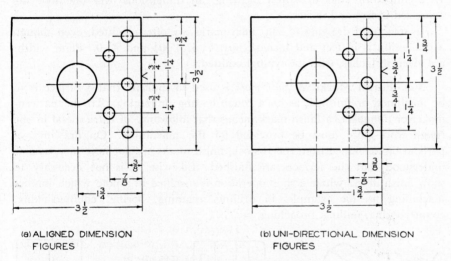

(a) ALIGNED DIMENSION
FIGURES

(b) UNI-DIRECTIONAL DIMENSION
FIGURES

FIG. 691   Direction of Dimension Figures.

364. Feet and Inches. *Inches* are indicated by the symbol ″ placed slightly above
and to the right of the numeral, thus: $2\frac{1}{2}''$.
Feet are indicated by the symbol ′ similarly
placed; for example: $3'-0''$, $5'-6''$, $10'-0\frac{1}{4}''$.

In machine drawing, inch marks are omitted,
except where there is a possibility of a misunderstanding; thus, 1 VALVE should be 1″
VALVE and 1 DRILL should be 1″ DRILL.

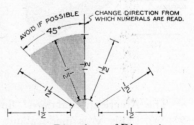

FIG. 692   Directions of Dimensions.

In some industries dimensions up to 72″ are expressed in inches, and
those greater than 72″ in feet and inches; in others, all dimensions are ex-

pressed in inches, regardless of the size. In locomotive, automotive, aircraft, and sheet-metal drafting, it is customary to express all dimensions in inches.

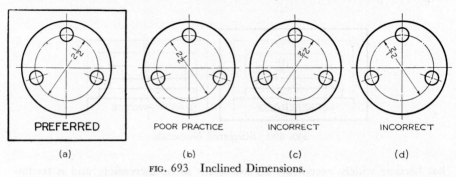

FIG. 693   Inclined Dimensions.

In architectural and structural drawing, all dimensions over one foot are expressed in feet and inches.

In structural drawing (§ 568) inch marks are often omitted, even though a dimension is in feet and inches, thus: $4'-3$, $4'-0\frac{1}{2}$ and $4'-0$. Plate widths are given in inches, with the symbol omitted.

365. Finish Marks. A *finish mark* is used to indicate that a surface is to be machined or finished, as on a rough casting or forging. To the pattern-maker or diemaker, a finish mark means that allowance of extra metal in the rough work-piece must be provided for the machining. On drawings of parts to be machined from rolled stock, finish marks are not necessary, as it is understood that the surfaces are finished. Likewise, it is not necessary to show finish marks where a shop operation is specified in a note which implies machining as, for example, in drilling, reaming, boring, countersinking, counterboring, milling, broaching, etc.

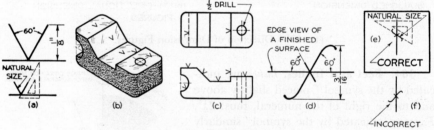

FIG. 694   Finish Marks.

The American Standard* finish mark is a capital $\vee$, as shown in Fig. 694 (a). This $\vee$ is made about $\frac{1}{8}''$ high, in conformity with the dimension figures, and for careful drawings should be made with the aid of the triangle, as shown.

*ASA Z14.1—1946. See Appendix 2.

In Fig. 694 (b) is shown an isometric drawing of a simple casting having several finished surfaces, each such surface being marked with a $\vee$ drawn in the isometric plane. At (c), two views of the same casting are given, showing the application of the finish marks on a working drawing. *The finish mark is shown only on the edge view of a surface to be finished, and is repeated in all views in which that surface is shown as a line, even if the line is a hidden line.* The point of the $\vee$ touches the line representing the finished surface, and is pointed inward toward the body of metal in a manner similar to a tool bit. Finish marks are given on curved surfaces, as shown at the left end of Fig. 694 (c), if not otherwise indicated to be finished.

Whenever it is necessary to specify the degree of smoothness of a finished surface, the $\vee$ may be used as a base for more elaborate symbols recommended by the ASA* to specify surface quality, as discussed in § 395.

Different forms of finish marks are used in almost every industrial drafting room, but the $\vee$-type finish mark is recommended by the ASA* and is rapidly gaining acceptance.

The old symbol "f" is still widely used, though it is executed in an annoying variety of forms. It is approved by the ASA* in the form shown in Fig. 694 (d) and (e), and probably will continue in use for many years. It is shown on edge views of finished surfaces as described above for the $\vee$-type finish mark.

If a part is to be finished all over, a note, such as FINISH ALL OVER, or F.A.O., or fAO may be used, and finish marks omitted.

Dimensions should always lead to finished surfaces wherever possible (Fig. 710).

366. Dimensions On or Off the Views. *Dimensions should not be placed upon a view unless the clearness of the drawing is promoted thereby.* The ideal form is shown in Fig. 695 (a), in which all dimensions are placed outside the view.

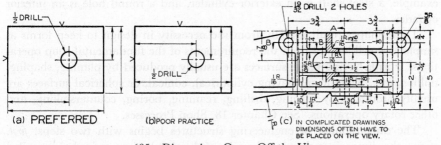

(a) PREFERRED   (b) POOR PRACTICE   (c) IN COMPLICATED DRAWINGS DIMENSIONS OFTEN HAVE TO BE PLACED ON THE VIEW.

FIG. 695   Dimensions On or Off the Views.

Compare this with the evidently poor practice shown at (b). This is not to say that a dimension should never be placed on a view, for in many cases, particularly in complicated drawings, this is not only unavoidable but pref-

* ASA Z14.1—1946. See Appendix 2.

erable, as shown at (c). Certain radii and other dimensions are given on the views, but in each case investigation will reveal a good reason for placing the dimension on the view.

The best rule to follow is to *place dimensions outside of views, except where directness of application and clarity are gained by placing them closer to the features dimensioned.*

367. Geometric Breakdown. Engineering structures are composed largely of simple geometric shapes, such as the prism, cylinder, pyramid, cone, sphere, etc., as shown in Fig. 696 (a). They may be exterior or interior forms. For

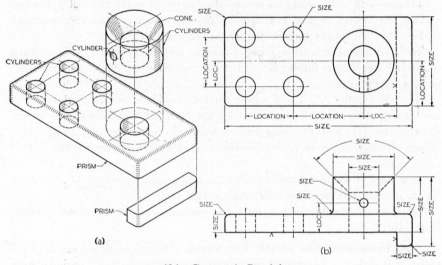

FIG. 696   Geometric Breakdown.

example, a steel shaft is an exterior cylinder, and a round hole is an interior cylinder.

These shapes result directly from the necessity in design to keep forms as simple as possible, and from the requirements of the fundamental shop operations. Forms having plane surfaces are usually produced by planing, shaping, milling, etc., while forms having cylindrical, conical, or spherical surfaces are usually produced by turning, drilling, reaming, boring, countersinking, and other rotary operations. See Chapter 18, Shop Processes.

The dimensioning of engineering structures begins with two steps: *first*, giving the dimensions showing the *sizes* of the simple geometric shapes, called *size dimensions*, and *second*, giving the dimensions *locating* these elements with respect to each other, called *location dimensions*. This method of geometric analysis is very helpful in dimensioning any object, but must be modified where there is a conflict with either the function of the part in the assembly or with the production requirements in the shop.

In Fig. 696 (b) is shown a multiview drawing of the object shown in isometric at (a). Here it will be seen that each geometric shape is dimensioned
with size dimensions, and these shapes are then located with respect to each
other with location dimensions. Note that a *location dimension locates a three-
dimensional geometric element*, and not just a surface; otherwise, all dimensions
would have to be classified as location dimensions.

368. Size Dimensions—Prisms. The prism is the most common shape
encountered. It is dimensioned by giving its height and width in the principal
view, and the depth in the side or top view, as shown in Fig. 697 (a) and (b).

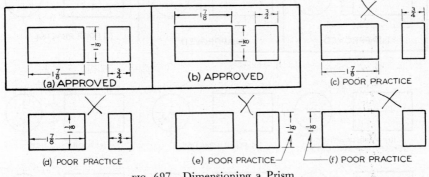

FIG. 697   Dimensioning a Prism.

Dimensions should "line up," if possible, and not be out of line without
reason as shown at (c).

Dimensions should not be given within the outlines of a view, or allowed to
cross as shown at (d), unless clearness of the drawing is improved by it. See
also § 366.

A dimension which applies to two adjacent views should be placed between
the views, as shown at (a) and (b), and not outside as in (e) and (f), unless
clearness of the drawing is improved by so doing. See also Figs. 687 and 696.
A dimension between two views should be attached to one view only; that is,
the extension lines should not connect the two views. See Fig. 713 (a).

Notice, in Fig. 697, that inch marks are omitted (§ 364).

For a triangular prism, two dimensions are given in the triangular view, and
the third dimension in another view. For a hexagonal or octagonal prism, one
dimension is given in the view showing the hexagon or octagon, the dimension
being given "across flats" or "across corners"; and the length is given in another view.

369. Size Dimensions—Cylinders. The cylinder is the next most common
form, and is commonly seen as a shaft or a hole. A cylinder is dimensioned by
giving *both its length and its diameter in the rectangular view*, as shown in Fig. 698
(a) and (b).

As mentioned before, it is poor practice to place a dimension on a view, as shown at (c).

Most of the errors made in dimensioning cylinders are those in specifying the circular size. Diagonal diameters, as shown at (d), are not approved except in cases where clearness is gained thereby. This could occur in the case of a large hole through thin material or in other cases where the diameter would not be clear in the rectangular view. The diameter of a circle of centers should

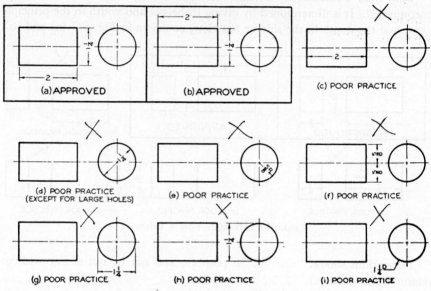

FIG. 698   Dimensioning a Cylinder.

be given diagonally, as shown in Fig. 693 (a), but this should not be regarded as a case of cylindrical dimensioning.

The radius of a cylinder should never be given, as shown at (e), since shop measuring tools, such as the micrometer caliper, are built to check diameters.

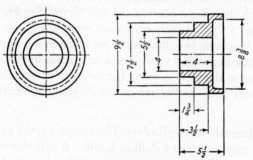

FIG. 699   Dimensioning Cylinders
(ASA Z14.1—1946).

The double radius at (f) is obviously bad. The diameter should not be given between extension lines running out from the circular view of a cylinder, as at (g) or at (h). Nor should a diameter be specified by note as at (i).

A practical example of dimensioning cylinders is shown in Fig. 699. This also illustrates how the dimension figures should be "staggered" to provide ample space for each dimension.

In dimensioning a cylindrical hole, it is customary to use a note, giving first the diameter, and second the operation, as in Fig. 689. See also the examples in Figs. 687 and 725. The depth of the hole is also often given in the note, as in Fig. 725 (a), but may be given in the rectangular view as a regular dimension, if the depth must be accurate (as when tolerances are given).

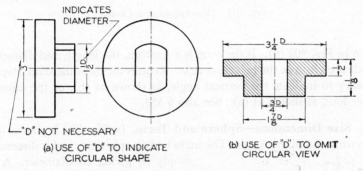

FIG. 700   Use of "D" in Dimensioning Cylinders.

When it is not clear from the views of the object that a dimension applies to a diameter, the abbreviation *D* should be given at the upper right side of the dimension figure, as shown in Fig. 700 (a). In some cases, the use of the *D* may be used to eliminate an entire view, as shown at (b).

A part of a cylinder, such as a fillet or round (§§ 444 and 467) is dimensioned by giving its *radius*, as discussed in § 380. In general, a circle is dimensioned by its diameter and an arc by its radius.

370. Size Dimensions—Pyramids. A pyramid is dimensioned by giving its length or altitude in the principal view (side of pyramid), and the dimensions of the base in the view showing its true size and shape, as in Fig. 701 (a).

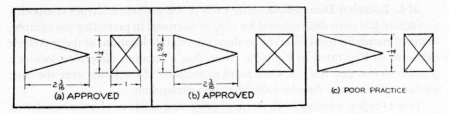

FIG. 701   Dimensioning a Pyramid.

If the base is square, one dimension only with the abbreviation *SQ.* may be given, as at (b). As shown at (c), a dimension between views is to be avoided, because of the long extension lines.

371. Size Dimensions—Cones. A cone is dimensioned by giving its length or altitude and the diameter of the base in the principal view (side of the cone),

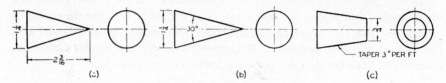

FIG. 702   Dimensioning a Cone.

as shown in Fig. 702 (a). If the cone is a frustum, the length and diameters of both ends are given in the principal view. Requirements in the shop may make it necessary to indicate the vertical angle, as shown at (b), or the amount of taper per foot, as shown at (c). See also § 388.

372. Size Dimensions—Sphere and Torus. In Fig. 703 is shown a two-view drawing of a plastic knob. The main body is spherical, and is dimensioned

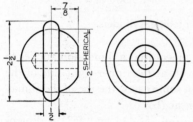

FIG. 703   Dimensioning Sphere and Torus.

simply by giving its diameter. A bead around the knob is in the shape of a torus, which is dimensioned by giving the thickness of the ring and the outside diameter of the torus.

373. Size Dimensions for Internal Shapes. As shown in § 367, the methods of dimensioning the basic geometric shapes are the same whether they are external or internal. The dimensioning of several internal shapes is illustrated in Fig. 704, where the prism, pyramid, cylinder, and cone shapes will be recognized. The holes at (c) and (d) would be dimensioned by means of notes (Fig. 725) if the operations are given.

374. Location Dimensions. After each of the geometric shapes composing a structure has been dimensioned for *size*, as discussed in preceding paragraphs, *location* dimensions must be given to show the relative locations of the geometric elements, as illustrated in Fig. 696. Note that a location dimension locates a *geometric element* and not just some point or surface. If the latter were the case, all dimensions could then be called location dimensions.

Prism shapes, whether in the form of projecting solids or of holes or recesses, are located with reference to their faces, as in Fig. 705 (a).

Cylindrical or conical holes or bosses or other symmetrical shapes are located with reference to their center lines, as in Fig. 705 (b).

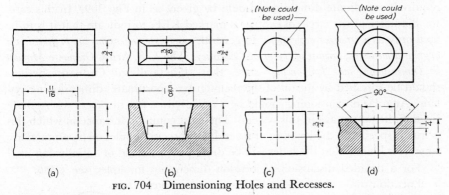

FIG. 704　Dimensioning Holes and Recesses.

Location dimensions for holes are preferably given in the view showing the shapes of the holes, as round, square, etc., as in Figs. 705 (b) and 706 (a).

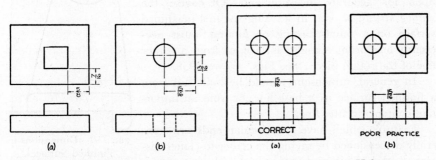

FIG. 705　Location Dimensions.　　　　　FIG. 706　Locating Holes.

Holes which are grouped symmetrically about a common center are located by giving the diameter (diagonally) of the *circle of centers*, or *bolt circle*, as in Fig. 707. This method may be used where great accuracy is not essential.

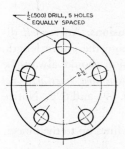

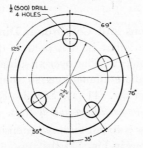

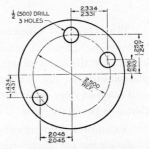

FIG. 707　Locating Holes,　　　FIG. 708　Locating Holes,　　　FIG. 709　Coordinate Di-
Equally Spaced about　　　Unequally Spaced about　　　mensions for Greater
a Center.　　　　　　　　a Center.　　　　　　　　Accuracy.

When the holes are not equally spaced, it is necessary to give the angles (§ 379) to *only one* of the center lines, as in Fig. 708. Where greater accuracy is required, coordinate dimensions should be given, as in Fig. 709. In this case, the diameter of the circle of centers is marked REF. to indicate that it is to be used only as a *reference dimension*. In general, *coordinate dimensions are preferred over angular dimensions, because of the greater accuracy.* The U.S. Army *Ordnance Manual on Dimensioning and Tolerancing** states that "Practically all Ordnance designs should be specified by means of the rectangular [coordinate] dimensioning system. Angular dimensioning should be used only in a few instances where there is a definite advantage in this system. The most common instance in which this is true is specifying the locating of several non-precision holes on a common arc when it is known that the holes will be drilled with the aid of an indexing jig."

For a detailed discussion of location dimensions for holes, see § 386.

Location dimensions (as well as size dimensions) should lead to finished surfaces wherever possible (Fig. 710), because rough castings and forgings vary in size, and unfinished surfaces cannot be relied upon for accurate measurements. Of course, the *starting dimension*, used in locating the first machined surface on a rough casting or forging, must necessarily lead from a rough surface, or from a center line of the rough piece. See Figs. 957 and 958.

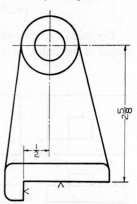

FIG. 710 Dimensions to Finished Surfaces.

In general, dimensions should be built out from a finished surface as a base line, or from an important center or center line.

Features which have semicircular ends are generally dimensioned by giving the center-to-center distance and the radii at the ends, and without an over-all dimension. For this and for several exceptions to this rule, see § 381.

When several cylindrical shapes have the same center line, it is not necessary to locate them with respect to each other. See Fig. 699. For a discussion of tolerances on concentricity, see § 405.

375. Over-all Dimensions and Continuous Dimensions. An *over-all* dimension is a total dimension; that is, it is used to denote the entire length, height, or thickness of an object. The over-all dimension should always be placed outside the intermediate dimensions so that *dimension lines will not cross extension lines*, as shown in Fig. 711 (a). See also Figs. 691 and 699. Notice that it is perfectly *correct to allow extension lines to cross*.

A common student's error is to fail to draw extension lines up to the object, as shown for the $\frac{1}{2}''$ dimensions in Fig. 711 (b).

---

* Published by Inspection Gage Office, Office of the Chief of Ordnance A.S.F., United States Army.

Dimensions should line up continuously, as shown at (a), and not "stepped" in conformity with the contour of the view, as shown at (c).

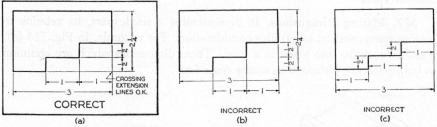

FIG. 711   Placement of Over-all Dimensions.

376. Contour Dimensioning. *Dimensions should be attached (by means of extension lines) to the view which most clearly represents the shape of the features dimensioned,* as shown in Fig. 712 (a) and (b), and Fig. 713 (a). Consequently, the view which shows most of the characteristic shapes of the object will also carry most of the dimensions.

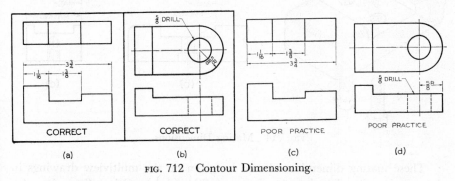

FIG. 712   Contour Dimensioning.

If individual dimensions are attached directly to the contour which shows the shape being dimensioned, this will prevent the attachment of dimensions to hidden lines and to object lines whose existence depends upon a contour shown in another view, as shown in Fig. 712 (c) and Fig. 713 (d). Follow this rule: *If possible, give a dimension in the view where the shape is shown.*

Although the placement of notes for holes follows the contour rule whenever possible, as shown in Fig. 712 (b), the diameter of general cylindrical shapes is preferably given in the rectangular view where it can be readily

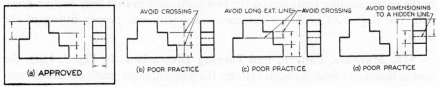

FIG. 713   Contour Dimensioning.

found near the dimension for the length of the cylinder. See Fig. 699. It would be particularly bad in this case if diagonal diameters were given in the circular view.

377. Mating Dimensions. In dimensioning a single part, its relation to mating parts must be taken into consideration. For example, in Fig. 714 (a), a guide block fits into a slot in a base. Those dimensions which are common to both parts are indicated as *mating dimensions*.

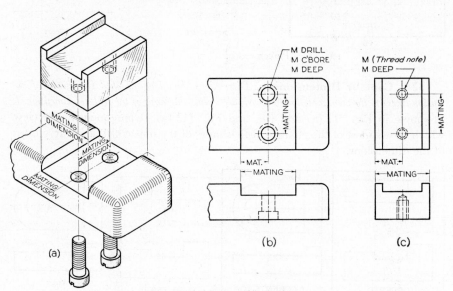

FIG. 714   Mating Dimensions.

These mating dimensions should be given on the multiview drawings in the corresponding locations, as shown at (b) and (c). Other dimensions are not mating dimensions since they do not control the accurate fitting together of the two parts. The actual *values* of two corresponding mating dimensions may not be exactly the same. For example, the width of the slot at (b) may be dimensioned $\frac{1}{32}''$ or several thousandths larger than the width of the block at (c), but these are mating dimensions figured from a single basic width.

It will be seen that the mating dimensions shown in Fig. 714 are those that might have been arrived at from a geometric breakdown (§ 367). However, the mating dimensions need to be identified so that they can be specified in the corresponding locations on the two parts, and so that they can be given with the degree of accuracy commensurate with the proper fitting of the parts.

378. Machine, Pattern, and Forging Dimensions. In Fig. 714 (a), the base is machined from a rough casting; the patternmaker needs certain dimensions to make the pattern, and the machinist needs certain dimensions for the machining. In some cases one dimension will be used by both. Again, in most cases, these dimensions will be the same as those resulting from a geometric breakdown (§ 367), but it is important to identify them in order to assign values to them intelligently.

The same part is shown in Fig. 715, with the machine dimensions and pattern dimensions identified by the letters M and P. The pattern-maker is interested only in the dimensions he needs to make the pattern, and the machinist, in general, is concerned only with the dimensions he needs to machine the part. If the part is large and complicated, two separate drawings are sometimes made, one showing the pattern dimensions, and the other the machine dimensions. The usual practice, however, is to prepare one drawing for the patternmaker and the machinist. See § 442.

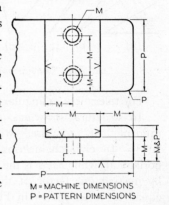

M = MACHINE DIMENSIONS
P = PATTERN DIMENSIONS

FIG. 715   Machine and Pattern Dimensions.

In the case of forgings, it is common practice to make separate forging drawings and machining drawings. A forging drawing of a connecting rod, showing only the dimensions needed in the forge shop, is shown in Fig. 855. A machining drawing of the same part, but containing only the dimensions needed in the machine shop, is shown in Fig. 857. See also Figs. 955–958.

Unless the complete decimal system is used (§ 397), the pattern dimensions are always nominal, usually to the nearest $\frac{1}{16}''$, and given in whole numbers and fractions. If a machine dimension is given in whole numbers and fractions, the machinist is usually allowed a tolerance (permissible variation in size) of $\frac{1}{64}''$, corresponding to his steel scale which has $\frac{1}{64}''$ divisions. Some companies specify a tolerance of .010″ on all common fractions. If greater accuracy is required, the dimensions are given in decimal form to three or more places (§ 397).

379. Angles. Two general methods are used in dimensioning angles, as shown in Fig. 716. The choice of method depends upon the degree of accuracy required, and the measuring equipment available in the shop.

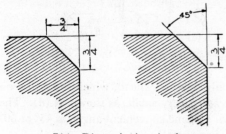

FIG. 716   Dimensioning Angles.

The use of angular dimensions to locate holes or other parts requiring accurate location (Figs. 707 and 708) should be avoided as much as possible in favor of the more accurate "coordinate" dimensioning, shown in Figs. 716 (left) and 709.

When angular dimensions are used, the dimension line is a circular arc with its center at the vertex of the angle, and terminated by arrowheads, as shown in Fig. 717. The dimension figures are lettered on horizontal guide lines, to be read from the bottom of the sheet. An exception is sometimes made in the aligned system (§ 363) in which, for large angles, the numerals may be lettered along an arc, as shown in Fig. 717 (e).

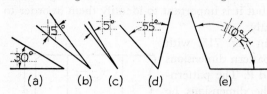

(a)   (b)   (c)   (d)   (e)

FIG. 717   Dimensioning Angles.

For tolerances in angular dimensions, see § 404.

In structural drawings, angular measurements are made by giving the ratio of "run" to "rise," with the larger side equal to 12″ (Figs. 1086 and 1088). In civil engineering drawings, *slope* represents the angle with the horizontal, while *batter* is the angle related to the vertical. Both are expressed by making one factor of the ratio equal to *1*, as shown in Fig. 718. *Grade* is the same as slope, but is generally related to lower angles, and is expressed in percentage of rise per 100 feet. Thus, a 20-foot rise in a 100-foot run is a grade of 20 per cent.

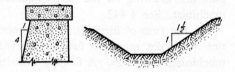

FIG. 718   Angles on Civil Engineering Projects (ASA Z14.1—1946).

380. Arcs and Curves. A circular arc is dimensioned in the view where the true shape of the curve is shown, by giving the numeral denoting its radius, followed by the abbreviation R placed above the dimension line, as shown in Fig. 719. The center is indicated by a small cross, as shown at (a) to (d). At (a) and (b) there is enough space to place the figure and the arrowhead inside the arc. At (c), the arrow is left inside, but the figure is moved outside. At (d), both the figure and the arrowhead had to be moved outside the arc. At (e) is shown an alternate method to (c) or (d), to be used when section lines or other lines are in the way.

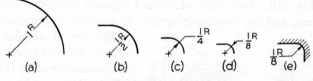

(a)   (b)   (c)   (d)   (e)

FIG. 719   Dimensioning Arcs.

The dimension line should have only one arrowhead, which should be on the inside of the arc except when the arc is very small, as shown at (d). The dimension line should always be drawn at some convenient angle, as 45° or 60° with horizontal, and never vertical or horizontal.

Individual fillets and rounds are dimensioned as shown in Fig. 719. Where there are many fillets or rounds having the same radius, a note may be given, such as "ALL CASTING RADII $\frac{1}{4}$R UNLESS OTHERWISE SPECIFIED."

Curved shapes may be dimensioned either by giving a series of radii, as shown in Fig. 720 (a), or by means of a series of offsets, as shown at (b).

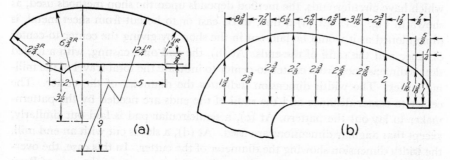

FIG. 720　Dimensioning Curves (ASA Z14.1—1946).

In dimensioning a large arc whose center is inaccessible, the center may be moved in on the drawing along a center line, as shown in Fig. 720 (a). A jog in the dimension line is made to indicate what has been done. Observe that the portion of the dimension line with the arrowhead is drawn toward the original center.

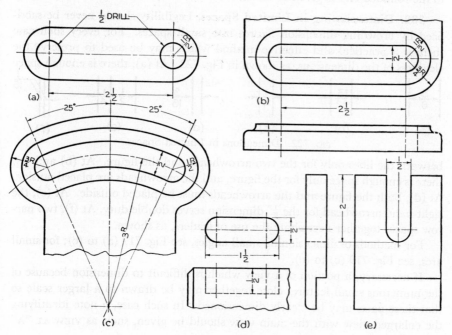

FIG. 721　Dimensioning Circular Ends.

When there are a large number of dimensions from a common reference point or surface, they may be placed in a single line so as to accumulate as shown in Fig. 720 (b). This is called *progressive dimensioning*. This is also good practice in structural drawing, as shown in Fig. 1086.

381. Dimensioning Circular Ends. In dimensioning objects or features which have circular ends, the method depends upon the shop methods used, as shown in Fig. 721. At (a) a link, to be cast or to be cut from sheet metal, is dimensioned as it would be laid out in the shop, by giving the center-to-center distance and the radii of the ends. At (b), the pad on a casting, with a milled slot, is dimensioned from center-to-center to indicate the total travel of the milling cutter. The width dimension indicates the diameter of the cutter. The center-to-center distance and the radii of the ends are needed by the pattern-maker to lay out the pattern. At (c), a semicircular pad is laid out similarly, except that angular dimensions are used. At (d), a slot is cut with an end mill, the width dimension showing the diameter of the cutter. In this case, the over-all dimension is given to facilitate inspection with gages, as in the case of Pratt and Whitney keys and keyseats. In general, when dimensioning machined internal or external rounded-end shapes where considerable accuracy is necessary, this method is recommended. When great accuracy is not required, the center-to-center distance at (d) might be preferred since it represents the travel of the cutter. At (e) a milling cutter is used, and the distance from the starting surface to the rounded end is given to indicate the travel of the cutter.

382. Dimensioning in Limited Spaces. Legibility should never be sacrificed by crowding dimension figures into small spaces. For every such case there is a practical and effective method which may be used to preserve the clearness of the dimensions, as shown in Fig. 722. At (a), there is enough space

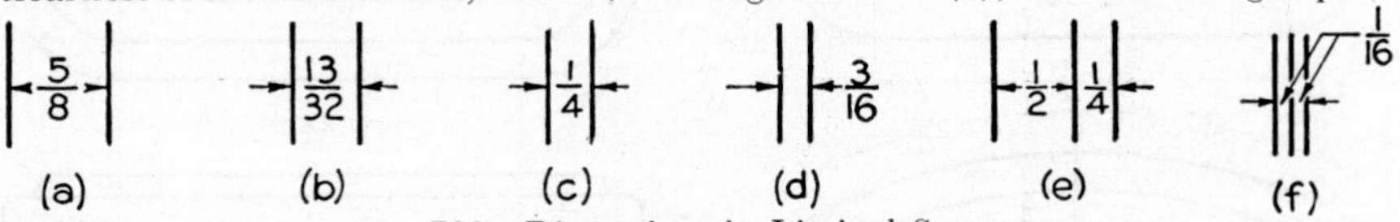

FIG. 722   Dimensions in Limited Spaces.

between the lines only for the two arrowheads and the figure. At (b) and (c), there is enough space only for the figure, and the arrowheads are placed outside. At (d), both the figure and the arrowheads must be placed outside. At (e), the right-hand arrowhead for the $\frac{1}{2}''$ dimension serves double duty. At (f), two narrow spaces together necessitate the use of leaders, as shown.

For methods of dimensioning small angles, see Fig. 717 (a) to (c); for small arcs, see Fig. 719 (c) to (e).

If necessary, a portion of a view which is difficult to dimension because of the numerous small features close together may be drawn to a larger scale so that these parts may be clearly dimensioned. In such case, a note identifying the enlarged view with the main view should be given, such as VIEW AT "A" ENLARGED.

383. Superfluous Dimensions. Although it is absolutely necessary to give all needed dimensions, the draftsman should avoid giving unnecessary or superfluous dimensions (Fig. 723). Dimensions should not be repeated on the same view or on different views, nor should the same information be given in two different ways.

In Fig. 723 (2) is shown a type of superfluous dimensioning which should generally be avoided, especially in machine drawing where accuracy is important. The workman should not be allowed a choice between two dimensions. *Avoid "chain" dimensioning*, in which a complete series of detail dimensions is given, together with an over-all dimension. In such cases, one dimension of the chain should be omitted, as shown, so that the machinist is obliged to work from

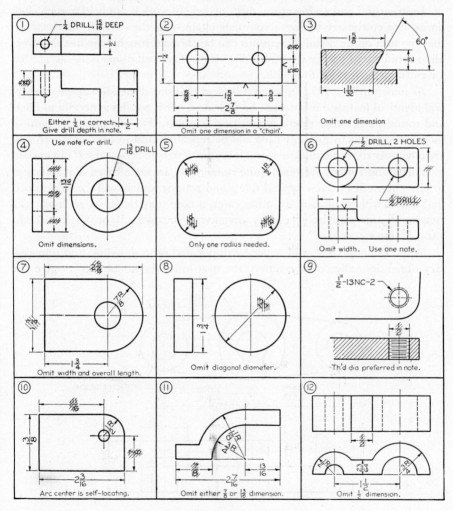

FIG. 723　Superfluous Dimensions.

one surface only. This is particularly important in limit dimensioning (§ 399), where an accumulation of tolerances can cause serious difficulties. See also § 403.

Some inexperienced draftsmen have the habit of omitting both dimensions, such as those at the right of Fig. 723 (2), on the theory that the holes are symmetrically located and will be understood to be centered. *This practice is not approved*, especially in production work or whenever accuracy is important.

Whenever it is necessary to give a complete chain plus the over-all dimensions for gaging or reference purposes, the extra dimension should be labeled REF. as shown in Fig. 724. It will be understood in the shop that this dimension will not be used except as a check.

In structural and architectural drafting, where work is not held to such close limits, it is customary to give a complete chain, plus the over-all dimension so that the sum of the detail dimensions can be checked roughly against the over-all to avoid a really large error. See Fig. 1088. Over-all dimensions are needed for cutting rough stock to length.

As shown in Fig. 723 (5), when it is clear that one dimension applies to several identical features, it need not be repeated. This applies generally to fillets and rounds, and other rough non-critical features. For example, the radii of the rounded ends in Fig. 721 need not be repeated; and in Fig. 687, both ribs are obviously the same thickness, and it is unnecessary to repeat the $\frac{3}{8}''$ dimension.

Fillets and rounds are often quite numerous. In some cases, it is sufficient to give the radii of a few typical fillets and rounds and it will be understood that others will be similar. In other cases, a note may be given, such as "ALL FILLETS $\frac{1}{4}^R$ AND ROUNDS $\frac{1}{8}^R$ UNLESS OTHERWISE SPECIFIED," or "ALL CASTING RADII $\frac{1}{4}^R$ UNLESS NOTED."

While dimensions should never be duplicated on a drawing, and unnecessary dimensions should be omitted, the draftsman should be sure to give the

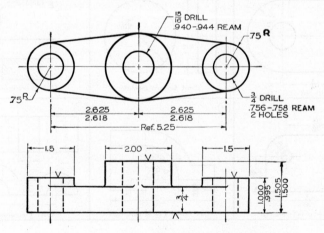

FIG. 724   Use of Reference Dimension.

dimensions needed to make the part as intended by the designer. The shop worker is not permitted to scale a blueprint to obtain a dimension; hence an incompletely dimensioned drawing will "bounce back" to the engineering department to the discomfiture of the draftsman. If this happens too often, he may be looking for another job.

384. Notes. It is frequently necessary to supplement the ordinary dimensions with notes. Notes should be kept to a minimum, since it takes time to letter them. The drawing plus the dimensions should be as clear and concise as can be and should need as little amplification by means of notes as possible. However, in production work, where the engineering department is attempting to control or "tie down" every detail so that the manufacturing will be carried out as planned, a great many notes are often necessary, as shown in Fig. 857. In architectural drawing, even notes are insufficient to carry all needed work information, and supplementary typed *specifications* are necessary (§ 552).

Notes should be brief and should be carefully worded so as to be capable of only one interpretation. *Notes should always be lettered horizontally on the sheet, and arranged in a systematic manner.* Notes are classified as *general notes* when they apply to an entire drawing, or *local notes* when they apply to specific items.

General Notes.—General notes should be lettered in the lower right-hand corner of the drawing, above or to the left of the title block, or in a central position below the view to which they apply; e.g.: "FINISH ALL OVER," or "BREAK SHARP EDGES TO $\frac{1}{32}$"R"; or "SAE–3345 - BRINELL 340 -380"; or "ALL DRAFT ANGLES 3° UNLESS OTHERWISE SPECIFIED."

In machine drawings the title strip or title block will carry many general notes, including material, general tolerances, heat treatment, pattern information, etc. See Fig. 742.

Local Notes. — Local notes apply to specific operations only and are connected by a leader to the point at which such operations are performed; e.g.: "$\frac{1}{4}$ DRILL–4 HOLES"; or "$\frac{1}{16} \times 45°$ CHAMFER"; or "33P. DIAMOND KNURL, RAISED." The leader should be attached at the front of the first word of a note, or just after the last word, and not at any intermediate place. For a large number of examples, see Fig. 725, which shows the wording of many notes commonly used. This wording is fairly well standardized, and should be used exactly as given where possible.

For additional information on notes, see § 471.

385. Size Dimensioning of Holes. Holes which are to be bored, drilled, reamed, punched, cored, etc., are specified by means of local notes, as shown in Fig. 726. In the case of a large hole, a diagonal diameter may be given together with the word indicating the operation.

A typical note includes, in this order, the following:

(1) Diameter of hole
(2) Operation (as DRILL, REAM, etc.)

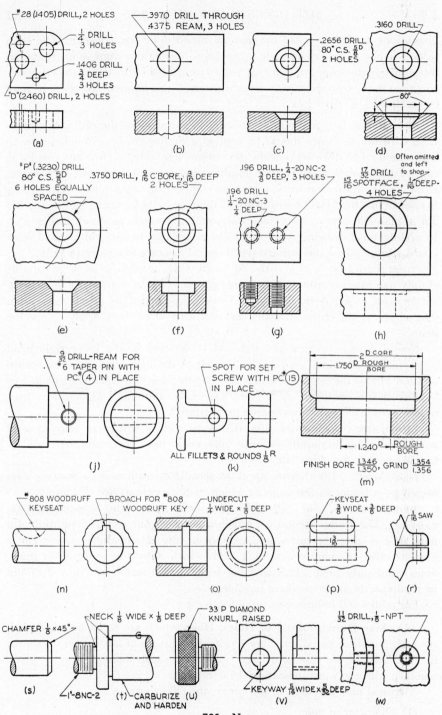

FIG. 725 Notes.

408

(3) Depth of hole

(4) Number of holes (if more than one)

(5) Spacing (if equally spaced, as in Fig. 707).

The leader of the note should lead to the circular view of the hole, if possible. In the case of counterbored, countersunk or tapped holes, or others where there are more than one circle, the arrowhead should touch the outer circle. See Fig. 725 (c) to (j) for a visual explanation.

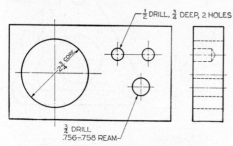

FIG. 726 Dimensioning Holes.

When there are several identical holes, there should be only one note, the leader pointing to only one hole, as shown at the top of Fig. 726. When there are several operations specified for one hole, the operations should be given in the note in the order they are to be performed, as shown at the bottom of Fig. 726. See also Fig. 725.

When the depth of a hole must be very accurate, a regular depth dimension may be given in the rectangular view of the hole, and the depth omitted from the note.

Notes and dimensions may be combined in the dimensioning of several concentric holes involving several operations, as shown in Fig. 727.

The use of decimal fractions to designate drill sizes is recommended by the ASA, and the practice is rapidly gaining in favor. If a fractional dimension is given, it is recommended that the decimal size be given also, but practice varies on this.

In all cases, where drills are specified by number (as #28) or by letter (as P), the decimal size should always be given, as shown in Fig. 725 (a) and (e).

A large number of notes are given in Fig. 725, the wording of which should be used for all similar cases.

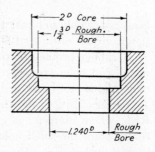

FIG. 727 Dimensioning Several Operations (ASA Z14.1–1946).

386. Location Dimensions of Holes. For accurate work, the coordinate method of locating holes is recommended, as shown in Fig. 728. The proper alignment of two or more mating parts (§ 377) requires similar dimensioning from a common datum plane or line, thus assuring accurate mating of the parts in assembly. A good example of this, called *base-line dimensioning*, is shown in Fig. 691. As shown, a base line may be a finished surface or an important center line. This arrangement makes each dimension independent of the others and avoids cumulative errors in a series of dimensions. See § 403.

In Fig. 728 (a) the three holes are on a common basic center line, and it

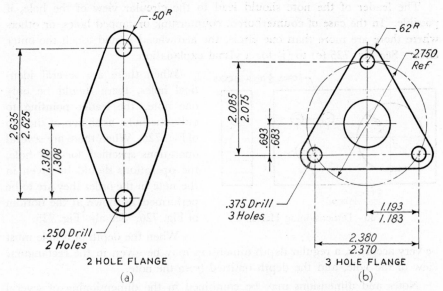

FIG. 728   Coordinate Location of Holes (ASA Z14.1—1946).

is necessary only to locate the holes along this line. Note that only one dimension from one of the end holes to the center is given.

A similar problem is shown in Fig. 724, in which both detail dimensions to the end holes are given, but note that the over-all is marked REF. to be used only for reference and checking.

In Fig. 728 (b), the three small holes are on a circle of centers marked REF. whose diameter is given only for reference purposes. From the main center point the small holes are located in two directions. A similar example is given in Fig. 709. *The use of angular dimensions (Figs. 707 and 708) for accurate work should be avoided as much as possible.*

387. Dimensioning of Threads. Local notes (§ 384) are used to specify dimensions of threads. For tapped holes the notes should, if possible, be attached to the circular views of the holes as shown in Fig. 725 (g). For external threads, the notes are usually placed in the side views, where the threads are more readily recognized, as in Fig. 770. For a detailed discussion of thread notes, see § 423.

388. Dimensioning of Tapers. The usual method of dimensioning a taper is to give the amount of taper per foot in a note (sometimes with "to gage" added), as shown in Fig. 729 (a), and then to give the diameter at one end plus the length, or give the diameters of both ends and omit the length. "*Taper per foot*" *is the difference in diameter in one foot of length.*

A standard taper is dimensioned by giving a note designating the taper by number taken from ASA B5.10–1943, and then giving the diameter at one end plus the length, as shown in Fig. 729 (b).

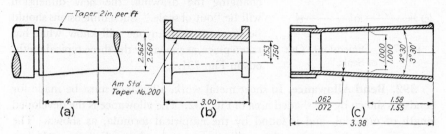

FIG. 729   Dimensioning Tapers (ASA Z14.1—1946).

Where considerable accuracy is required to obtain a close fit between internal and external parts, a taper should be dimensioned as shown in Fig. 729 (c). A gage line is selected and the tolerance at this point is taken as ± 0. The tolerance for locating the gage line varies according to the variation in entry distance permitted. Angular tolerance is then specified in accordance with the closeness of fit required. Notice the method of offsetting the extension lines for the gage line diameter. This is done to separate the extension lines from the internal object lines.

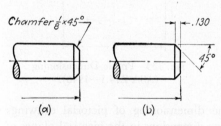

FIG. 730   Dimensioning Chamfers
(ASA Z14.1—1946).

389. Dimensioning of Chamfers. *A chamfer* is a beveled or oblique edge. The most common chamfer is 45°, and it is dimensioned by means of a note, as shown in Fig. 730 (a), or by means of dimensions, as shown at (b). If the angle is not 45°, the method at (b) must be used.

390. Dimensions of Standard Parts. The dimensions for many commonly used machine elements such as bolts, screws, nails, keys, tapers, wire, pipes, sheet metal, chains, ropes, pins, rolled steel shapes, etc., have been standardized, and the draftsman must obtain these sizes from company standards manuals, from handbooks, from American Standard pamphlets, or from manufacturers' tables. Tables covering some of the more common items are given in the Appendix of this text.

Such parts are not shown on detail working drawings unless the parts are to be altered for use, but are drawn conventionally on assembly drawings and are listed, according to standard tables, in the parts lists (§ 473).

391. Changes of Dimensions. It is often necessary to change a dimension in order to avoid making a drawing over. Such changes come under the general heading of alterations and are discussed at length in § 474.

(a)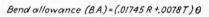

When a dimension is changed without changing the drawing, the new dimension will be "out of scale." Such dimensions should be given so that anyone will know what has taken place, as shown by the three typical methods in Fig. 731.

FIG. 731   Dimensions "Out of Scale."

392. Bend Allowance. In sheet metal work, allowance must be made for bends, as shown by the shaded area of Fig. 732. The allowance is the developed length of material, and is found by the empirical formula, as shown. The intersection of the plane surfaces adjacent to a bend is called the *mold line*, and this line is used rather than the center of the arc to terminate dimensions. as shown in Fig. 733.

Bend allowance (B.A.) = (.01745 R + .0078 T) θ

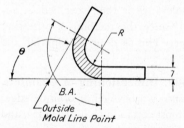

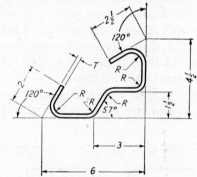

FIG. 732   Bend Allowance
(ASA Z14.1—1946).

FIG. 733   Profile Dimensioning
(ASA Z14.1—1946).

393. Pictorial Dimensioning. The dimensioning of pictorial drawings consists largely in drawing the multiview dimensions in the pictorial planes of the object represented. For the dimensioning of isometric drawings, see § 277, and for oblique drawings, see § 294.

There are many examples of both isometric and oblique dimensioning in the problems at the ends of Chapters 7 and 19. For examples of isometric dimensioning, see especially Figs. 866, 870, 885, and 893, and for examples of oblique drawing, see especially Figs. 934–937, 939 and 945.

All dimension figures should be isometric or oblique projections of vertical numerals.

394. Tabular Dimensions. A series of objects having like features but varying in dimensions may be represented by one drawing (Fig. 734). Letters are substituted for the numerals, and the varying dimensions are given in tabular form. The dimensions of standard parts are given in this manner in the various handbooks.

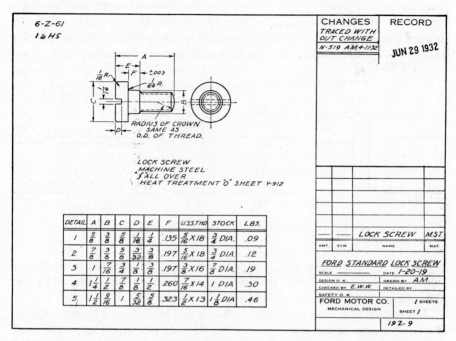

FIG. 734 Tabular Dimensions.

395. Surface Quality Symbols. A proposed American Standard (ASA B46) has now been developed on surface quality, which defines *roughness, waviness,* and *lay,* sets up specifications for each, and recommends symbols to indicate the desired surface quality. *Surface roughness* is the term used with reference to the small peaks and valleys which will be found on any surface. *Waviness* refers to the larger undulations of a surface. *Lay* refers to the direction of the tool marks or scratches on a surface.

Surface finish is intimately related to the functioning of a surface, and proper specification of finish of such surfaces as bearings, seals, etc., is very important. Where the finish of a surface is not important, it may not be necessary to specify the surface quality. However, surface finish specification may be used to prevent the shop from overdoing the matter of finish and thus running up the cost unnecessarily.

When surface quality is to be specified, the ASA ∨ finish mark is used as a base, and the right side is extended upward like a check mark, as shown in Fig. 735 (a). When it is necessary to specify only roughness height, and the width between ridges or direction of tool marks is unimportant, the simple symbol shown at (a) should be used. The roughness is indicated by the numeral in microinches (one microinch = one-millionth inch [0.000001]), designating maximum peak-to-valley height, average-peak-to-valley height, or average deviation from the mean. Since the average deviations from the mean can be easily measured with an instrument called a *profilometer*, this method is generally used. Surface roughness may be inspected visually or by touch by comparison of a surface with sample surfaces having accurately measured surface ridges.

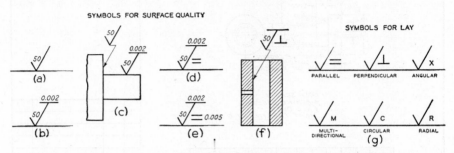

FIG. 735   Surface Quality Symbols (ASA Z14.1—1946).

Where it is desired to specify "waviness height" in addition to roughness height, a horizontal bar is added on top of the symbol, and the numerical value of waviness height is shown above the line, as shown in Fig. 735 (b).

If it is further desired to specify the lay, it will be indicated by the addition of a combination of lines, as shown in Fig. 735 (d) and (g). The parallel and perpendicular line symbols indicate that the ridges on the surface are parallel or perpendicular to the boundary line of the surfaces in contact with the symbol.

The complete symbol, including the roughness *width* to the right of the lay symbol, is shown in Fig. 735 (e). The number for height or width of roughness or waviness is understood to be the maximum value. When it is desired to indicate maximum and minimum permissible values, two numbers separated by a dash may be used.

Applications are shown at (c) and (f).

396. Do's and Don'ts of Dimensioning. The following check list summarizes briefly most of the situations in which a beginning draftsman is likely to make a mistake in dimensioning. The student should check his drawing by this list before submitting it to his instructor.

1. Dimensions should not be duplicated or the same information be given in two different ways, and no dimensions should be given except those needed to produce or inspect the part.
2. Dimensions should be given between points or surfaces which have a functional relation to each other or which control the location of mating parts.
3. Dimensions should be given to finished surfaces or important center lines in preference to rough surfaces wherever possible.

4. Dimensions should be so given that it will not be necessary for the workman to calculate, scale, or assume any dimension.

5. Dimensions should be attached to the view where the shape is best shown (contour rule).

6. Dimensions should be placed in the views where the features dimensioned are shown true size.

7. Avoid dimensioning to hidden lines wherever possible.

8. Dimensions should not be placed upon a view unless clearness is promoted thereby.

9. Dimensions which apply to two adjacent views should be placed between views, unless clearness is promoted by placing them outside.

10. Over-all dimensions should be placed outside of all intermediate dimensions, so that dimension lines will not cross extension lines.

11. In machine drawing, omit all inch marks, except where necessary for clearness; e.g.: 1″ VALVE.

12. Do not expect the workman to assume a feature is centered (as a hole on a plate), but give one location dimension in each direction.

13. A dimension should be attached to only one view (extension lines not connecting two views).

14. Detail dimensions should "line up" in a continuous line.

15. Avoid a complete chain of detail dimensions, but omit one; otherwise, one detail dimension or the over-all dimension may be marked REF.

16. A dimension line should never be drawn through a dimension figure. A figure should never be lettered over any line of the drawing.

17. Dimension lines should be spaced uniformly throughout the drawing. (Small drawings: $\frac{1}{4}$″ spacing; larger drawings: $\frac{3}{8}$″ to $\frac{1}{2}$″ spacing.)

18. No line of the drawing should be used as a dimension line or coincide with a dimension line.

19. A dimension line should never be joined end-to-end with any line of the drawing.

20. Dimension lines should not cross, if avoidable.

21. Dimension lines and extension lines should not cross, if avoidable.

22. When extension lines cross extension lines or object lines, no break in either line should be made.

23. A center line may be extended and used as an extension line, in which case it is still made like a center line.

24. Center lines should generally not extend from view to view.

25. Leaders for notes should be straight, not curved, and pointing to the circular views of holes wherever possible.

26. Leaders should slope at 45°, 30°, or 60°, with horizontal but may be made at any odd angle except vertical or horizontal.

27. Leaders should extend from the beginning or end of a note, the horizontal shoulder extending from the mid-height of the lettering.

28. Dimension figures should all be lettered to read from the bottom of the sheet or from the right side (aligned), or should all be lettered to read from the bottom of the sheet (unidirectional).

29. Dimension figures should be centered between the arrowheads, except that in a "stack" of dimensions, the figures should be "staggered."

30. Dimension figures should be about $\frac{1}{8}''$ high for whole numbers and $\frac{1}{4}''$ high for fractions.

31. Dimension figures should never be crowded or in any way made difficult to read.

32. Dimension figures should not be lettered over sectioned areas unless necessary, in which case, a clear space should be left for the dimension figures.

33. Dimension figures for angles should generally be lettered horizontally.

34. Fraction bars should always be parallel to the dimension line, never inclined.

35. The numerator and denominator of a fraction should never touch the fraction bar.

36. Notes should always be lettered horizontally on the sheet.

37. Notes should be brief and clear, and the wording should be standard in form (Fig. 725).

38. Finish marks should be placed on the edge views of all finished surfaces, including hidden edges and the contour and circular views of cylindrical surfaces.

39. Finish marks should be omitted on holes or other features where a note specifies a machining operation.

40. Finish marks should be omitted on parts made from rolled stock.

41. If a part is finished all over, omit all finish marks, and use the general note: FINISH ALL OVER, or F.A.O.

42. A cylinder is dimensioned by giving both its diameter and length in the rectangular view (except when notes are used for holes).

43. Holes which are to be bored, drilled, reamed, etc., are completely size-dimensioned by notes in which the leaders preferably point toward the circular views of the holes.

44. Drill sizes are preferably expressed in decimals. For drills designated by number or letter, the decimal size must also be given.

45. In general, a circle is dimensioned by its diameter, an arc by its radius.

46. Avoid diagonal diameters, except for very large holes and for circles of centers.

47. A diameter dimension figure should be followed by the letter D except when it is obviously a diameter.

48. A radius dimension figure should always be followed by the letter R. The radial dimension line should have only one arrowhead, and it should touch the arc.

49. Holes should be located by their center lines.

50. Holes should be located in their circular views, if possible.

51. Holes should be located by coordinate dimensions in preference to angular dimensions where accuracy is important.

52. Where there are several rough non-critical features obviously the same size (fillets, rounds, ribs, etc.) it is necessary to give only typical dimensions, or to use a note.

53. When a dimension is not to scale it should be underscored or marked "Not to scale."

54. Mating dimensions should be given correspondingly on drawings of mating parts.

55. Pattern dimensions should be given in common whole numbers and fractions to the nearest $\frac{1}{16}''$.

56. Decimal dimensions should be used where greater accuracy than $\frac{1}{64}''$ is required on a machine dimension.

57. Avoid cumulative tolerances, especially in limit dimensioning described in § 399.

397. Fractional and Decimal Dimensioning. In the early days of machine manufacturing in this country much reliance was placed on the skill of the workman. Often the original design drawing, which had few if any dimensions, was used in the shop, and through personal supervision and verbal instructions the machines were built to suit the designer. The workman would scale the drawing to obtain any needed dimensions, and it was his responsibility to see to it that the parts fitted together properly.

When blueprinting came into use, workmen in widely separated localities used the same drawings, and it became the practice to dimension the drawings, more or less completely, in inches and common fractions, such as $\frac{1}{4}''$, $\frac{1}{8}''$, $\frac{1}{16}''$, $\frac{1}{32}''$, and $\frac{1}{64}''$. The smallest dimension the workman was supposed to measure directly was $\frac{1}{64}''$, which was the smallest division on the ordinary machinist's scale.* (However, a good machinist could "split" sixty-fourths with ease.) Where close fits were required, the drawing would carry a note, such as "running fit," or "drive fit," and the workman would make considerably finer adjustment of size than $\frac{1}{64}''$. Workmen were skilled, and it should not be thought that very accurate and excellent fits were not obtained. Hand-built machines were often beautiful examples of precision workmanship.

This system of units and common fractions is still used in architectural and structural work where close accuracy is relatively unimportant, and where the steel tape or framing square is used to set off measurements. Architectural and structural drawings are therefore dimensioned in this manner.

Also today there are many types of manufacturing in which units and common fractions are almost universally used, because extreme accuracy is not necessary. An example of this is locomotive drawing in which the structure is very large and extremely fine measurements are generally not required. However, there are also many small articles manufactured today in which the ordinary machinist's scale is sufficiently accurate, and units and common fractions for dimensions on drawings are considered perfectly satisfactory and suitable for the purpose.

As industry has progressed, there has been greater and greater demand for more accurate specifications of the important functional dimensions—more accurate than the $\frac{1}{64}''$ permitted by the machinist's scale. It was cumbersome to use smaller fractions, such as $\frac{1}{128}$ or $\frac{1}{256}$, and it became the practice to give decimal dimensions, such as 4.2340, 3.815, etc., for the dimensions requiring accuracy. Along with this, many of the dimensions, such as pattern dimensions, forging dimensions and relatively unimportant machine dimensions, were

---

* Many machinist's scales are now graduated in hundredths.

still expressed in units and common fractions. This practice is the most common method of dimensioning drawings today—that is, using a combination of units and common fractions for relatively rough dimensions, and using units and decimal fractions where greater accuracy is required. See Fig. 742. The tendency is definitely to shift responsibility for size control from the shop to the engineering department, where it obviously belongs.

The use of two systems of dimensioning at the same time has caused a great deal of confusion, and there is a strong movement toward a complete decimal system for all dimensions. The metric system has many advantages and undoubtedly would be adopted if it were not necessary to scrap all present measuring devices and undergo the upheaval of making the change from the inch system.

In 1932, the Ford Motor Company decided to adopt a complete decimal system based on the inch as the unit of measure, thereby obtaining one of the major advantages of the metric system. The scale adopted (Fig. 736) is divided on one edge into inches and tenths, and on the other edge into inches, tenths, and fiftieths. The division lines on this latter edge are of three different lengths

FIG. 736   Ford Special Rule.

and grouped in an ingenious manner to facilitate easy reading. The smallest division is thus one-fiftieth, or .02″; two divisions would be .04″, three-fiftieths would be .06″, etc., so that when it is necessary to halve any measurement, the result will still be a two-place decimal. This scale has now been widely adopted, especially in the automotive industry.

Under this decimal system, measurements formerly expressed in common fractions are expressed in decimals to one place, as 2.1, 5.6, etc. A second place is added where greater accuracy is important, as 2.10, 5.62, but always in multiples of two. For still more accurate dimensions, in which the micrometer is used, a three-, four- (or more) place decimal is used. An example is shown in Fig. 737.

The ASA has now recommended a similar complete decimal system,* for use in industries where such a system would be advantageous, as follows:

"The fundamental basis of the complete decimal system is the use of a two-place decimal, i.e., a decimal consisting of two figures after the decimal point. In all dimensions where a fraction would ordinarily be used, the two-place decimal can be applied. The figures after the decimal point, where applicable, should be in fiftieths (e.g., .02, .04, .08, .84) so that when halved (e.g., diameters to radii) two-place decimals will result. Exceptions, of course, will have to be made, but they should be kept to a minimum.

"When a decimal value obtained by converting a common fraction to decimals is to be rounded off to a lesser number of places than the total number available, the procedure should be as indicated in ASA Z25.1—1940."

* ASA Z14.1—1946. See Appendix 2.

The method of rounding off decimals* is as follows:

"When the figure beyond the last figure to be retained is less than 5, the last figure retained should not be changed. *Example:* 3.46325, if cut off to three places, should be 3.463.

"When the figures beyond the last place to be retained amount to more than 5, the last figure retained should be increased by 1. *Example:* 8.37652 if cut off to three places, should be 8.377.

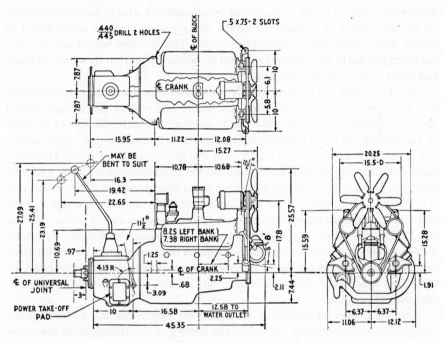

FIG. 737   Assembly of Ford V-8 Motor.

"When the figure beyond the last place to be retained is exactly 5 with only zeros following, the preceding number, if even, should be unchanged; if odd, it should be increased by 1. *Example:* 4.365 becomes 4.36 when cut off to two places. Also 4.355 becomes 4.36 when cut off to two places."

The use of the complete decimal system means not only an expensive change-over of measuring equipment, but also a change-over in thinking on the part of draftsmen and designers. They must discontinue thinking in terms of units and common fractions, and think in terms of tenths, fiftieths, and hundredths of an inch. However, once the new system is installed, it is obvious that the advantages in computation, in checking, and in simplified dimensioning technique will be considerable. There is no question but that industry in general is moving toward the adoption of a complete decimal system.

* ASA Z25.1—1940.

398. Tolerances. As has been stated in § 397, the use of decimal dimensions, such as 3.598″, or .002″, came into use because of the desire to specify on drawings more exactly the sizes desired by the designer—to shift the responsibility for exact size control from the judgment of the workman to the judgment of the trained engineer. Quantity production was made possible by the design and use of special tools, jigs, fixtures, and automatic machines which could in many cases be handled by semi-skilled workmen. The idea of depending upon highly skilled hand work had to be abandoned, and it became necessary for the draftsman or designer to decide exactly what sizes he wanted and to specify them unmistakably on the drawings. The designer would not be present when the parts were completed, and elaborate inspection by means of gages and other measuring devices had to be used.

But it was not sufficient to specify a dimension in decimals, say 3.598″, for it is impossible, even for a skilled mechanic, and especially for semi-skilled machine operators, to make anything to *exact size*. There will always be some variation from the exact theoretical size, though in some cases (e.g.: gage blocks) it is possible to make parts accurate to a few millionths of an inch. However, exact sizes are not needed, and would be too expensive even if they could be obtained, and a single product might require a large range of different degrees of accuracy. The answer to the problem was specification of a *tolerance* on each dimension, tolerance being "the amount of variation permitted in the size of a part." Thus, it becomes the problem of the draftsman or designer to specify the allowable error which may exist for a given dimension and still permit satisfactory functioning of the part. Since greater accuracy costs more money, he would not specify the closest tolerance, but instead would specify as generous tolerance as possible.

Another reason for specifying tolerances on dimensions was to make interchangeable manufacturing possible. The history of interchangeable manufacturing, by means of which parts could be made in widely separated localities and then brought together for assembly where the parts would all fit together properly, is a fascinating story in itself. Without interchangeable manufacturing, modern industry could not exist, and without tolerance dimensioning, interchangeable manufacturing could not have been achieved; for, in order to have parts made by different people in different places fit together properly, a definite size-control system by the engineer is essential.

399. Limit Dimensions. The old method of indicating dimensions of two mating parts was to give the nominal dimensions of the two parts in common whole numbers and fractions and to indicate by a note the kind of fit that is desired, as shown in Fig. 738 (a), and then to depend upon the workman to produce the parts so that they would fit together and function properly. Other types of fit included "drive fit," "sliding fit," "tunking fit," "force fit," etc.

In the example shown at (a), the machinist would make the hole close to $1\frac{1}{4}''$ diameter and would then make the shaft, say .003″ less in diameter. It would not matter if the hole were several thousands more or less than *1.250"*; he could make the shaft about *.003"* less and obtain the desired fit. But this method would not work in quantity production, since the sizes would vary considerably and would not be interchangeable; that is, any given shaft would not fit properly in any hole.

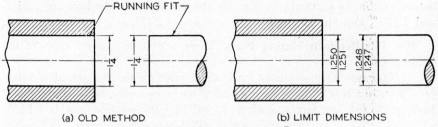

(a) OLD METHOD   (b) LIMIT DIMENSIONS

FIG. 738   Fits between Mating Parts.

In order to control the dimensions of quantities of the two parts so that any two mating parts would be interchangeable, it is necessary to assign limits to the dimensions of the parts, as shown in Fig. 738 (b). The diameter of the hole may be machined not less than *1.250"* and not more than *1.251"*; these two figures representing the *limits* and the difference between them, *.001"*, being the *tolerance.* Likewise, the shaft must be produced between the limits of *1.248"* and *1.247"*, the tolerance on the shaft being the difference between these, or *.001"*.

Here it will be seen that minimum difference between the two parts of *.002"* and a maximum difference of *.004"* is permitted, the average difference being *.003"*, which is the same as the difference allowed in the example at (a), but any hole will fit any shaft interchangeably.

400. Definitions of Terms. At this point it is well to fix in mind the definitions of certain terms used in limit dimensioning. The following are a list of the commonly used terms:

Nominal Size. — A close approximation to a standard size, without any specified limits of accuracy. In Fig. 738 (b), the nominal size of both hole and shaft is $1\frac{1}{4}''$.

Basic Size. — The exact theoretical size from which limits are figured. In Fig. 738 (b), the basic size is the decimal equivalent of $1\frac{1}{4}''$, or *1.250"*.

Allowance. — The minimum clearance space (or maximum interference) intended between mating parts. In Fig. 738 (b), the allowance is the difference between the smallest hole, *1.250"*, and the largest shaft, *1.248"*, or *.002"*. Allowance, then, represents the tightest permissible fit, or the condition where the largest internal member is mated with the smallest external member. The allowance is simply the smallest hole minus the largest shaft; and for clearance fits this difference will be positive, while for interference fits, it will be negative. See § 401 (2).

Tolerance. — The total permitted variation in the size of a part or in the location of points or surfaces; or the difference between the limits. In Fig. 738 (b), the tolerance on the hole is the difference between *1.250″* and *1.251″*, or *.001″*, and the tolerance on the shaft is the difference between *1.248″* and *1.247″*, or *.001″*.

Limits.—The maximum and minimum permitted dimensions of a part, or between points or surfaces. In Fig. 738 (b) the limits for the hole are *1.250″* and *1.251″*, and for the shaft are *1.248″* and *1.247″*.

401. Fits Between Mating Parts. There are three general types of fits between parts:

(1) *Clearance fit*, in which an internal member fits in an external member (as a shaft in a hole), and leaving an air space or clearance between the parts. In Fig. 738 (b), the largest shaft is *1.248″* and the smallest hole is *1.250″*, which permits a minimum air space of *.002″* between the parts. This space is the allowance, and in this case it is positive.

(2) *Interference fit*, in which the internal member is larger than the external member such that there is an actual interference of metal. In Fig. 739 (a), the smallest shaft is *1.2513″*, and the largest hole is *1.2506″*, so that there is an actual interference of metal amounting to at least *.0007″*.

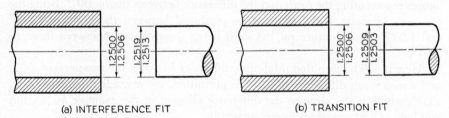

(a) INTERFERENCE FIT   (b) TRANSITION FIT

FIG. 739   Fits between Parts.

(3) *Transition fit*, in which the fit might be either a clearance fit or an interference fit. In Fig. 739 (b), the smallest shaft, *1.2503″*, will fit in the largest hole, *1.2506″*, with *.0003″* to spare. But the largest shaft, *1.2509″*, will have to be forced into the smallest hole, *1.2500″*, with an interference of metal (negative allowance) of *.0009″*.

Since a transition fit may or may not represent an interference of metal, *interchangeable assembly* is not generally satisfactory, and *selective assembly* is used. In selective assembly, all parts are classified into several grades, according to size, so that "small" shafts can be matched with "small" holes, "medium" shafts with "medium" holes, etc. In this way, very close fits may often be obtained at much less expense than by machining all mating parts to very accurate dimensions to ensure interchangeability.

Since standard reamers and other standard tools can be used to produce holes, and since shafting can easily be machined to any size desired, limit dimensions are most commonly figured on the so-called *basic hole system*. In this system, the *minimum hole is taken as the basic size*, an allowance is assigned, and limit dimensions applied on both sides of, and away from, this allowance.

In some branches of industry, as textile machinery manufacturing where use is made of a great deal of cold-finished shafting, the *basic shaft system* is often used. This system is preferred when several parts having different fits, but one nominal size, are required on a single shaft. In this system the *maximum shaft is taken as the basic size*, an allowance is assigned, and limit dimensions are applied on both sides of, and away from, this allowance.

The basic shaft size may be changed to the basic hole size simply by the addition or subtraction of the allowance, depending upon whether the allowance represents clearance of metal or interference. The specified limits are then applied to this new basic size for both shaft and hole.

402. Specification of Tolerances. For fractional dimensions, the worker is not expected to work closer than he can be expected to measure with a steel rule. It is customary to indicate an over-all tolerance for all fractional dimensions by means of a printed note in, or just above, the title block, such as ALL FRACTIONAL DIMENSIONS ±.010 UNLESS OTHERWISE SPECIFIED, or HOLD FRACTIONAL DIMENSIONS TO ±$\frac{1}{64}$ UNLESS OTHERWISE NOTED. See Figs. 846 and 861.

General tolerances on decimal dimensions in which limits are not given may also be covered in a general printed note, such as DECIMAL DIMENSIONS TO BE HELD TO ±.001. Thus, if a dimension *3.250* is given, the worker machines between the limits *3.249* and *3.251*. See Figs. 855-857.

Three methods of lettering tolerances are recommended by the ASA*. The *first method*, to be used on the smaller parts and where accurate dimensions are to be established with limit gages or micrometers, is to give the upper and lower limits for each dimension, as shown in Fig. 740. For external dimensions, the maximum dimension is placed above the line, while for internal dimensions, the maximum is placed below the line.

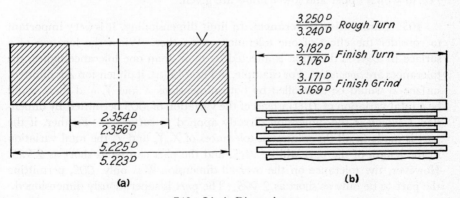

FIG. 740   Limit Dimensions.

* ASA Z14.1—1946. See Appendix 2.

A *second method* is to give the basic size to the desired number of decimal places, followed by a plus tolerance and a minus tolerance, with the plus above the minus, as shown in Figs. 741 (a) and 746.

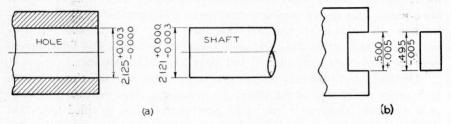

(a)   (b)

FIG. 741   Plus and Minus Tolerances.

A *third method*, sometimes used, is to give the desired dimension with a unilateral tolerance which is either plus or minus, but not both. This method is the one adopted by the U.S. Army Ordnance Department.* See Fig. 741 (b).

All three methods given above are examples of *unilateral tolerances*, in which a basic size is chosen and the tolerance is assigned from it, either plus or minus, but not both. See Figs. 740 and 741 (a). The figure used for the basic size is that which is nearest the critical or dangerous condition, and the tolerance is then given in a direction away from this condition.

When the basic size is selected, and then the tolerances in both directions from this value are given, the result becomes *bilateral tolerances*, as, for example, $8.625 \begin{smallmatrix} +.002 \\ -.002 \end{smallmatrix}$. This system is used when a variation in one direction is no more critical than in another, as in the location of holes. Bilateral tolerances are commonly used in specifying general tolerances by means of notes, as discussed above.

A typical commercial example of limit dimensioning is illustrated in Fig. 742, in which upper and lower limits are given.

403. Cumulative Tolerances. In limit dimensioning, it is very important to consider the effect of one tolerance on another. When the location of a surface in a given direction is affected by more than one tolerance figure, the tolerances are *cumulative*. For example, in Fig. 743 (a), if dimension Z is omitted, surface A would be controlled by both dimensions X and Y, and there could be a total variation of .010 instead of the variation of .005 permitted by dimension Y which is the dimension directly applied to surface A. Further, if the part is made to all the minimum tolerances of X, Y, and Z, the total variation in the length of the part will be .015, and the part can be as short as 2.985. However, the tolerance on the over-all dimension W is only .005, permitting the part to be only as short as 2.995. The part is superfluously dimensioned.

---

* See *Ordnance Manual on Dimensioning and Tolerancing*, issued by Inspection Gage Sub-Office, Office of Chief of Ordnance, A.S.F., United States Army.

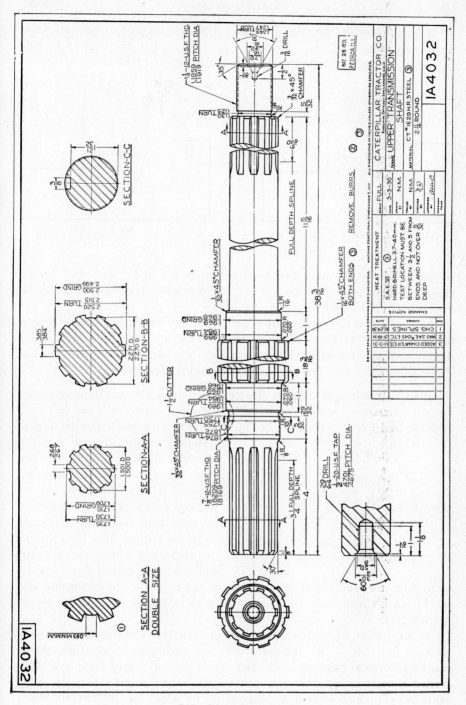

FIG. 742   Limit Dimensions.

425

In some cases, for functional reasons, it may be desired to hold all three small dimensions X, Y, and Z closely without regard to the over-all length. In such a case the over-all dimension should be marked REF. In other cases,

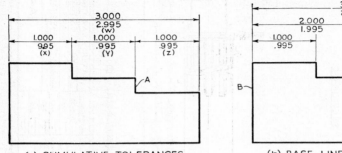

(a) CUMULATIVE TOLERANCES   (b) BASE-LINE DIMENSIONING

FIG. 743   Cumulative Tolerances.

it may be desired to hold two small dimensions X and Y and the over-all closely, without regard to dimension Z. In that case, dimension Z should be omitted, or marked REF.

As a rule, it is best to dimension each surface so that it is affected by only one dimension. This can be done by referring all dimensions to a single datum surface, such as B, as shown in Fig. 743 (b). This is called *base-line dimensioning*, and its use is generally recommended. See also Fig. 691.

404. Tolerances of Angles. Bilateral tolerances are generally given on angular dimensions where considerable accuracy is required, as $60° \pm \frac{1°}{2}$, $\pm 0°10'$, and $\pm 0'30''$, as shown in Fig. 744. In figuring tolerances on angles,

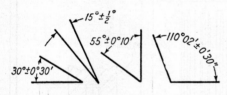

FIG. 744   Tolerances on Angles
(ASA Z14.1—1946).

it should be kept in mind that the tolerance increases as the distance from the vertex of the angle increases. The tolerance should be figured, therefore, after considering the total allowable displacement at the point farthest from the vertex of the angle, and a tolerance specified which will not exceed this. The use of angular tolerances may be avoided by using gages. Taper turning and machining is usually handled by machining to fit a gage, or by fitting to the mating part.

In most cases, angle tolerances are not desirable, and coordinate dimensions at the ends of the angular surface are preferable where these points can be accurately controlled. In cases where the end points cannot be controlled accurately or where the function of the part is such that the angle must be maintained without reference to the surfaces which intersect the angle, angle tolerances are recommended.

405. Tolerance of Concentricity. When two or more closely fitting machined cylindrical surfaces must be accurately concentric, tolerances of concentricity are sometimes necessary. Since the center lines of concentric cylinders coincide on the drawing, ordinary dimensions for concentricity cannot be given, but instead, notes are used. One method is to use reference letters near the diameters in question and to give a note, as in Fig. 745 (a). Another method

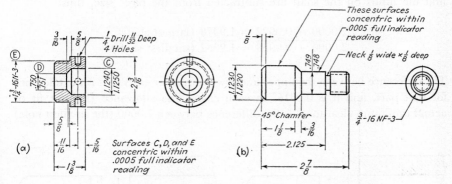

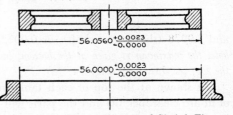

FIG. 745   Tolerances of Concentricity (ASA Z14.1—1946).

is to use notes with leaders pointing directly to the cylindrical surfaces to be toleranced, as shown at (b).

406. ASA Standard Tables. The American Standards Association has recommended* eight standard fits, from *Loose Fit,* an example of which is shown in Fig. 741 (a), which has a large positive allowance, to *Heavy Force and Shrink Fit,* an example of which is the locomotive wheel in Fig. 746, which has a considerable negative allowance. Tables of limits for these eight fits are given in Appendix 18.

These tables give tolerances in the basic hole system (§ 401), in which tolerances are figured from the basic hole size (smallest hole).

To illustrate the use of the tables for a clearance fit, let it be given that a 2″ shaft is to have a

FIG. 746   Heavy Force and Shrink Fit (American Standard).

Class 2 fit in a 2″ hole. The nominal size is then 2″, and the basic hole size is 2.0000″.

From the limit table "Free Fit (Class 2)" on p. 796, the hole size is found in the column headed "Size." The size 2″ is between $1\frac{7}{8}″$ and $2\frac{1}{8}″$, and reading across horizontally to the right to the column headed "Limits," it will be found that the hole may vary from 0.0000″ to +0.0016″ (which is the tolerance for

* ASA B4a—1925.

the hole), and the shaft may vary from $-0.0022''$ to $-0.0038''$ (which is the tolerance for the shaft). The limits on the hole are added to the basic size, thus:

$$\overline{2.0000 + 0.0000} = 2.0000 \text{ (smallest hole)}$$
$$2.0000 + 0.0016 = 2.0016 \text{ (largest hole)}$$

and the limits on the shaft are subtracted from the basic size, thus:

$$\overline{2.0000 - 0.0022} = 1.9978 \text{ (largest shaft)}$$
$$2.0000 - 0.0038 = 1.9962 \text{ (smallest shaft)}$$

The difference between the upper and lower limits for each part is the tolerance for that part, and it is $0.0016''$ in each case. The allowance (tightest fit or actual minimum clearance) is the difference between 2.0000 (the smallest hole)

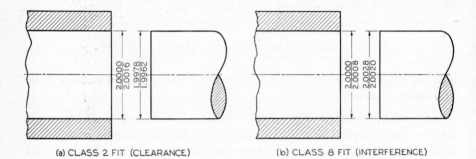

(a) CLASS 2 FIT (CLEARANCE)   (b) CLASS 8 FIT (INTERFERENCE)

FIG. 747   Limit Dimensions.

and 1.9978 (the largest shaft), or 0.0022. Note that *in giving the limits for the hole, the maximum is given at the bottom, but for the shaft, the maximum is given at the top*, as shown in Fig. 747 (a).

As shown at the top of each table in the Appendix, the first four classes of fit are clearance fits and the parts will be interchangeable. For the remaining four classes the allowances are negative, and selective assembly is required for accurate fits.

To illustrate the use of the tables for an interference fit, let it be given that a 2″ shaft is to have a Class 8 fit in a 2″ hole. The nominal size is 2″, and the basic hole size is 2.0000″.

From the limit table "Heavy Force and Shrink Fit (Class 8)" on p. 802, the size 2″ is between $1\frac{7}{8}''$ and $2\frac{1}{8}''$, and reading across horizontally to the right to the columns headed "Limits," it will be found that the hole may vary from $0.0000''$ to $+0.0008''$ (which is the tolerance for the hole), and the shaft may vary from $+0.0020''$ to $+0.0028''$ (which is the tolerance for the shaft).

The limits on the hole are added to the basic size, thus:

$$\frac{2.0000 + 0.0000 = 2.0000 \text{ (smallest hole)}}{2.0000 + 0.0008 = 2.0008 \text{ (largest hole)}}$$

and the limits on the shaft are added to the basic size, thus:

$$\frac{2.0000 + 0.0028 = 2.0028 \text{ (largest shaft)}}{2.0000 + 0.0020 = 2.0020 \text{ (smallest shaft)}}$$

The difference between the upper and lower limits for each part is the tolerance for that part, and it is 0.0008″ in each case. The allowance (tightest fit, or maximum interference of metal) is the difference between 2.0000 (the smallest hole) and 2.0028 (the largest shaft), or 0.0028. These limits applied to the drawing are shown in Fig. 747 (b).

DIMENSIONING PROBLEMS*

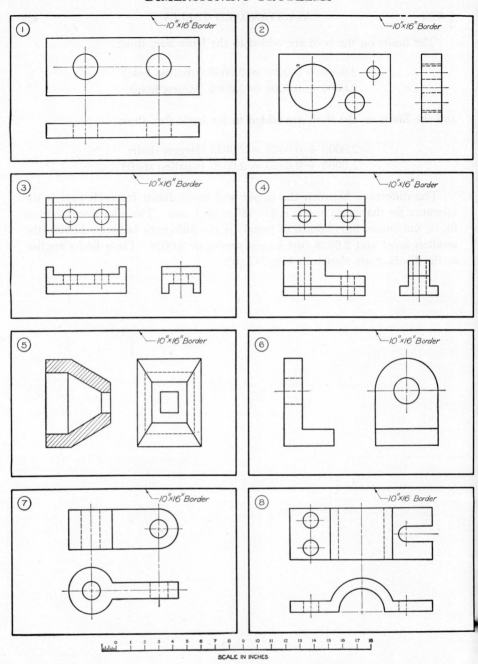

FIG. 748 Using Layout B4, draw assigned problem with instruments. To obtain sizes, place dividers on the views on this page and transfer to scale at the bottom to obtain values in inches (nearest $\frac{1}{16}''$). Dimension drawing completely.

* Dimensioning problems in convenient form for solution may be found in *Technical Drawing Problems*, by Giesecke, Mitchell, and Spencer, and in *Technical Drawing Problems—Series 2*, by Spencer and Grant, both designed to accompany this text and published by The Macmillan Company.

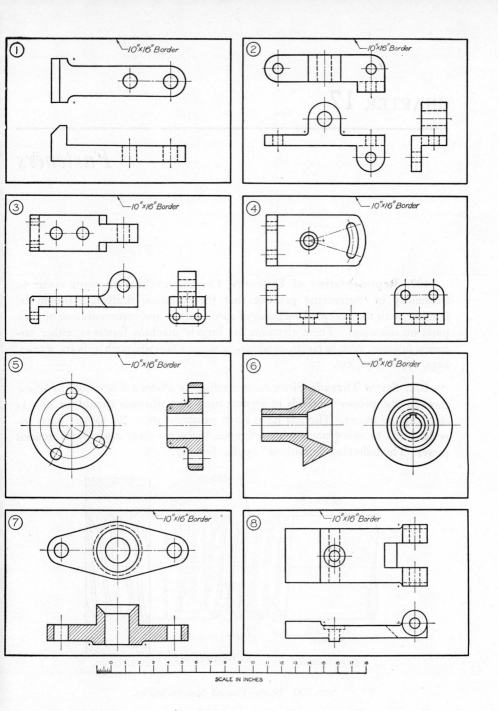

FIG. 749 Using Layout B4, draw assigned problem with instruments. To obtain sizes, place dividers on the views on this page and transfer to scale at the bottom to obtain values in inches (nearest $\frac{1}{16}''$). Dimension drawing completely.

* These problems are intended to provide practice in elementary dimensioning. Additional assignments for more advanced work may be made from problems at the end of Chapter 19.

431

CHAPTER 17

Fasteners

407. Representation of Fasteners. Certain machine elements occur so frequently in engineering practice that the technical draftsman should be familiar with the accepted methods of specification and representation of such parts on drawings. These elements are largely machine fasteners, either *permanent fasteners*, such as rivets, or welds, or *movable fasteners*, such as bolts, screws, keys, cotter keys, etc.

408. Screw Threads. Since most machine fasteners are actuated by screw threads, the proper methods of representing such threads should be understood at the outset. Threads have three principal uses: (1) to *hold* parts together; (2) to *adjust* parts with reference to each other; and (3) to *transmit* power. The following definitions* apply. See Fig. 750.

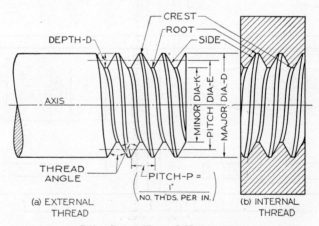

FIG. 750   Screw-Thread Nomenclature.

Screw Thread.—A ridge of uniform section in the form of a helix (§ 125) on the external or internal surface of a cylinder.

External Thread.—A thread on the outside of a member.

* From *American Standard Screw Threads*, ASA B1.1—1935.

432

Internal Thread.—A thread on the inside of a member.

Major Diameter.—The largest diameter of a screw thread (applies to both internal and external threads).

Minor Diameter.—The smallest diameter of a screw thread (applies to both internal and external threads).

Pitch.—The distance from a point on a screw thread to a corresponding point on the next thread measured parallel to the axis. The pitch P is equal to 1″ divided by the number of threads per inch.

Pitch Diameter.—The diameter of an imaginary cylinder passing through the threads so as to make equal the widths of the threads and the widths of the spaces cut by the cylinder.

Lead.—The distance a screw thread advances axially in one turn.

Angle of Thread.—The angle included between the sides of the thread measured in a plane through the axis of the screw (Fig. 750).

Crest.—The top surface joining the two sides of a thread (Fig. 750).

Root.—The bottom surface joining the sides of two adjacent threads (Fig. 750).

Side.—The surface of the thread which connects the crest with the root (Fig. 750).

Axis of Screw.—The longitudinal center line through the screw.

Depth of Thread.—The distance between the crest and the root of the thread measured normal to the axis.

Form of Thread.—The cross section of thread cut by a plane containing the axis.

Series of Thread.—Standard number of threads per inch for various diameters.

409. Screw-Thread Forms. Various *forms* of threads are in use to meet the general functions listed above (Fig. 751). For holding parts together, the

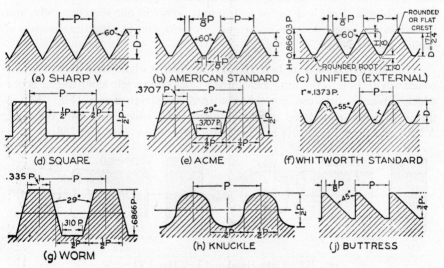

FIG. 751   Screw-Thread Forms.

American (*National*) *Standard thread* is used most in the United States, it having superseded the old 60° *sharp-V thread*. The flattened roots and crests make the former the stronger thread. This thread was originally called the United States Standard, or the Sellers thread. For purposes of certain adjustments the sharp-V thread is still useful because of the friction resulting from the increased area of the thread-face. It is also used in brass pipe work.

On November 18, 1948, representatives of the United States, Canada and Great Britain signed an agreement on unification of American and British screw threads. The new thread is called the *Unified Thread* and is illustrated in Fig. 751 (c). It represents a compromise between the American Standard and Whitworth systems, and allows complete interchangeability of threads in the three countries.

The *Whitworth thread* (British Standard) is used mostly in Great Britain, but is also found frequently in the United States. Its uses correspond roughly to those of the American Standard thread.

The *square thread* is theoretically the ideal thread for power transmission, since its face is nearly at right angles to the axis; but, owing to the difficulty of cutting it with dies, and because of other inherent disadvantages, such as the fact that split nuts will not readily disengage, the square thread has been displaced to a large extent by the Acme thread.

The *Acme thread* is a modification of the square thread. It is stronger than the square thread and is easier to cut.

The *standard worm thread* is similar to the Acme thread, but is deeper. It is used on shafts to carry power to worm wheels.

The *knuckle thread* is usually rolled from sheet metal but is sometimes cast, and is used in electric bulbs and sockets, bottle tops, etc.

The *buttress thread* is designed to transmit power in one direction only, and is used in the breech-locks of large guns, in jacks, and in other mechanisms of similar requirements.

410. Right-Hand and Left-Hand Threads. A right-hand thread is one which advances into the nut when turned clockwise; a left-hand thread is one which advances into the nut when turned counterclockwise (Fig. 752). A thread is always considered to be righthand (RH) unless otherwise specified. A left-hand thread is always marked LH on a drawing. See Fig. 768.

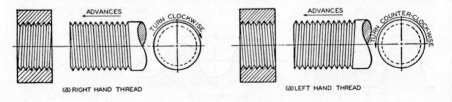

FIG. 752   Right-Hand and Left-Hand Threads.

411. Single and Multiple Threads. A *single* thread, as the name implies, is composed of one ridge; in this thread the lead is equal to the pitch. *Multiple* threads are composed of two or more ridges running side by side. In *double* threads the lead is twice the pitch; in *triple* threads the lead is three times the pitch, etc. See Fig. 753. On a drawing of a single or triple thread, a root is opposite a crest; in the case of a double or quadruple thread, a root is drawn opposite a root. Therefore, in one turn, a double thread advances twice as far as a single thread; a triple thread advances three times as far, etc.

Multiple threads are used wherever quick motion, but not great power, is desired, as on fountain pens, toothpaste caps, valve stems, etc. The threads on a valve stem are frequently multiple threads, to impart quick action in

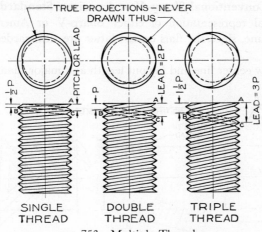

FIG. 753   Multiple Threads.

opening and closing the valve. Multiple threads in a shaft can be recognized and counted by observing the number of thread ends on the end of the screw, as shown in the top views of Fig. 753. These curves are never drawn in practice.

412. Semi-Conventional Representation of Threads. The true projection of the helical curves of a screw thread (Figs. 750 and 758, a) presents a pleasing appearance, but this advantage does not compensate for the laborious

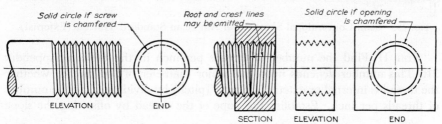

FIG. 754   Semi-Conventional American Standard Threads.

task of plotting the helices (§ 125). Consequently, the true projection representation is never used in practice.

Where the diameter of the thread is over one inch (approximately) on the drawing, a very satisfactory representation may be made by the *semi-conventional method*, in which the true profiles of the threads are drawn, but the helical curves are represented by straight lines, as shown in Fig. 754* for American Standard threads. The flats for the roots and crests are disregarded; consequently Sharp-V and American Standard threads are represented in the same way.

Steps in drawing Sharp-V, American Standard, Square, and Acme threads are given in the following paragraphs.

413. Semi-Conventional Sharp-V or American Standard Threads. The semi-conventional representation of either Sharp-V or American Standard threads is the same, since the flats on the latter are disregarded, as shown in Fig. 755:

STEP I. Draw center line and lay out length and major diameter of thread.

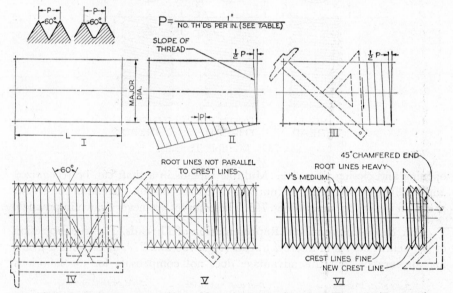

FIG. 755 Semi-Conventional Sharp-V, or American Standard Threads (External).

STEP II. Find the number of threads per inch in the table in Appendix 21. This number depends upon the major diameter of the thread, whether the thread is internal or external. Find P (pitch) by dividing 1″ by the number of threads per inch. Establish the slope of the thread by offsetting the slope

---

* The crest and root lines of internal threads in section shown at (b) may be omitted if necessary for clearness. ASA-Z14.1—1946 is inconsistent on this as regards American Standard, Square, and Acme thread representation.

line $\frac{1}{2}P$ for single threads, P for double threads, $1\frac{1}{2}P$ for triple threads, etc.*
For right-hand threads, the slope line slopes upward to the left, as shown in
Fig. 752 (a); for left-hand threads the slope line slopes upward to the right,
as at (b). Set off pitch distances, as shown.

STEP III. From pitch-points, draw crest lines parallel to slope line. These
should be dark, sharp lines. Slide triangle on T-square (or another triangle)
to make lines parallel.

STEP IV. Draw 60° V's lightly. These V's should stand vertically; i.e.,
they should not "lean" with the thread.

STEP V. Draw root lines heavy at once. Root lines will *not* be parallel to
crest lines. Slide triangle on straightedge to make root lines parallel.

STEP VI. Accent the V's and finish the drawing. Relief is obtained on
external threads by accenting the root-diameter lines as shown.

When the end is chamfered (usually 45°, sometimes 30°, with end of shaft),
the chamfer extends to the thread depth. The chamfer creates a new crest
line, which is then drawn between the two new crest points.

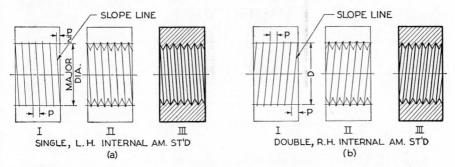

FIG. 756   Semi-Conventional Sharp-V, or American Standard Threads (Internal).

The corresponding internal semi-conventional threads are drawn as shown
in Fig. 756. Notice that for LH threads, the lines slope upward to the left, as
shown at (a), while for RH threads, the lines slope upward to the right, as at
(b). Relief is obtained on internal threads by accenting the major-diameter
lines, as shown.

414. Semi-Conventional Square Threads. The steps in drawing semi-
conventional square threads where the major diameter is over one inch (approximately) are shown in Fig. 757. The number of threads per inch is found in
Appendix 24. This number depends upon the major diameter of the thread,
whether the thread is internal or external.

STEP I. Draw center line, and lay out length and major diameter of thread.
The pitch P is equal to $1''$ divided by the number of threads per inch. For a
single RH thread the lines slope upward to the left, and the slope line is offset

* These offsets are the same amounts in terms of P for any kind of thread.

$\frac{1}{2}P$ *as for all single threads of any kind.* The points set off on the upper line are spaced at intervals of $\frac{1}{2}P$, as shown.

STEP II. From the $\frac{1}{2}P$ points on the upper line, draw crest lines parallel to slope line. These should be made dark and fairly sharp. Draw guide lines for the root of the thread, making the depth $\frac{P}{2}$, as shown.

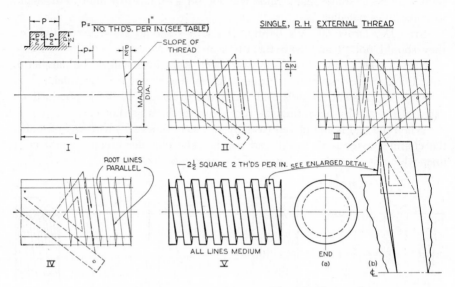

FIG. 757   Semi-Conventional Square Threads (External).

STEP III. Draw parallel visible back edges of threads.

STEP IV. Draw parallel visible root lines. (Note enlarged detail.)

STEP V. Accent the lines. All lines should be medium in thickness, and dark.

Note the end view of the shaft at (a). The root circle is hidden, and no attempt is made to show the true projection. If the end is chamfered, a solid circle would be drawn instead of the hidden circle.

A comparison of the true projection and the semi-conventional representation of the square thread is shown in Fig. 758. The true projection, in which the true helical curves are drawn, is shown at (a). The construction of a helix is explained in § 125. This difficult construction is never used in practice and is included here for illustration purposes only. The semi-conventional method is shown at (b), in which all helical curves have been represented by straight lines.

A careful study of Fig. 758 should enable the student to visualize clearly the details of square thread construction. Note particularly the differences in representation of the screw alone, the screw and nut in section, and the nut alone in section. Observe also that the thread lines representing the front side of the screw slope in the opposite direction from the thread lines for the back portion of the internal thread (shown in section).

Steps in drawing a single RH internal square thread in section are illustrated in Fig. 759. Note in Step II that a crest is drawn opposite a root for

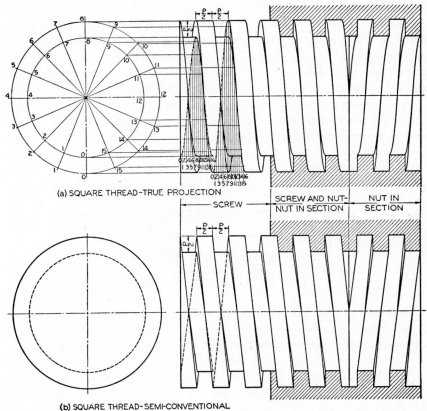

FIG. 758   Square Threads.

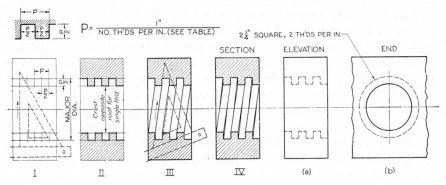

FIG. 759   Semi-Conventional Square Threads (Internal).

this thread. For single or triple threads, a crest is opposite a root; for double or quadruple threads, a crest is opposite a crest. Thus, the construction in Step I is the same for the single, double, triple, or quadruple threads. The differences between them are developed in Step II, where the threads are distinguished from the spaces.

The same internal thread is shown in elevation in Fig. 759 (a). The profiles of the threads are drawn in their normal position, but with hidden lines, and the sloping lines are omitted for simplicity. The end view of the same internal thread is shown at (b). Note that the hidden and solid circles are opposite those for the end view of the shaft. See Fig. 757 (a).

A simplified method of drawing square threads is shown in Fig. 760, in which the visible root lines and some visible crest lines are omitted. This method is recommended only where the drawing is so small that the regular semi-conventional method becomes too compact. When the diameter is too small even for the simplified method of Fig. 760, the conventional method (§§ 416–418) should be used.

FIG. 760   Simplified Representation.

Note also in Fig. 760 the use of ditto lines (Fig. 85) to eliminate drawing all the threads on a long screw. This may be done on detail drawings, but is not recommended on assembly drawings when the screw is engaged.

The American Standards Association has approved* a modified square thread which is similar to the old square thread but has sides sloping slightly with a 10° included angle. Except for the angle, the thread is the same as that illustrated above. In drawing the modified square thread, the slight angle may be disregarded.

415. Semi-Conventional Acme Threads. The steps in drawing semi-conventional Acme Threads* where the major diameter is over one inch (approximately) are shown in Fig. 761. The number of threads per inch is found in the table in Appendix 23. The number depends upon the major diameter of the thread, whether the thread is internal or external.

STEP I. Draw center line, and lay out length and major diameter of thread. The pitch P is equal to $1''$ divided by the number of threads per inch. Draw intermediate construction lines for the root diameter, making the thread depth $\frac{P}{2}$. Draw construction lines halfway between the crest and root guide lines.

STEP II. On the intermediate construction lines, lay off $\frac{P}{2}$ spaces, as shown.

*ASA B1.3—1941.

STEP III. Through alternate points, draw construction lines for sides of threads at 15° with vertical.

STEP IV. Draw construction lines for opposite sides of threads. Note that for single and triple threads a crest is opposite a root, while for double and quadruple threads a crest is opposite a crest.

STEP V. Draw parallel crest lines *sharp* and dark.

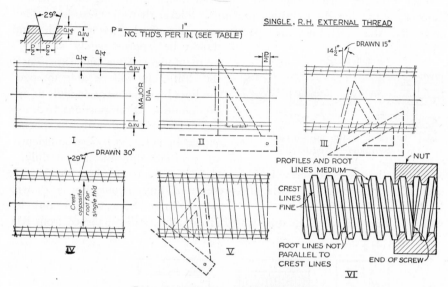

FIG. 761   Semi-Conventional Acme Threads.

STEP VI. Accent root lines and thread profiles, as shown. Note that the internal threads in the back of the nut slope in an opposite direction to the external threads on the front side of the screw. Observe also that the internal cres⁺ lines are made heavy to give the appearance of being in shadow.

End views of Acme-threaded shafts and holes are drawn exactly like those of the square thread (Figs. 757 and 759).

The American Standards Association has approved* a General Purpose Acme thread, which has been illustrated above, and also a 29-Degree Stub thread, which is similar to the Acme thread but has a depth of only *0.3P*. Included also are standard proportions for a 60-Degree Stub thread, which is similar to the American Standard but has wider flats, and a Modified Square thread, which is similar to the old square thread but has sides slightly sloping with a 10° included angle.

416. Conventional Representation of Threads. Conventional thread symbols are used in representing *all forms of threads* on assembly and detail

* ASA B1.3—1943.

drawings. It is recommended that threads be represented in this manner wherever the thread is *an inch or less in diameter on the drawing*.

Two types of thread symbols, a *regular* (Figs. 762 and 763) and a *simplified* (Figs. 765 and 766) have been approved as American Standard.*

417. Regular Thread Symbols. External threads in elevation and end view are shown in Fig. 762 (b). The threads are indicated by alternate long and short dashes at right angles to the center line, representing the crests and roots of the threads, the root lines preferably thicker than the crest lines. Theoretically, the crest lines are spaced according to the actual pitch, and should be approximately so drawn by the student. After some experience, the draftsman will be able to space the lines by eye closely enough to approximate actual proportions. In drawing extremely fine threads, the spacing should be enlarged by eye sufficiently to avoid crowding the lines unduly.

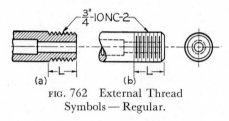

FIG. 762   External Thread Symbols — Regular.

When the threaded screw is sectioned, it is necessary to show the V's, as shown in Fig. 762 (a); otherwise the presence of threads could not be shown.

Internal threads tapped through are shown in end view, section, and elevation in Fig. 763 (a). The only way LH threads are distinguished from RH

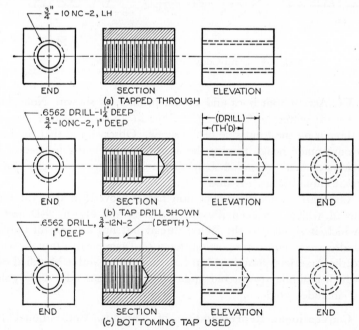

FIG. 763   Internal Thread Symbols — Regular.

*ASA Z14.1—1946. See Appendix 2.

threads is in the note. In the elevation view the hidden dashes should be staggered.

Internal threads where the tap drill does not go through are shown at (b). The drill point should be drawn at 60° with the center line, and the drill depth should extend about four pitches beyond the thread depth to account for the imperfect threads on the tap.

The method shown at (c) should be used to indicate a bottoming tap, when the depth of thread is the same as the depth of drill, or when it is not necessary to specify both depth of drill and depth of thread.

The steps in drawing an external thread are as follows (Fig. 764):

Step I. Lay out length and major diameter of thread with construction lines. Obtain pitch P by dividing 1″ by the number of threads per inch (see

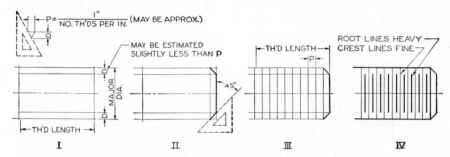

FIG. 764   Steps in Drawing Conventional Threads.

table in Appendix 21) or by estimating it to the nearest convenient distance. If a thread has 16 threads per inch, the pitch is $\frac{1}{16}''$. If a thread has 14 threads per inch, the pitch can be estimated as slightly more than $\frac{1}{16}''$. If a thread has 32 or 40 threads per inch, the pitch should be as small as possible and still keep the root lines separated clearly from the crest lines.

Find depth of thread, D, by constructing one V-thread profile, as shown at the upper left of Fig. 764. Since the depth is slightly less than P, it can be easily estimated, and guide lines for the root diameter drawn.

Step II. Draw 45° chamfer with final heavy dark lines.

Step III. Draw crest lines with final fine dark lines, the last crest away from the end being at the thread length terminal or slightly beyond if it comes out that way.

Step IV. Draw root lines final weight, spacing them by eye midway between the crest lines, and go over construction lines as required to complete the drawing.

418. Simplified Thread Symbols. The simplified symbols are recommended where it is desirable to simplify drafting. They are increasing in use, and are favored in the automotive industries especially.

External threads are shown in Fig. 765, and internal threads in Fig. 766. The threaded portions are indicated by dashed lines parallel to the axis at the approximate depth of the thread. Note that end views and elevation views of

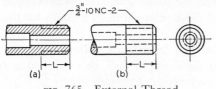

internal threads are the same for both the regular and simplified symbols.

The external simplified symbol is drawn as shown in Steps I and II of Fig. 764. Instead of proceeding to Step III, the dashed lines are drawn at the root diameter, and the threads finished to conform to Fig. 765.

FIG. 765   External Thread
Symbols — Simplified.

419. Threads in Section. Semi-conventional representations of large American Standard threads in section are shown in Figs. 754 and 756. As indicated in the footnote at the bottom of p. 436, the root lines and crest lines of internal threads in section may be omitted if necessary for clearness. If

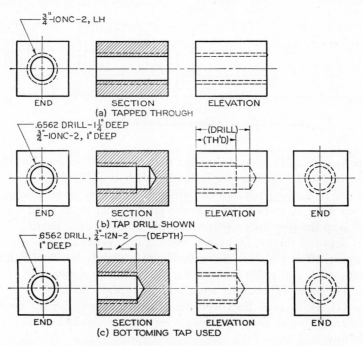

FIG. 766   Internal Thread Symbols — Simplified.

these lines are drawn, they should slope in a direction opposite to those of the visible external threads, as shown in Fig. 754 (b).

Semi-conventional representations of large square and Acme threads in section are shown in Figs. 758, 759 and 761. In all cases, the root lines and crest lines of the internal threads are shown in conformity with the American Standard.*

Conventional external threads are sectioned as shown in Figs. 762 (a) and 765 (a). Note that in the regular symbol, the V's must be drawn. Conventional internal threads are sectioned as shown in Figs. 763 and 766.

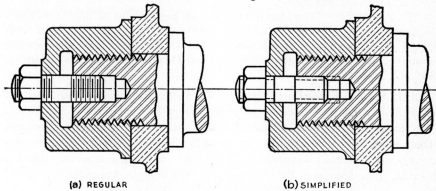

(a) REGULAR   (b) SIMPLIFIED
FIG. 767   Screw Threads in Assembly (ASA Z14.1—1946).

Threads in an assembly drawing are illustrated in Fig. 767. It is customary not to section a stud or a nut unless necessary to show some internal shapes. Note that when both the internal and external threaded members are sectioned, the V's must be shown; otherwise no threads would be evident.

420. American Standard Screw Threads. The present American (National) Standard thread was adopted in 1935.** The *form* or profile (Fig. 751) is the same as the old Sellers' profile or United States Standard, and is known now as the *National Form*. See table in Appendix 21. For methods of representation, see §§ 412, 413, 416, 417 and 418.

Five *series* of screw threads are embraced in the Standard. All have the same form of thread but have different numbers of threads per inch for given diameters.

(1) The *Coarse Thread* is a general-purpose thread for holding purposes. It is designated NC (National Coarse). See table in Appendix 21.

(2) The *Fine Thread* has a greater number of threads per inch, and is used extensively in automobile and aircraft construction where threads are subjected to extreme vibration. It is designated NF (National Fine). See table in Appendix 21.

(3) The *8-Pitch Thread* has eight threads per inch for all diameters, ranging from 1″ to 6″. It is used on bolts for high-pressure pipe flanges, cylinder-head studs, and similar fastenings against pressure to secure a necessary initial tension. For such uses, the torque required to assemble the fastening would be excessive if the pitch should be increased according to the diameter of the thread. It is designated by N (National Form, eight threads per inch). See table in Appendix 25.

*ASA Z14.1—1946. See Appendix 2.   **ASA B1.1—1935.

(4) The *12-Pitch Thread* has twelve threads per inch for all diameters, ranging from $\frac{1}{2}''$ to 6″. Sizes from $\frac{1}{2}''$ to $1\frac{3}{4}''$ are used in boiler work, where it is customary to re-tap worn stud holes with the next larger size. The 12-pitch thread is also used a great deal in machine construction for thin nuts on shafts and sleeves. It is designated 12N (National Form, twelve threads per inch). See table in Appendix 25.

(5) The *16-Pitch Thread* has sixteen threads per inch for all diameters ranging from $\frac{3}{4}''$ to 4″. It is used where it is necessary to have a fine thread regardless of the diameter, primarily for threaded adjusting collars and bearing retaining nuts. It is designated 16N (National Form, sixteen threads per inch). See table in Appendix 25.

421. S.A.E.* Extra Fine Threads. *The S.A.E. Extra Fine Thread Series* has many more threads per inch for given diameters than any series of the American Standard. The form of thread is the same as the American Standard. These small threads are used in thin metal where the length of thread engagement is small, in cases where close adjustment is required, and where vibration is great. It is designated EF (Extra Fine). See table in Appendix 22.

422. American Standard Screw Thread Fits. The American Standards Association also established for general use four distinct classes of screw thread *fits* between mating threads (as between bolt and nut). Fit is defined as "the relation between two mating parts with reference to ease of assembly." These four fits are produced by the application of tolerances which are listed in the standards. The four fits are described as follows:**

Class 1 Fit.—Recommended only for screw thread work where clearance between mating parts is essential for rapid assembly and where shake or play is not objectionable.

Class 2 Fit.—Represents a high quality of commercial thread product, and is recommended for the great bulk of interchangeable screw thread work.

Class 3 Fit.—Represents an exceptionally high quality of commercially threaded product and is recommended only in cases where the high cost of precision tools and continual checking are warranted.

Class 4 Fit.—Intended to meet very unusual requirements more exacting than those for which Class 3 is intended. It is a selective fit if initial assembly by hand is required. It is not, as yet, adaptable to quantity production.

The class of fit desired on a thread is indicated by the number of the fit in the thread note, as shown in Fig. 768.

423. Thread Notes on Drawings. A set of symbols** has been approved for specifying American Standard Threads on drawings, in correspondence, on shop and store-room cards, and in specifications for parts, taps, dies, tools, and gages.

A thread note for a blind tapped hole is shown in Fig. 768. The tap drill diameter should always be given, and the depth of drill should be given, unless

* Society of Automotive Engineers.
** ASA B1.1—1935.

the hole is a through hole. See table in Appendix 21 for tap drill sizes. The symbols in the thread specification should be given exactly in the form shown. If the LH symbol is omitted, it is understood that the thread is right-hand. If the thread is a multiple thread, the word Double, Triple, or Quad-ruple should precede the thread depth. If the thread is single, no symbol is given and the thread is understood to be single.

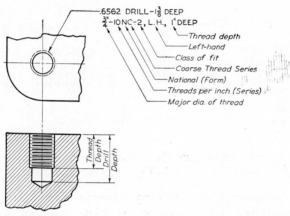

FIG. 768　Thread Note.

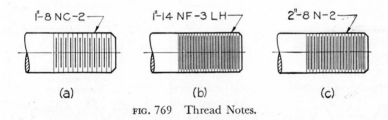

(a)　　　　　　　(b)　　　　　　　(c)

FIG. 769　Thread Notes.

Examples of notes for typical American Standard Threads are as follows:*

American Standard Coarse-Thread Series: To specify a threaded part 1 inch in diameter, 8 threads per inch, right-hand, and
Class 2 Fit.............................1″–8NC–2. See Fig. 769 (a).

American Standard Fine-Thread Series: A threaded part 1 inch in diameter, 14 threads per inch, left-hand thread, and
Class 3 Fit.............................1″–14NF–3LH. See Fig. 769 (b).

American Standard 8-Pitch, 12-Pitch, and 16-Pitch Thread Series: A threaded part 2 inches in diameter in these three special series and
Class 2 Fit.............................2″– 8N–2. See Fig. 769 (c).
$$2″–12N–2$$
$$2″–16N–2$$

* ASA B1.1—1935.

American Standard Thread, Special Pitch: To specify a threaded part $1\frac{1}{2}''$ in diameter, 7 threads per inch (special pitch), and left-hand . . . . $1\frac{1}{2}''$–7N–LH.

Other forms of threads, such as square threads or Acme threads, are designated as shown in Fig. 770. See Appendixes 23 and 24.

Thread notes for external threads should be attached to the longitudinal view of the thread, as shown in Figs. 769 and 770.

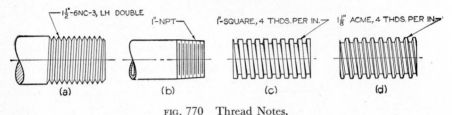

FIG. 770   Thread Notes.

Thread notes for internal threads are preferably attached to the circular view of the thread, as shown in Figs. 725 (g) and 768.

424. American Standard Pipe Threads. The American Standard for Pipe Threads, originally known as the Briggs Standard, was formulated by Robert Briggs in 1882. Two general types of pipe threads have been approved

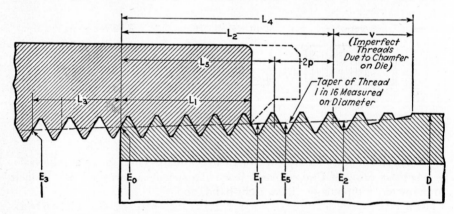

FIG. 771   American Standard Taper Pipe Thread (ASA B2.1—1945).

as American Standard: *Taper Pipe Threads* and *Straight Pipe Threads.** The profile of the taper pipe thread is illustrated in Fig. 771 (see table in Appendix 10). The taper of the thread is 1 in 16 or 0.75″ per foot measured on the diameter and along the axis. The angle between the sides of the thread is 60°. The depth of the sharp V is $0.8660p$, and the basic maximum depth of the

* ASA B2.1—1945.

truncated thread is $0.800p$ (where p is the pitch). The basic pitch diameters E_0 and E_1 (Fig. 771) are determined by the formulas:

$$E_0 = D - (0.050 D + 1.1) \tfrac{1}{n}$$
$$E_1 = E_0 + 0.0625 L$$

where D = basic outside diameter of pipe,

      E_0 = pitch diameter of thread at end of pipe,

      E_1 = pitch diameter of thread at the large end of internal thread,

      L_1 = normal engagement by hand between external and internal threads,

      n = number of threads per inch.

The basic length of the effective external taper thread, L_2, is determined by the formula:

$$L_2 = (0.80 D + 6.8) \tfrac{1}{n}$$

The ASA has also recommended two modified taper pipe threads for: (1) Dryseal Pressure-Tight Joints, and (2) Rail Fitting Joints. The former is used to provide a metal-to-metal joint which eliminates the need for a sealer, and is used in refrigeration, marine, automotive, aircraft, and ordnance work. The latter is used to provide a rigid mechanical thread joint as required in rail fitting joints. For further information, see ASA B2.1–1945.*

While taper pipe threads are recommended for general use, there are certain types of joints where straight pipe threads are used to advantage. The number of threads per inch, the angle, and the depth of thread are the same as on the taper pipe thread, but the threads are cut parallel to the axis. Straight

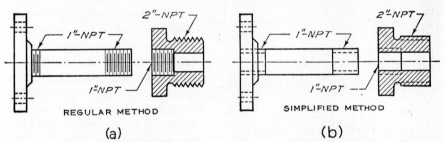

REGULAR METHOD   SIMPLIFIED METHOD

(a)   (b)

FIG. 772   Conventional Representation of Pipe Threads (ASA Z14.1—1946).

pipe threads are used for pressure-tight joints for pipe couplings, fuel and oil line fittings, drain plugs, free-fitting mechanical joints for fixtures, loose-fitting mechanical joints for locknuts, and loose-fitting mechanical joints for hose couplings. For further information, see ASA B2.1–1945.*

Pipe threads are represented conventionally or semi-conventionally in a manner similar to the representation of American Standard Threads. The conventional representation (regular or simplified) is recommended for general

* American Standards Association, 70 East 45th Street, New York 17, New York.

use, regardless of diameter (Fig. 772), the semi-conventional method being approved only when the threads are large and when it is desired to show the profile of the thread, as for example in a sectional view of an assembly. See Figs. 980, 982 and 988.

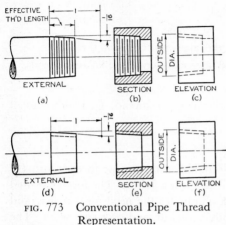

FIG. 773   Conventional Pipe Thread
Representation.

It is not necessary to draw the taper on the threads (Fig. 772) unless it is desired to emphasize this, since the thread note indicates whether the thread is straight or tapered. If it is desired to show the taper, it should be exaggerated, as shown in Fig. 773, where the taper is drawn $\frac{1}{16}''$ per $1''$ *on radius*, instead of the actual taper of $\frac{1}{16}''$ *on diameter*. American Standard Taper Pipe Threads are indicated by a note giving the nominal diameter followed by the letters *NPT* (National Pipe Taper), as shown in Fig. 772. When straight pipe threads are specified, the letters *NPS* (National Pipe Straight) are used.

For numbers of threads per inch and other data on pipe threads, see Appendix 10. For a general discussion of piping drawings, see Chapter 21.

425. Bolts, Studs, and Screws.

The term *bolt* is generally used to denote a "through bolt" which has a head on one end and is passed through clearance holes in two or more aligned parts and is threaded on the other end to receive a nut to tighten and hold the parts together. See Fig. 774

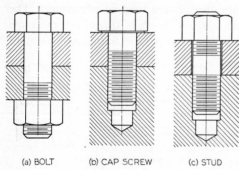

FIG. 774   Bolt, Screw, and Stud.

(a), and §§ 426 and 427 on American Standard bolts.

A hexagon head *cap screw* is similar to a through bolt, except that it generally has a greater length of thread because it is used without a nut, one of the members held together being threaded to act as a nut. See Fig. 774 (b). It is screwed on with a wrench. Cap screws are not screwed into thin materials if strength is desired. See § 430.

A *stud* is a steel rod threaded on both ends, and is screwed into place with a pipe wrench or, preferably, with a stud driver. As a rule, a stud is passed through a clearance hole in one member and is screwed into another member, a nut being used on the free end, as shown in Fig. 774 (c). See § 428.

A *machine screw* is similar to the slotted-head cap screws, but is in general smaller. It may be used with or without a nut. See § 431 which discusses American Standard machine screws in detail.

A *set screw* is a screw with or without a head which is screwed through one member and whose special point is forced against another member to prevent relative motion between the two parts. See § 432 on American Standard set screws and Fig. 786.

The bottom of a drilled hole is conical in shape, as formed by the point of the twist drill (Fig. 775). On drawings, an angle of 30° is used to approximate the actual 31°.

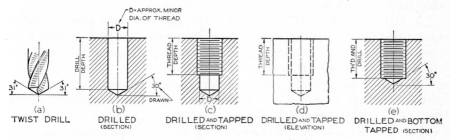

FIG. 775   Drilled and Tapped Holes.

The drill depth is the depth of the cylindrical portion of the hole and does not include the cone point. The drill depth shown beyond the thread depth in Fig. 775 (c) includes the several imperfect threads produced by the chamfered portion at the end of the tap. A good rule is to make this distance equal to four pitches of the thread. In this way the thread depth includes only effective threads, and the remaining depth provides needed space for chips.

It is good practice to make the thread depth equal to at least $1\frac{1}{2}$ times the outside diameter for steel, and somewhat more for softer materials. When bolts or screws are used for holding purposes, and are passed through a clear hole in one member, the hole is usually drilled $\frac{1}{32}''$ larger in diameter than the shank of the bolt or screw. This clearance is usually not shown on the drawing unless needed for clearness. If it is drawn, it should be exaggerated to about double size, or $\frac{1}{32}''$ on each side of the shank, as shown in Fig. 774 (c).

426. American Standard Bolts. The American Standards Association* has approved three series of bolts and nuts as follows:

1. *Regular Series Bolt Heads and Nuts.*—These are for general use. The dimensions are based on theoretical analysis of stresses and on results of numerous tests.

2. *Heavy Series Bolt Heads and Nuts.*—These are for use where greater bearing surface is necessary; i.e., where a large clearance between the bolt and hole or a greater wrench-bearing surface is essential. These are practically the same

* ASA B18.2—1941.

as the old United States Standard, except that the latter had a 45° chamfer instead of 30°.

3. *Light Series Nuts.*—These have smaller dimensions across flats than regular series nuts.

These bolt heads and nuts are classified according to finish as follows:

1. *Unfinished* (Square or Hexagon Bolts).—Except for the threads, these are not machined on any surface.

2. *Semi-finished* (Hexagon Bolts).—These are machined or otherwise formed or treated on the bearing surface so as to provide (a) for bolt heads, a washer face and (b) for nuts, a washer face or a circular bearing surface formed by chamfering the edges.

3. *Finished* (Hexagon Cap Screws).—These are the same as semi-finished except that in addition to the finished bearing surface, all other surfaces have been so treated as to provide a special finished appearance. The purchaser will specify the finish of all non-bearing surfaces.

A *washer-face* is a circular boss turned or otherwise produced on the bearing surface of a bolt head or nut to relieve the corners. It is applicable to the finished or semi-finished forms listed above. See Fig. 776 (b).

Bolt ends are generally chamfered at 45° by the thread depth. American Standard dimensions of bolt heads and nuts are listed in Appendix 27 for reference.

427. To Draw American Standard Bolts. In practice, standard bolts and nuts need not be shown on detail drawings unless they are to be altered, but they appear so frequently on assembly drawings that a suitable but rapid method of drawing them must be used. They may be drawn from exact dimensions taken from tables* if accuracy is important, as in figuring clearances; but in the great majority of cases the conventional representation, in which proportions based upon diameter are used, will be sufficient, and a considerable amount of time may be saved.

Three typical bolts illustrating the use of these proportions for the regular series bolts are shown in Fig. 776. In all cases, heights of the heads are $\frac{2}{3}$ the diameter of the shaft, and the heights of the nuts are $\frac{7}{8}$ the diameter of the shaft. These heights can be spaced off with bow dividers on the shaft diameter, then transferred as shown at (a), and should not be figured arithmetically. Note that the washer-faces are included in the heights.

For the heavy series the width across flats should be drawn $1\frac{1}{2}D + \frac{1}{8}''$, the height of the head should be $\frac{3}{4}D$, and the thickness of the nut should be D. The $\frac{1}{64}''$ washer-face is shown in the semi-finished hexagon bolt only, and is included in the heights of the head and nut.

Bolt lengths have not been standardized because of the endless variety re-
-quired in engineering practice. However, the Bureau of Standards publica-

* See pp. 808-811 in Appendix.

tion SPR 169–45 lists stock sizes of bolts and gives the following increments of length:

SQUARE HEAD BOLTS

Lengths $\frac{1}{2}''$ to $\frac{3}{4}''$ = $\frac{1}{8}''$ increments.
Lengths $\frac{3}{4}''$ to $4\frac{3}{4}''$ = $\frac{1}{4}''$ increments.
Lengths $4\frac{3}{4}''$ to $11\frac{1}{2}''$ = $\frac{1}{2}''$ increments.
Lengths $11\frac{1}{2}''$ to $20''$ = $1''$ increments.
Lengths $20''$ to $24''$ = $2''$ increments.

HEXAGON HEAD BOLTS

Lengths $\frac{1}{2}''$ to $\frac{3}{4}''$ = $\frac{1}{8}''$ increments.
Lengths $\frac{3}{4}''$ to $3''$ = $\frac{1}{4}''$ increments.
Lengths $3''$ to $6''$ = $\frac{1}{2}''$ increments.
Lengths $6''$ to $8''$ = $1''$ increments.

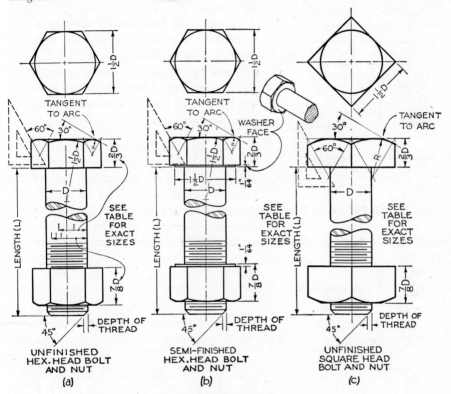

FIG. 776   Bolt Proportions.

For thread lengths, see table in Appendix 31.

As shown in Fig. 674 (c), the curves produced by the chamfer on the bolt heads and nuts are hyperbolas. However, in actual practice, these curves are always represented approximately by means of circular arcs, as demonstrated in Fig. 776.

Generally, bolt heads and nuts should be drawn "across corners" in all views, regardless of projection, as shown in Figs. 905–908. This conventional violation of projection is used to prevent confusion between the square and hexagon heads and nuts and to show actual clearances. Only when there is a special reason should bolt heads and nuts be drawn across flats. In such cases, the conventional proportions shown in Fig. 777 are recommended.

Steps in drawing hexagon bolts and nuts are illustrated in Fig. 778 and those for square bolts and nuts in Fig. 779. Before starting, the diameter of the bolt, the length from the under side of the bearing surface to the tip, the type of head (square or hexagon), and the series (regular or heavy), as well as the type of finish must be known.

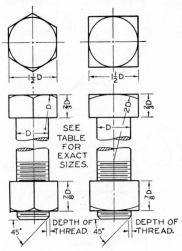

FIG. 777 Bolts "Across Flats."

If only the longitudinal view of a bolt is needed, it is necessary to draw only the lower half of the top views in Figs. 778 and 779 *with light construction lines* in order to project the corners of the hexagon or square to the front view. These construction lines may then be erased if desired.

428. Specifications of Bolts and Studs. In detail drawings, the lengths of bolts are always given from the under side of the bearing surface of the head to the extreme end, and the length of the threads is given from the extreme end. The diameter may be given in the side view of the bolt or in the thread note, as shown in Fig. 780.

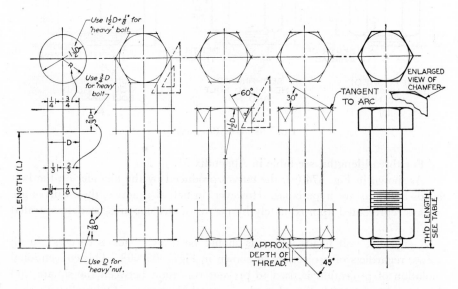

FIG. 778 Steps in Drawing a Hexagon-Head Bolt and Hexagon Nut.

In specifying bolts in parts lists, in correspondence, or elsewhere, the following information must be covered in order:

(1) Diameter of bolt shank　　　　(4) Finish of bolt
(2) Length of bolt　　　　　　　　(5) Type of head
(3) Thread specification (see § 423)　(6) Name

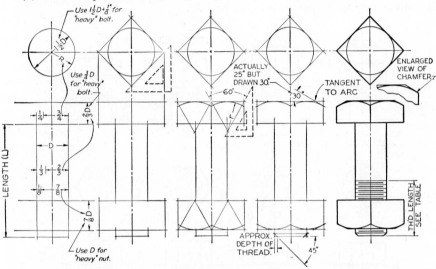

FIG. 779　Steps in Drawing a Square-Head Bolt and Nut.

Example (Complete): $\frac{3}{4}'' \times 1\frac{3}{4}''$–10NC–2 SEMI-FINISHED HEXAGON-HEAD BOLT
Example (Abbreviated): $\frac{3}{4}'' \times 1\frac{3}{4}''$ SEMI-FIN HEX HD BOLT

On detail drawings of studs, the length is given from one extreme end to the other, and the diameter and thread information are given as for bolts.

In parts lists and elsewhere, studs are specified as follows:

Example (Complete): $\frac{7}{16}'' \times 3\frac{1}{4}''$–14NC–2 STUD
Example (Abbreviated): $\frac{7}{16}'' \times 3\frac{1}{4}''$ STUD

429. Nut Locks. Many types of special devices to prevent nuts from unscrewing are available, the most common of which are illustrated in Fig. 781. The American Standard Jam Nuts* (a) and (b) are the same as the

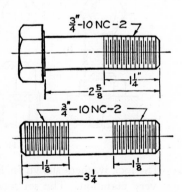

FIG. 780　Dimensioning of Bolts.

Regular Hexagon Nuts, except that they are thinner. The application at (b) where the larger nut is on top and the top nut is screwed on more tightly is recom-

* ASA B18.2—1941.

mended. They are drawn in the manner shown for regular hexagon nuts in Fig. 778, but with a thickness equal to $\frac{1}{2}D$ (approx. height). They are available, unfinished, and semi-finished in the regular and heavy series, and semi-finished in the light series. The tops of all are flat and chamfered at 30°, and the semi-finished nut has either a washer-face or a chamfered bearing surface. For exact measurements, see Appendixes 27, 28 and 30.

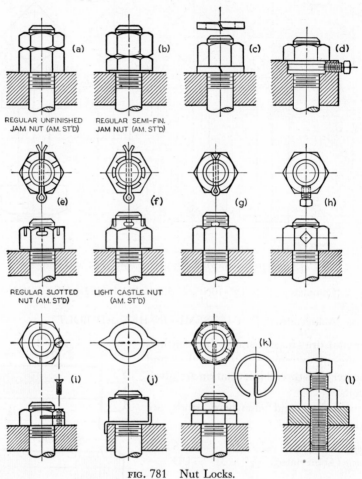

REGULAR UNFINISHED JAM NUT (AM. ST'D)   REGULAR SEMI-FIN. JAM NUT (AM. ST'D)

REGULAR SLOTTED NUT (AM. ST'D)   LIGHT CASTLE NUT (AM. ST'D)

FIG. 781   Nut Locks.

The lock washers shown in Fig. 781 (c) and the cotter key (e), (f), and (g) are very common. The set screw (h) is frequently made to press against a plug of softer material, such as brass, which in turn presses against the threads without deforming them.

For use with cotter keys, the ASA* recommends a Regular Slotted Nut, illustrated in Fig. 781 (e), and slotted nuts in the heavy, light and light-thick

* ASA B18.2—1941.

series, all semi-finished and in hexagon form, as well as a Light Castle Nut shown in Fig. 781 (f). For dimensions, see Appendixes 29 and 30.

The Dardelet Thread is self-locking, and is illustrated in Fig. 782. The form of the thread is similar to that of the Acme, but the crest of the thread in the nut and the root of the thread on the screw are tapered at about 6° with the axis of the screw, so that when the nut is tightened in place the crest of the thread of the nut is wedged against the root of the thread on the screw.

430. American Standard Cap Screws. There are six standard heads for cap screws, as shown in Figs. 783 and 784. They are regularly produced in finished form and are used on machine tools and other machines where accuracy and appearance are

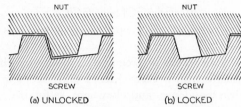

FIG. 782　Dardelet Self-Locking Thread.

important. They are available in diameters ranging from $\frac{1}{4}''$ to $1\frac{1}{4}''$. Cap screws ordinarily pass through a clearance hole in one member and screw into another. The clearance hole is usually drilled $\frac{1}{32}''$ larger, and is generally not drawn unless necessary for clearness, in which case it is drawn about $\frac{1}{16}''$ larger in diameter than the shank of the screw. Cap screws are inferior to studs

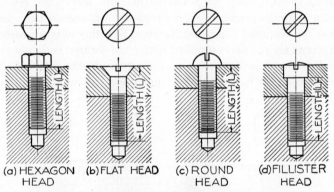

(a) HEXAGON HEAD　(b) FLAT HEAD　(c) ROUND HEAD　(d) FILLISTER HEAD

FIG. 783　American Standard Cap Screws.

if frequent removal is necessary; hence they are used on machines requiring few adjustments. The slotted head or socket types are best under crowded conditions.

The hexagon head cap screw, shown in Fig. 783 (a), is drawn conventionally in the same manner as the semi-finished hexagon head bolt, as shown in Fig. 776 (b), but the head is made $\frac{3}{4}D$ in height.

The socket head cap screw (Fig. 784) has a head height equal to the diameter of the screw. Other dimensions should be taken directly from the table in Appendix 33.

The slotted-head types are also easily drawn from dimensions given in the table in Appendix 32. Note that the screw-driver slots are drawn at 45° in the circular views without regard to true projection (Fig. 783).

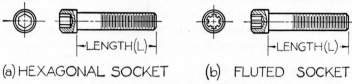

FIG. 784 American Standard Socket Cap Screws.

Cap screws are regularly produced with National Coarse or Fine threads, usually with a Class 3 fit (§ 422). They are specified in bills of material, in correspondence, and elsewhere, as follows:

Example (Complete): $\frac{3}{8}'' \times 2\frac{1}{2}''$–16NC–3 HEXAGON HEAD CAP SCREW
Example (Abbreviated): $\frac{3}{8}'' \times 2\frac{1}{2}''$ HEX HD CAP SCR

431. American Standard Machine Screws. Machine screws are similar to cap screws but are in general smaller (0.060 dia. to 0.750). The ASA has approved eight forms of heads, as shown in Appendix 34. The hexagon head may be slotted if desired. All others are available in either slotted or recessed-head forms. American Standard machine screws are regularly produced with a naturally bright finish, not heat-treated, and are threaded according to either the National Coarse or National Fine thread series with a Class 2 fit. These screws are regularly supplied with plain-sheared ends, not chamfered.

An application of the four most common types is shown in Fig. 785. Note that the threads in the bottom of the tapped hole are omitted so that the end

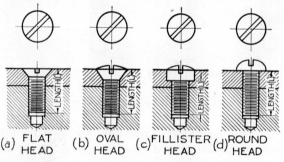

FIG. 785 American Standard Machine Screws.
(For other types, see Appendix 34.)

of the screw is clearly shown. Observe also that it is conventional practice to draw the screw-driver slots at 45° in the circular view without regard to true projection. On assembly drawings the screw heads may thus be more quickly spotted, and also, the close slot lines are not confused with the center lines.

Machine screws are particularly adapted to screwing into thin materials, and all the smaller-numbered screws are threaded to the head. They are used extensively in firearms, jigs, fixtures, and dies.

Machine screw nuts are used mainly on the round head and flat head types of screws, and are hexagonal in form.

Machine screws are specified in bills of material, in correspondence, and elsewhere, as follows:

Example (Complete): No. 10 × $\frac{5}{8}''$–32NF–3 FILLISTER HEAD MACHINE SCREW

Example (Abbreviated): No. 10 × $\frac{5}{8}''$ FILL HD MACH SCR

432. American Standard Set Screws. The function of set screws (Fig. 786) is to prevent relative motion, usually rotary, between two parts, such as the

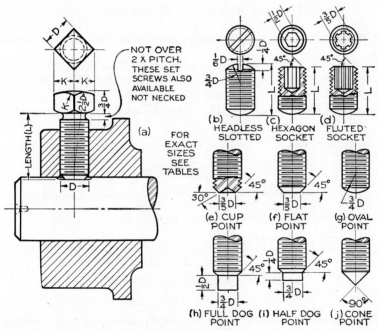

FIG. 786   Set Screws.

motion of the hub of a pulley on a shaft. A set screw is screwed into one part so that its point bears firmly against another part. If the point of the set screw is cupped (e), or if a flat is milled on the shaft (a), the screw will hold much more firmly.

The American Standard Square Head Set Screw is shown in Fig. 786 (a). Two American Standard sockets for headless set screws are illustrated at (c) and (d). American Standard set screw points are shown from (e) to (j). The headless set screws have come into greater use because the projecting head of headed set screws has caused many industrial casualties; this has resulted in legislation prohibiting their use in many states.

Most of the dimensions in Fig. 786 are American Standard formula dimensions,* and the resulting drawings are almost exact representations.

Set screws are threaded in either the National Coarse or National Fine thread series. The Coarse thread is generally used in the square head set screw, which as a rule is used on the rougher grades of work. It is obvious that set screws are not efficient where the load is heavy, or is applied suddenly. Usually they are manufactured of steel and are case hardened.

The difference in consecutive lengths of set screws is as follows:

    (a) For screw lengths $\frac{1}{4}''$ to $\frac{5}{8}''$, difference $= \frac{1}{16}''$.
    (b) For screw lengths $\frac{5}{8}''$ to $1''$, difference $= \frac{1}{8}''$.
    (c) For screw lengths $1''$ to $4''$, difference $= \frac{1}{4}''$.
    (d) For screw lengths $4''$ to $6''$, difference $= \frac{1}{2}''$.

Set screws are specified in a manner similar to that for other screws, as follows:

Example (Complete): $\frac{3}{8}'' \times \frac{3}{4}''$–16NC–2 SQUARE HEAD SET SCREW
Example (Abbreviated): $\frac{3}{8}'' \times \frac{3}{4}''$ SQ HD SET SCR
Example (Abbreviated): $\frac{3}{8}'' \times \frac{1}{2}''$ H'DLESS SET SCR

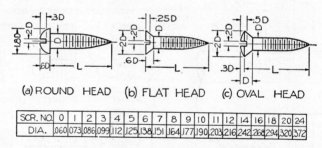

(a) ROUND HEAD   (b) FLAT HEAD   (c) OVAL HEAD

SCR. NO.	0	1	2	3	4	5	6	7	8	9	10	11	12	14	16	18	20	24
DIA.	.060	.073	.086	.099	.112	.125	.138	.151	.164	.177	.190	.203	.216	.242	.268	.294	.320	.372

FIG. 787 American Standard Wood Screws.

433. American Standard Wood Screws. Wood screws with three types of head have been standardized** (Fig. 787). The dimensions shown are not exact but closely approximate the actual dimensions and are more than sufficiently accurate for use on drawings.

Instead of the screwdriver slot, the Phillips recessed head is becoming more popular. Two styles of cross recesses have been standardized by the ASA.** Many examples may be seen on the automobile. A special screw-driver is used, as shown in Fig. 788 (v), and results in rapid assembly without damage to the head.

* ASA B18.3—1936.
** ASA B18.6—1947.

434. Miscellaneous Fasteners. Many other types of fasteners have been devised for specialized uses. Some of the more common types are shown in Fig. 788.

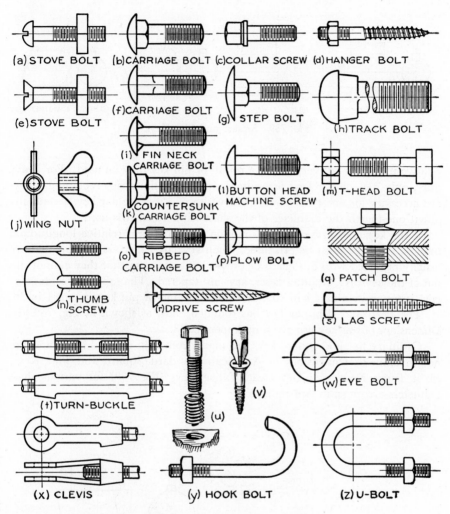

FIG. 788   Miscellaneous Bolts and Screws.

Aero-Thread Inserts or Heli-Coil Inserts, as shown in Fig. 788 (u), are shaped like a spring except that the cross section of the wire conforms to threads in the screw and in the hole. These are made of phosphor bronze or stainless steel and they provide a hard, smooth protective lining for tapped threads in soft metals and in plastics. These inserts have many applications in aircraft engines and accessories, and are coming into wider use.

435. Keys. Keys are used to prevent relative movement between shafts
and wheels, couplings, cranks, and similar machine parts attached to or supported by shafts (Fig. 789). For light duty, that is, where the tendency for

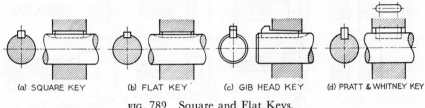

(a) SQUARE KEY   (b) FLAT KEY   (c) GIB HEAD KEY   (d) PRATT & WHITNEY KEY

FIG. 789   Square and Flat Keys.

relative motion is not very great, a round or pin key may be used. For heavy
duty, only rectangular keys are suitable, and sometimes two rectangular keys
are necessary for one connection. The width of a rectangular key is generally
about one-fourth the diameter of the shaft with which it is used.

If the key is to prevent rotary motion and to permit relative longitudinal
motion, its shape must be prismatic. Such keys are called *feather* keys and are
usually provided with gib heads or otherwise fastened so that they cannot slip
out of the keyway. In other cases, keys are tapered. The taper of rectangular
keys is generally about 1 in 100, and that of round or pin keys about 1 in 50.

The Pratt and Whitney key has rounded ends, as shown in Fig. 789 (d).
Dimensions of this key are given in Appendix 38.

Ordinary flat and square keys are made from cold-finished stock and are
not machined. Dimensions of American Standard Square and Flat Keys,
Plain Taper Keys, and Gib Head Taper Keys (Fig. 789) for various shaft
diameters are given in Appendix 35.

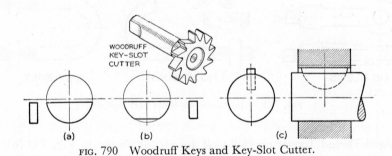

WOODRUFF
KEY–SLOT
CUTTER

(a)   (b)   (c)

FIG. 790   Woodruff Keys and Key-Slot Cutter.

The Woodruff key is semicircular in shape (Fig. 790). The key fits into a
semicircular key slot cut with a Woodruff cutter, as shown. Dimensions of
American Standard Woodruff keys are given in Appendix 36.

Keys are specified as shown in the following:

Example: $\frac{1}{4}''$ SQ. $\times$ $1\frac{1}{2}''$ SQUARE KEY
Example: $\frac{1}{4}''$ $\times$ $\frac{3}{16}''$ $\times$ $1\frac{1}{2}''$ FLAT KEY
Example: No. 204 WOODRUFF KEY
Example: No. 10 PRATT & WHITNEY KEY

Standard notes for keyways and keyseats are shown in Fig. 725 (n), (p), and (v). For production work, keyways on shafts should be dimensioned* as shown in Fig. 791 (a), and on the hub or external member the keyway should be dimensioned as shown at (b).

Keys need not be drawn on detail drawings unless they are to be altered or are of special design, but are drawn to scale on assembly drawings.

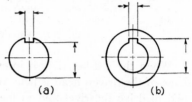

(a) (b)

FIG. 791   Dimensioning Keyways
(ASA Z14.1—1946).

436. Taper Pins and Dowel Pins. For light work, the taper pin is effective in fastening hubs or collars to shafts, as shown in Fig. 792, in which the hole through the collar and shaft is drilled and reamed when the parts are assembled. For slightly heavier duty, the taper pin may be used parallel to the shaft as for square keys, as shown in Fig. 789 (a).

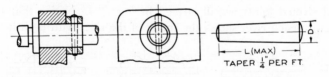

L(MAX)
TAPER $\frac{1}{4}''$ PER FT.

FIG. 792   Taper Pin.

Dowel pins are cylindrical or conical in form, and are used for a variety of purposes, chief of which is to keep two parts in a fixed position or to preserve alignment. The taper dowel pin is most commonly used and is favored where absolute alignment is essential. Dowel pins are usually made of machinery steel and are hardened and ground in a centerless grinder.

437. Rivets. Rivets are regarded as permanent fastenings as distinguished from removable fastenings, such as bolts and screws. They are generally used to hold sheet metal or rolled steel shapes together, and are made of wrought iron, soft steel, or copper, or occasionally other metals.

To fasten two pieces of metal together, holes are punched, drilled, or punched and then reamed, slightly larger in diameter than the shank of the rivet. Rivet diameters in practice are made from $d = 1.2 \sqrt{t}$ to $d = 1.4 \sqrt{t}$, where d is the rivet diameter and t is the metal thickness. The larger size

* ASA Z14.1—1946. See Appendix 2.

is used for steel and single-riveted joints, and the smaller may be used for multiple-riveted joints. In structural work it is common practice to make the hole $\frac{1}{16}''$ larger than the rivet.

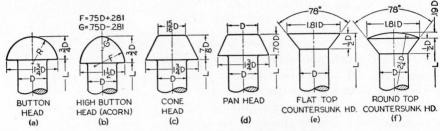

BUTTON HEAD (a) HIGH BUTTON HEAD (ACORN) (b) CONE HEAD (c) PAN HEAD (d) FLAT TOP COUNTERSUNK HD. (e) ROUND TOP COUNTERSUNK HD. (f)

FIG. 793   American Standard Large Rivets.

When the red-hot rivet is inserted, a "dolly bar" having a depression the shape of the driven head is held against the head. A riveting machine is then used to drive the rivet and to form the head on the plain end. This action causes the rivet to swell and fill the hole tightly.

American Standard Large Rivets are used in structural work of bridges, buildings, and in ship and boiler construction, and are shown in their exact formula proportions in Fig. 793. The button head and countersunk head types (a) and (c) are the rivets most commonly used in structural work. The button head and cone heads are commonly used in tank and boiler construction.

Typical riveted joints are illustrated in Fig. 794. Notice that the longitudinal view of each rivet shows the shank of the rivet with both heads made

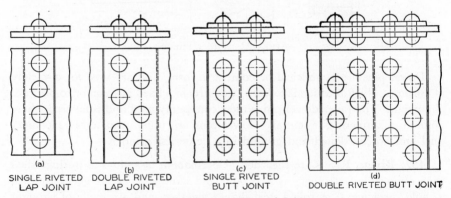

(a) SINGLE RIVETED LAP JOINT   (b) DOUBLE RIVETED LAP JOINT   (c) SINGLE RIVETED BUTT JOINT   (d) DOUBLE RIVETED BUTT JOINT

FIG. 794   Common Riveted Joints.

with circular arcs, and the circular view of each rivet is represented by only the outside circle of the head. In structural drafting where there may be many such circles to draw, the drop spring bow (§ 31) is a popular instrument.

Since many engineering structures are too large to be built in the shop, they are built in the largest units possible and then transported to the desired

location. Trusses are common examples of this. The rivets driven in the shop
are called *shop rivets,* and those driven on the job are called *field rivets.* Solid
black circles are used to represent field rivets, and other standard symbols are
used to show other features, as shown in Fig. 795.

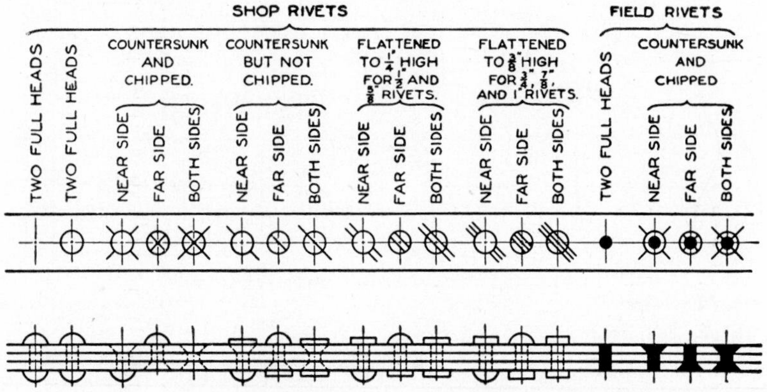

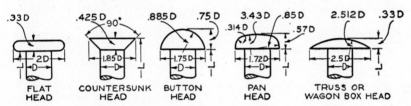

FIG. 795   Conventional Rivet Symbols (American Standard*).

For light work, small rivets are used. American Standard Small Rivets
are illustrated with dimensions showing their standard proportions in Fig. 796.
The American Standards Association has also approved a standard on Tinners',
Coopers', and Belt Rivets.**

FIG. 796   American Standard Small Rivet Proportions.

* ASA Z32.2—1941.

** ASA B18g—1929.

FASTENER PROBLEMS*

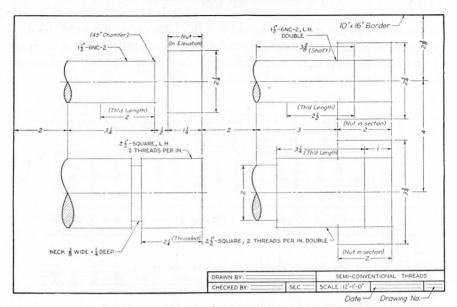

FIG. 797 Draw specified semi-conventional threads arranged as shown. Layout B4 (Appendix 1). Omit all dimensions and notes given in inclined letters. Letter only the thread notes and the title strip.

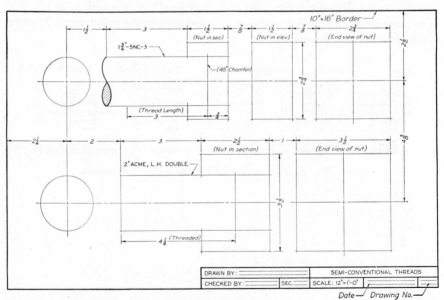

FIG. 798 Draw specified semi-conventional threads, arranged as shown. Layout B4 (Appendix 1). Omit all dimensions and notes given in inclined letters. Letter only the thread notes and the title strip.

* Fastener problems in convenient form for solution may be found in *Technical Drawing Problems*, by Giesecke, Mitchell, and Spencer, and in *Technical Drawing Problems—Series 2*, by Spencer and Grant, both designed to accompany this text, and published by The Macmillan Company.

466

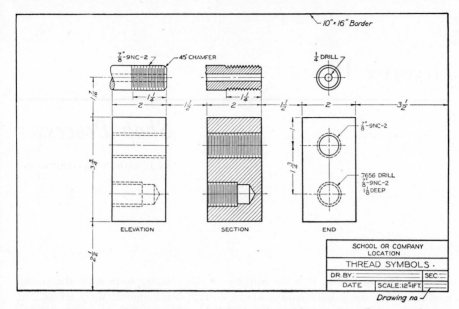

FIG. 799 Draw specified conventional threads, arranged as shown. Draw regular or simplified symbols, as assigned by instructor. Layout B6 (Appendix 1). Omit all dimensions and notes given in inclined letters. Letter only the drill and thread notes, the titles of the views, and the title strip.

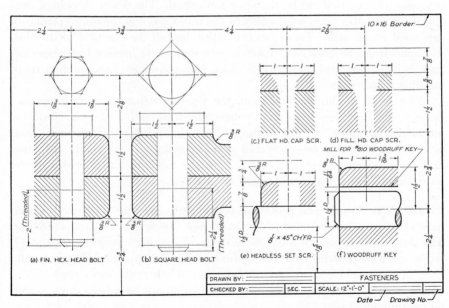

FIG. 800 Draw fasteners, arranged as shown. Layout B6 (Appendix 1). At (a) draw $\frac{7}{8}''$ x 4"–9NC–2 Fin. Hex. Hd. Bolt. At (b) draw $1\frac{1}{8}''$ x 4"–7NC–2 Sq. Hd. Bolt. At (c) draw $\frac{3}{8}''$ x $1\frac{1}{2}''$–16NC–3 Flat Hd. Cap Screw. At (d) draw $\frac{7}{16}''$ x $1\frac{1}{8}''$–14NC–3 Fill. Hd. Cap Screw. At (e) draw $\frac{1}{2}''$ x 1" Headless Set Screw. At (f) draw front view of No. 1010 Woodruff Key. Letter titles under each figure, as shown.

467

CHAPTER **18**

Shop Processes

By J. GEORGE H. THOMPSON*

438. Introduction. It is the purpose of this chapter to provide the young engineer with some information about certain fundamental shop terms and processes and to assist him in using this information on his drawings, so that he can bridge the gap between the ideal design and the practical design that can be economically produced.

As explained in § 357, the designing and production functions were closely allied in the early years of machine manufacturing. In many cases these processes were carried out by the same individual. The design drawings, usually of the assembly type, were scaled by the workman, and the results primarily depended on his skill. Today, specialization has set the engineer off to himself, apart from the workman. Likewise, the shops have become highly specialized, being subdivided into pattern shop, foundry, forge shop, welding shop, machine shop, and so on.

As a result of this specialization, the drafting department must prepare drawings so that they may readily be understood and used as a guide for production in each of the several shops. To do this requires that the individual processes in each shop be considered as the drawings are prepared. It follows that the draftsman must be familiar with the fundamental processes of the several shops where his drawings will be used.

439. The Shops. The process of producing a machine part may be seen more clearly if it is considered to consist of *rough-forming, finishing,* and *assembling.* The three most important rough-forming operations are *casting* (in a foundry), *forging* (in a forge shop), and *welding* (in a welding shop). Finishing is usually done in the machine shop. Assembling the various parts into complete machines often requires certain operations that could not have been done so well on the individual parts.

Engineering drawings are first used for estimating and planning. They are

* Associate Professor of Mechanical Engineering, Agricultural and Mechanical College of Texas.

468

then used for making patterns which are needed before castings can be poured, for making dies before forgings can be struck, or for precutting material before welding can be started. The detail drawings are necessary for these preliminary operations, but they are usually not as much needed in the casting, forging, and welding processes.

It is in the machine shop that the detail drawings are most important. Here the parts which are already rough-formed by casting, forging, and welding are finished, often to close tolerances (§§ 398-406). The detail drawings are usually not used during assembly, but assembly drawings should include all notes necessary for the joining together of the individual parts.

440. Inspection. Throughout the process of making a part the drawings will be referred to by inspectors who must decide if the work has been done satisfactorily. Therefore, it is essential to think of the inspector as well as the machinist when drawings are dimensioned.

The inspector checks the finished part with measuring instruments which have been carefully calibrated. For example, Fig. 801 illustrates the use of micrometers to inspect outside diameters of machined parts. When mass production warrants special tooling,* the inspector uses special-purpose gages and checking equipment designed and constructed to facilitate measurement. In

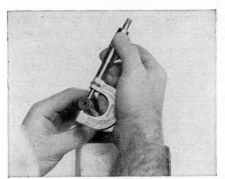

Courtesy Brown & Sharpe Mfg. Co.

FIG. 801   Use of Micrometer Calipers.

many instances, however, and particularly for small-quantity production, the inspector uses such measuring devices as micrometers, vernier height gages, sine bars, gage blocks, dial indicators, and "go" and "no-go" gages.

441. Shop Processes. An understanding of shop processes starts with the drawing itself, since it is the drawing that indicates what is to be accomplished in the shop. A detail drawing specifies shape, size, and material for the machine part it describes. Since the job of the shop is to produce the item shown on the drawing, it follows that the shop starts with what may be described as

---

* Machine tools hold work and guide small tools. Any device which performs either of these functions belongs to that class of mechanical equipment known, collectively, as "tooling."

raw stock and then modifies this piece of material until it agrees with the detail drawing. Thus, the shape of the raw material may have to be altered before the piece agrees with the drawing. For example, an automobile body must be pressed out of sheet steel on a massive press before it conforms with the drawing. Also, the size of the raw stock may have to be changed to satisfy the specified dimensions. For example, a 2″ round bar may have to be turned down on a lathe until it becomes 1.774″ in diameter. The characteristics of the material may have to be varied to agree with the properties called for on the drawings. For instance, the part might require a Brinell* hardness of 400. Since steel ordinarily is not supplied in this degree of hardness, it would be necessary to heat-treat such a part. The function of the shop, then, is to effect changes in the shape, size, and properties of the raw material in accordance with the specifications indicated on the detail drawing.

To change the shape and size of the raw stock which is being fashioned to conform with the drawing requires one or more of the following: (1) *removal* of part of the original material; (2) *addition* of more material; (3) *redistribution* of original material. Cutting, as turning on a lathe, or punching holes in sheet metal in a power press, removes material. Welding, brazing, soldering, metal spraying, and electrochemical plating add material. Forging, pressing, drawing, extruding, and spinning redistribute material.

To change the properties of the raw material usually requires heat treatment. This becomes very technical and involves such properties of the material as ductility, toughness, elastic limit, hardness, and resilience. The subject is beyond the scope of this chapter, but it should be made clear that heat treating is just as important a shop process as are any of the cutting or forming operations. Two examples will illustrate this point. First, it is common to use heat treatment to stress-relieve welded parts to reduce internal stresses. Second, it is also common practice to machine a part when it is soft (the material is heat treated to make it soft before machining) and then to harden the part after machining. During this hardening process a slight distortion often takes place, and grinding is employed to finish the piece. The student should note that grinding is used not only because it is so accurate a process, but also because ordinary cutting tools do not work well on hard steel. See § 445.

The student should seize every opportunity to familiarize himself with manufacturing processes by means of observation in shops and by reading available books and periodicals.** It is the purpose of the following pages to lay the basis for this acquaintance with shop processes by describing, simply, some of the more common shop operations. Certain phases of work in pattern

---

* *Brinell* is a scale for measuring hardness which is obtained by measuring the diameter of indentation produced by a standard steel ball loaded according to specified conditions. A steel of "150 Brinell" is moderately soft. "250 to 400 Brinell" is as hard as can ordinarily be cut with single-pointed steel cutting tools. Harder materials can be machined by grinding or by the use of non-ferrous cutting tools such as Stellite or Tungsten-Carbide.

** See Technical Bibliography in Appendix 44.

shop, foundry, forge shop, welding shop, and machine shop will now be discussed in the order listed.

442. The Pattern Shop. *Patterns* (Fig. 802) are usually made of white pine, sugar pine, mahogany, and other durable woods. If the same pattern is to be used repeatedly in production, a metal pattern of aluminum, brass, or other metal may be made from a wooden pattern. This wooden pattern is called a *master pattern.*

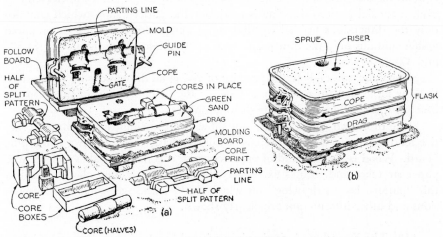

FIG. 802   Sand Molding.

Since shrinkage occurs when metal cools, patterns are made slightly oversize. Therefore, the patternmaker uses a *shrink rule* whose units are oversize according to the shrinkage characteristics of the metal to be used. For example, cast iron shrinks $\frac{1}{8}''$ per foot. Allowance for shrinkage is not shown on the working drawing, but is taken care of entirely by the pattern shop. Notice that the wooden master pattern referred to at the end of the preceding paragraph would have to allow for the shrinkage of the metal pattern as well as for the shrinkage of the casting.

Draft (see § 443) is the taper given to a pattern to permit it to be easily withdrawn from the sand mold. It is also taken care of by the pattern shop, and is generally not shown on the working drawing. Draft is one of the most troublesome problems that arise. The way the pattern is drafted often determines how the mold has to be made in the foundry, and the design engineer should be able to think in terms of the pattern shop and the foundry as he proportions his part.

It is from considerations of shrinkage and of draft that one arrives at a general rule that small holes (even if so placed as to draw out of the sand) are better drilled from a solid casting and that large holes are better cored and bored.

Finish marks are as important to the patternmaker as to the machinist, because additional material on each surface which is to be machined must be provided. For small and medium-sized castings, $\frac{1}{16}''$ to $\frac{1}{8}''$ is usually sufficient; larger allowances are made where there is probability of distortion or warping.

The pattern shop receives the working drawing showing the object in its completed state, including all dimensions and finish marks. Usually the same drawing is used by the pattern shop and by the machine shop; hence, it should contain all dimensions and notes needed by both shops. In some cases, however, a special pattern drawing is made for the pattern shop, which contains only the dimensions needed by that shop, and another drawing is prepared which contains only the dimensions needed by the machine shop. See §§ 378 and 477.

Some companies follow the practice of giving all dimensions for the pattern shop or forge shop in pencil and those for the machine shop in ink. On the blueprint, the difference is easily distinguishable.

Since draft and shrinkage are not shown on drawings, it is common practice for the pattern shop to prepare a full-size pattern layout on a white pine board. Wood is used instead of paper because it is more durable and because paper stretches and shrinks excessively. The pattern is then checked against this "pattern layout drawing" on which draft, shrinkage, coreprint* dimensions and other information are clearly shown.

443. The Foundry. A casting is produced by pouring molten metal into a mold, or cavity, the shape of which the metal retains after it has solidified. Molds are made of various materials. Sand and steel are the most common, but plaster of Paris, wood, and even paper are used commercially today.

Sand molds are relatively inexpensive to make, and it is in these that the majority of castings are produced. Plaster of Paris molds are superior to sand molds because they produce castings possessing better appearing surfaces, sharper corners, and more accurate dimensions. Although plaster molds are more expensive than sand molds, and are somewhat limited in their use, they are of practical importance today. Stainless steel, for example, has been cast in plaster of Paris molds. The *lost wax process*,** like the plaster mold, has been used for generations but only recently has assumed a position of real engineering significance. *Precision cast* steam turbine blades are produced by the lost wax process. Each of the above-mentioned methods of producing castings has the disadvantage that the mold is destroyed each time a casting is made and consequently the entire cost of the mold must be borne by the product of one pouring.

---

* A coreprint is a projection added to a pattern to form a cavity in a mold into which a corresponding portion of a core will seat, as shown in Fig. 802, thus forming an anchor to hold the core in place.

** See *Materials and Processes*, edited by James F. Young of General Electric Company. (John Wiley, 1944.)

Sometimes expensive metal molds are produced. These have the advantage that they may be used more than once and thereby have their cost shared by a number of castings. Because of their long life, metal molds are sometimes referred to as *permanent molds*. When only the force of gravity is used, as in the case of sand molds, to force the molten metal into the permanent mold, the resulting casting is called a *gravity casting*. When a considerable pressure is exerted to force the liquid metal into the mold, and when such pressure is maintained until solidification is complete, the resulting casting is called a *die casting*. When pressure is so employed the metal mold is referred to as a *die*. (Note the use of the word die to describe a steel mold which gives shape to a plastic steel in § 446.)

Die castings are accurate in size and shape and possess surfaces superior in appearance and accuracy to those produced by other casting processes. Their production is rapid and, for large quantities, they are relatively inexpensive. Die castings are often not machined to any great degree. This is partly because of their fine surface finish and high degree of accuracy as cast and partly because any degree of cutting, unless done with discretion, could result in both distortion and loss of strength. There are, however, many instances where a considerable amount of machining is done on die castings. For the most part die castings cannot be heat-treated nor be put into service at high temperatures since they are usually limited to non-ferrous alloys of reasonably low melting point.

A casting process of growing importance is *centrifugal casting*. Molten metal is poured into a mold which is already rotating and which may be made to continue to rotate until the metal has solidified. The effect of centrifugal force may thus be employed to produce a casting which is less porous than that produced in a sand mold. The process is extensively used for the manufacture of cast iron pipe, and for steel gears and discs.

While there are many interesting processes used to produce castings, it should be noted that the first step toward an understanding of what goes on in a foundry is to see how a simple casting is produced in a common sand mold.

The sand mold is used far more extensively than is any other type of mold. Sand molds are made by ramming sand around a pattern (§ 442) and then carefully withdrawing the pattern, leaving a cavity to receive the molten metal, as shown in Fig. 802 (a). The sand is contained in a two-part box called a *flask* (b); the upper part is called the *cope* and the lower the *drag*. For more complicated work, one or more intermediate boxes (called *cheeks*) may be introduced between the cope and the drag. The pattern must be of such shape that it will "pull away" from both the cope and the drag. The plane of separation of the two halves of the pattern marks the *parting line* on the pattern (Fig. 802). On each side of the parting line the pattern must be tapered slightly inward to permit the withdrawal of the pattern from the sand unless loose pieces are used. This taper is the draft. Though the draft is usually not shown, and dimensions for it are not given on working drawings, the design must be such that the draft can be properly built into the pattern by tne patternmaker.

A *sprue stick*, or round peg, is placed in position during the ramming process and then removed to leave a hole through which the metal may be poured. The part of the hole adjacent to the casting is called the *gate*, and the vertical part the *sprue* (Fig. 802).

When it is necessary to form the sand into shapes that would ordinarily not permit the necessary adhesion and strength or in instances where the shape of the casting would interfere with the removal of the pattern, a *dry sand core* is used. Dry sand cores are made by ramming a prepared mixture of sand and a binding substance into a *core box*. See Fig. 802 (a). The core is then removed from the core box and baked in a core oven to make the core sufficiently rigid. The most common use of a core is to extend it through a casting to form a cored hole. (Sometimes a dry sand [baked] core forms the bottom half of a core, and a green sand [not baked] core forms the top half of a core.) The baked or dried sand is sufficiently rigid to form the desired hole in the casting during the pouring process, but is brittle enough to permit removal or disposal of the core sand after the casting has cooled.

Often, symmetrical cores are made in two pieces and then pasted together to form the core, as shown in Fig. 802 (a).

444. Fillets and Rounds. A rounded interior angle on a machine or structural member is called a *fillet;* on an exterior angle it is called a *round*. Fillets and rounds as applied to patterns and castings are illustrated in Fig. 803. A

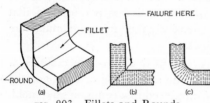
FIG. 803   Fillets and Rounds.

round on a pattern is formed by shaping the wood by planing, sandpapering, etc. A fillet on a pattern is made of wood, leather, or wax, applied to the pattern. The fillets and rounds on the pattern, which were put there according to the dimensions on the drawing, will be reproduced in the casting. Sharp corners should be avoided, not only because they are difficult to obtain in a casting, but because the crystals of the cooling metal arrange themselves normal to the exterior surfaces, which may cause a weak area that may later result in failure, as shown in Fig. 803 (b).

If the corners of the pattern are rounded and filleted properly, the crystals form as shown at (c), and produce a stronger casting. One company makes it a practice to cast a large fillet where a particular piece has to have a square inside corner, and to add a note to the drawing: "CAST WITH $\frac{3}{4}''$ RADIUS FILLET, MACHINE SQUARE."

It has been noted that a fillet of small radius tends to weaken a casting. Also, from design considerations other than those related to the solidification of castings in molds, a fillet should have as large a radius as possible. The term *stress concentration* is used to describe the increase in stress in the vicinity of a fillet. The load a part can safely carry may sometimes be doubled by simply increasing the radius of a fillet.

Fillets are considered carefully, therefore, in order to minimize stress concentrations as well as to reduce the severity of the cooling stresses. Fillets must be designed thoughtfully on *all* types of stress-bearing structural and machine parts, whether castings, forgings, welded parts, or pieces made in any other manner. See also § 467.

Typical of the best practice with regard to fillets and rounds is that of General Electric Company:

"It is General Electric Company's regular practice to specify on drawings the dimensions for fillets and rounds, due to recognizing corner cracks as one of the most frequent causes of mechanical failure. This company expects it to be almost second nature for each mechanical engineer and designer to specify properly-considered dimensions for transitions in cross section. The sizes of fillets and rounds are determined by the designer who must dimension to prevent the hazards of concentrated strains, corner cracks, and whose decision usually in part depends upon the proportion of the parts, the relationship of mating parts, the stresses to be encountered in service, and the requirements incidental to the plan of processing."*

445. Heat-Treating. The process of effecting changes in the properties of metals by heating and cooling is known as heat-treating or heat-treatment. *Annealing* and *normalizing* are generally used for the purpose of softening the metal or improving its grain structure, and involve heating to the critical temperature and then permitting slow cooling. *Hardening* requires heating to above the critical temperature range followed by rapid cooling (*quenching*) in oil, water, or brine, or in some instances in air (air-hardening steels). Hardening may be followed by *tempering*, a low temperature reheating treatment which reduces the internal stresses caused by the hardening process and improves the toughness and ductility of the material. *Case hardening* involves the surface hardening of low carbon steels by adding carbon from an external source, with subsequent hardening and tempering. In *carburizing*, the highly carbonized surface is obtained by heating the part in contact with carbonizing material, such as wood charcoal or bone dust. In *cyaniding*, the surface carbon is obtained from potassium cyanide, and is usually only a few thousandths of an inch in depth. *Nitriding* is a surface hardening process used for alloy steels by heating in an atmosphere of partially dissociated ammonia; hardening results from the formation of nitrides of iron and alloying elements in the steel.

446. Mechanical Working of Metals. In the casting operations, the objects usually take on their final shape while the metal is still liquid. Only after castings take the shape of the mold do they cool and solidify.

* J. E. Burmester, Supervisor of Drawings, General Electric Company.

Many manufacturing processes, however, involve the changing of the shape and size of a piece of metal after it has solidified. If these processes involve slowly pressing the part (squeezing) or rapidly and repeatedly striking the part (hammering) the term *mechanical working* is used to describe the operation. If mechanical working is done when the metal is relatively cold, the metal tends to become brittle, and parts may require annealing (§ 445). If several annealing cycles are required, the cost may place a limit on the economy of mechanical working of cold metal.

If, on the other hand, a metal part is sufficiently hot to be plastic, the pressing and hammering will not make it brittle, and severe changes in shape may be made as long as the "recrystallization" temperature is maintained, which is defined as the temperature above which there is "hot working" and below which there is "cold working." *

By hot working it is possible to form larger parts than could economically be formed by cold working. Proper hot working produces a part superior to a casting in that it is stronger, more uniform in properties, more ductile, and usually requires less finishing. Cold working produces a better surface finish and more accurate shape than hot working. In many instances cold working is used as a sizing or finishing operation after a part has been formed to approximate size by hot working.

Forging is an example of hot working. *Stamping* is an example of cold working. Most hot-working processes have their cold-working counterparts. For example, *swedging* is a cold-working counterpart to the hot-working process called forging.

Figure 855 is an example of forging. Hot working may be accomplished by *hand forging* in which the forming is accomplished by manual operations such as hand hammering, or by *die forging* in which the hot metal is deformed to fill a die. The die controls and defines the flow of metal. Drop forging, forging-machine work, and hot pressing are the three most common types of die forging.

Since forging is a process of flow of metal under pressure, the distribution and balance of adjacent sections of a drop forging must be carefully considered. Attention must also be paid to fillet design. Drastic changes of section may require that the forging of the part be accomplished in several steps. Draft, to permit removal of the forging from the die, should ordinarily not be less than 7° although, under special conditions, much less than this may be tolerated.

The working drawing, as it comes to the forge shop, may show the finished or machined part; in such cases, the necessary forging and machining allowances are made by the die-maker. Separate forging drawings are often made which contain only the dimensions needed by the forge shop, as shown in Figs. 855, 955, and 956.

* See Chapter I of *Materials and Processes*, by J. F. Young.

447. Stock Forms. Many forms of metal, plastic, wood, or other materials are so often used that their composition and sizes have been standardized and may be obtained readily from the manufacturer in stock sizes. Among these are bars of various shapes, as square, hexagonal, or round, the common structural shapes (Fig. 1083), plate, and sheet.

448. Welding. *Welding* (Fig. 804) is a process of joining metals by fusion into a single homogeneous mass. Arc welding, gas welding, resistance welding, and atomic hydrogen welding are commonly used as well as the old method of forge welding which is still employed to a certain extent. Welding drawings are discussed in Chapter 22.

Courtesy Dallas Tank Co.

FIG. 804   Welding.

Welded structures are built up in most cases from stock forms, particularly plate, tubing, and angles. Often both heat-treating and machine shop operations must be performed on welded machine parts. In general it is a good rule for the young engineer to remember always to design a welded part such that no welding will be done after any surface has been finished by machining.

449. Machine Shop. The welded parts, castings, forgings, or rough stock must come to the machine shop for final machining. As a rule, the same working drawings used by the preceding shops are also used in the machine shop to bring the product to completion. When the work warrants it, special drawings are prepared which contain only the information needed by the machine shop. See Figs. 856, 857, and 958, and § 378.

The work of the machine shop is effected by cutting tools, which are used for one or more of three purposes: metal removal, dimensional or size accuracy, and surface refinement. Cutting tools are applied either manually or by means of a machine tool, which is usually defined as any power-driven, non-portable machine for shaping and sizing metal parts. Machine tools are usually classified as *general-purpose* and *special-purpose* machines; the *engine lathe, drill press, boring mill, planer, shaper,* and *grinder* are examples of the first classification, while *automatic* and *semiautomatic milling* and *drilling machines* are illustrative of the special-purpose group.

Machine shops may be broadly classified into two categories: the *job shop* and the *mass-production shop.* The former is usually equipped with general-purpose machine tools, operated by skilled machinists, and is able to handle a wide variety of work, almost always in limited or comparatively small quantities. The mass-production shop is usually equipped with special-purpose machinery, operated by workmen whose skills (although often very high) are limited in scope, since they are usually trained for specific repetitive tasks on larger quantities of parts. The automotive industry furnishes many outstanding examples of mass-production machine shops. The typical operations in each classification, however, are alike in principle, and may be resolved into *drilling, boring, reaming, turning, facing, shaping, milling, planing, threading, broaching,* and *grinding.*

450. Holes. Finished holes may be produced on the lathe, the drill press, the milling machine, the boring mill, the jig borer, and many special machines. Such holes are most commonly produced by a drill, as shown in Fig. 805 (a),

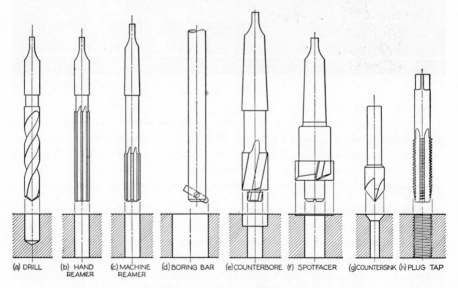

(a) DRILL (b) HAND REAMER (c) MACHINE REAMER (d) BORING BAR (e) COUNTERBORE (f) SPOTFACER (g) COUNTERSINK (h) PLUG TAP

FIG. 805 Types of Holes.

boring bar (d) and reamer, (b) and (c). These drilling, boring and reaming operations may be performed on any one of a number of different machines. The basic operations of cutting holes and the basic tools used are the same whether lathe, drill press, milling machine, or any other machine tool be employed. Furthermore, the same basic tools and the same basic principles are found even in the most complicated special machine tools used in mass production shops.

A drill is essentially a tool for originating cylindrical holes. In many cases the drilled hole is not accurate in size, is not truly cylindrical, and is not straight. Under ordinary conditions the drilled hole may be as much as .005″ oversize, with respect to its nominal diameter, and may be several thousandths of an inch out of round. Modern practice, using the latest techniques, the best equipment and specially trained labor, can produce very satisfactory work with drilled holes, but under average shop conditions, the drill is still to be regarded as a roughing tool. Drilling on the lathe is illustrated in Fig. 806.

FIG. 806   Drilling $\frac{31}{64}''$ Hole in Gear Blank.*

The boring bar cannot be used to originate holes, but can be used only to enlarge a hole that has already been produced by one of the common operations such as drilling, coring, or piercing. Such an enlarged hole produced by boring, being a generated hole, is largely independent of the condition of the original hole. Boring will straighten the hole and will make it more nearly

* Original photographs for Figs. 806, 807, 808, 810, 811, 813, 814, 818 and 822 were made at Texas A. & M. College through courtesy of Prof. Walter Downard.

cylindrical. The accuracy with which a hole can be produced by this operation depends upon the equipment used and, in many instances, on the skill of the machine operator. Boring on a lathe to improve a drilled hole is illustrated in Fig. 807.

FIG. 807   Boring to Improve Drilled Hole.

It is difficult to give a figure for accuracy of a bored hole because holes are bored under varying conditions. On S.I.P. (Swiss) jig-boring machines, holes are said to be within 0.00008″ of true size and are said to be located to within 0.00005″ accuracy. Diamond-boring machines* are said to hold holes to the following limits: 0.0001″ for out of round, 0.0001″ for straightness, and 0.0001″ for size. Thus, the boring operation is capable of very accurate results.

Reamers are used ordinarily for finishing existing holes which are close to the required size. Basically, reamers are intended to improve surface quality and accuracy of diameter of holes, and are not intended to improve such conditions as errors in direction of the hole. While the boring bar tends to generate an ideal hole, the reamer tends to follow the hole left by the drill. Good practice is to drill, bore, and ream, in that order; and in some cases these operations are followed by *honing*.** Reaming on a lathe to finish a $\frac{1}{2}″$ hole is illustrated in Fig. 808.

---

* A diamond is the material used for the cutting tool.

** Honing is a process of improving a surface by rubbing a fine abrasive stone over the surface so that very little material is removed but the surface itself is improved.

Reaming, in general, is approximately half as accurate as boring so far as size and roundness are concerned. In straightness, reamed holes will usually be inaccurate compared with bored holes. Schneider gives 0.002″ error in 6″ of depth of hole as the best degree of accuracy that should be ordinarily expected

FIG. 808   Reaming to Finish $\frac{1}{2}$″ Hole.

for straightness of reamed holes and 0.0002″ as the corresponding error in bored holes. The reamed hole normally will be within 0.001″ of size. *

The reamer should not ordinarily be called upon to enlarge the diameter of a hole by an amount in excess of $\frac{1}{64}$″ (0.0156″), and a smaller cut is recommended for accurate work. Thus, if a hole be reamed to .500″ diameter after drilling, the drill size would be $\frac{31}{64}$″. The hand reamer is used for very accurate work and only a few thousandths of an inch of the diameter should be removed by such an operation for best results.

The location of holes is a subject which is as important as the production of the holes themselves. Details are beyond the scope of this chapter, but it should be mentioned that the layout of the part to be machined is usually a necessary operation before cutting begins. See § 386.

For the production of holes, this layout is customarily accomplished by first treating the surface with copper sulphate, Prussian blue, or other suitable substance so that scratches will be clearly visible. Then sharp-pointed instruments (scribers) are used to scratch center lines on the work. The surface table or

* A. W. Schneider: *Finishing Internal Surfaces;* from Mechanical Engineering, April 1936.

layout table is often used for such layout. Frequently the work is clamped to a toolmaker's angle and the center lines scratched on with a vernier height gage.

Of the several methods commonly used to locate work relative to the cutting tool, the use of toolmaker's buttons is probably the most common. Buttons are small hardened-steel rings which may temporarily be attached to the work so that the centers of the rings are precisely where the centers of the holes are to be. The work is then set up with the center of one of the buttons in the center of rotation of, say, the faceplate of an engine lathe. The button is then unscrewed and a hole drilled, bored, and reamed in proper location. By repeating this process the required number holes may be produced in their proper locations.

451. The Engine Lathe. The *engine lathe* (Fig. 809) is one of the most useful of all machine tools. Usually rotating work is cut on this machine by

Courtesy Lodge & Shipley Co.

FIG. 809   Engine Lathe.

means of non-rotating cutters. Work is supported on centers by means of a *mandrel* (Fig. 810), supported in a *chuck*—essentially a rotating vise—(Fig. 811) or supported in other ways as will be described in detail in reference books suggested in Appendix 44. The most common operations performed on an engine lathe are *drilling* (Fig. 806), *boring* (Fig. 807), *reaming* (Fig. 808), *turning* (Fig. 810), and *facing* (Fig. 811). Also *threading, cutting a taper, producing a contour*, and many other special operations are possible on an engine lathe.

Sometimes the shape of a surface is determined by the *shape of the cutting tool*, examples of which are shown in Figs. 818, 819 and 822. A surface so formed may be said to be "form cut" or "contour cut." Sometimes the shape of a surface is determined by the *motion of the cutting tool*, examples of which are shown in Figs. 807, 810, 811, and 814. A surface so produced is said to be "generated." While some form cutting is done on lathes, the majority of lathe work produces generated surfaces.

FIG. 810   Turning Outside Diameter of Gear Blank.

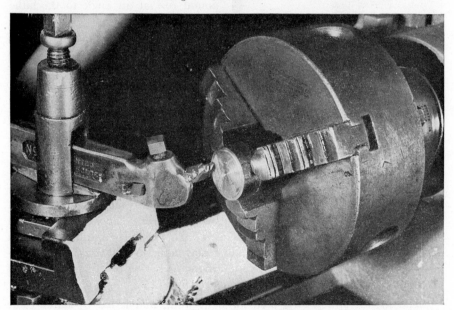

FIG. 811   Facing End of Stock in Universal Chuck in Engine Lathe.

An inside right circular cylindrical surface is *bored* (Fig. 807) and an outside right circular cylindrical surface is *turned* (Fig. 810) when the tool is moved in a straight line parallel to the axis of rotation of the work. A plane surface is *faced* (Fig. 811) when the tool is moved in a straight line perpendicular to the axis of rotation of the work. Examination of an engine lathe in action will reveal many other ways in which surfaces are generated as, for instance, the cutting of screw threads.

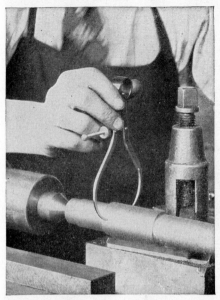

FIG. 812   Use of Spring Caliper.

Figures 810 and 811 show how the *cutting tool* is supported. The cutting tool, or *tool bit*, is seen to be held in a *tool holder* by means of a set screw. Note that both right- and left-hand tool holders are used. The tool holder is locked in a *tool post*. This tool post rests in a T-slot in the top of a *compound rest*. The compound rest, in turn, is secured to a *cross slide* mounted on a carriage. A *cross feed* moves the whole compound rest across the carriage at right angles to the axis of rotation of the work. It is also possible to move the entire carriage parallel to the axis of rotation, and to move the compound rest at an angle to the lathe spindle axis.

Work is bored (Fig. 807) and turned (Fig. 810) by moving the carriage parallel to the axis of rotation. Work is faced (Fig. 811) by using the cross feed to move the cross slide or the compound rest across the carriage while the carriage is kept stationary.

For checking diameters within limits of .010″, the *spring caliper* is commonly used (Fig. 812). For measurements requiring more accuracy, the *micrometer caliper* is generally used (Fig. 801).

452. Drill Press. The drill press (Fig. 813) is one of the most-used machine tools in the shop. The drill is held in a chuck which is made to revolve at a cutting speed appropriate to the metal worked upon. The work is clamped to the table, or held in a *drill vise*, or in a *drill jig*. The use of a drill jig is shown in Fig. 813. See § 459. Other operations may be performed merely by changing the cutting tool to a reamer, counterbore, or boring bar. For methods of indicating these operations on a drawing, see Fig. 725.

The *sensitive drill press* is used for light work, and is fed by hand. The *heavy-duty drill press* is used for heavy work. A *multiple-spindle drill press* supports a number of spindles driven from the same shaft. The *radial drill press* (Fig. 813) is designed so that the spindle may be removed to the desired position on the work instead of adjusting the work to the position of the spindle. This machine is, therefore, very flexible, and especially suitable for large work.

High speeds for small-diameter drills may be obtained through the use of a *drill speeder* (Fig. 929).

FIG. 813   Radial Drill Press.

453. The Shaper. In the *shaper* (Figs. 814 and 815), work is machined by being held in a vise while a single-pointed cutting tool cuts as it is forced

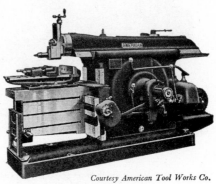

Courtesy American Tool Works Co.

FIG. 814   Machining Plane Surface on Shaper.

FIG. 815   Shaper.

to move in a straight line past stationary work. A comparison of Fig. 814 with Figs. 810 and 811 will reveal that tools and tool holders used on shapers are similar to those employed in lathe work. Fig. 814 shows the tool about to start on a cutting stroke. The work will remain stationary as the tool cuts.

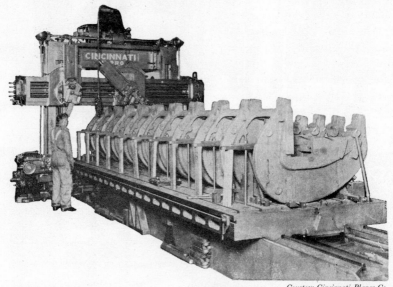

Courtesy Cincinnati Planer Co.

FIG. 816   Planer.

After this, the tool will be returned so as to be in position to take another cut, and the work is "fed," or moved slightly so that a fresh portion of the work will be in the path of the tool for the next cut.

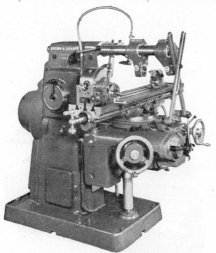

Courtesy Brown & Sharpe Mfg. Co.

FIG. 817   Milling Machine.

454. The Planer. Figure 816 shows a *planer*. Work is fixed to a table which is moved so that cutting takes place between stationary tools and moving work. Usually planers are used for large work, whereas shapers (Fig. 815) are used to cut small pieces. Sometimes a number of small parts are mounted on the planer and cut simultaneously. Like the shaper, the planer is used primarily to cut plane surfaces. The length of stroke is rather closely regulated in shapers but may vary somewhat in planers. Thus it is good practice to cut close to a shoulder on a shaper, but it would not be as good practice to do this on a planer.

455. The Milling Machine. Figure 817 shows the *milling machine*. In this machine, cutting is accomplished by feeding the work into a rotating cutter.

Figure 818 shows a small gear being cut on a milling machine. The gear is seen to be fed into the cutter much as wood is fed into a circular saw in a wood shop. Close examination of Fig. 818 will reveal that the profile of the gear tooth space is dependent upon the shape of the teeth on the milling cutter. Figure 819 shows a few other shapes of hardened steel cutters. A variety of such cutters is available today. Some of these cut on their sides, as shown. Others cut on their ends and are known as "end milling cutters."

By means of equipment supplied with the milling machine it is possible to turn the gear blank

FIG. 818   Cutting Teeth on Gear in Milling Machine.

through exactly the same angle between each cut. This insures uniformity of thickness and spacing of gear teeth being cut.

The milling machine is capable of producing almost every surface cut on a shaper, and in addition will perform work not possible on the shaper. Milled surfaces are essentially formed, not generated, and are therefore usually not as accurate as those produced by a planer or shaper, but the milling machine usually has a higher production rate than the single-point-tool machines.

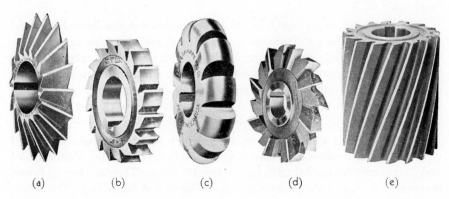

(a)   (b)   (c)   (d)   (e)

Courtesy Brown & Sharpe Mfg. Co.

FIG. 819   Milling Cutters.

Drilling, reaming, and boring are also practicable on the milling machine; in small shops with limited equipment, the milling machine may be used as a boring machine for great accuracy of hole location.

456. The Boring Machine. A *boring machine* is primarily a machine tool for boring holes. The *vertical boring mill* (Fig. 820), sometimes called vertical

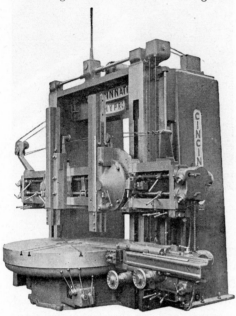

boring and turning mill, has an action between the rotating work and the non-rotating cutting tool essentially as though a lathe were set on end, having a vertical instead of a horizontal axis of rotation. The vertical boring mill is used for operations such as facing, turning, and hole boring. It is a simple, accurate machine and is suited for heavy work. Castings weighing 20 tons are commonly handled on such a machine tool. The *horizontal boring machine* and the *jig borer* are essentially similar to milling machines. In these two machine tools a rotating tool bores holes into non-rotating work.

The horizontal boring machine is suitable for accurate boring, reaming, facing, counterboring,

Courtesy Cincinnati Planer Co.

FIG. 820   Vertical Boring Mill.

and milling of holes for pieces larger than could be handled on a milling machine.

The two most important parts of this machine are the large horizontal spindle to which the rotating cutting tool is fixed and the table to which the work is secured. Once the machine is adjusted, all movements except two are locked. These two motions, which may take place when cutting is being done, are rotation of the spindle and movement of the table in a direction parallel to the axis of rotation of the spindle. The latter feeds the work into the cutting tool and fixes the depth to which holes will be bored.

The jig borer is a specialized machine which somewhat resembles a drill press in its basic features of a rotating vertical spindle supporting a cutting tool and a stationary horizontal table for holding the work. The precision jig borer, however, is equipped with a table which can be locked in position while a hole is being cut but which may be moved between cutting operations so as to locate one hole with respect to another. The work is not moved relative to the table;

instead, the table may be accurately positioned in two perpendicular directions by means of precise compensating lead screws or by micrometer measuring bars.

457. Grinding Machine. A *grinding machine* (Fig. 821) is used for removing a relatively small amount of material to bring the work to a very accurate and fine finish. The work is fed against the grinding wheel. For roughing, the depth of cut may be from .001″ to .004″; and for finishing, from .00025″ to .0005″. If a surface is to be ground, the draftsman should so indicate with the notation GRIND, as shown in Fig. 742.

Grinding machines with attachments for grinding plane surfaces and both internal and external cylindrical and conical surfaces are very common. Also, specially formed grinding wheels are often used to cut gear teeth, threads, and other shapes.

Courtesy Brown & Sharpe Mfg. Co.

FIG. 821   Grinding Machine.

458. Broaching Machine. *Broaching* is illustrated in Fig. 822, in which a broach is shown in an arbor press cutting a keyway in a small gear. Broaching is basically similar to a single-stroke filing operation. Close inspection will reveal that, as the broach is forced through the work, each succeeding tooth bites deeper and deeper into the metal, thus enlarging and forming the keyway as the broach passes through the hole. Another typical broach, together with the drawing, showing the rectangular hole it produces, is shown in Fig. 823. Some broaches are pushed and others are pulled through the work.

The illustrations in Figs. 822 and 823 are examples of *internal broaching*. Square, cylindrical, hexagonal, and other shaped holes are produced by this process. An initial hole, produced by drilling, punching, or otherwise, is necessary in order to permit the broach to enter the work. Thus, internal broaching only enlarges and improves the shape of a hole which has already been produced by some other operation.

In addition to internal broaching, there is *surface broaching*, which is used to produce flat surfaces on such parts as engine blocks and cylinder heads.

Broaching is distinctly a mass-production process in which there is usually involved a large expenditure of money both for the broaches themselves and for the special machines developed for their use in mass production. Broaching is one of our most accurate cutting processes, and work produced by it is of a high order of precision. It is common to hold holes to within .0005″ of the desired diameter with this process. In some instances, cylindrical holes can be more accurately and economically finished by this process than by reaming.

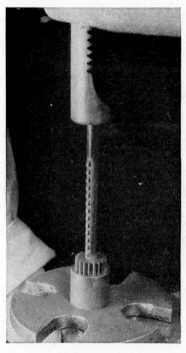

FIG. 822   Broaching.

459. Jigs and Fixtures. A general-purpose machine tool may have its effectiveness on a specific job increased by means of *jigs* or *fixtures*. A jig is a device which holds the work and guides the tool; it is usually not rigidly fixed to a machine. A *drilling jig* (Fig. 813) is a common device by means of which holes on many duplicate parts may be drilled exactly alike. A fixture is rigidly attached to the machine, becoming in reality an extension of it, and holds the work in position for the cutting tools without acting as a guide for them. Drawings of one of the important fixtures used in the production of the Ford V–8 connecting rod, shown in Figs. 855–858, are shown in Figs. 947–952. It was built at considerable expense for the sole purpose of holding the connecting rod in the exact position required for the efficient and speedy execution of a single operation.

Jigs and fixtures are usually designed in a tooling department by tool designers. Usually they are built by machinists of much better than average ability, using especially accurate equipment. Such tooling devices are commonly held to tolerances one tenth of those applied to the parts to be produced on these jigs and fixtures.

Jigs and fixtures may be grouped into two general classes: *manufacturing tooling* and *assembly tooling*. Manufacturing tooling consists of devices used in producing individual parts. An example of this is a fixture for holding a connecting rod in a milling machine when the ends are being faced by straddle milling.

Assembly tooling is an important subject in itself and consists of devices to hold work and guide tools as parts are being assembled. For example, the center section of the wing of the B–24 airplane was assembled in a special jig in which parts were held in place, drilled when together, and riveted. The assembly jig was so built that the component parts could only fit together when correctly located, and so that no measurement was ever made and no blueprint ever referred to by the worker assembling the wing. Such assembly tooling enables a small group of highly skilled workers to produce jigs or fixtures by means of which precision products may be produced and assembled by cheaper and less-skilled labor than would otherwise be required.

460. Analyzing the Job. Now, how can these ideas be effectively applied to the work in technical drawing? How can a beginning student learn something about manufacturing processes without actual shop experience? A simple method is suggested here which has been used both in industry and in the classroom to hasten the progress of inexperienced students in applying principles of good shop practice to their designs. No such method is a substitute for actual experience, but it may be said definitely that students who first master this simple technique will increase the speed with which they will learn to design for efficient manufacture when they do get practical experience.

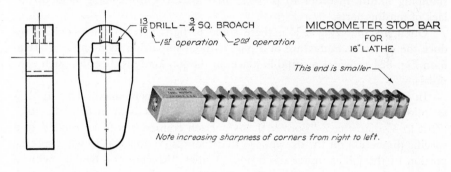

FIG. 823　Broaching.

The method is to fill out a "job analysis sheet" (Fig. 824) for each detail drawing. List, one by one, each operation to be performed on a given part. The number of parts required to be made at one time (see item 2 on Fig. 824) will affect the process by which the part is to be made. If several thousand forgings are required, for example, special dies would be justified; whereas, if only two forgings are ordered, each part would be formed by a skilled craftsman in the forge shop using general-purpose dies. Usually it is cheaper to weld if only one or two pieces are wanted, and cheaper to cast if many are desired. This is not always true, however, and each design must be judged on merit in light of progress in the various fields and on the ability of a given organization to use those processes. The use of progressive forming operations would not be economical for sheet metal stampings unless a reasonably large number of pieces were called for.

The material (see item 3 on Fig. 824) affects the manufacturing process by means of which a part is to be made and vice versa. Since plain carbon steel requires a much more drastic quench during heat-treatment than does alloy steel of the same carbon content, greater distortion results and there is greater chance of failure in the heat-treating of plain carbon steel. Thus, a part requiring a certain combination of hardness and toughness might be cheaper to make with more expensive alloy steel than with the less expensive carbon steel.

By raw stock (see item 4 on Fig. 824) is meant the stock or material in the condition one finds it as it arrives at the first operation covered by the job analysis sheet. Thus, raw stock may mean a piece which has already been machined to a considerable degree. If raw stock is neither bar, sheet, forging, nor casting, then check "OTHER" in item 4 and explain in item 5.

Special instructions (see item 5 on Fig. 824) are sometimes desirable in order that lessons learned (and paid for) in previous production experiences on this part or on similar parts be called to the attention of those responsible for the performance of the operation or operations involved. For example, one nationally known manufacturer makes it a practice to produce right-hand and left-hand members of a certain part simultaneously in the same stamping fixture in order to prevent final assembly from being held up for lack of mating parts.

Often, in analyzing a job, there come to light minor changes which reduce the cost of manufacture of a part without impairing its usefulness. Item 6 on Fig. 824 provides a suitable place on the job analysis sheet for such proposals.

In item 7 one simply lists each operation to be performed. Under "Description of operation" will be written such comments as "Cut to 8″ length," "Cut to 4″ diameter," "Bore to 1.364″. Each comment is to be related to a specific dimension on the drawing so that there is no doubt as to what specific portion of the job is under discussion. Under "Machine or Bench" will be written such comments as "Hack Saw," "Inspection Bench," "Engine Lathe," etc. Under "Remarks" will be written such comments as "Use drill jig #3462," "Check with template #1392," etc.

The eight jobs suggested in Fig. 825 will illustrate the problems that come to light as the job analysis sheet is used to check a detail drawing. For example, the tolerance indicated in job 2 would be impractical unless it is intended to finish the bore of the bushings after these bushings have been pressed into position and even then only on highly accurate equipment and with highly skilled labor. In job 3 it would be better to finish the hole before finishing the square end because the accurate location of a reamed hole is a most painstaking task unless unusually precise equipment is on hand, whereas the accurate location of a flat surface relative to a hole that has already been reamed is a relatively simple task on a surface grinder. In job 5 the $\frac{1}{16}''$ holes should be drilled before cutting to the .316″ dimension because this piece most likely will be cut from a tool steel block not less than $1\frac{1}{8}''$ x $2\frac{1}{8}''$ x $\frac{5}{8}''$ and if the corners of this block are removed before drilling the $\frac{1}{16}''$ holes, then the drill would tend to drift towards the open space where the corner had been removed.

As a specific example of the use of the job analysis sheet, take the case of the small gear, Fig. 824. If only one spur gear is required it would probably be cut out of a $1\frac{3}{8}''$ diameter bar of cold-rolled steel or a $1\frac{1}{2}''$ diameter bar of hot-rolled steel. Hot-rolled steel is quite rough and covered with a black scale, called *mill scale*, whereas cold-rolled steel is supplied with a smooth finish. Obviously, a greater amount of finishing is required to remove the scale from the hot-rolled steel than would be required in the case of cold-rolled steel. To offset the extra machining cost of hot-rolled steel there is, among other things, the major consideration that hot-rolled steel is cheaper than cold-rolled steel.

Item 7 in the job analysis sheet should be filled in somewhat as follows for the manufacture, in small quantities, of the small gear:

DESCRIPTION OF OPERATION	MACHINE OR BENCH	REMARKS
1. Cut off to $\frac{5}{8}''$ length	Cut off, band saw	
2. Chuck	Engine lathe	Use universal chuck.
3. Face one end of stock	Engine lathe	(See Fig. 811.)
4. Cut center to receive drill	Engine lathe	Use centering tool.
5. Drill to $\frac{31}{64}''$ dia.	Engine lathe	Use drill chuck in tail stock. (See Fig. 806.)
6. Bore to $\frac{.493}{.497}$ dia.	Engine lathe	(See Fig. 807.)
7. Ream to $\frac{.4997}{.5000}$ dia.	Engine lathe	Use $\frac{1}{2}''$ reamer. (See Fig. 808.)
8. Chamfer bore	Engine lathe	Use scraper.
9. Press on to $\frac{1}{2}''$ mandrel	Arbor press	
10. Put on centers in lathe	Engine lathe	Drive with dog. The unfinished side is to be placed toward the tail stock.
11. Face to $\frac{1}{2}''$ thickness of gear blank	Engine lathe	
12. Turn to $\frac{1.313''}{1.310''}$ OD	Engine lathe	(See Fig. 810.)
13. Chamfer outside corners	Engine lathe	Use file.
14. Set dividing head for number of teeth	Milling machine	
15. Mount cutter on milling machine arbor	Milling machine	This cutter was selected on basis of pitch and number of teeth.
16. Mount gear blank and mandrel on centers	Milling machine	
17. Lock dog to driving member of dividing head	Milling machine	This is to insure positive rotation of gear blank.
18. Align profile cutter with dividing head cutter	Milling machine	This is done by moving table parallel to arbor.
19. Raise table until blank contacts rotating cutter	Milling machine	
20. Move gear blank out from under cutter	Milling machine	This is done by moving table at right angles to arbor.
21. Raise table by amount of whole depth of cut	Milling machine	

DESCRIPTION OF OPERATION	MACHINE OR BENCH	REMARKS
22. Cut first tooth	Milling machine	Cutter rotates and table feeds at a uniform rate, causing gear blank to move past the cutter. (See Fig. 818.)
23. Return table to starting position	Milling machine	(See Fig. 818.)
24. Index	Milling machine	This means to turn the gear blank so that it will be in position for the next tooth to be cut.
25. Repeat until all teeth are cut	Milling machine	(See Fig. 818.)
26. Remove burrs	Bench	Use file.
27. Cut keyway	Arbor press	Use special hand broach. (See Fig. 822.)
28. Remove burrs	Bench	Use file.
29. Inspect	Inspection bench	Special devices are often used to inspect machined parts.

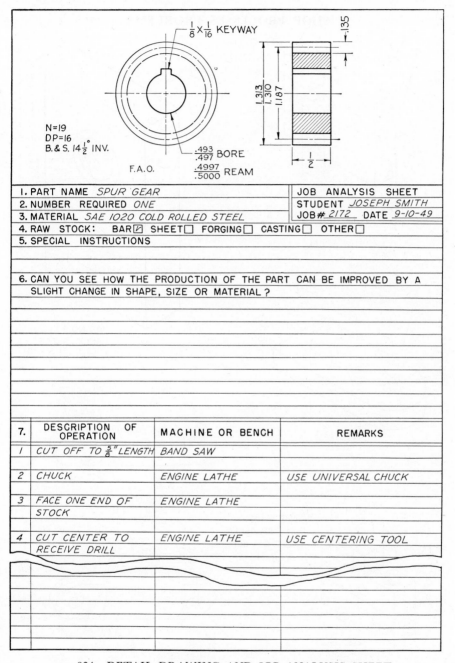

$\frac{1}{8} \times \frac{1}{16}$ KEYWAY

.135

N=19
DP=16
B.& S. 14$\frac{1}{2}$° INV.

1.313
1.310
1.187

$\frac{.493}{.497}$ BORE

$\frac{1}{2}$

F.A.O.

$\frac{.4997}{.5000}$ REAM

1. PART NAME *SPUR GEAR*	JOB ANALYSIS SHEET
2. NUMBER REQUIRED *ONE*	STUDENT *JOSEPH SMITH*
3. MATERIAL *SAE 1020 COLD ROLLED STEEL*	JOB # *2172* DATE *9-10-49*

4. RAW STOCK: BAR ☑ SHEET☐ FORGING☐ CASTING☐ OTHER☐

5. SPECIAL INSTRUCTIONS

6. CAN YOU SEE HOW THE PRODUCTION OF THE PART CAN BE IMPROVED BY A SLIGHT CHANGE IN SHAPE, SIZE OR MATERIAL ?

7.	DESCRIPTION OF OPERATION	MACHINE OR BENCH	REMARKS
1	CUT OFF TO $\frac{5}{8}$" LENGTH	BAND SAW	
2	CHUCK	ENGINE LATHE	USE UNIVERSAL CHUCK
3	FACE ONE END OF STOCK	ENGINE LATHE	
4	CUT CENTER TO RECEIVE DRILL	ENGINE LATHE	USE CENTERING TOOL

FIG. 824 DETAIL DRAWING AND JOB ANALYSIS SHEET.

Below the detail drawing of the gear is seen a *job analysis sheet*. Inclined lettering indicates information to be supplied by the student. The operations required to produce this gear appear on pp. 493 and 494. Figures 806, 807, 808, 810, 811, 818, and 822 illustrate several of the operations used to produce this gear.

495

SHOP PROCESSES PROBLEMS

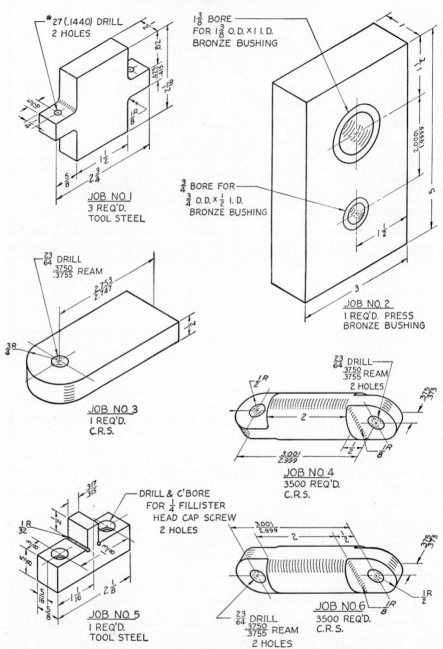

FIG. 825 JOB ANALYSIS PROBLEMS. Prepare a job analysis sheet similar to Fig. 824 ($8\frac{1}{2}''$ x 11" sheet), including detail drawing at the top, as shown. Fill in sheet completely.

CHAPTER 19

Working Drawings

461. Introduction. The outstanding characteristic of modern manufacturing industry is *specialization*. The general engineer has been replaced by the structural engineer, the sanitary engineer, the heating and ventilating engineer, the highway engineer, etc. The language of technical drawing has therefore undergone many changes in meeting the new demands of these specialized fields. While the fundamentals are the same today in all industrial fields, the applications vary greatly.

462. Evolution of Design. An engineering structure must exist in the mind of the engineer before it can exist in reality. This original conception is generally placed on paper in the form of a rough freehand sketch (Fig. 826),* and is then followed by other sketches developing more fully the idea in the mind of the engineer. At this stage, approximate calculations are made to determine the practicability of the idea.

The sketches are followed by the design assembly drawing, or *design layout*, which is usually full size and is executed with instruments. All parts of the structure are carefully designed for strength and function, and all cost calculations are completed at this time. The design drawing rarely passes the pencil stage. From it, trained draftsmen prepare the *detail* and *assembly* drawings. These drawings are usually made in pencil directly on tracing paper or pencil tracing

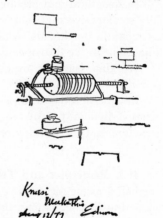

FIG. 826 Edison's Phonograph.

cloth (§ 68). The drawings may be traced in ink (§ 70), usually on tracing cloth, if the job is important enough to justify the additional expense. Finally, the pencil drawings or ink tracings are reproduced by one of the methods explained in §§ 611–615.

* Original sketch of Thomas A. Edison's first conception of the phonograph; published here by special permission from Mrs. Edison.

463. Empirical Design. There are two general types of design: *scientific design* and *empirical design*. In scientific design, use is made of the principles of physics, mathematics, chemistry, mechanics, etc., in the design of new structures which are intended to function under assigned conditions. In empirical design, use is made of data compiled in handbooks which, in turn, have been determined with the aid of the sciences, or have been learned by experience. Practically all ordinary design is a combination of scientific and empirical design. A designer should therefore be equipped with adequate scientific knowledge, and should have access to handbooks relating to his field.

464. Working Drawings. A working drawing of an object is one which completely describes the object represented. Working drawings are used by engineers, architects, and draftsmen to convey ideas to those who are to execute their designs. Such drawings should describe the objects so completely that no additional information will be needed by those who are to erect, construct, or manufacture the object represented. Working drawings should give the necessary information in the simplest manner possible and according to conventions adopted by the respective professions and trades. A working drawing should include a graphical representation of the object, dimensions showing its size, explanatory notes or indications of the materials to be used, the methods by which they are to be finished, and a descriptive title, as explained in § 472.

In structural and architectural drawing, the explanatory notes are generally so extensive that they are not lettered on the drawing but are prepared as separate documents, which are known as *specifications*, and which are as important as the drawings themselves.

Working drawings are classified as *detail drawings* (Figs. 856 and 857) and *assembly drawings* (Fig. 858).

In general a detail drawing is one which describes a single part, or several parts individually. An assembly drawing is one which shows the complete structure and the working relationship of the component parts.

DETAIL DRAWINGS

465. Principles and Technique. The technique of producing an instrumental drawing or tracing is discussed in Chapter 3, and lettering, multiview drawing, sectioning, dimensioning, etc., are discussed in the succeeding chapters. The following articles are concerned chiefly with the idioms and usages which have grown up in present-day practice.

466. Conventional Violations of Projection. In some cases, *true projections* are either decidedly awkward or actually confusing. Conventional methods of treating such cases have been generally adopted.

Conventional violations as related to sectioning are discussed in § 233. Conventional representations of intersections are shown in Fig. 827. It is not necessary to draw the true line of intersection between two bodies or two parts of a solid body unless this line is prominent or of special importance. In space *1*, the intersection is large enough to warrant the true projection, as shown, while in space *2*, the intersection is so small that a conventional representation is sufficient. Similarly, in space *3*, the curve of intersection is prominent enough to justify plotting points and drawing the true curve of intersection. In space *4*,

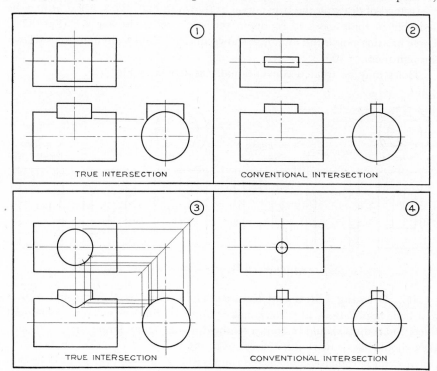

FIG. 827   Intersections.

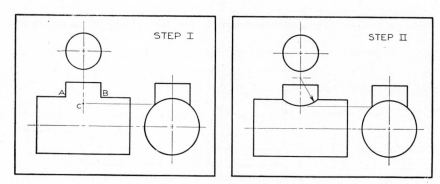

FIG. 828   Conventional Intersections.

however, the curve of intersection is so small as to approximate a straight line, and is so represented, conventionally. The method of plotting points on the curve in space *3* is explained in § 351, and other intersections are explained in succeeding paragraphs. The irregular curve (§ 72) is used to draw the resulting curves.

Instead of drawing the true curve, as shown in Fig. 827, space *3*, it may be desirable in some cases to represent the curve by a circular arc (Fig. 828). Three limiting points are found, as shown in step I, and a circular arc is drawn through them (§ 103).

Holes may be treated conventionally as shown in Fig. 829.

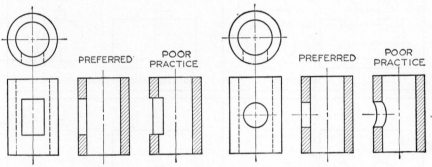

FIG. 829   Conventional Representation of Intersections.

467. Drawing Fillets and Rounds. The definitions of fillets and rounds and their applications to patternmaking and founding are given in § 444. All fillets and rounds should be shown on the drawing, and if larger than $\frac{1}{8}''$ radius, they should be drawn with the compass (§§ 105–107). It has often been the practice not to dimension fillets and rounds unless they are important in design. In such cases, the patternmaker uses his shop judgment in deciding upon their sizes. However, the best practice is to dimension all fillets and rounds, as indicated in §§ 380 and 444.

The correct method of representing fillets in connection with plane surfaces which are tangent to cylinders is shown in Fig. 830. These small curves are

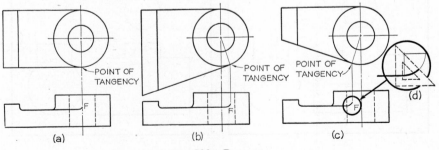

FIG. 830   Runouts.

called *runouts*. Note that the runouts, *F*, have a radius equal to that of the fillet and are equal to one-eighth of a circle (d).

The manner of showing runouts depends somewhat upon the relative sizes of intersecting fillets and rounds. In Fig. 831 (a) the top of the web is nearly flat, while the top of the left-end member is rounded considerably. The extended runout lines in the top view show that the flat surface extends over the rounded surface. At (b), the central member is rounded and the end piece is flat, so that the runout lines of the flat piece tend to extend over the rounded web.

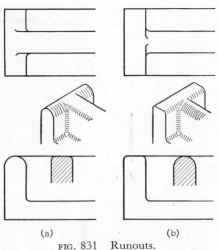

(a)   (b)

FIG. 831   Runouts.

Additional filleted intersections and runouts are illustrated in Fig. 832. The runouts at (a),(b), and (c) differ because of the different shapes of the horizontal intersecting members. At (d) and (e) the runouts differ because the top edge of the web at (d) is flat, with only slight rounds along the edges, while the top edge of the web at (e) is considerably rounded.

Frequently, owing to rounded edges, the true projection is very misleading, as shown in Fig. 833. The true projection of the rail (side view) appears quite

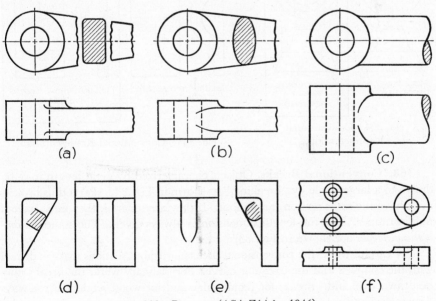

(a)   (b)   (c)

(d)   (e)   (f)

FIG. 832   Runouts (ASA Z14.1—1946).

blank (a) and is better represented as shown at (b) or (c). Note that the added
lines are projected from the approximate intersections of the surfaces, disre-
garding the fillets and rounds. Similar examples are shown in Figs. 834 and
835. Note the small Y's at the ends of the lines in Fig. 835 (b). These are

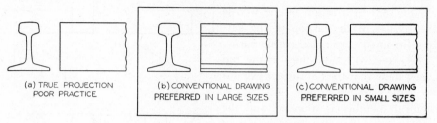

(a) TRUE PROJECTION   (b) CONVENTIONAL DRAWING   (c) CONVENTIONAL DRAWING
POOR PRACTICE   PREFERRED IN LARGE SIZES   PREFERRED IN SMALL SIZES

FIG. 833   Conventional Representation of a Rail.

drawn freehand and represent the intersection of filleted or rounded edges with
rough surfaces. If the side surfaces in the right side view were finished, the lines
would intersect without the Y's.

On working drawings, fillets and rounds are never shaded. The presence
of the curved surfaces is indicated only in the views where they appear as arcs.

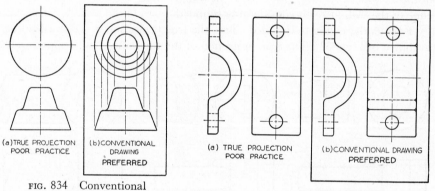

(a) TRUE PROJECTION   (b) CONVENTIONAL
POOR PRACTICE   DRAWING
PREFERRED

FIG. 834   Conventional
Representation.

(a) TRUE PROJECTION   (b) CONVENTIONAL DRAWING
POOR PRACTICE   PREFERRED

FIG. 835   Conventional Representation.

468. Conventional Breaks. Objects characterized by great length may be
drawn to a larger scale by "breaking," as shown in Fig. 836. Parts thus broken
must have the same section throughout. If they are tapered, they must have a
uniform taper. The full-length dimension is always given. The standard *conventional breaks* are shown in Fig. 837.

For careful work, the conventional breaks for round sections may be drawn
with the compass and the irregular curve. For ordinary work, the breaks may
be drawn freehand. Breaks for rectangular and for wood sections are always
drawn freehand.

One of the most common applications of breaks is in connection with re-volved sections. See Fig. 838 and § 228.

469. Use of Ditto Lines. In representing objects having a series of identi-cal features, time may be saved and satisfactory representation effected by the use of ditto lines, as in Fig. 839 and § 64. Threaded shafts thus represented

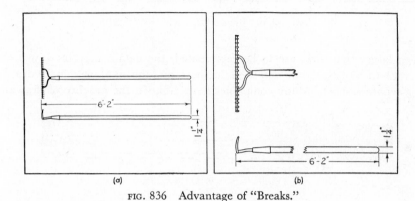

(a)   (b)

FIG. 836   Advantage of "Breaks."

may be shortened without the use of conventional breaks, but must always be correctly dimensioned. The same procedure may be applied to springs, as shown in Fig. 851 (d).

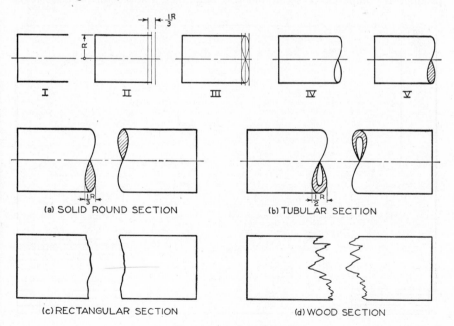

I   II   III   IV   V

(a) SOLID ROUND SECTION   (b) TUBULAR SECTION

(c) RECTANGULAR SECTION   (d) WOOD SECTION

FIG. 837   Conventional Breaks.

470. Number of Details per Sheet. Two general methods are followed in commercial practice regarding the grouping of details on sheets. If the structure is small, the details and the assembly may be shown on one large sheet.

FIG. 838   Conventional Breaks Used with Revolved Sections.

When larger structures are to be represented, the details may be drawn on several large sheets, several details to the sheet, and the assembly may be drawn on a separate sheet. Many companies have adopted the practice of drawing

FIG. 839   Use of Ditto Lines.

only one detail per sheet, to simplify filing, as shown in Fig. 843. Many have adopted letter-size sheets ($8\frac{1}{2}'' \times 11''$ — American Standard, § 21) to facilitate correspondence, as well as filing. This method is most convenient when the product is composed of small parts. Companies manufacturing cash regis-

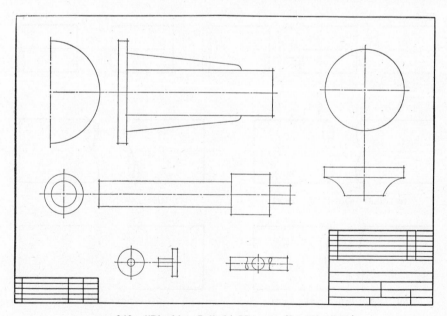

FIG. 840   "Blocking In" the Views.   (See Fig. 901.)

ters, adding machines, typewriters, and similar products find this practice advantageous.

When several details are drawn on one sheet, careful consideration must be given to spacing. The draftsman should decide upon the views which will be required for each detail, and "*block-in*" *all views before beginning to draw any view*, as shown in Fig. 840. This drawing was made from the problem in Fig. 901. The same scale should be used on all details throughout one sheet. When this is not possible, the scales for the dissimilar details should be clearly noted underneath each.

471. Notes. Dimensioned multiview projections alone are usually inadequate to describe completely a part to be produced. It may be necessary to specify the kind of material, its treatment, the number of parts required, the patterns, special tools or dies required, and many other such items.

Notes may be roughly classified as (1) *general notes* (Fig. 841) and (2) *local notes* (Fig. 842).

The information conveyed by notes must be brief, clear, accurate, and complete. See § 384.

To facilitate reading, notes should be lettered horizontally, and leaders (Fig. 689) should be freely used to insure correct application. Good commer-

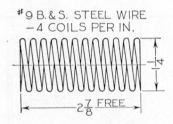

cial drawings (Figs. 855–858) should be studied to secure an adequate understanding of the use of notes. Standard shop notes to be used in specifying holes to be drilled, reamed, cored, etc., are shown in Fig. 725. An intimate knowledge of shop practice, as described in Chapter 18, is essential, and should be acquired by every draftsman.

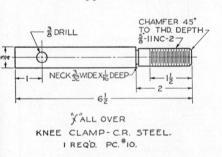

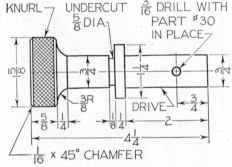

FIG. 841　General Notes.　　　　FIG. 842　Local Notes.

472. Title and Record Strip. The function of the title and record strip is to show *in an organized manner* all necessary information not given by the drawing with its dimensions and notes, as in Fig. 843. Obviously, the type of title used depends upon the filing system in use, the processes of manufacture, and the requirements of the product. The following information should generally be given in the title form:

(1) Name of the object represented.
(2) Name and address of the manufacturer.
(3) Name and address of the purchasing company, if any.
(4) Signature of the draftsman who made the pencil drawing, and the date of completion.
(5) Signature of the tracer, and the date of completion.
(6) Signature of the checker, and the date of completion.
(7) Signature of the chief draftsman, engineer, or other authority, and the date of approval.
(8) Scale.
(9) Number of the drawing.

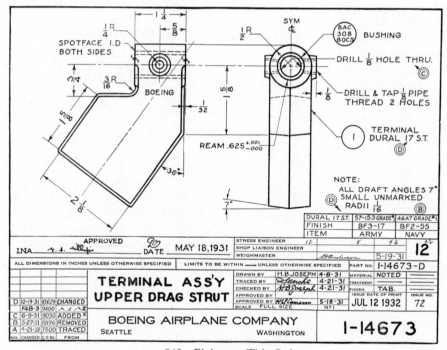

FIG. 843   Elaborate Title Strip.

Other information may be given, such as material, quantity, heat treatment, finish, hardness, pattern number, estimated weight, superseding and superseded drawing numbers, symbol of machine, and many other items, depending upon the plant organization and the peculiarities of the product. Some typical commercial titles are shown in Figs. 844, 845, and 846.

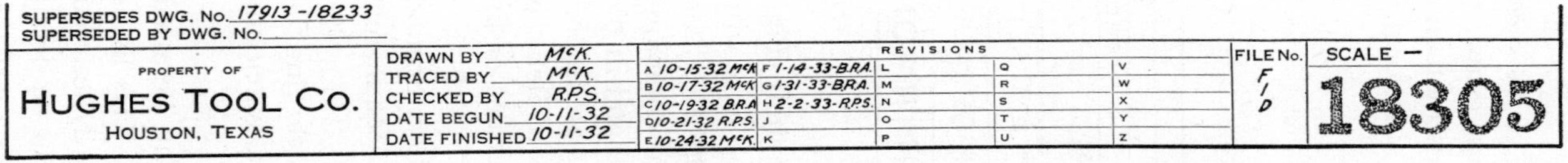

Fig. 844

SUPERSEDES DWG. NO. 17913 -18233
SUPERSEDED BY DWG. NO.

PROPERTY OF

HUGHES TOOL CO.

HOUSTON, TEXAS

DRAWN BY	M^cK
TRACED BY	M^cK
CHECKED BY	R.P.S.
DATE BEGUN	10-11-32
DATE FINISHED	10-11-32

REVISIONS			
A 10-15-32 M^cK	F 1-14-33-BRA	L	Q
B 10-17-32 M^cK	G 1-31-33-BRA	M	R
C 10-19-32 BRA	H 2-2-33-RP.S.	N	S
D 10-21-32 R.P.S.	J	O	T
E 10-24-32 M^cK	K	P	U

V		
W	X	
	Y	
	Z	

FILE No. SCALE —

F/o

18305

FIG. 844 Title Strip.

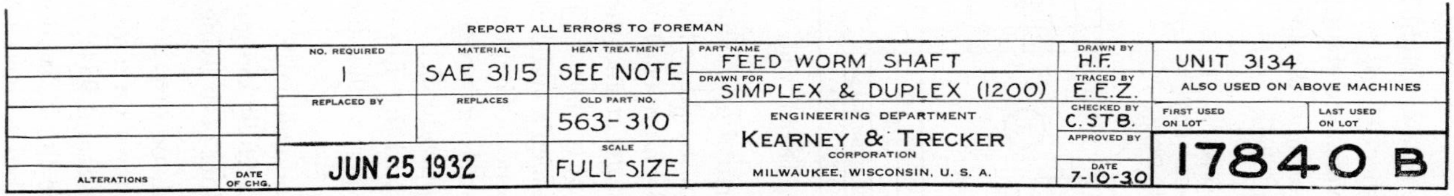

Fig. 845

REPORT ALL ERRORS TO FOREMAN

NO. REQUIRED	MATERIAL	HEAT TREATMENT	PART NAME
1	SAE 3115	SEE NOTE	FEED WORM SHAFT
REPLACED BY		OLD PART NO.	DRAWN FOR
		563-310	SIMPLEX & DUPLEX (1200)
		SCALE	ENGINEERING DEPARTMENT
		FULL SIZE	**KEARNEY & TRECKER**
DATE OF CHG.			CORPORATION
ALTERATIONS	JUN 25 1932		MILWAUKEE, WISCONSIN, U. S. A.

DRAWN BY	H.F.	UNIT 3134
TRACED BY	E.E.Z.	ALSO USED ON ABOVE MACHINES
CHECKED BY	C.S^TB.	FIRST USED	LAST USED
APPROVED BY		ON LOT	ON LOT
DATE	7-10-30		

17840 B

FIG. 845 Title Strip.

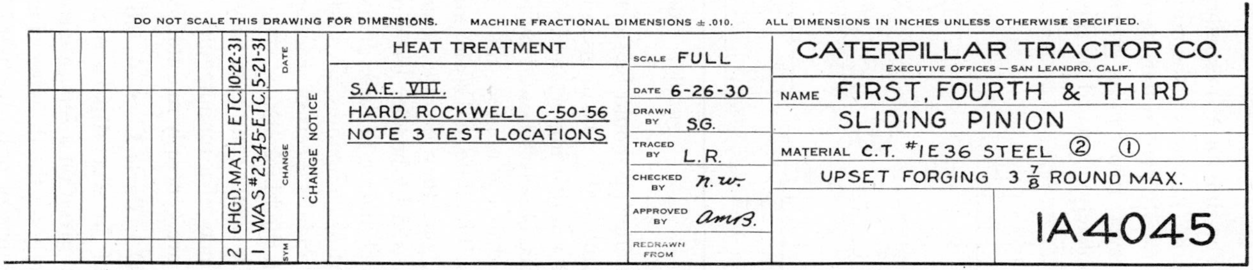

Fig. 846

DO NOT SCALE THIS DRAWING FOR DIMENSIONS. MACHINE FRACTIONAL DIMENSIONS ±.010. ALL DIMENSIONS IN INCHES UNLESS OTHERWISE SPECIFIED.

CHANGE NOTICE			HEAT TREATMENT
SYM	CHANGE	DATE	S.A.E. VIII.
1	WAS #2345-ETC.	5-21-31	HARD. ROCKWELL C-50-56
2	CHGD.MATL.ETC.	10-22-31	NOTE 3 TEST LOCATIONS

CATERPILLAR TRACTOR CO.

EXECUTIVE OFFICES — SAN LEANDRO, CALIF.

SCALE FULL	NAME FIRST, FOURTH & THIRD
DATE 6-26-30	SLIDING PINION
DRAWN BY S.G.	MATERIAL C.T. #1E 36 STEEL ② ①
TRACED BY L.R.	UPSET FORGING 3 7/8 ROUND MAX.
CHECKED BY N. W.	
APPROVED BY Am.B.	
REDRAWN FROM	

1A4045

FIG. 846 Title Strip.

507

The title form is usually placed in the lower right-hand corner of the sheet (Fig. 847), or along the bottom of the sheet (Figs. 844–846), because drawings are usually filed in flat, horizontal drawers, and the title must be easily found. However, many filing systems are in use, and the location of the title form is completely governed by the system employed.

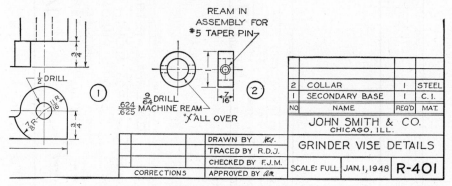

FIG. 847   Identification of Details with Parts List.

Lettering should be single-stroke vertical or inclined Gothic capitals (Figs. 182 and 200). The items in the title form should be lettered in accordance with their relative importance. The drawing number should receive greatest emphasis, closely followed by name of the object and the name of the company. The drawing number must be prominent so that it can be easily found in the files. The date and scale, and the draftsmen's and checkers' names are important, but they do not deserve prominence. Greater importance of items is indicated by heavier lettering, larger lettering, wider spacing of letters, or by a combination of these methods. See Appendix 2.

Most companies have adopted standard title forms and have them printed on standard sheets of tracing cloth or paper, so that the draftsmen need merely fill in the blank spaces.

Drawings constitute very important and valuable information regarding the products of a manufacturer. Hence, carefully designed, well-kept, systematic files are generally maintained for the filing of drawings.

473. Parts Lists. A bill of material, or *parts list*, consists of an itemized list of the several parts of a structure shown on a given drawing. This list is often given on a separate sheet (Figs. 928 and 954), but is frequently lettered directly on the drawing (Fig. 859). The title strip alone is sufficient on detail drawings of only one part (Fig. 843), but a parts list is necessary on detail drawings of several parts (Fig. 949).

Parts lists on machine drawings contain the part numbers or symbols, a descriptive title of each part, the number required, the material specified, and frequently other information such as pattern numbers, stock sizes of materials, weights of parts, etc.

Parts are listed in general order of size or importance. The accepted procedure is to list main castings first and standard parts last. Parts are listed from the bottom upward, so that new items may be added later. In some cases the parts list may be placed in the upper right corner of the drawing, and the parts listed from the top down.

Each detail in the drawing may be identified with the parts list in the strip by the use of a small circle containing the part number, placed adjacent to the detail, as in Fig. 847. One of the sizes that are shown in Fig. 848 will generally be found suitable for this purpose.

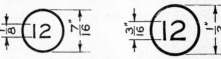

FIG. 848   Identification Numbers.

Standard parts are not drawn, but are listed in the parts list (§ 390).

474. Alterations. Changes on drawings are necessitated by changes in design, inadequacy of shop equipment, desires of customers, or by errors in design or in production. In order that the sources of all changes of information on drawings may be understood, verified, and accessible, a complete record of all drawing changes must be made on the drawings. The record must show that a change was made, the character of the change, by whom, when, and why made.

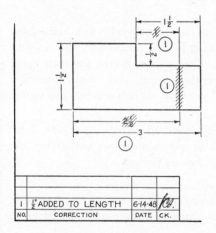

FIG. 849   Alterations.

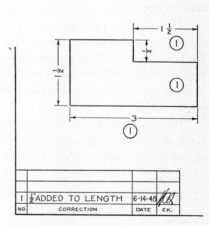

FIG. 850   Alterations.

Some companies follow the practice of drawing diagonal lines through lines and numerals which are to be superseded, as shown in Fig. 849. A numeral or letter, or other symbol, is placed nearby, usually in a small circle, to identify the change with the information in the alteration strip. See also § 391.

Other companies follow the practice of erasing lines and numerals which are to be superseded, making all changes, and keeping blue prints on file of each issue to show the features before the change, as in Fig. 850. In any case, new prints are issued to replace the old ones each time a change is made.

If considerable change of a drawing is necessary, a new drawing may be made and the old one is then stamped OBSOLETE and placed in the obsolete file. In the title block of the old drawing, under "Superseded by . . . " or "Replaced by . . . " (see Figs. 844 and 845) the number of the new drawing is entered. On the new drawing, under "Supersedes . . . " or "Replaces . . ." is entered the number of the old drawing.

See § 615 for some of the latest techniques in making changes on drawings.

The alteration strip may be placed in any convenient place on the drawing—in the lower left-hand corner of the drawing, as in Figs. 849 and 850, or attached to the title form, as in Figs. 843 to 846.

475. Checking. The importance of accuracy in technical drawing cannot be overestimated. In commercial offices, errors sometimes cause tremendous unnecessary expenditures. *The draftsman's signature on a drawing identifies him and he is held responsible for the accuracy of his work.*

In small offices, checking is usually done by the designer or by one of the draftsmen. In large offices, experts are employed who devote their entire time to checking.

The pencil drawing, upon completion, is carefully checked and signed by the draftsman who made it. The drawing is then checked by the designer for function, economy, practicability, etc. Corrections, if any, are then made by the original draftsman. The drawing is then traced and upon completion the tracing is checked against the original drawing. If it is correct, it is signed by the tracer.

The final checker should be able to discover all remaining errors. If his work is to be effective, he must proceed in a systematic way, studying the drawing with particular attention to the following points:

(1) Choice of views, partial views, auxiliary views, sections, etc.
(2) Dimensions, with special reference to repetition, ambiguity, legibility, omissions, errors, and finish marks. Special attention should be given to tolerances.
(3) Standard parts. In the interest of economy, as many parts as possible should be standard.
(4) Notes, with special reference to clear wording and legibility.
(5) Clearances. Moving parts should be checked in all possible positions to assure freedom of movement.
(6) Title form information.

476. Helical Springs. The true projection of a helical spring is usually not drawn in practice because of the labor involved. As is the case with screw threads (§§ 412–4 8), *semi-conventional* and *conventional* methods, involving straight lines only, are used as shown in Fig. 851.

The elevation view of the square-wire spring is similar to the square thread with the core of the shaft removed (Fig. 757). Standard section lining is used if the areas in section are large, as shown in Fig. 851 (a) and (b). If

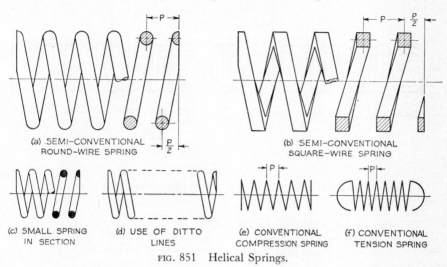

(a) SEMI–CONVENTIONAL   (b) SEMI–CONVENTIONAL
    ROUND–WIRE SPRING   SQUARE–WIRE SPRING

(c) SMALL SPRING   (d) USE OF DITTO   (e) CONVENTIONAL   (f) CONVENTIONAL
   IN SECTION   LINES   COMPRESSION SPRING   TENSION SPRING

FIG. 851   Helical Springs.

these areas are small, the sectioned areas may be made solid black (c). In cases where a complete picture of the spring is not necessary, ditto lines may be used to save time in drawing the coils (d). If the drawing of the spring is too small to be represented by the outlines of the wire, it may be drawn by the conventional method, in which single straight lines are used (e) and (f).

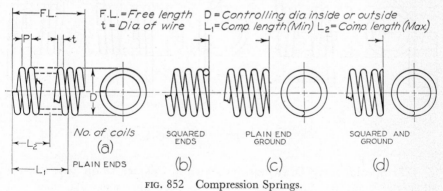

F.L.=*Free length*   D =*Controlling dia. inside or outside*
t = *Dia. of wire*   L₁=*Comp. length (Min)* L₂= *Comp. length (Max)*

No. of coils   SQUARED   PLAIN END   SQUARED AND
   (a)   ENDS   GROUND   GROUND

PLAIN ENDS   (b)   (c)   (d)

FIG. 852   Compression Springs.

The various types of ends of *compression springs*, together with dimensions required, are shown in Fig. 852. The diameter given is ID or OD (inside or outside diameter), whichever is required.

The types of ends and the dimensioning of *tension springs* are shown in Fig. 853. Methods of representing and dimensioning some typical *torsion springs* are shown in Fig. 854.

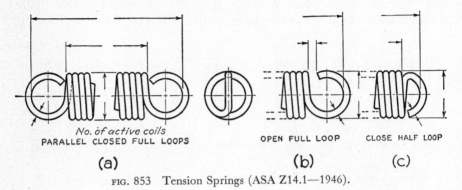

No. of active coils
PARALLEL CLOSED FULL LOOPS   OPEN FULL LOOP   CLOSE HALF LOOP

(a)   (b)   (c)

FIG. 853   Tension Springs (ASA Z14.1—1946).

In general, the following information must be given for any spring:

(1) Free length.
(2) Size, shape, and kind of material.
(3) Inside diameter, if the spring works on a rod; outside diameter, if the spring works in a hole.
(4) Pitch or number of coils.
(5) Style of ends.

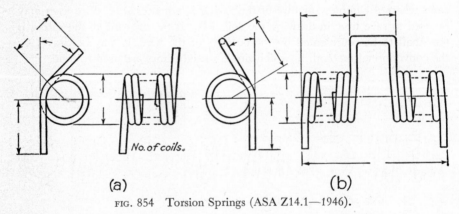

No. of coils.

(a)   (b)

FIG. 854   Torsion Springs (ASA Z14.1—1946).

477. Special Shop Drawings. As shown in Chapter 18 on *Shop Processes*, all special shops, as pattern shop, forge shop, machine shop, etc., may each obtain the information needed from one drawing. However, in modern *mass production* it is frequently advantageous to prepare special drawings for each main process. Such drawings are known as *process drawings*. See also §§ 378 and 442.

The forge shop is furnished with a *forging drawing* (Figs. 855, 955, and 956), which shows the object as it should be when it leaves the forge shop, omitting all information for machining, etc. No effort is made to hold sizes of forgings to close dimensions; hence dimensions on forging drawings are nominal.

A *pattern drawing* conveys only the information required by the pattern shop, and is generally used only for the larger or more complicated castings.

A *machine-shop drawing* (Figs. 756 and 757) omits all information concerning the pattern or the forging processes and conveys only that needed for machining.

A simple *operation drawing* conveys only the information needed to perform a single shop operation. Such drawings are used in interchangeable manufacturing where effort is made to specialize every operation performed.

Job sheets give a brief description of each operation necessary in performing a given job or unit of work. These sheets are frequently combined with working drawings or operation drawings.

ASSEMBLY DRAWINGS

478. Function. The purpose of an assembly drawing is to represent the proper working relationships of the several component parts of a structure or mechanism. Assembly drawings have many specific uses; hence there are many types.

479. Design Assemblies. The designer of a new machine or structure is primarily interested in the relationships of the mating parts, and secondarily in the exact requirements of each part. Assembly drawing is the natural vehicle of design. When general problems of function have been disposed of, attention is given to the design of each detail so that it may carry out its purpose. The design drawing is generally drawn full size except for very large machines or other structures, and is executed with instruments. It may include any auxiliary views or sections which are helpful, and generally is not dimensioned. The completed design assembly is used as a basis for the preparation of complete detail and assembly drawings.

480. General Assemblies. Frequently the design drawing is traced, with some modifications, to produce the final assembly. The details and assembly may be shown on the same sheet in the representation of small structures, but usually the assembly is drawn on a separate sheet (Figs. 858 and 859). The drawing shown in Fig. 858 is an assembly of the Ford V-8 Connecting Rod, the details of which are shown in Figs. 855, 856, and 857.

(a) *Sectioning.*—In order to show the working relationships of interior parts, it is generally advantageous to use sectioning more often than in detail drawing (Fig. 859). Usually conventional section lining (Fig. 405) is used to indicate different materials. Section lining of adjacent parts must run in opposite directions, as shown in Figs. 407 and 408. Shafts, keys, bolts, etc.,

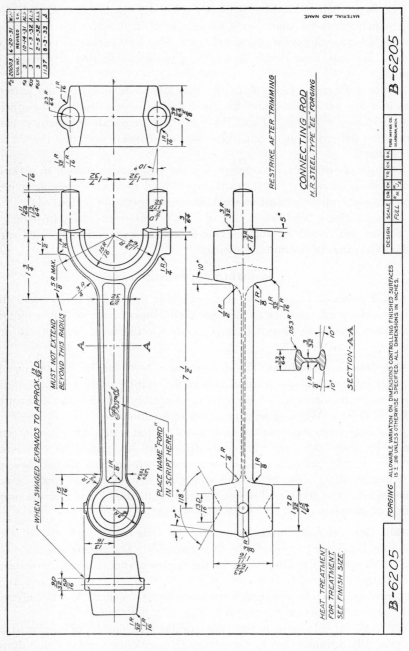

FIG. 855   FORGING DRAWING OF CONNECTING ROD. *Problem:* Draw forging drawing.

514

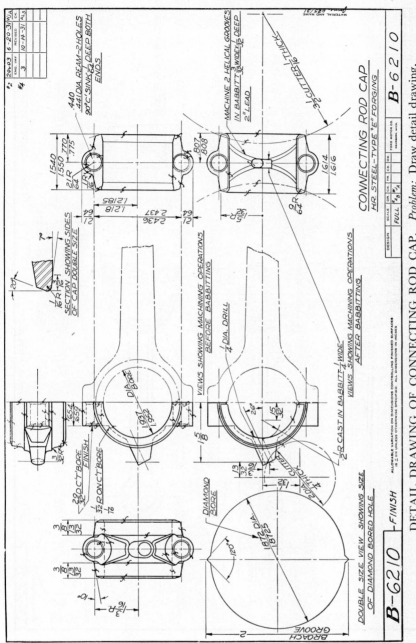

DETAIL DRAWING OF CONNECTING ROD CAP. *Problem:* Draw detail drawing.

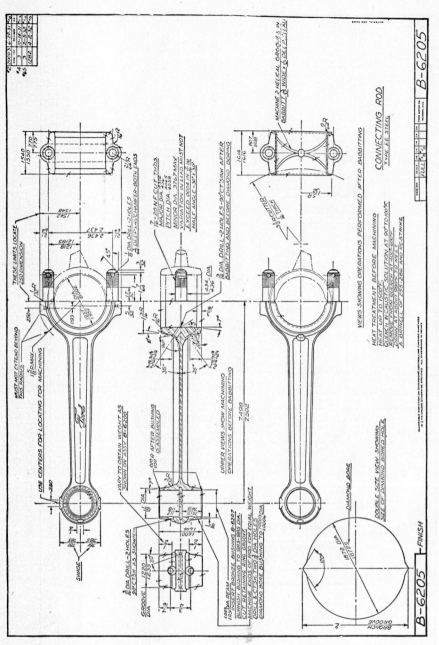

FIG. 857 DETAIL DRAWING OF CONNECTING ROD. *Problem:* Draw detail drawing.

516

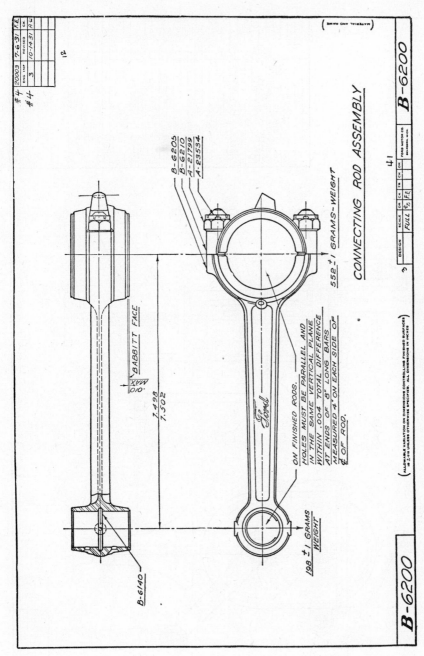

FIG. 858 ASSEMBLY DRAWING OF CONNECTING ROD. *Problem:* Draw assembly.

517

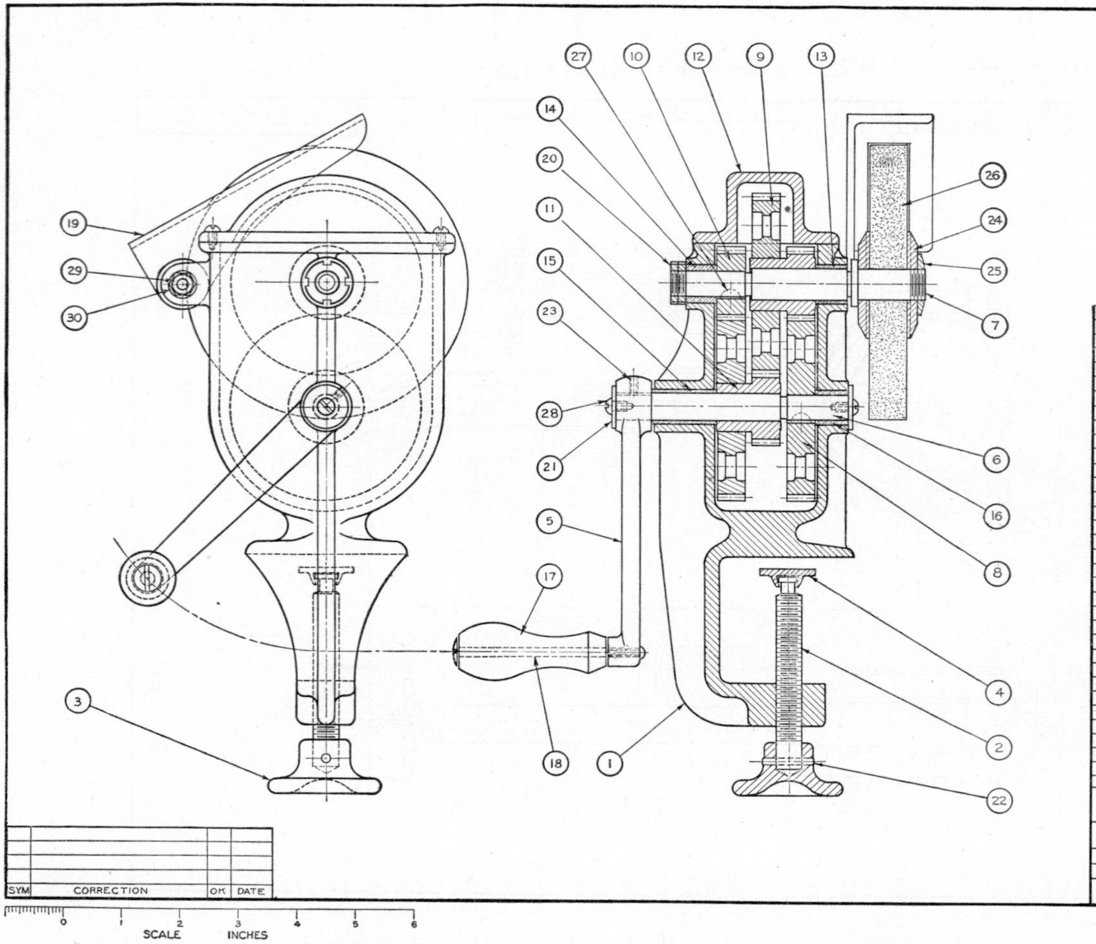

NO.	PART NAME	REQD	MAT.
30	¼ LOCK WASHER	1	STEEL
29	¼ X 1 FIN. HEX. HD. BOLT & NUT	1	STEEL
28	⅜ X ⅝ LG. RND. HD. MACH. SCR.	4	
27	WOODRUFF KEY " 204	2	
26	5 X ½ ALUNDUM WHEEL	1	
25	WHEEL NUT	1	STEEL
24	WHEEL WASHER	2	STEEL
23	⅜ X ⅜ SET SCREW-CUP POINT	1	
22	CLAMP PIN	1	STEEL
21	CRANK SPINDLE WASHER	2	STEEL
20	SPECIAL LOCK NUT	4	STEEL
19	TOOL REST	1	C.I.
18	HANDLE BOLT	1	STEEL
17	CRANK HANDLE	1	WOOD
16	BUSHING	1	BRONZE
15	BUSHING	1	BRONZE
14	BUSHING	1	BRONZE
13	BUSHING	1	BRONZE
12	HOUSING COVER	1	C.I.
11	SMALL PINION, PRESSED	2	C.I.
10	SMALL PINION, KEYED	1	C.I.
9	LARGE GEAR, PRESSED	2	C.I.
8	LARGE GEAR, KEYED	1	C.I.
7	WHEEL SPINDLE	1	STEEL
6	CRANK SPINDLE	1	STEEL
5	CRANK	1	C.I.
4	CLAMP SCREW CAP	1	C.I.
3	CLAMP SCREW HANDLE	1	C.I.
2	CLAMP SCREW	1	STEEL
1	HOUSING	1	C.I.

GRINDER ASSEMBLY

JOHN SMITH AND CO.
ST. LOUIS, MO.

DR. BY	6-2-48	CK. BY	6-2-48		R-145
TR. BY	R.D.J.	6-2-48	APP. BY	6-2-48	
SCALE: FULL		SECTION BOX			

FIG. 859 ASSEMBLY DRAWING OF GRINDER. Problems: (1) Draw details. (2) Draw assembly.

518

are not sectioned (§ 234). For a complete treatment of sectioning, the student is referred to Chapter 8.

(b) *Views.* — Since most structures are symmetrical about a center line or a central plane, it is possible to expose nearly all parts by a full section, and one main view is frequently sufficient. However, any additional views or sections may be used. No effort should be made to describe completely the *forms* of parts, since this information is shown on the detail drawings. The views chosen should be those which show most clearly how the parts fit together and how the mechanism functions.

(c) *Dimensions.* — When dimensions are necessary, only those applying to the structure as a whole are given. These may include overall dimensions, dimensions between important centers, and any others necessary to show the relationships of the parts (Fig. 862). Detail dimensions should be omitted.

(d) *Title Strip.* — Title strips on assemblies are similar to those on detail drawings. See § 472, and Figs. 858, 859, 861, and 863.

(e) *Identification.* — The methods of identification of parts in an assembly are similar to those used in detail drawings where several parts are shown on one sheet, as in Figs. 847 and 859. Circles containing the numbers of the parts are placed adjacent to the parts with leaders terminated by arrowheads touching the parts, as in Fig. 859. The circles shown in Fig. 848 for detail drawings are, with the addition of radial leaders, satisfactory for assembly drawings. Note, in Fig. 859, that these circles are placed systematically, preferably in vertical or horizontal rows, and not scattered over the sheet in disorder. Leaders are never allowed to cross, and adjacent leaders are parallel or nearly so. The parts list includes the parts numbers or symbols, a descriptive title of each part, the number required, the material specified, and frequently other information, such as pattern numbers, stock sizes of materials, weights of parts, and so on. Frequently, the parts list is carried on a separate sheet, as shown in Figs. 928 and 954.

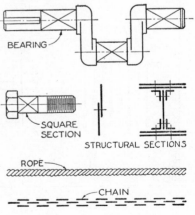

FIG. 860   Standard Parts.

Another method of identification is to letter the name of each part, together with other necessary information, adjacent to the part, with a leader having an arrowhead touching the part indicated as in Fig. 861.

(f) *Alterations.* — Methods of recording changes are the same as those for detail drawings. See § 474 and Figs. 844–846, 855–858, and 861.

(g) *Hidden Lines.* — The use of hidden lines in assembly drawings is the

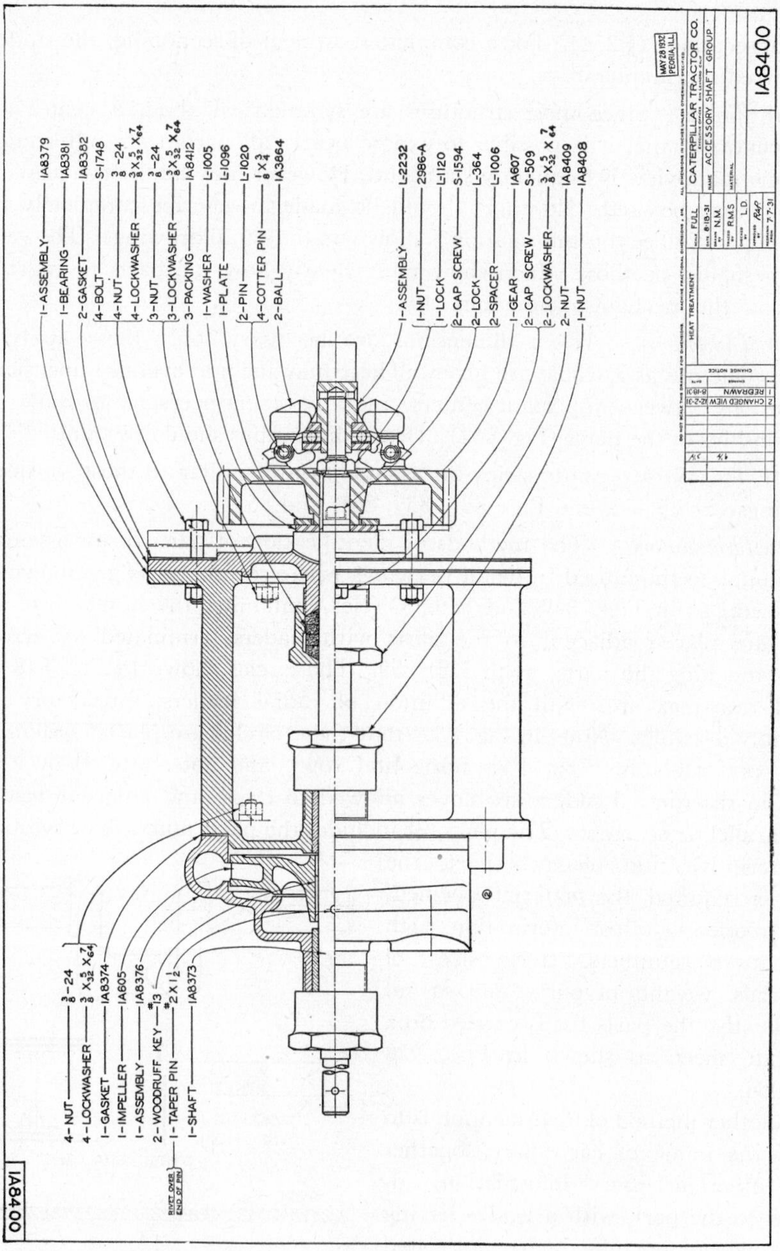

4 – NUT ———— 3 – 24
4 – LOCKWASHER ———— 3/8 X 5/32 X 7/64
1 – GASKET ———— IA8374
1 – IMPELLER ———— IA605
1 – ASSEMBLY ———— IA8376
2 – WOODRUFF KEY ———— #13
1 – TAPER PIN ———— 2 X 1 1/2
1 – SHAFT ———— IA8373

SHAFT OVER
END OF PIN

1 – ASSEMBLY ———— IA8379
1 – BEARING ———— IA8381
2 – GASKET ———— IA8382
4 – BOLT ———— S-1748
4 – NUT ———— 3/8 – 24
4 – LOCKWASHER ———— 3/8 X 5/32 X 7/64
3 – NUT ———— 3/8 – 24
3 – LOCKWASHER ———— 3/8 X 5/32 X 7/64
3 – PACKING ———— IA8412
1 – WASHER ———— L-1005
1 – PLATE ———— L-1096
2 – PIN ———— L-1020
4 – COTTER PIN ———— 1/8 X 3/4
2 – BALL ———— IA3864

1 – ASSEMBLY ———— L-2232
1 – NUT ———— 2986-A
1 – LOCK ———— L-1120
2 – CAP SCREW ———— S-1594
2 – LOCK ———— L-364
2 – SPACER ———— L-1006
1 – GEAR ———— IA607
2 – CAP SCREW ———— S-509
2 – LOCKWASHER ———— 3/8 X 5/32 X 7/64
2 – NUT ———— IA8409
1 – NUT ———— IA8408

MAY 28 1932
PEORIA, ILL.

CATERPILLAR TRACTOR CO.
PEORIA, ILL.

ACCESSORY SHAFT GROUP

SCALE FULL
DATE 8-18-31
DR. N.M.
CK. R.M.S.
APP. R.L.D.

HEAT TREATMENT   MATERIAL

7-2-31

IA8400

FIG. 861   Group Assembly.

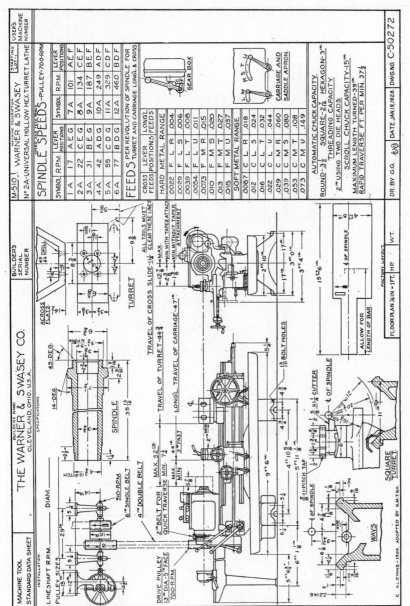

FIG. 862 Installation Assembly.

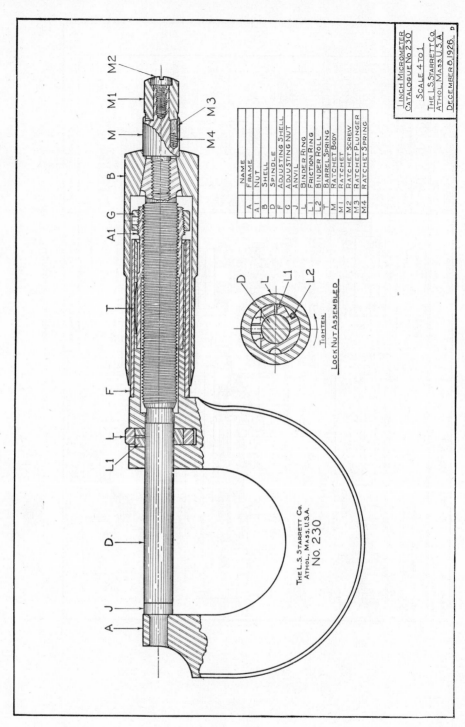

1 INCH MICROMETER
CATALOGUE No. 230
SCALE 4 TO 1
THE L.S.STARRETT CO.
ATHOL, MASS. U.S.A.
DECEMBER 8, 1926.

LOCK NUT ASSEMBLED

TIGHTEN

THE L.S. STARRETT CO.
ATHOL, MASS, U.S.A.
NO. 230

FIG. 863   Display Assembly.

same as that in all other types of drawing. *Hidden lines should be used only when their use results in added clearness.*

(h) *Standard Parts.* — Standard parts, such as rolled sections, rope, chains, cables, bearings, pipes, bolts, nuts, screws, etc., are represented symbolically by approximate methods. See Fig. 860 and § 390.

481. Working-Drawing Assemblies. The details of simple mechanisms are sometimes dimensioned completely in the assembly drawings. This is common practice in drawings of valves, jigs, and fixtures. Methods of identification are the same as those in general assembly drawings.

482. Group Assemblies. It is impossible to show the relationships of all the parts in some complicated structures in a single assembly drawing. Generally, such mechanisms are divided into natural units, or groups of parts, such as the carburetor or the transmission system of an automobile. An assembly of the "Accessory Shaft Group" of a Caterpillar tractor is shown in Fig. 861.

483. Installation Assemblies. An assembly which is made for the specific purpose of showing how to erect or install a structure is an *installation assembly* (Fig. 862). This type of drawing is often called an outline assembly, because it shows only the outlines and the relationships of exterior surfaces.

484. Display Assemblies. There are various types of display assemblies. Salesmen must be furnished with literature containing reproductions of drawings showing the assembled structure in attractive form (Fig. 863). If artistic results are desirable, shade lines and surface shading may be used (§§ 524–526). Ornamental lettering may be used if properly executed. Colors or monotone washes may be used; but when highly artistic effects are required, a commercial artist should be employed.

Pictorial assemblies (Fig. 864) are useful with prospective customers who cannot read a projection drawing, or when it is desired to show the appearance of an object. See Chapters 11, 12, and 13.

FIG. 864   Pictorial Assembly.

485. Check Assemblies. After all detail drawings of a structure have been finished, it may be necessary to make a *check assembly*. Such a drawing is an assembly of all details drawn accurately to scale in order to check each one graphically. After the check assembly has served its purpose, it may be converted into an assembly drawing of any type desired. Therefore the assembly drawing usually may be employed to check against the detail drawings and the general computations.

PROBLEMS

486. Working Drawing Problems.—Figs. 865-962. These problems are presented here to provide practice in making regular working drawings of the type used in industry. Owing to the variation in sizes and in scales which may be used, the student is to select his own sheet sizes and scales, subject to the approval of the instructor. Standard sheet layouts are shown in Appendix 1.

The statements for each problem are intentionally brief so that the instructor may amplify or vary the requirements when making assignments. Some tracings in pencil and in ink should be assigned, but this also is left to the instructor.

The student should clearly understand that in problems presented in pictorial form, the placement of dimensions and finish marks cannot always be followed in the drawing. *The dimensions given are in most cases those needed to make the parts, but due to the limitations of pictorial drawing they are not in all cases the dimensions which should be shown on the drawing.* In the pictorial problems finish marks obviously cannot be placed according to the rule for working drawings; i.e., *finish marks should be placed upon the edge views of finished surfaces.* The student should, of course, follow this rule strictly on his drawing.

Each problem should be preceded by a thumbnail sketch or a complete technical sketch, fully dimensioned. Any of the title blocks in Appendix 1 may be used, or the student may design the title block if so assigned by the instructor.

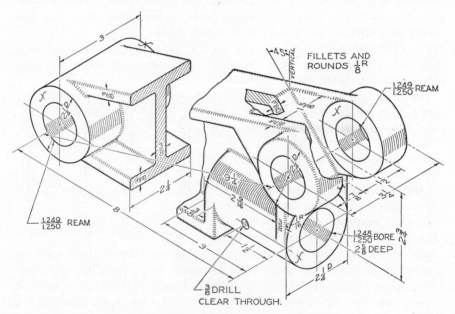

FIG. 865 ROCKER LINK. Make detail drawing.

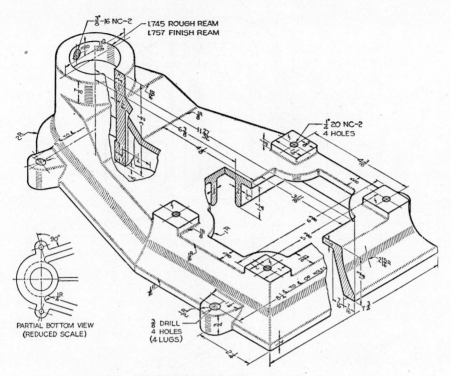

FIG. 866 DRILL PRESS BASE. Make detail drawing.

FIG. 866   DRILL PRESS BASE.   Make detail drawing.

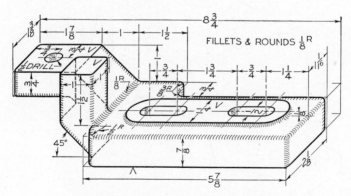

FIG. 867   REST HOLDER.   Make detail drawing.

525

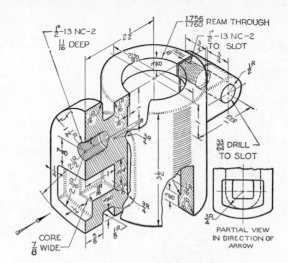

FIG. 868 TABLE BRACKET.
Make detail drawing.

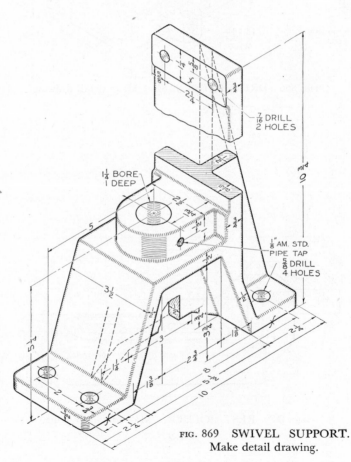

FIG. 869 SWIVEL SUPPORT.
Make detail drawing.

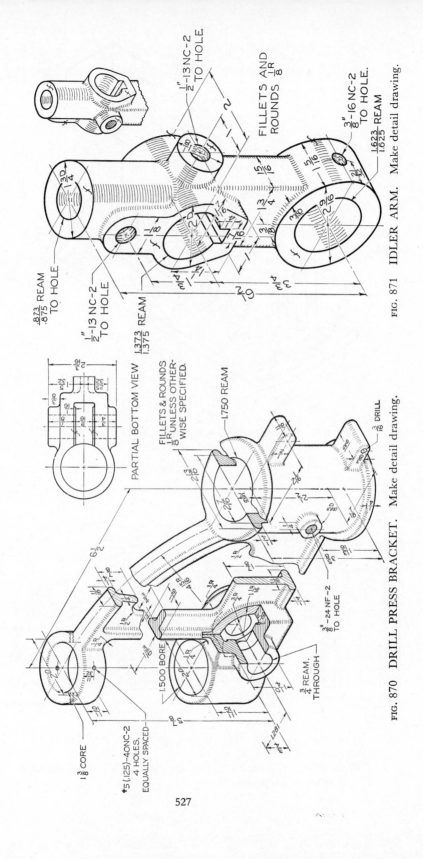

FIG. 871 IDLER ARM. Make detail drawing.

FIG. 870 DRILL PRESS BRACKET. Make detail drawing.

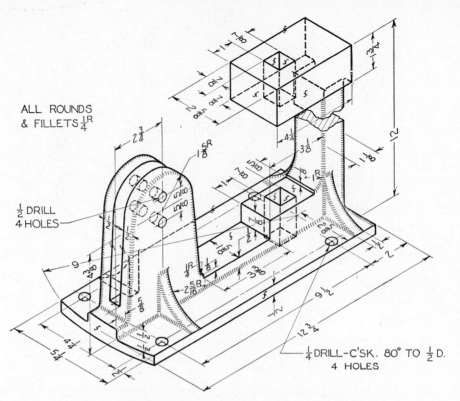

ALL ROUNDS
& FILLETS $\frac{1}{4}$R

$\frac{1}{2}$ DRILL
4 HOLES

$\frac{1}{4}$ DRILL-C'SK. 80° TO $\frac{1}{2}$ D.
4 HOLES

FIG. 872 SOAP PRESS BRACKET. Make detail drawing.

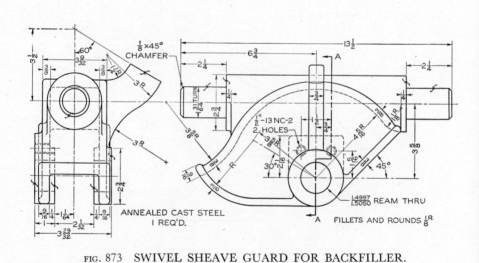

$\frac{1}{8}$×45°
CHAMFER

$\frac{1}{2}''$-13 NC-2
2 HOLES

3 R

3 R

60°

$\frac{3}{32}$

ANNEALED CAST STEEL
1 REQ'D.

$13\frac{1}{2}$

$6\frac{3}{4}$

$2\frac{1}{4}$

A

$2\frac{1}{4}$

30°

45°

.4997
.5050 REAM THRU

A   FILLETS AND ROUNDS $\frac{1}{8}$R

FIG. 873 SWIVEL SHEAVE GUARD FOR BACKFILLER.
Given: Front and left side views.
Required: Front, right side in half section on A-A (section right half
of view), and top view.

528

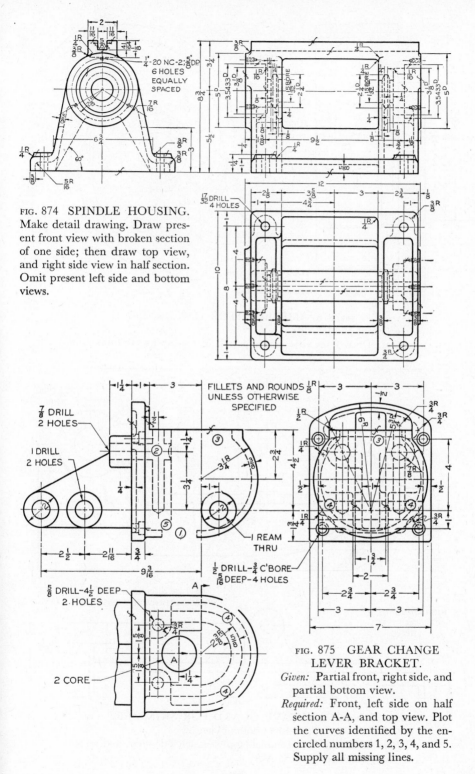

FIG. 874 SPINDLE HOUSING. Make detail drawing. Draw present front view with broken section of one side; then draw top view, and right side view in half section. Omit present left side and bottom views.

FIG. 875 GEAR CHANGE LEVER BRACKET.

Given: Partial front, right side, and partial bottom view.

Required: Front, left side on half section A-A, and top view. Plot the curves identified by the encircled numbers 1, 2, 3, 4, and 5. Supply all missing lines.

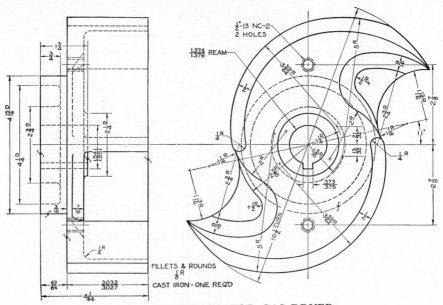

FIG. 876   IMPELLER FOR GAS DRYER.

Given: Front and left side views.

Required: Draw front view, and top and right side views in full section.

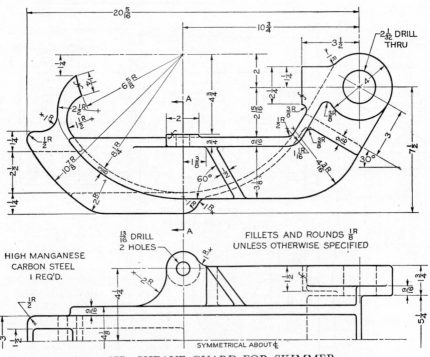

FIG. 877   SHEAVE GUARD FOR SKIMMER.

Given: Front view, and half-bottom view.

Required: Front view, complete top view, left side view, and right
side view sectioned on A-A.

530

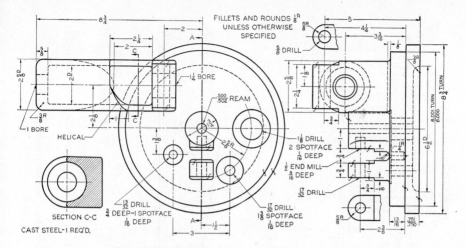

FIG. 878   TRIP GEAR CASE FOR STEAM TURBINE.

Given: Front view, right side view, and Section C-C.

Required: Draw front view, right side view sectioned on A-A, bottom view, and Section C-C.   Omit small partial views.

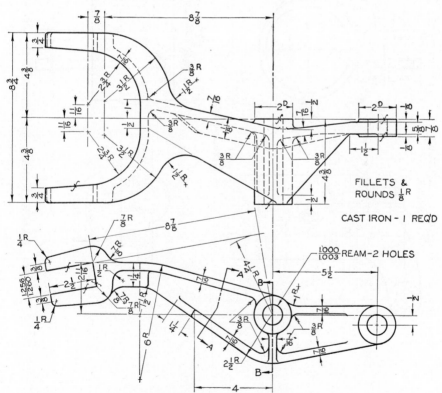

FIG. 879   CLUTCH SHIFTING FORK FOR POWER SHOVEL.

Given: Front and top views.

Required: Draw front and bottom views, and detail sections A-A and B-B.

531

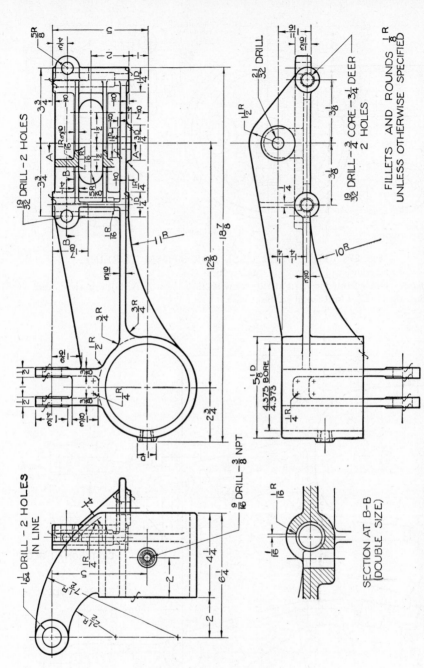

FIG. 880   BRACKET. Make detail drawing. Draw present front view; then draw top and right side views, and removed section A-A. Omit present left side view, bottom view, and both sections.

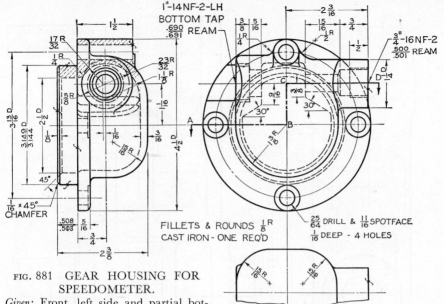

FIG. 881 GEAR HOUSING FOR
        SPEEDOMETER.

Given: Front, left side and partial bottom views.

Required: Draw front view, top view sectioned on A-B-C-D, and right side in full section.

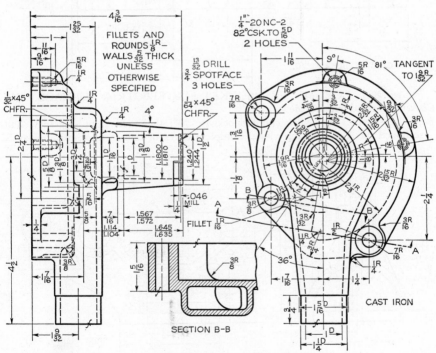

FIG. 882 WATER PUMP BODY.

Given: Front and left side views, with detail section B-B.

Required: Draw front view, right side in full section, and Section A-A. Include in Section A-A all visible lines behind the cutting plane. Omit Section B-B.

533

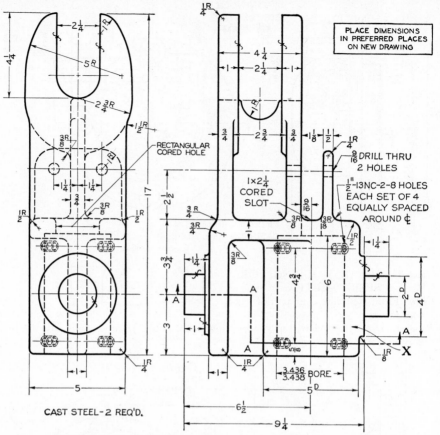

FIG. 883 COLUMN TILT SOCKET FOR ELECTRIC FURNACE.

Given: Front and left side views.

Required: Revolve front view counterclockwise 90°; then add right side view half-sectioned on A-A, and top view. Complete curve of intersection indicated at X.

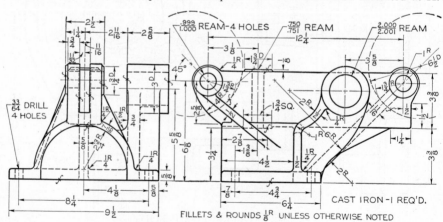

FIG. 884 BELT TIGHTENER BRACKET FOR MILLING MACHINE.

Given: Front and left side views.

Required: Front, right side, and top views.

534

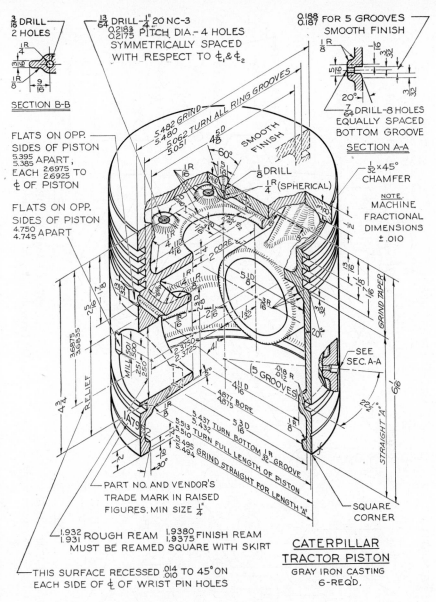

SECTION B-B

¾ DRILL 2 HOLES

¼R

³⁄₁₆

⅛R

⁹⁄₁₆

¹³⁄₆₄ DRILL - ¼" 20 NC-3
0.2183
0.2175 PITCH DIA.- 4 HOLES
SYMMETRICALLY SPACED
WITH RESPECT TO ₵₁ & ₵₂

0.188
0.187 FOR 5 GROOVES
SMOOTH FINISH

⅛R

⁵⁄₁₆

³⁄₃₂

-16

³⁄₃₂

20°

⁷⁄₆₄ DRILL-8 HOLES
EQUALLY SPACED
BOTTOM GROOVE

SECTION A-A

FLATS ON OPP.
SIDES OF PISTON
5.395
5.385 APART,
EACH 2.6975
2.6925 TO
₵ OF PISTON

FLATS ON OPP.
SIDES OF PISTON
4.750
4.745 APART

5.482 GRIND
5.480
5.052 TURN ALL RING GROOVES
5.051

45 D
4 8

60°

SMOOTH FINISH

⅛ DRILL
¼R (SPHERICAL)

1R
16

½

¹⁄₃₂ ×45°
CHAMFER

NOTE.
MACHINE
FRACTIONAL
DIMENSIONS
±.010

4.110
4.16

2 CORE

5 1D
8

3R
16

⅛

¹⁄₃₂

20°

GRIND TAPER

3.6875
3.6835

RELIEF

MILL .501
.500
.251
.250

2.3750
2.3725

4¼

4°

5°

5°

411 D
16

4877 BORE
4875

(5 GROOVES)

.018 R
.012

SEE
SEC. A-A

STRAIGHT "A"

6 1
16

1A79
12

1R
8

5.437 TURN BOTTOM 1R GROOVE
5.432   32

5 3 D
16

1R
8

SQUARE
CORNER

5513 TURN FULL LENGTH OF PISTON
5510

5.498 GRIND STRAIGHT FOR LENGTH "A"
5.494

30°

PART NO. AND VENDOR'S
TRADE MARK IN RAISED
FIGURES. MIN SIZE ¼"

1.932
1.931 ROUGH REAM

1.9380
1.9375 FINISH REAM
MUST BE REAMED SQUARE WITH SKIRT

THIS SURFACE RECESSED .014 TO 45° ON
.010
EACH SIDE OF ₵ OF WRIST PIN HOLES

CATERPILLAR
TRACTOR PISTON
GRAY IRON CASTING
6-REQ'D.

FIG. 885   CATERPILLAR TRACTOR PISTON.   Make detail drawing

535

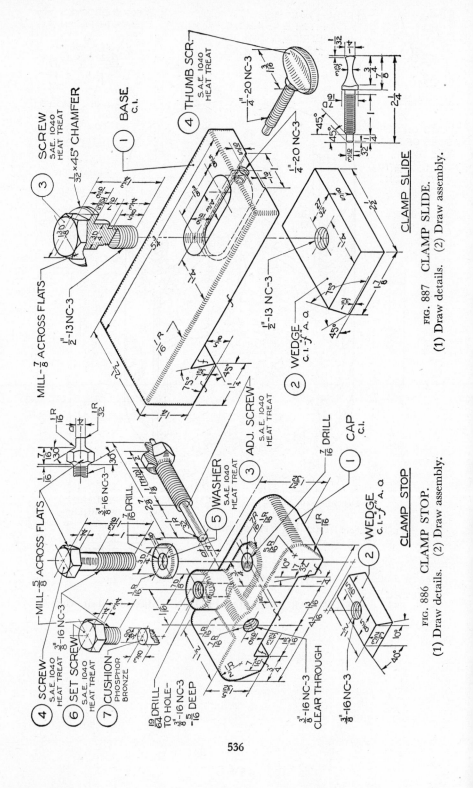

CLAMP SLIDE.

FIG. 887 CLAMP SLIDE.
(1) Draw details. (2) Draw assembly.

CLAMP STOP.

FIG. 886 CLAMP STOP.
(1) Draw details. (2) Draw assembly.

536

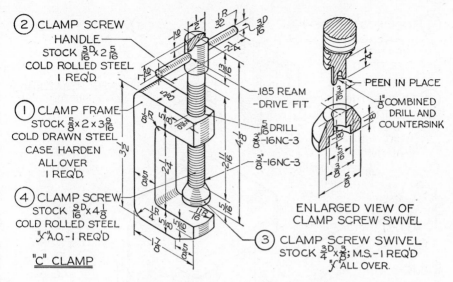

FIG. 888 "C" CLAMP. Draw details and assembly.

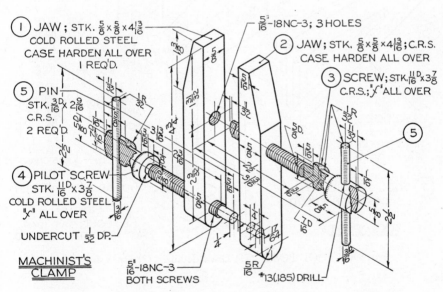

FIG. 889 MACHINIST'S CLAMP. Draw details and assembly.

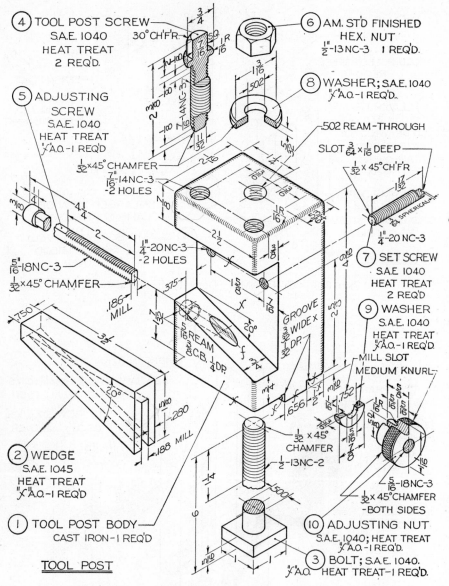

FIG. 890 **TOOL POST.** (1) Draw details. (2) Draw assembly.

538

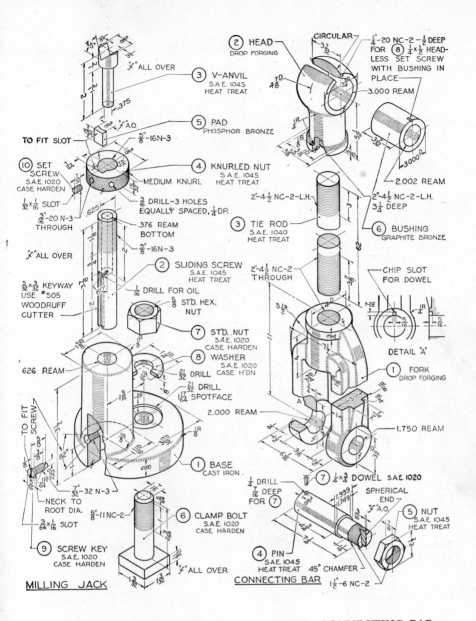

③ V-ANVIL
S.A.E. 1045
HEAT TREAT

② HEAD
DROP FORGING

CIRCULAR

¼"-20 NC-2-½ DEEP
FOR ⑧ ¼x½ HEAD-
LESS SET SCREW
WITH BUSHING IN
PLACE

3.000 REAM

⑤ PAD
PHOSPHOR BRONZE

TO FIT SLOT

⑤-16N-3

⑩ SET
SCREW
S.A.E. 1020
CASE HARDEN

⅛ x 1/16 SLOT

5/16"-20 N-3
THROUGH

④ KNURLED NUT
S.A.E. 1045
HEAT TREAT

MEDIUM KNURL

¾ DRILL-3 HOLES
EQUALLY SPACED, ¼ DP.

2.002 REAM

2"-4½ NC-2-L.H.
3¼ DEEP

"X"ALL OVER

.376 REAM
BOTTOM
⅝-16N-3

2"-4½ NC-2-L.H.

③ TIE ROD
S.A.E. 1040
HEAT TREAT

⑥ BUSHING
GRAPHITE BRONZE

5/32 x 3/32 KEYWAY
USE #505
WOODRUFF
CUTTER

② SLIDING SCREW
S.A.E. 1045
HEAT TREAT

1/16 DRILL FOR OIL

2"-4½ NC-2
THROUGH

CHIP SLOT
FOR DOWEL

⅝ STD. HEX.
NUT

⑦ STD. NUT
S.A.E. 1020
CASE HARDEN

DETAIL "A"

626 REAM

⑧ WASHER
S.A.E. 1020
CASE H'DN

21/32 DRILL

21/32 DRILL
17/64 SPOTFACE

① FORK
DROP FORGING

2.000 REAM

1.750 REAM

TO FIT
SCREW

82°

⑦ ¼x¾ DOWEL S.A.E. 1020

① BASE
CAST IRON.

7/32"-32 N-3

NECK TO
ROOT DIA.

3/64 x 1/16 SLOT

⑤-11NC-2

⑥ CLAMP BOLT
S.A.E. 1020
CASE HARDEN

¼ DRILL
7/16 DEEP
FOR ⑦

SPHERICAL
END

⑤ NUT
S.A.E. 1045
HEAT TREAT

1.999
1.749

⑨ SCREW KEY
S.A.E. 1020
CASE HARDEN

"X"ALL OVER

④ PIN
S.A.E. 1045
HEAT TREAT   45° CHAMFER

1½"-6 NC-2

MILLING JACK

CONNECTING BAR

FIG. 891 MILLING JACK.
(1) Draw details. (2) Draw assembly.

FIG. 892 CONNECTING BAR.
(1) Draw details. (2) Draw assembiy.

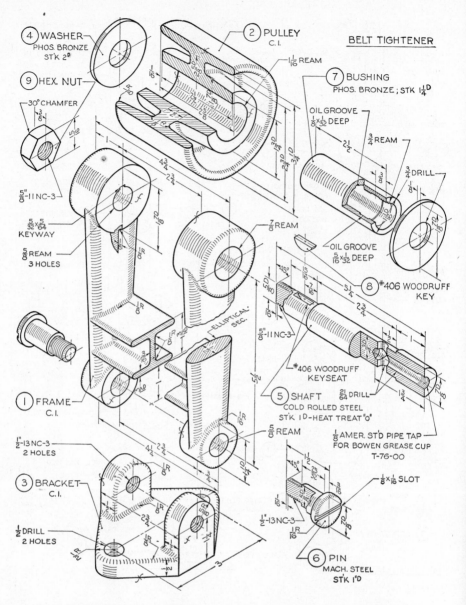

FIG. 893 **BELT TIGHTENER.** (1) Draw details. (2) Draw assembly.

It is assumed that the parts are to be made in quantity and they are to be dimensioned for interchangeability on the detail drawings. Using Tables of Limits in Appendix, give dimensions as follows:

1. Bushing fit in pulley: Class 6 fit.
2. Shaft fit in bushing: Class 2 fit.
3. Shaft fit in frame: Class 2 fit.
4. Pin fit in frame: Class 2 fit.
5. Pulley hub length plus washers fit in frame: Class 1 fit.
6. Bracket fit in frame: Class 1 fit.
7. Make bushing 0.010″ shorter than pulley hub.

540

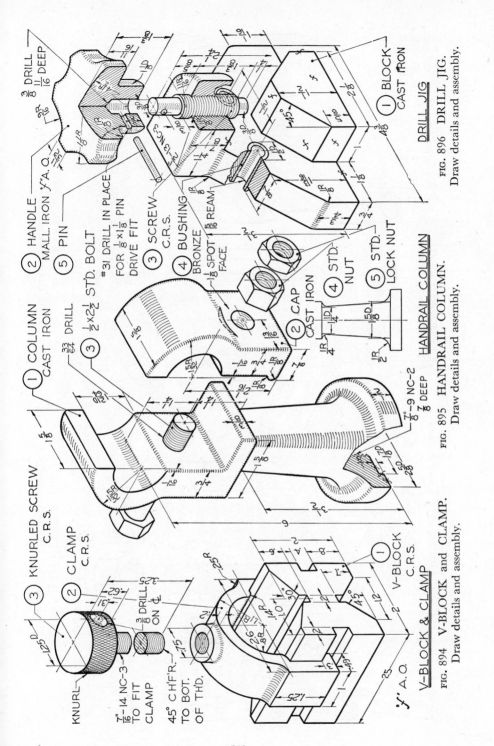

① COLUMN
CAST IRON

③ 33/64 DRILL

③ 1/2 × 2 1/2 STD. BOLT

② CAP
CAST IRON

④ STD.
NUT

⑤ STD.
LOCK NUT

HANDRAIL COLUMN.

FIG. 895 HANDRAIL COLUMN.
Draw details and assembly.

② HANDLE
MALL. IRON 'f'A.Q.

⑤ PIN

#31 DRILL IN PLACE
FOR 1/8 × 1 1/8 PIN
DRIVE FIT

③ SCREW
C.R.S.

④ BUSHING
BRONZE

① BLOCK
CAST IRON

DRILL JIG

FIG. 896 DRILL JIG.
Draw details and assembly.

③ KNURLED SCREW
C.R.S.

② CLAMP
C.R.S.

① V-BLOCK
C.R.S.

V-BLOCK & CLAMP

FIG. 894 V-BLOCK and CLAMP.
Draw details and assembly.

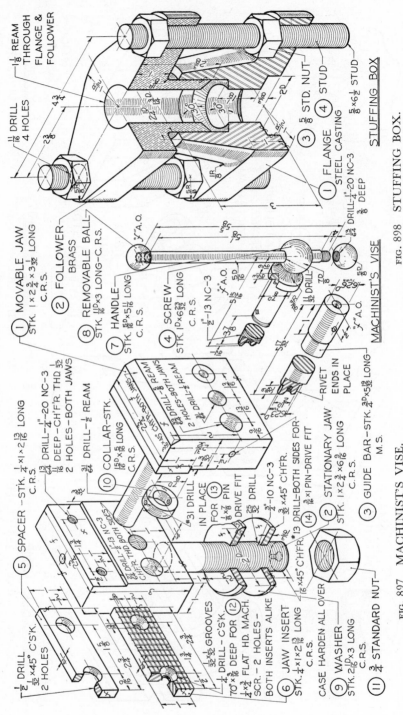

① MOVABLE JAW
STK. 1 × 2¼ × 3³⁄₃₂ LONG
C.R.S.

② FOLLOWER
BRASS

⑧ REMOVABLE BALL
STK. 1¹⁄₁₆D × 3 LONG—C.R.S.

⑦ HANDLE
STK. ⅝D × 5¹¹⁄₁₆ LONG
C.R.S.

④ SCREW
STK. 1D × 6²³⁄₃₂ LONG
C.R.S.
1"–13 NC-3

MACHINIST'S VISE

FIG. 897 MACHINIST'S VISE.
(1) Draw details.   (2) Draw assembly.

⑤ SPACER – STK. ¼ × 1 × 2¹³⁄₁₆ LONG
C.R.S.

⑩ COLLAR–STK.
1⅝D × 1D LONG
C.R.S.

② STATIONARY JAW
STK. 1 × 2¼ × 6¹⁄₁₆ LONG
C.R.S.

③ GUIDE BAR–STK. ¾D × 5¹⁹⁄₃₂ LONG
M.S.

⑥ JAW INSERT
STK. ¼ × 1 × 2¹³⁄₁₆ LONG
C.R.S.

⑨ WASHER
STK. 2¹⁄₁₆D × 3 LONG
C.R.S.

⑪ ¾ STANDARD NUT

CASE HARDEN ALL OVER

① FLANGE
STEEL CASTING

③ ⅝ STD. NUT

④ STUD
⅝ × 6⅝ STUD

STUFFING BOX

FIG. 898 STUFFING BOX.
(1) Draw details.   (2) Draw assembly.

1⅛ REAM
THROUGH FLANGE &
FOLLOWER

1¹⁄₁₆ DRILL
4 HOLES

542

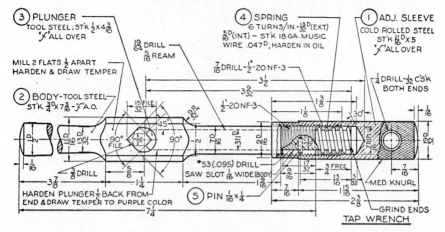

FIG. 899 TAP WRENCH. (1) Draw details. (2) Draw assembly.

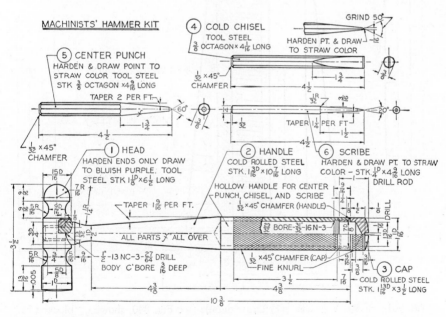

FIG. 900 MACHINIST'S HAMMER KIT. (1) Draw details. (2) Draw assembly.

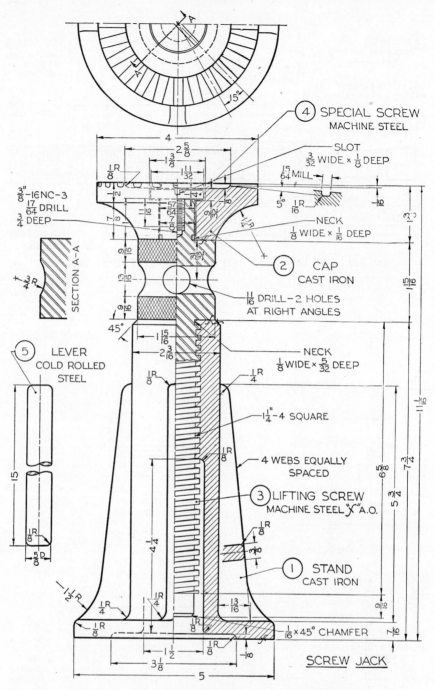

FIG. 901 SCREW JACK. (1) Draw details (see Fig. 840, showing "blocked-in" views on Sheet Layout C789). (2) Draw assembly.

544

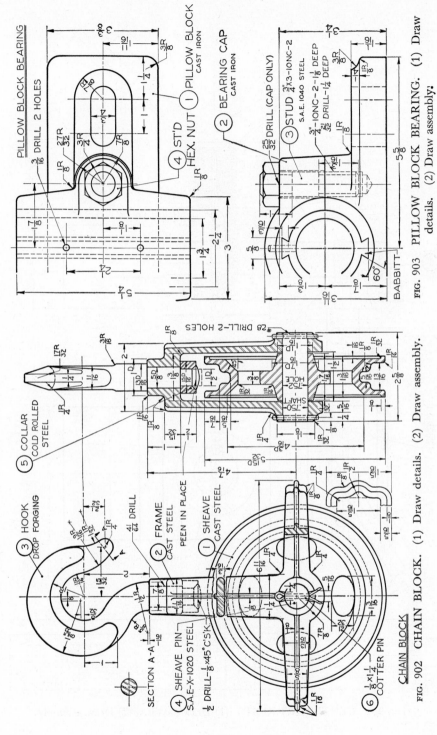

PILLOW BLOCK BEARING

PILLOW BLOCK BEARING. (1) Draw details. (2) Draw assembly.

FIG. 903

CHAIN BLOCK

FIG. 902 CHAIN BLOCK. (1) Draw details. (2) Draw assembly.

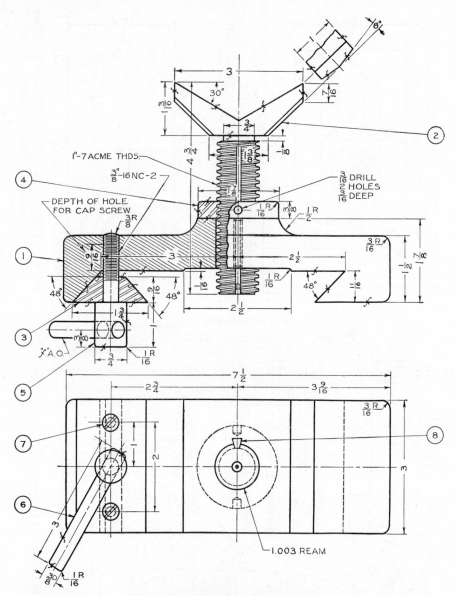

CENTERING REST

PARTS LIST									
NO.	PART NAME	MAT.	REQ'D.	NO.	PART NAME		MAT.	REQ'D.
1	BASE	C.I.	1	5	CLAMP SCREW		S.A.E.1020	1
2	REST	S.A.E.1020	1	6	CLAMP HANDLE		S.A.E.1020	1
3	CLAMP	S.A.E.1020	1	7	$\frac{1}{4} \times 1$ FILL. HD. CAP SCREW			2
4	ADJUSTING NUT	S.A.E.1020	1	8	$\frac{7}{32} \times \frac{7}{32} \times \frac{1}{8} - 1$ LONG - KEY		S.A.E.1030	1

FIG. 904   CENTERING REST.   (1) Draw details.   (2) Draw assembly.

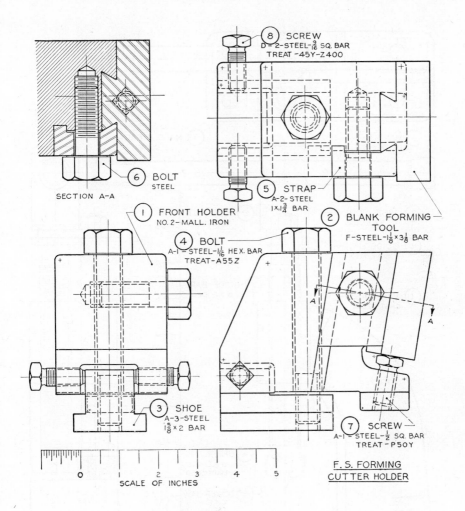

SECTION A-A

⑥ BOLT
STEEL

⑧ SCREW
D-2-STEEL-$\frac{3}{16}$ SQ. BAR
TREAT -45Y-Z400

⑤ STRAP
A-2-STEEL
1×1$\frac{3}{4}$ BAR

① FRONT HOLDER
NO. 2- MALL. IRON

② BLANK FORMING
TOOL
F-STEEL-1$\frac{1}{8}$×3$\frac{1}{8}$ BAR

④ BOLT
A-1-STEEL-1$\frac{1}{16}$ HEX. BAR
TREAT-A55Z

③ SHOE
A-3-STEEL
1$\frac{5}{8}$×2 BAR

⑦ SCREW
A-1-STEEL-$\frac{1}{2}$ SQ. BAR
TREAT-P50Y

F. S. FORMING
CUTTER HOLDER

0   1   2   3   4   5
SCALE OF INCHES

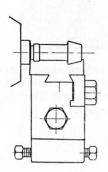

FIG. 905 F. S. FORMING CUTTER HOLDER.
(1) Draw details. (2) Draw assembly. To obtain
dimensions take distances directly from figure with
dividers; then set dividers on printed scale and read
measurements in inches.

547

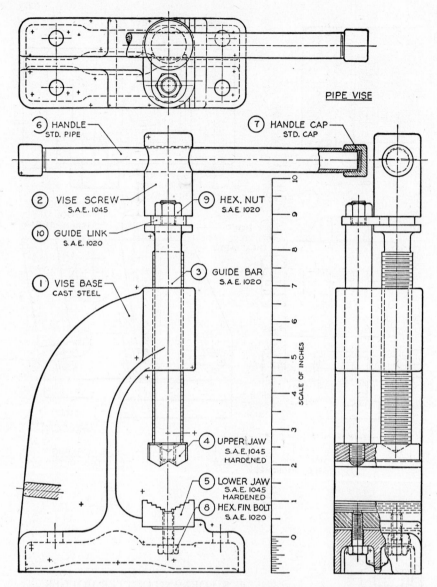

FIG. 906 PIPE VISE. (1) Draw details. (2) Draw assembly. To obtain dimensions take distances directly from figure with dividers; then set dividers on printed scale and read measurements in inches. All threads are American Standard Coarse Threads except the American Standard Pipe Threads on handle and handle caps.

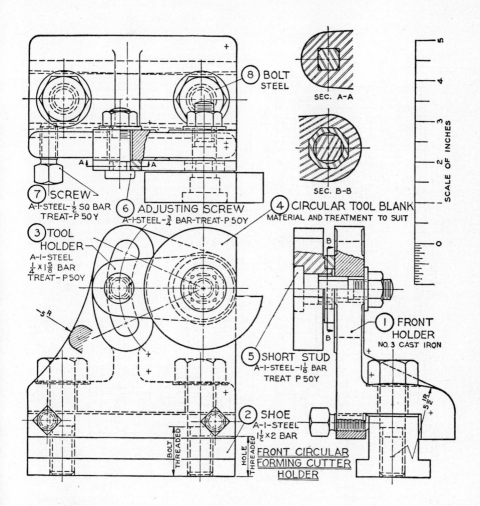

⑧ BOLT
STEEL

SEC. A-A

SEC. B-B

⑦ SCREW
A-I-STEEL-½ SQ BAR
TREAT-P 50 Y

⑥ ADJUSTING SCREW
A-I-STEEL-¾ BAR-TREAT-P 50Y

④ CIRCULAR TOOL BLANK
MATERIAL AND TREATMENT TO SUIT

③ TOOL
HOLDER
A-I-STEEL
¼ ×1⅝ BAR
TREAT-P 50Y

.5 R

⑤ SHORT STUD
A-I-STEEL-1⅛ BAR
TREAT P 50Y

① FRONT
HOLDER
NO. 3 CAST IRON

5½ R

② SHOE
A-I-STEEL
1½×2 BAR

BOLT THREADED

HOLE THREADED

FRONT CIRCULAR
FORMING CUTTER
HOLDER

SCALE OF INCHES

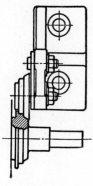

FIG. 907   FRONT CIRCULAR FORMING
CUTTER HOLDER. (1) Draw details. (2) Draw
assembly. To obtain dimensions, take distances
directly from figure with dividers; then set dividers
on printed scale and read measurements in inches.

549

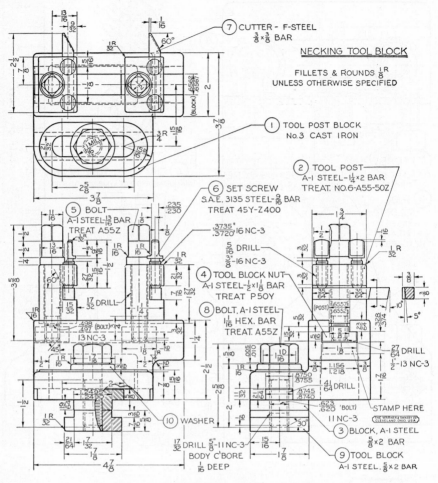

FIG. 908 NECKING TOOL BLOCK.
(1) Draw details. (2) Draw assembly.

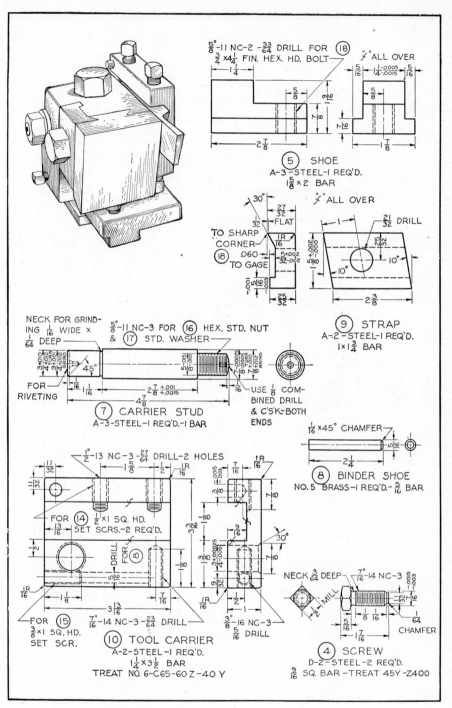

FIG. 909 FORMING CUTTER HOLDER DETAILS. (1) Draw details.
(2) Draw assembly (see also Fig. 910).

551

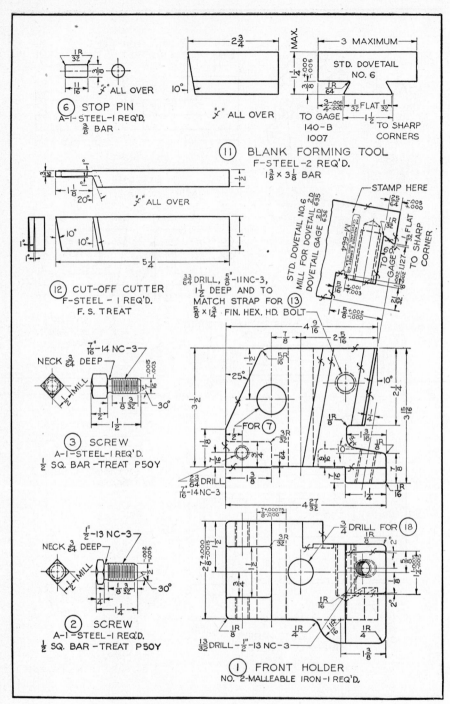

FIG. 910 FORMING CUTTER HOLDER DETAILS (*Continued*). (1) Draw details. (2) Draw assembly (see also Fig. 909).

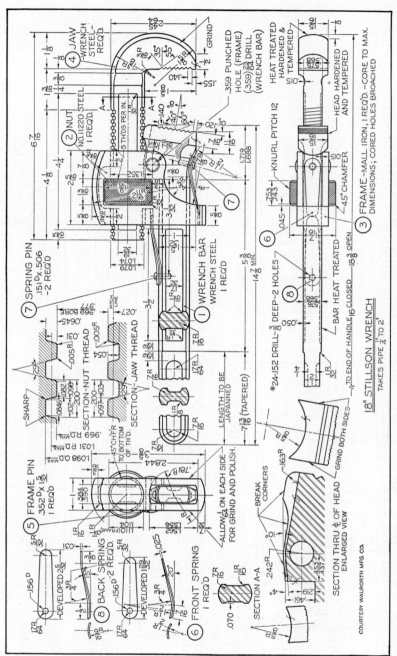

FIG. 911   18″ STILLSON WRENCH.   (1) Draw details.   (2) Draw assembly.

553

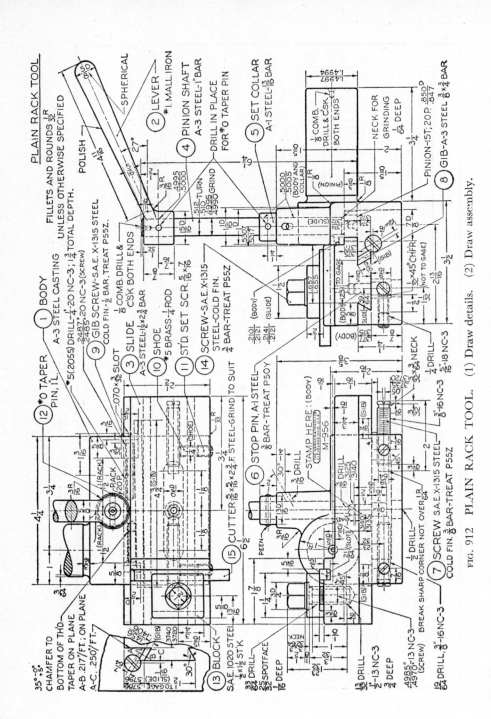

FIG. 912 PLAIN RACK TOOL. (1) Draw details. (2) Draw assembly.

554

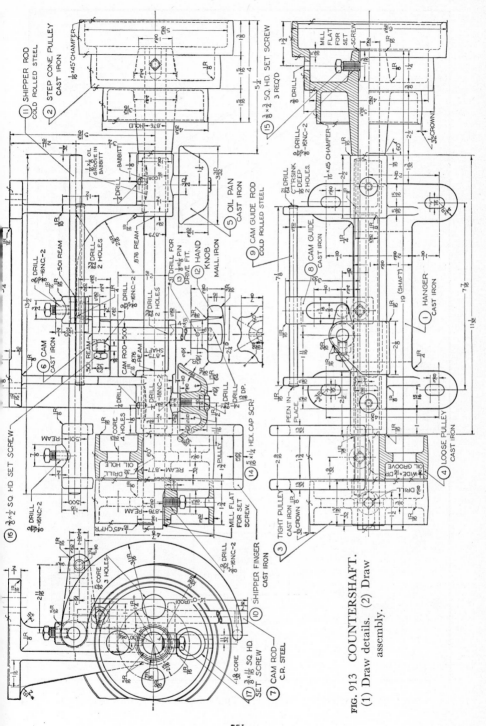

FIG. 913   COUNTERSHAFT.
(1) Draw details.   (2) Draw assembly.

555

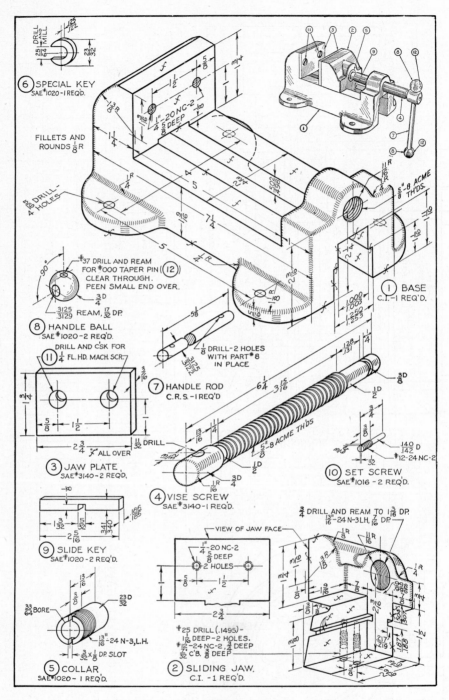

FIG. 914 MACHINE VISE. (1) Draw details. (2) Draw assembly.

556

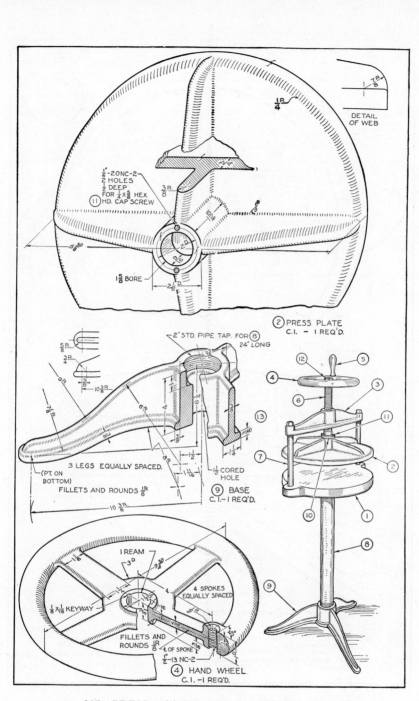

DETAIL OF WEB

$\frac{7}{8}$R

$\frac{1}{4}$R

f

$\frac{1}{4}$"-20NC-2
2 HOLES
$\frac{1}{2}$ DEEP
FOR $\frac{1}{4}$ X $\frac{5}{8}$ HEX.
⑪ HD. CAP SCREW

$\frac{3}{8}$R

$1\frac{5}{8}$ BORE

$2\frac{1}{2}$ D.

② PRESS PLATE
C.I. – I REQ'D.

2" STD. PIPE TAP. FOR ⑧
24" LONG

3 LEGS EQUALLY SPACED.
(PT. ON BOTTOM)
FILLETS AND ROUNDS $\frac{1}{8}$R

$1\frac{1}{2}$ CORED HOLE

⑨ BASE
C.I. – I REQ'D.

10 $\frac{3}{8}$R

⑫ ⑤
④ ③
⑥ ⑬
⑪ ⑦ ②
⑩ ①
⑧
⑨

I REAM
3^D
$\frac{1}{8}$ X $\frac{1}{16}$ KEYWAY
4 SPOKES EQUALLY SPACED
FILLETS AND ROUNDS $\frac{1}{8}$R
$\frac{1}{2}$-13 NC-2

④ HAND WHEEL
C.I. – I REQ'D.

FIG. 915   PRESS.   (1) Draw details.   (2) Draw assembly.

557

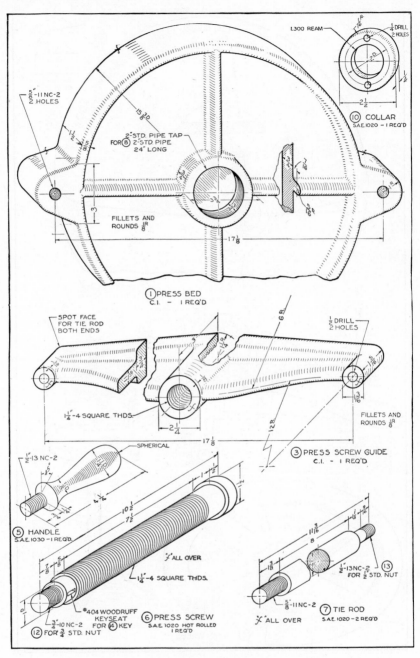

FIG. 916　PRESS (*Continued*).　Draw details.

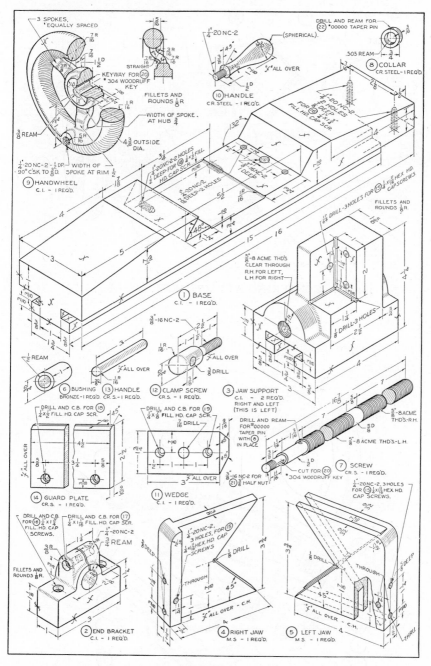

FIG. 917   CENTERING ATTACHMENT.   (1) Draw details.   (2) Draw assembly.
(See Fig. 918.)

559

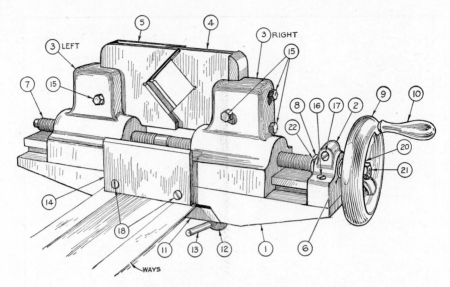

FIG. 918   CENTERING ATTACHMENT.   (See Fig. 917.)

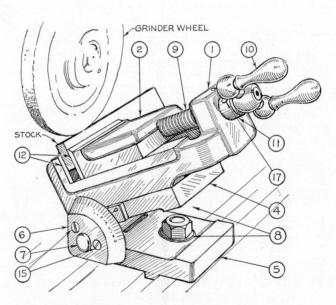

FIG. 919   GRINDER VISE.   (See Figs. 920 and 921.)

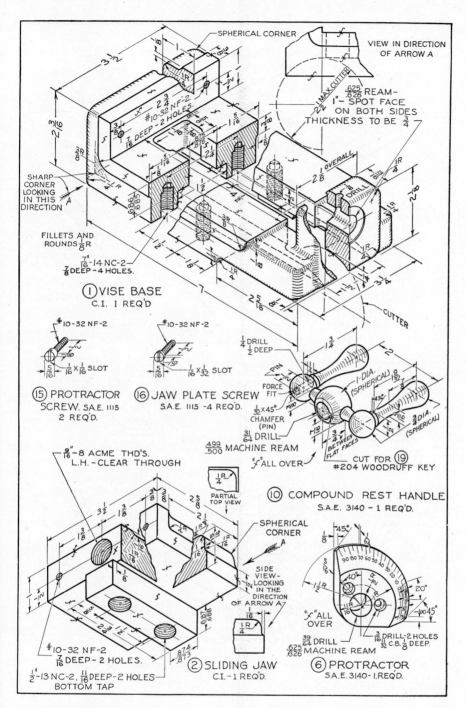

FIG. 920   GRINDER VISE.   (1) Draw details.   (2) Draw assembly.   (See Fig. 919.)

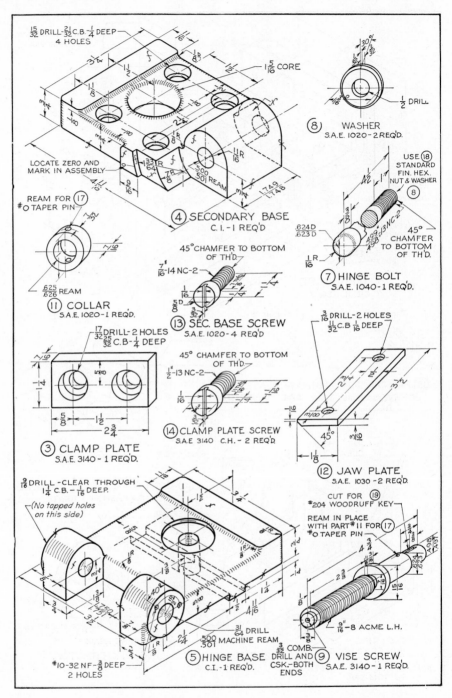

FIG. 921 **GRINDER VISE** (*Continued*). Draw details. (See Fig. 919.)

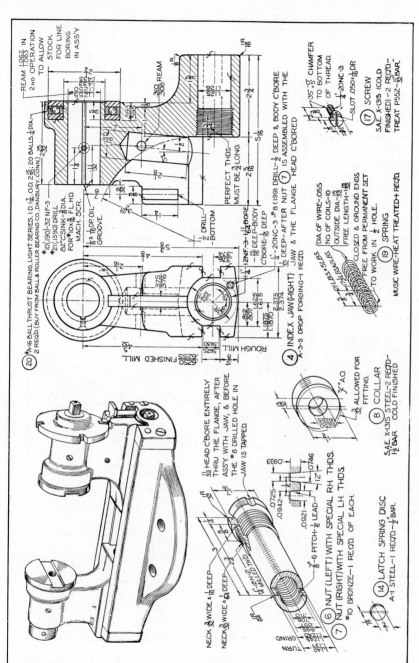

FIG. 922 REVOLVING JAW CHUCK. (1) Draw details. (2) Draw assembly.

563

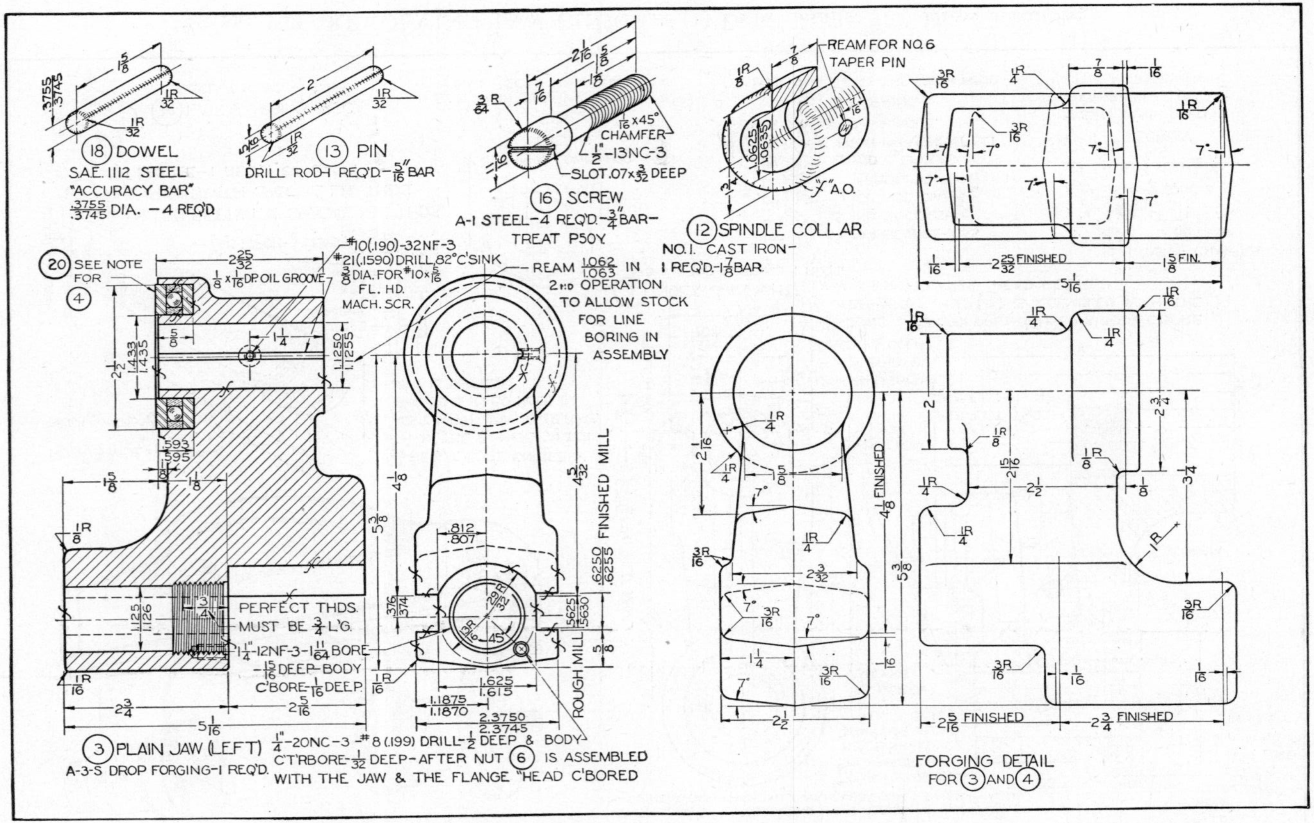

FIG. 923 REVOLVING JAW CHUCK (Continued). Draw details.

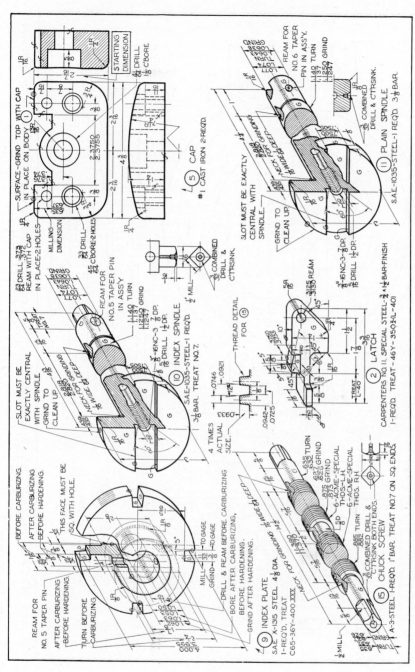

FIG. 924 REVOLVING JAW CHUCK (*Continued*). Draw details. For *Part No. 5:* Revolve given front view 180°; then add right side and bottom views.

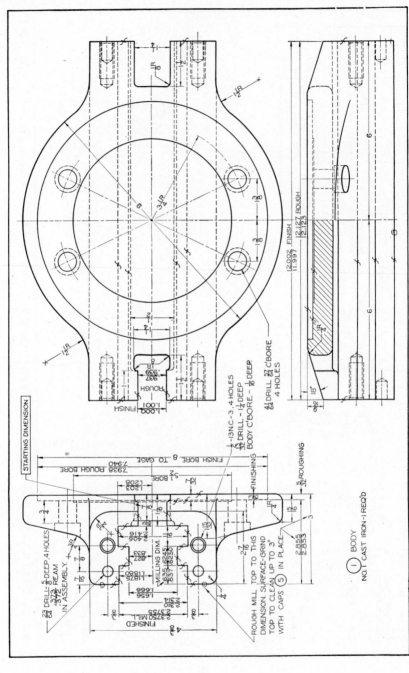

FIG. 925 REVOLVING JAW CHUCK (*Continued*). Draw detail drawing. Take given left side view as the right side view in the new drawing; then add front view and bottom view in half section.

566

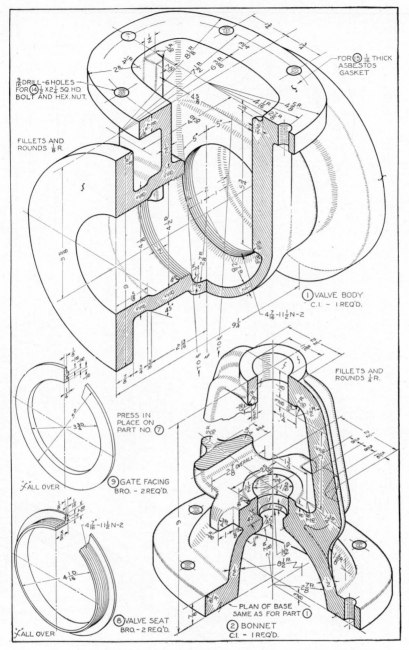

FIG. 926 GATE VALVE. (1) Draw details. (2) Draw assembly.

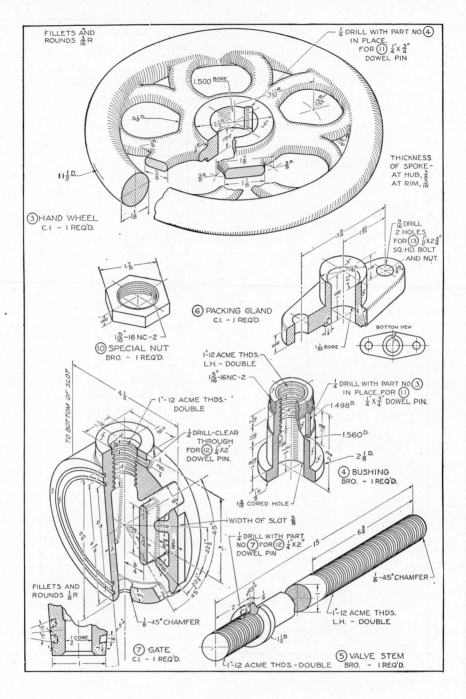

FIG. 927   GATE VALVE (*Continued*).   Draw details.

568

ITEM	DRAWING	PATT.	NO. PER MACH.	MAT'L	PIECE	REMARKS	IDENTIFICATION
	PAGE				NO. 3 DRILL SPEEDER		PRODUCTION LIST
1	335	335	1	C.I.	BODY - UPPER HALF		$1\frac{3}{4}$
2	336	336	1	C.I.	BODY - LOWER HALF		$3\frac{1}{4}$
3	351	—		SPECIAL STEEL	SHANK		$9\frac{1}{4}$
4	338	—	1	SPECIAL STEEL	SPINDLE		15 T 12 P
5	337	337	2	C.I.	INTERMEDIATE GEAR		26 T 12 P.
6	337	—	2	AJAX STEEL	INTERMEDIATE PINION		15 T 12 P.
7	337	—	1	M.S.	SHANK GEAR	C.H.	26 T. 12 P.
8	342	—	2	M.S.	GEAR STUD	C.H.	$\frac{1}{2}$
9	341	341	1	BRONZE	SPINDLE BUSHING		$2\frac{1}{8}$
10	344	—	1	M.S.	ADJUSTMENT NUT-UPPER	C.H.	
11	344	—	1	M.S.	ADJUSTMENT NUT-LOWER	C.H.	SAME
12	413	—	1	PHOS. BRONZE	SHANK BUSHING		$\frac{5}{8}$
13	341	—	1	CRS	SPINDLE WASHER	.015 THICK	$1\frac{3}{8}$ O.D. $\frac{15}{16}$ HOLE
14	343	—	1	CRS	STOP ROD		$\frac{7}{16}$
15	398	—	1	M.S.	STOP ROD SET SCREW		
16	—	—	2	M.S.	GEAR STUD NUTS	C.H	$\frac{1}{2}$ FIN. HEX.
17	—	—	1	—	SPINDLE THRUST BEARING	BALL TYPE	$1\frac{1}{32}$ X $\frac{3}{16}$ X $\frac{5}{8}$ HOLE
18	341	—	1	M.S.	SPINDLE BUSHING ADJUSTMENT SCREW		$\frac{3}{8}$ STD.
19	351	—	1	M.S.	SHANK COTTER PIN	FOR OIL	#13-$\frac{3}{32}$ X $\frac{3}{4}$
20	342	—	2	M.S.	GEAR STUD COTTER PIN	FOR OIL	#13-$\frac{3}{32}$ X $\frac{3}{4}$
21	351	—	3	T.S.	GEAR KEY BALL		$\frac{1}{8}$ D.
22		—	1	BRASS	NAME PLATE		
23		—	2	BRASS	NAME PLATE PINS	#13 ESCUTCHEON PINS, CUT TO $\frac{1}{4}$	
24	—	—	1	STOCK	CHUCK, $\frac{1}{2}$ JACOBS 6A, RECESS $1\frac{15}{32}$ X $\frac{3}{32}$		HOLE $\frac{17}{64}$
25	—	—	—	—	PAINT, STAR ENAMEL	2 COATS	
26	—	—	1	WOOD	PACKING BOX, $6\frac{3}{4}$ X 4 X 17	$\frac{13}{16}$ STOCK	
27	380	—	—	—	ASSEMBLY DRAWING	12 X 18	

FIG. 928   Drill Speeder Parts List.

FIG. 929   Use of Drill Speeder.

FIG. 930   Drill Speeder.
(See Figs. 931, 932, and 933.)

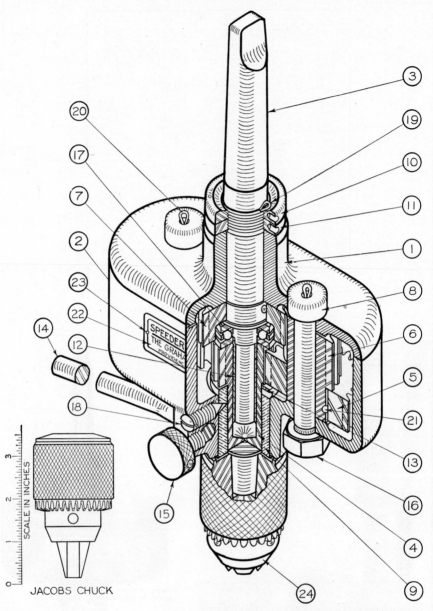

SCALE IN INCHES

JACOBS CHUCK

FIG. 931   Drill Speeder (*Continued*). See Figs. 928–930, 932, and 933.

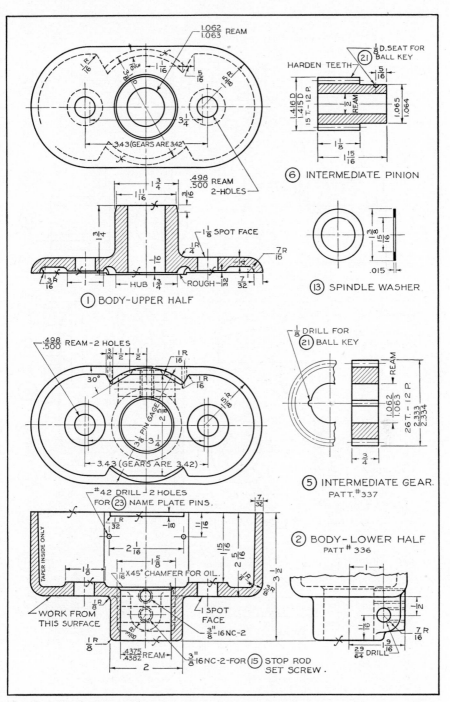

FIG. 932 DRILL SPEEDER (*Continued*). (1) Draw details. (2) Draw assembly.

571

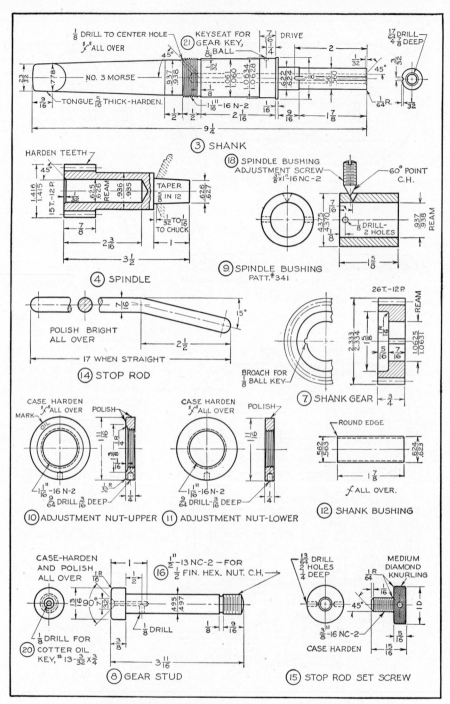

FIG. 933   DRILL SPEEDER (*Continued*).   Draw details.

572

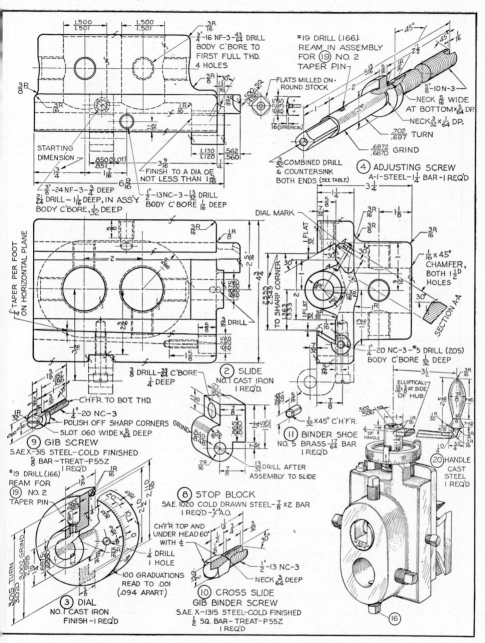

FIG. 934 VERTICAL SLIDE TOOL. (1) Draw details. (2) Draw assembly. *Part No. 2:* Take given top view as front view in the new drawing; then add top and right side views.

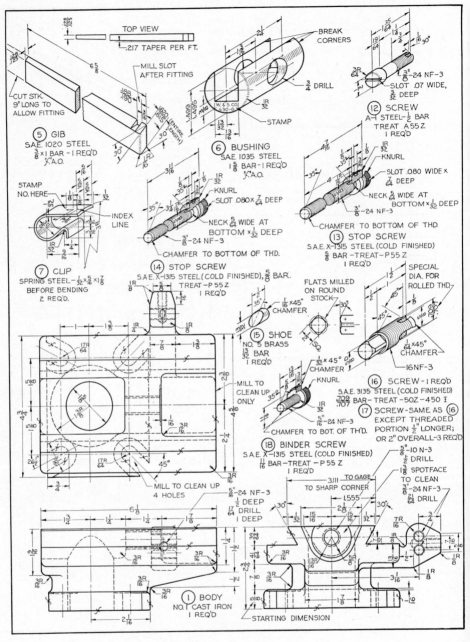

FIG. 935 VERTICAL SLIDE TOOL (*Continued*). *Part No. 1:* Take top view as front view in the new drawing; then add top and right side views.

574

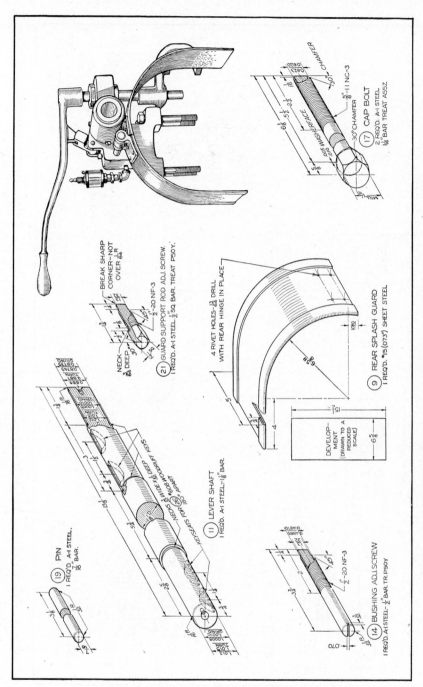

FIG. 936 OVERHEAD PILOT ATTACHMENT. (1) Draw details. (2) Draw assembly.

575

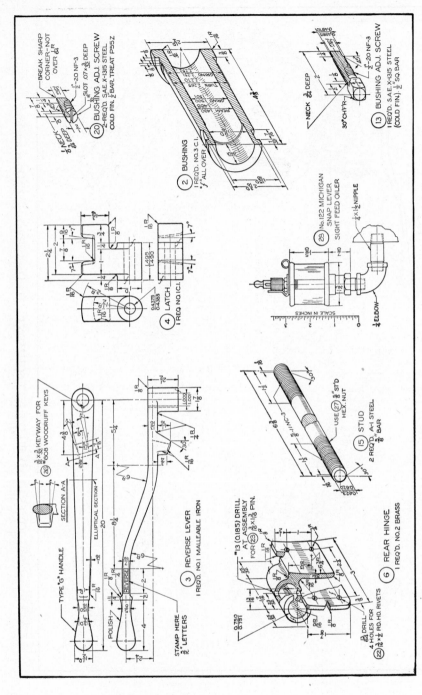

FIG. 937 OVERHEAD PILOT ATTACHMENT (*Continued*). Draw details. *Part No. 4:* Draw front, top, and right side views.

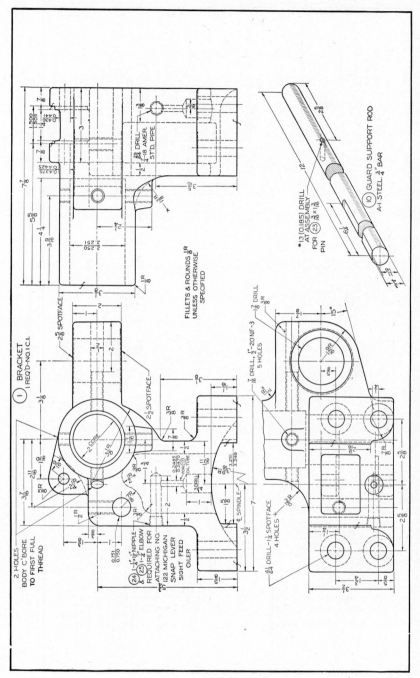

FIG. 938 OVERHEAD PILOT ATTACHMENT (*Continued*). *Part No. 1:* Draw present front view and add top and left side views, omitting present right side view and partial bottom view.

577

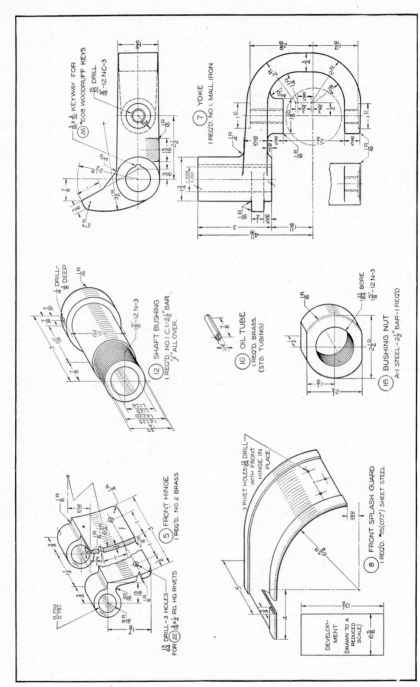

FIG. 939 OVERHEAD PILOT ATTACHMENT (*Continued*). *Part No. 7:* Revolve given top view 180°; then add front and right side views.

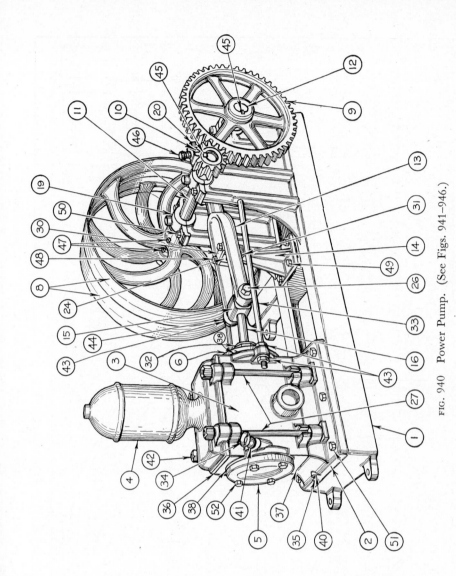

FIG. 940 Power Pump. (See Figs. 941–946.)

579

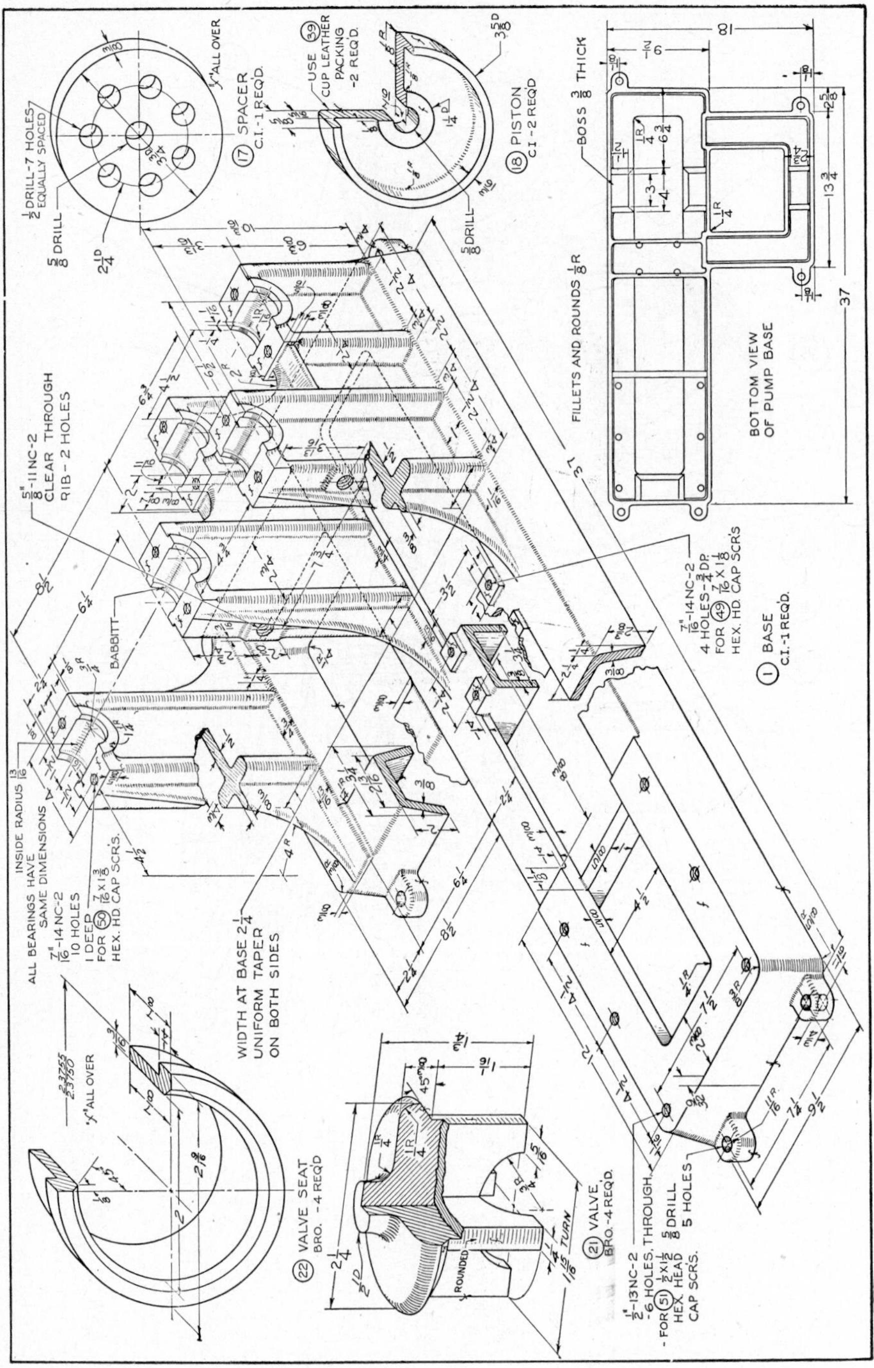

FIG. 941 POWER PUMP. (1) Draw details. (2) Draw assembly.

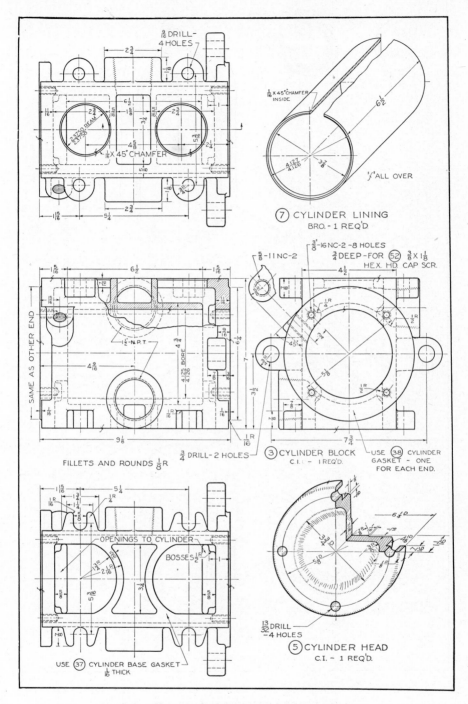

FIG. 942 POWER PUMP (*Continued*). Draw details.

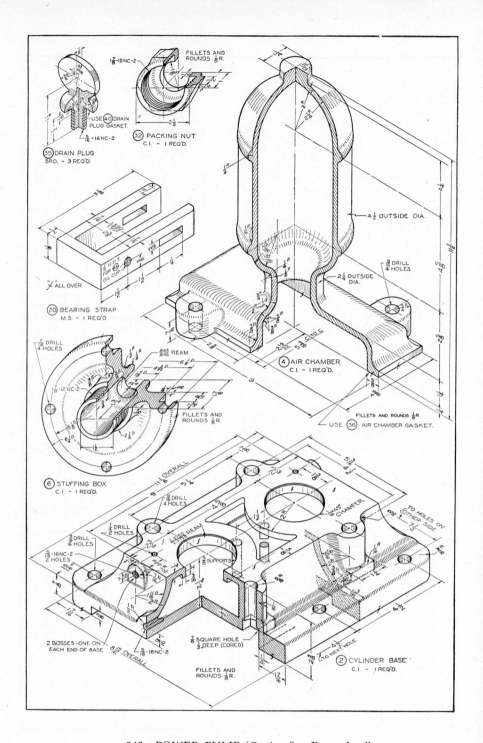

FIG. 943 POWER PUMP (*Continued*). Draw details.

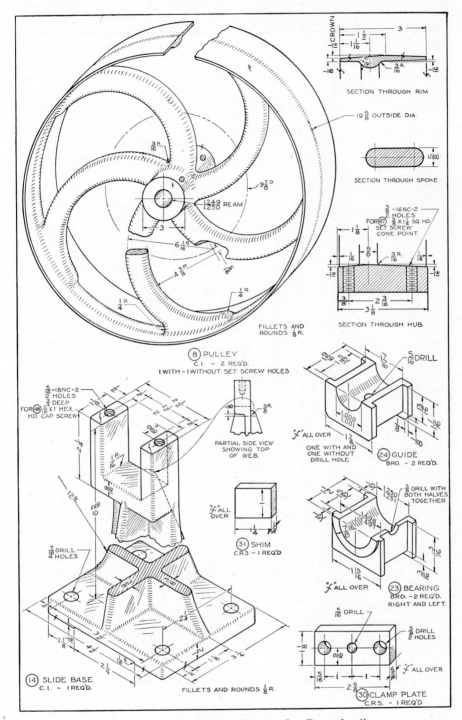

SECTION THROUGH RIM

SECTION THROUGH SPOKE

SECTION THROUGH HUB

⑧ PULLEY
C.I. – 2 REQ'D.
1 WITH – 1 WITHOUT SET SCREW HOLES

PARTIAL SIDE VIEW
SHOWING TOP
OF WEB.

"f" ALL OVER
ONE WITH AND
ONE WITHOUT
DRILL HOLE

㉔ GUIDE
BRO. – 2 REQ'D.

"f" ALL OVER

㉛ SHIM
C.R.S – 1 REQ'D

㉓ BEARING
BRO. – 2 REQ'D.
RIGHT AND LEFT.

⑭ SLIDE BASE
C.I. – 1 REQ'D.

FILLETS AND ROUNDS ⅛ R.

㉚ CLAMP PLATE
C.R.S. – 1 REQ'D.

FIG. 944 POWER PUMP (*Continued*). Draw details.

583

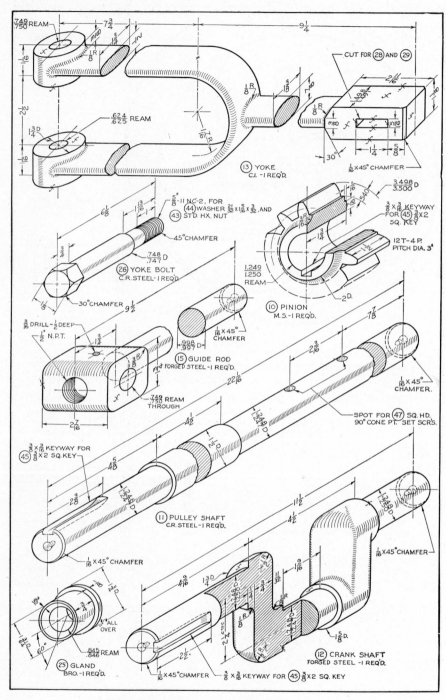

FIG. 945 POWER PUMP (*Continued*). Draw details.

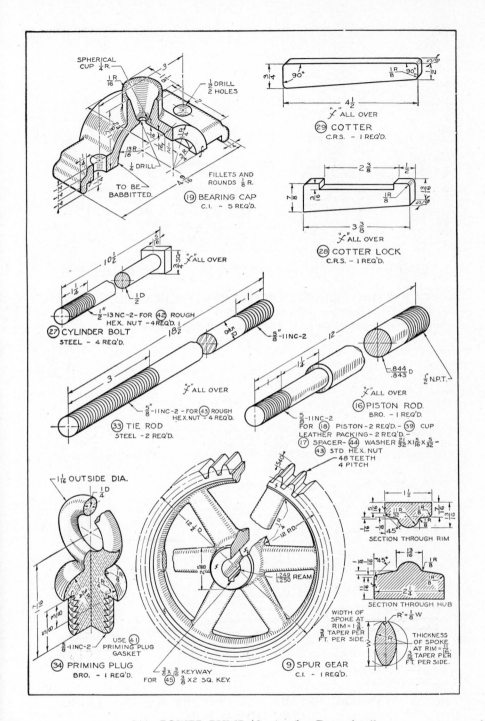

FIG. 946 POWER PUMP (*Continued*). Draw details.

585

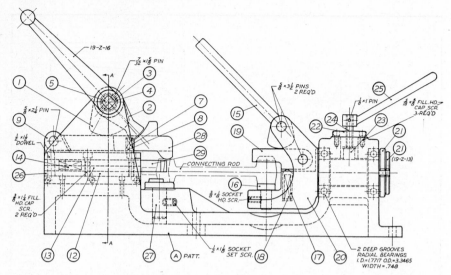

FIG. 947 PARTIAL ASSEMBLY OF FIXTURE FOR CENTERING CONNECT-
ING ROD. Draw complete assembly, including given front view, a top view, and a
right side view in section on A-A. For details, see Figs. 948–952.

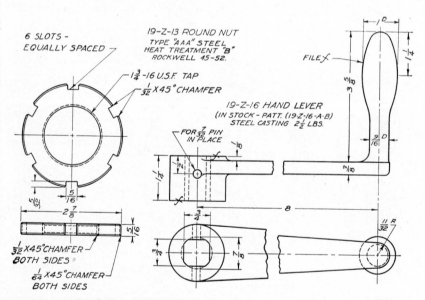

FIG. 948 STANDARD DETAILS FOR FIXTURE FOR CENTERING
CONNECTING ROD.

586

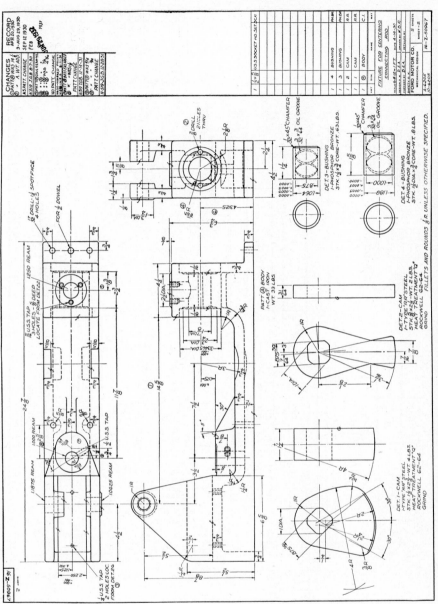

FIG. 949   DETAILS OF FIXTURE FOR CENTERING CONNECTING ROD (*Continued*).   Draw details.

587

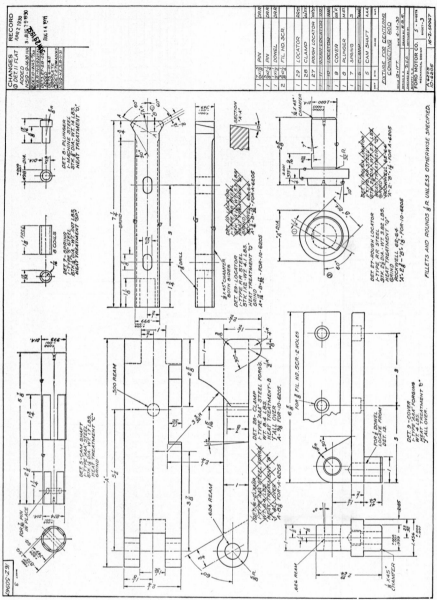

FIG. 950   DETAILS OF FIXTURE FOR CENTERING CONNECTING ROD (*Continued*).   Draw details.

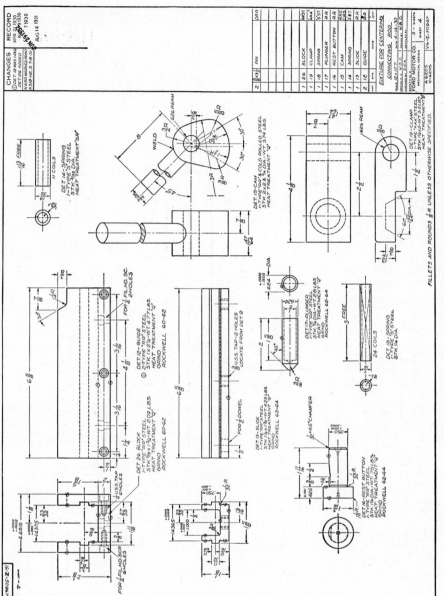

FIG. 951   DETAILS OF FIXTURE FOR CENTERING CONNECTING ROD (*Continued*).   Draw details.

589

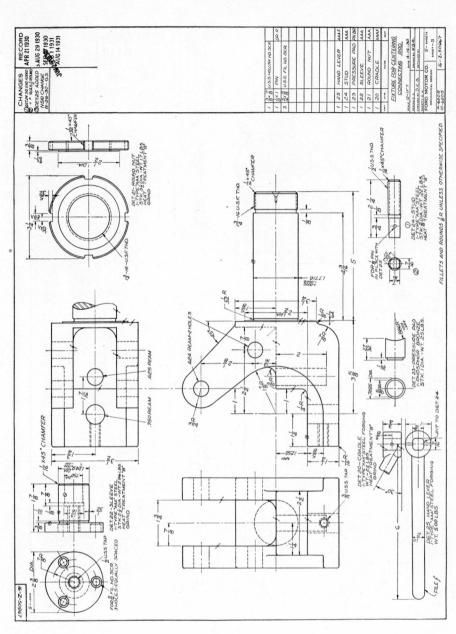

FIG. 952 DETAILS OF FIXTURE FOR CENTERING CONNECTING ROD (*Continued*). Draw details

FIG. 953 SLIDE TOOL. Make assembly drawing. (See Figs. 954–962.)

PARTS LIST   NO. OF SHEETS___2___   SHEET NO.___1___   MACHINE NO. *M-219*

NAME___NO. 4 SLIDE TOOL (SPECIFY SIZE OF SHANK REQ'D.)___   LOT NUMBER

NO. OF PIECES

TOTAL ON MACH.	NO. PCS.	NAME OF PART	PART NO.	CAST FROM PART NO.	TRACING NO.	MATERIAL	ROUGH WEIGHT PER PC.	DIA.	LENGTH	MILL	PART USED ON	NO. REQ. FINISH
	1	Body	219-12		D-17417	A-3-S D.F.						
	1	Slide	219-6		D-19255	A-3-S D.F.					219-12	
	1	Nut	219-9		E-19256	#10 BZ.					219-6	
	1	Gib	219-1001		C-11129	S.A.E. 1020					219-6	
	1	Slide Screw	219-1002		C-11129	A-3-S					219-12	
	1	Dial Bush	219-1003		C-11129	A-1-S					219-1002	
	1	Dial Nut	219-1004		C-11129	A-1-S					219-1002	
	1	Handle	219-1011		E-18270	(Buy from Cincinnati Ball Crank Co.)					219-1002	
	1	Stop Screw (Short)	219-1012		E-51950	A-1-S					219-6	
	1	Stop Screw (Long)	219-1013		E-51951	A-1-S					219-6	
	1	Binder Shoe	219-1015		E-51952	#5 Brass					219-6	
	1	Handle Screw	219-1016		E-62322	X-1315 C.F.					219-1011	
	1	Binder Screw	219-1017		E-63927	A-1-S					219-6	
	1	Dial	219-1018		E-39461	A-1-S					219-1002	
	2	Gib Screw	219-1019		E-52777	A-1-S		$\frac{1}{4}$-20	1		219-6	
	1	Binder Screw	280-1010		E-24962	A-1-S					219-1018	
	2	Tool Clamp Screws	683-F-1002		E-19110	D-2-S					219-6	
	1	Fill. Hd. Cap Scr.	1-A			A-1-S		$\frac{3}{8}$	$1\frac{3}{8}$		219-6 219-9	
	1	Key	No.404 Woodruff								219-1002	

FIG. 954 Slide Tool Parts List.

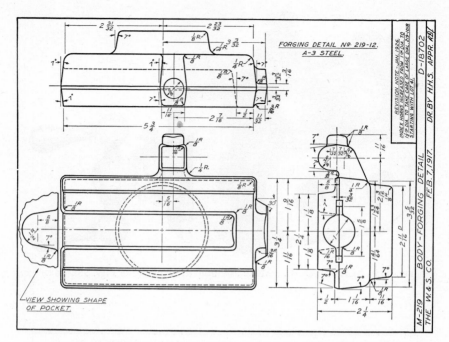

FIG. 955   SLIDE TOOL BODY (*Continued*).   Make forging drawing.

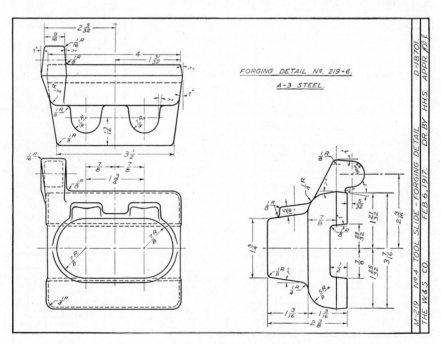

FIG. 956   SLIDE TOOL SLIDE (*Continued*).   Make forging drawing.

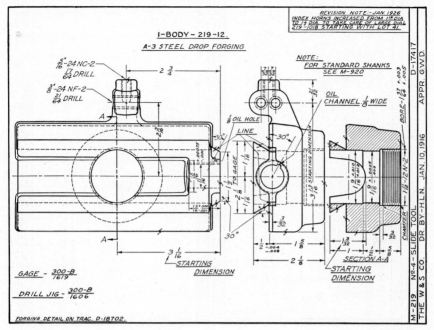

FIG. 957   SLIDE TOOL BODY (*Continued*).   Make machine shop drawing.

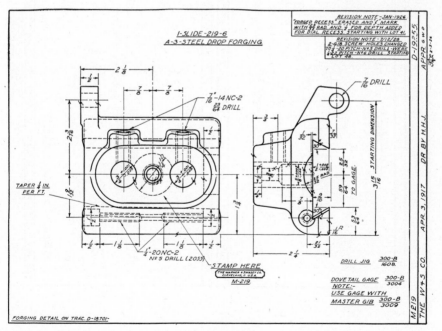

FIG. 958   SLIDE TOOL SLIDE (*Continued*).   Make machine shop drawing.

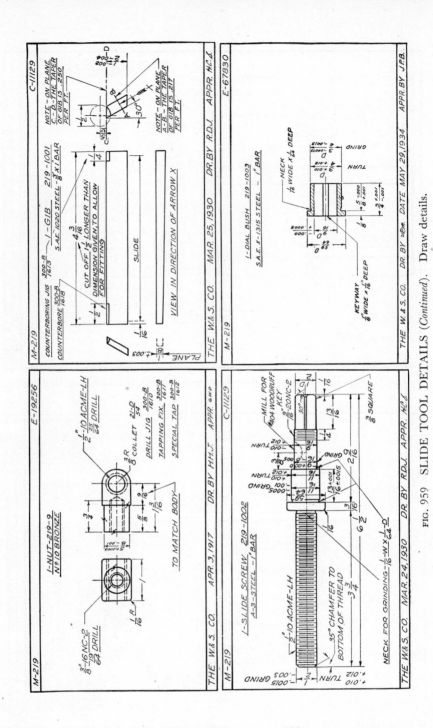

FIG. 959 SLIDE TOOL DETAILS (*Continued*). Draw details.

594

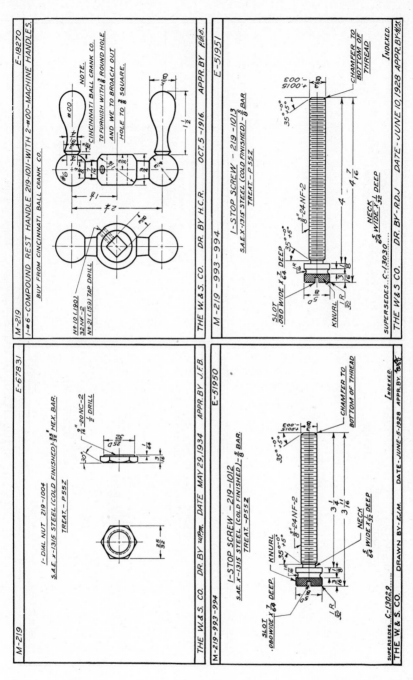

FIG. 960 SLIDE TOOL DETAILS (*Continued*). Draw details.

595

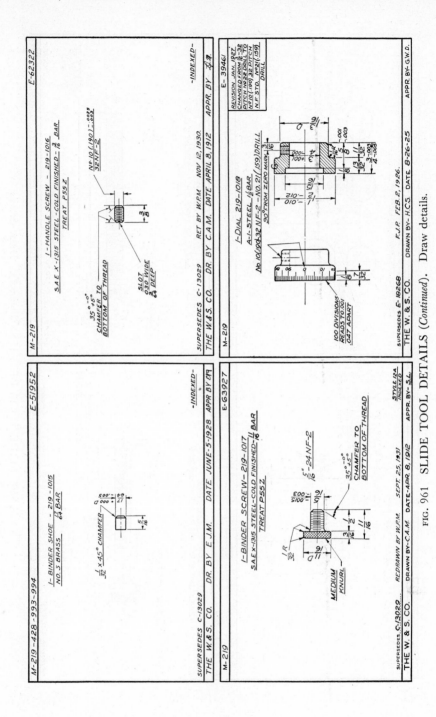

FIG. 961 SLIDE TOOL DETAILS (*Continued*). Draw details.

596

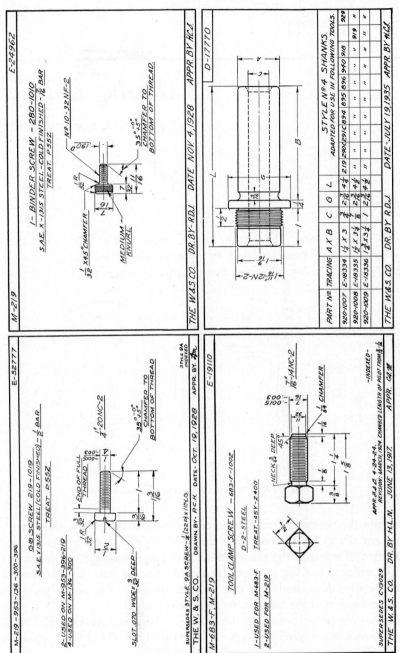

FIG. 962 SLIDE TOOL DETAILS (*Continued*). Draw details.

CHAPTER 20

Gearing and Cams

By B. LEIGHTON WELLMAN*

487. Spur Gears. The friction wheels shown in Fig. 963 (a) will transmit motion and power from one shaft to a parallel shaft. However, friction gears are subject to slipping, and excessive pressure is required between the wheels

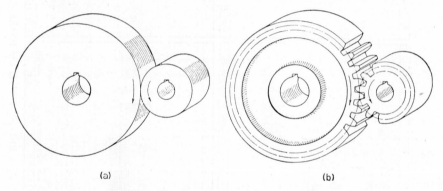

(a)   (b)

FIG. 963   Friction Gears and Toothed Gears.

to obtain the necessary frictional force. If teeth of the proper shape are provided on the cylindrical surfaces, the resulting *spur gears*, as shown in Fig. 963 (b), will transmit the same motion and power without slipping and with greatly reduced bearing pressures. It should be noted that these gears rotate in opposite directions, and that the rotative speeds are inversely proportional to the diameters of the tangent, or pitch, circles.

Spur-gear proportions and the shape of the teeth are well standardized. The nomenclature given on pp. 599–600 and in Fig. 964 is common to practically all spur gears. The dimensions relating to the tooth height are for full-depth $14\frac{1}{2}°$ involute teeth.

* Professor of Mechanical Engineering and Head of Division of Engineering Drawing, Worcester Polytechnic Institute.

Pitch Circle. — An imaginary circle that corresponds to the circumference of the friction gear from which the spur gear has been derived.

Pitch Diameter (PD). — The diameter of the pitch circle.

Number of Teeth (N). — The number of teeth on the gear.

Diametral Pitch (DP). — A ratio equal to the number of teeth on the gear per inch of pitch diameter. $DP = N/PD$.

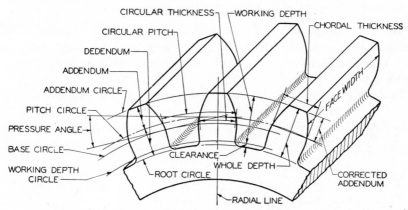

FIG. 964   Gear Tooth Nomenclature.

Circular Pitch (CP). — The distance in inches measured along the pitch circle from a point on one tooth to the corresponding point on the adjacent tooth. $CP = \pi PD/N$. Also note that $CP \times DP = \pi$.

Addendum (A). — The radial distance from the pitch circle to the top of the tooth. $A = 1/DP$.

Dedendum (D). — The radial distance from the pitch circle to the bottom of the tooth space. $D = 1.157/DP$.

Outside Diameter (OD). — The diameter of the addendum circle. It is equal to the pitch diameter plus twice the addendum.

Root Diameter (RD). — The diameter of the root circle. It is equal to the pitch diameter minus twice the dedendum.

Whole Depth (WD). — The total height of the tooth. It is equal to the addendum plus the dedendum.

Working Depth (WkD). — The distance that a tooth projects into the mating space. It is equal to twice the addendum.

Clearance (C). — The distance between the top of a tooth and the bottom of the mating space. It is equal to the dedendum minus the addendum.

Circular Thickness (CT). — The thickness of a tooth measured along the pitch circle. It is equal to one-half the circular pitch.

Chordal Thickness (ChT). — The thickness of a tooth measured along a chord of the pitch circle. $ChT = PD \sin (90°/N)$.

Corrected Addendum (CA). — The radial distance from the top of a tooth to the chord of the pitch circle. $CA = A + \frac{1}{2} PD [1 - \cos (90°/N)]$.

Base Circle. — The circle from which the involute tooth profile is generated. It may be obtained graphically. (See § 488.)

Pressure Angle. — The angle that determines the direction of the pressure between contacting teeth, and that designates the shape of involute teeth, e.g., $14\frac{1}{2}°$ involute. It also determines the size of the base circle.

Pinion. — The smaller of two mating gears.

Gear. — The larger of two mating gears.

488. The Shape of the Tooth. If gears are to operate smoothly with a minimum of noise and vibration, the curved surface of the tooth profile must be of a definite geometric form. The most common form in use today is the *involute* profile.

In the involute system, the shape of the tooth depends basically upon the *pressure angle*, which is ordinarily $14\frac{1}{2}°$. This pressure angle determines the size of the base circle, from which the involute curve is generated, in the following manner: at any point on the pitch circle (Fig. 965) a line is drawn tangent to

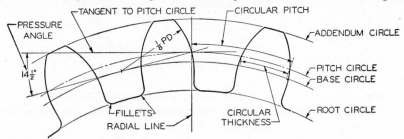

Fig. 965   Approximate Representation of Involute Spur Gear Teeth.

it; a second line is drawn through the point of tangency at an angle of $14\frac{1}{2}°$ (frequently approximated as 15° on the drawing) with the tangent; the base circle is then drawn tangent to the $14\frac{1}{2}°$ line.

If the exact shape of the tooth is desired, the portion of the profile from the base circle to the addendum circle can be drawn as the involute of the base circle. The method of construction is shown in Fig. 160 (d) and (e). That part of the profile below the base circle is drawn as a radial line which terminates in the *fillet* at the root circle. The fillet should be equal in radius to one and one-half times the clearance.

For display drawings and more rapid construction, the involute curve may be approximated (Fig. 965). The base circle is drawn as described above, and the spacing of the teeth is set off along the pitch circle. With a radius equal to one-eighth the pitch diameter, and with centers on the base circle, circular arcs are drawn through the spaced points on the pitch circle, and are extended from the addendum circle to slightly below the base circle. Below the base circle a radial line and fillet complete the profile.

If the pressure angle is increased to 20° and the height of the tooth is reduced, the teeth are called *stub* teeth. Such teeth are drawn in the same manner except that $A = 0.8/DP$, $D = 1/DP$, and the pressure angle is made 20°. The major advantage of stub teeth is that they are stronger than the $14\frac{1}{2}$° standard involute teeth.

When the gear teeth are formed on a flat surface, the result is a *rack* (Fig. 966). In the involute system, the sides of rack teeth are straight, and are inclined at an angle equal to the pressure angle. To mesh with a gear, it is obvious that the linear pitch of the rack must be the same as the circular pitch of the gear, and the rack teeth must have the same height proportions as the gear teeth.

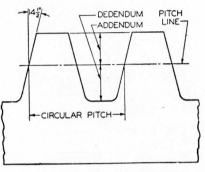

FIG. 966   Involute Rack Teeth.

489. Working Drawings of Spur Gears. Figure 967 shows a typical working drawing of a spur gear. The individual teeth are not drawn; the addendum circle is a fine solid line; the pitch circle is a center line; and the root circle is

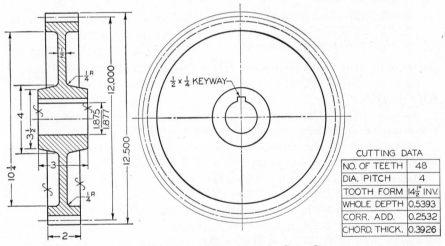

CUTTING DATA	
NO. OF TEETH	48
DIA. PITCH	4
TOOTH FORM	$14\frac{1}{2}°$ INV.
WHOLE DEPTH	0.5393
CORR. ADD.	0.2532
CHORD. THICK.	0.3926

FIG. 967   Working Drawing of a Spur Gear.

a dashed line. On the drawing, only dimensions for the gear blank are given. The data necessary to cut the teeth in the blank are given in a note or table. The note or table should include, for the machinist, the number of teeth, the pitch, the whole depth, and the tooth form. The corrected addendum and chordal thickness are given to aid in checking the finished gear.

490. Bevel Gears. *Bevel gears* are used to transmit power between shafts whose axes intersect. The analogous friction drive would consist of a pair of cones having a common apex at the point of intersection of the axes. The axes may intersect at any angle, but axes at right angles occur most frequently, and the latter is the only position that will be considered here.

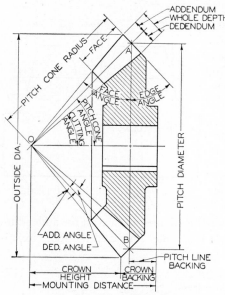

Figure 968 illustrates the important dimensions and angles on a bevel gear. The *pitch cone* is shown as the triangle OAB. Examination of Fig. 969 will reveal the pitch cones for the mating gear and the pinion shown there. Evidently, the pitch-cone angle of each gear depends upon the relative diameters of the gears. Therefore the pitch-cone angles (PCA) are determined from the following equations:

$$\tan (PCA)_g = \frac{PD_g}{PD_p},$$

$$\tan (PCA)_p = \frac{PD_p}{PD_g}.$$

The other dimensions shown in Fig. 968 are defined below:

FIG. 968　　Bevel Gear Nomenclature.

Pitch Diameter (PD). — The diameter of the base of the pitch cone, $PD_g = N_g/DP$ and $PD_p = N_p/DP$.

Pitch-Cone Radius (PCR). — The slant height of the pitch cone. $PCR = PD/2 \sin PCA$.

Addendum (A). — The same as for a spur gear of the same diametral pitch. It is measured at the large end of the tooth. $A = 1/DP$.

Dedendum (D). — The same as for a spur gear of the same diametral pitch. It is measured at the large end of the tooth. $D = 1.157/DP$.

Addendum Angle (AA). — $\tan AA = A/PCR$.

Dedendum Angle (DA). — $\tan DA = D/PCR$.

Edge Angle (EA). — Equal to the pitch-cone angle (PCA).

Face Angle (FA). — $FA = 90° - (PCA + AA)$.

Cutting Angle (CA). — $CA = PCA - DA$.

Outside Diameter (OD). — $OD = PD + 2 A \cos PCA$.

Pitch Line Backing (PB). — The distance from the base of the pitch cone to the rear end of the hub.

Crown Backing (CB). — $CB = PB + A \sin PCA$.

Crown Height (CH). — $CH = \frac{1}{2} OD \tan FA$.

Mounting Distance (MD). — The sum of the crown backing and the crown height. It is given by the equation $MD = PB + \frac{1}{2} PD/\tan PCA$.

Face (F). — The face should not exceed $\frac{1}{3} PCR$.

Formative Number of Teeth (N'). — $N' = N/\cos PCA$. This information is needed in selecting the proper cutter to form the teeth.

491. Working Drawings of Bevel Gears. As in the case of spur gears, a working drawing of a bevel gear gives only the dimensions of the gear blank. The necessary data for cutting the teeth are given in a note or table. A single sectional view (Fig. 969) usually will provide all necessary information. If a

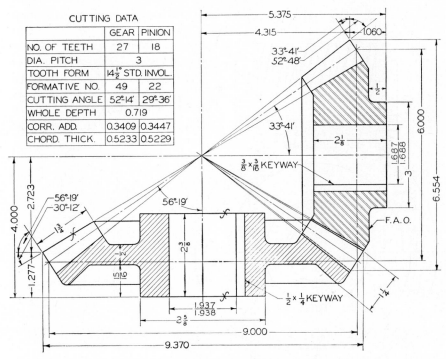

CUTTING DATA		
	GEAR	PINION
NO. OF TEETH	27	18
DIA. PITCH	3	
TOOTH FORM	$14\frac{1}{2}°$ STD. INVOL.	
FORMATIVE NO.	49	22
CUTTING ANGLE	52°14'	29°36'
WHOLE DEPTH	0.719	
CORR. ADD.	0.3409	0.3447
CHORD. THICK.	0.5233	0.5229

FIG. 969   Working Drawing of Bevel Gears.

second view is required, only the gear blank is drawn, and the tooth profiles are omitted. Figure 969 shows two gears in their operating relationship. On detail drawings, each gear is usually drawn separately (Fig. 968).

Proper placing of the gear-blank dimensions is largely dependent upon the shop methods used in producing the gear, but the scheme employed in Fig. 969 is commonly followed.

492. Worm Gears. *Worm gears* are used to transmit power between non-intersecting shafts that are at right angles to each other. The *worm* is a screw having a thread of the same shape as a rack tooth. The *worm wheel* is similar to a spur gear except that the teeth have been twisted and curved to conform to the shape of the worm. A large speed ratio is obtainable with worm gearing, since a *single-thread worm* in one revolution advances the worm wheel only one tooth and space.

In Fig. 970, a worm and worm wheel are shown engaged. The section taken through the center of the worm and perpendicular to the axis of the worm wheel shows that the worm section is identical with a rack, and that the wheel section is identical with a spur gear. Consequently, in this plane

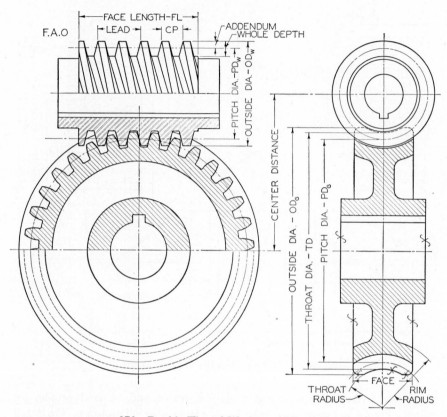

FIG. 970   Double Thread Worm and Worm Gear.

the height proportions of thread and gear teeth are the same as for a spur gear of corresponding pitch. *Pitch* and *lead* of the worm have the same meaning as for screw threads (§ 411), and the pitch of the worm equals the circular pitch of the worm gear. The *helix angle* of the worm is the angle between a tangent to the helix at the pitch diameter and a plane perpendicular to the axis of the worm. It is the angle whose tangent is equal to the lead divided by the pitch circumference of the worm.

For $14\frac{1}{2}°$ standard involute teeth and single-thread or double-thread worms, the following proportions are the recommended practice of the

A.G.M.A. (American Gear Manufacturers' Association). (CP = circular pitch, and N = teeth on gear.)

For the worm:

Pitch Diameter (PD_w). — $PD_w = 2.4\ CP + 1.1$ (recommended value, but may be varied).

Outside Diameter (OD_w). — $OD_w = PD_w + 0.636\ CP.$

Face Length (FL). — $FL = CP\ (4.5 + N/50)$

For the gear:

Pitch Diameter (PD_g). — $PD_g = N \times CP/\pi.$

Throat Diameter (TD). — $TD = PD_g + 0.636\ CP.$

Outside Diameter (OD). — $OD = TD + 0.4775\ CP.$

Throat Radius (TR). — $TR = \frac{1}{2}\ PD_w - 0.318\ CP.$

Rim Radius (RR). — $RR = \frac{1}{2}\ PD_w + CP.$

Face (F). — $F = 2.38\ CP + 0.25.$

493. Working Drawings of Worm Gears. Figure 970 illustrates the conventional representation of a worm and a worm wheel. On detail drawings, the worm and worm wheel are usually drawn separately. The worm is frequently shown with one view in half-section, as shown, the helices being approximated by straight lines (§ 412). A single view showing a section through the axis of the worm wheel will usually convey sufficient information for the gear. If another view is necessary, the gear blank can be represented conventionally, as shown in the lower half of the circular view (Fig. 970). No teeth need be drawn on the gear.

Dimensioning of the worm and worm wheel is again largely dependent upon the method of production. The blanks should be completely dimensioned, and the cutting data peculiar to the proposed shop methods may be given in a note.

494. Cams. Cams provide a simple means for obtaining unusual and irregular motions that would be difficult to produce otherwise. Figure 971 (a) illustrates the basic principle of the cam. A shaft rotating at uniform speed carries

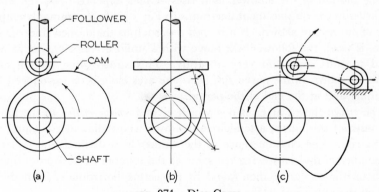

FIG. 971   Disc Cams.

an irregularly shaped disc called the *cam;* a reciprocating plunger, called the *follower*, presses a small roller against the curved surface of the cam; rotation of the cam thus causes the follower to reciprocate with a definite cyclic motion according to the shape of the cam profile. The roller is held in contact with the cam by gravity or a spring. The problem of the draftsman is to construct the cam profile necessary to obtain the desired motion of the follower.

Figure 971 (b) shows an automobile valve cam that operates a flat-faced follower. The profile of this particular cam is composed of circular arcs for ease in manufacture. Figure 971 (c) shows a disc cam with the roller follower attached to a swinging arm.

495. Displacement Diagrams. Since the motion of the follower is of primary importance, its rate of speed and its various positions should be carefully planned in a displacement diagram before the cam profile is constructed. A displacement diagram (Fig. 972) is a curve showing the displacement of the

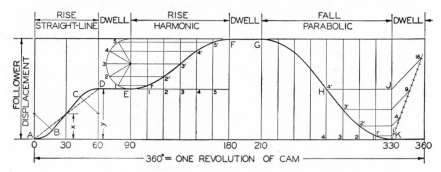

FIG. 972   Displacement Diagram with Typical Curves.

follower as ordinates erected on a base line that represents one revolution of the cam. The follower displacement should be drawn to scale, but any convenient length can be used to represent the 360° of cam rotation.

The motion of the follower as it rises or falls depends upon the shape of the curves in the displacement diagram. In Fig. 972, four commonly employed types of curves are shown. If a *straight line*, such as the dashed line *AD* in the figure, is used, the follower will move with a uniform velocity, but it will be forced to start and stop very abruptly. This straight-line motion can be *modified* as shown in the curve *ABCD*, where arcs have been introduced at the beginning and at the end of the period.

The curve shown at *EF* is one which gives *harmonic motion* to the follower. To construct this curve, a semicircle is drawn whose diameter is equal to the desired rise. The circumference of the semicircle is divided into equal arcs, the number of divisions being the same as the number of horizontal divisions. Points on the curve are then found by projecting horizontally from the divisions on the semicircle to the corresponding ordinates.

The *parabolic* curve shown at *GHK* gives the follower constantly accelerated and decelerated motion. This motion is analogous to that of a falling body. The half of the curve from *G* to *H* is exactly the reverse of the half from *H* to *K*. To construct the curve *HK*, the vertical height from *K* to *J* is divided into distances proportional to 1^2, 2^2, 3^2, etc., or 1, 4, 9, etc., the number of such divisions being the same as the number of horizontal divisions. (See §§ 85 and 120.) Points on the curve are found by projecting horizontally from the divisions on the line *JK* to the corresponding ordinates.

496. The Cam Profile. Figure 973 illustrates the general procedure in constructing a cam profile. The disc cam rotating counterclockwise on its shaft raises and lowers the roller follower in a straight line. The axis of the

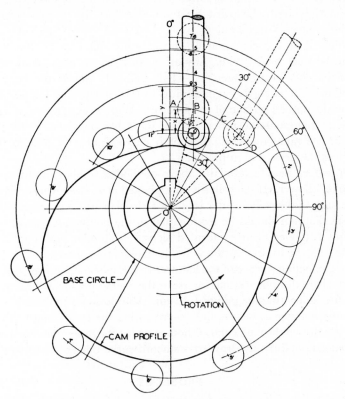

FIG. 973   Disc Cam Profile Construction.

follower is offset from the center line of the cam. The cam profile shown corresponds to the displacement diagram in Fig. 972.

The follower in Fig. 973 has been shown in its lowest position. A *base circle* is drawn tangent to the roller; this is the minimum diameter of the cam. The cam disc is then divided into equal angular divisions corresponding to the divisions used in the abscissa of the displacement diagram. The 0° division is conveniently selected as vertical.

Reference to the displacement diagram (Fig. 972) shows that when the cam has rotated 30° the follower should rise a distance x, and after 60° of rotation, a distance y, etc. The distances x, y, etc., can be transferred from the displacement diagram to Fig. 973, where they locate the points 1, 2, etc., on the vertical center line of the follower. The points 1, 2, etc., thus indicate the successive positions of the center of the roller.

It should now be observed that while the center of the roller follower has moved from its initial position 0, to position 1, for example, the cam has rotated *counterclockwise* 30°. This same rotative effect can be obtained by assuming that the cam remains stationary, and that the follower rotates 30° in a *clockwise* direction. The point 1 should, therefore, be rotated 30° clockwise about the center of the cam. This is most easily accomplished as follows: with radius O–1, and center at O, draw an arc AD, which extends from the 0° line to beyond the 30° line. Lay off on this arc the chordal distance C–$1'$ equal to the chordal distance A–B. This point $1'$ locates the center of the roller follower in its correct relationship to the cam profile for position 1, as shown by the dashed outline of the follower. With $1'$ as a center, a light circle is drawn to represent the roller. All of the other positions of the roller are located in the same manner. A smooth curve drawn tangent to the roller circles gives the desired cam profile.

With proper modification the above method is fundamentally correct for any type of follower. If the roller is on a pivoted arm, as shown in Fig. 971 (c), then the path of the roller center is along a circular arc. The height of the displacement diagram should be made equal to the rectified length of this path. The points 1, 2, etc., are then located along this circular path, and the points $1'$, $2'$, etc., can be located in the same manner as that shown in Fig. 973.

If the contacting surface of the follower is flat, as shown in Fig. 971 (b), then the point where the follower axis intersects the contacting surface is a convenient point to use in locating the points 1, 2, etc. After locating the points $1'$, $2'$, etc., in the same manner as before, lines representing the contacting surface of the follower are drawn through each of these points at the proper angle. The correct cam profile is obtained by drawing a smooth curve tangent to these lines.

PROBLEMS

497. Problems on Gearing and Cams.

Gearing

Prob. 1 A 12-tooth, 1 DP, pinion engages a 15-tooth gear. Make a full-size drawing of a segment of each gear showing how the teeth mesh. Construct the $14\frac{1}{2}°$ involute teeth exactly, noting any points where the teeth appear to interfere.

Prob. 2 The same as Prob. 1, but use 20° stub teeth.

Prob. 3 The same as Prob. 1, but use a rack in place of the 12-tooth pinion.

Prob. 4 Make a display drawing of the pinion in Fig. 945. Show two views, drawing the teeth by the approximate method shown in Fig. 965. Draw twice the actual size.

Prob. 5 A spur gear has 40 teeth of 5 DP. The face width is $1\frac{1}{2}''$. The shaft is $1\frac{3}{16}''$ in diameter. Make the hub 2″ long, and $2\frac{1}{4}''$ in diameter. Calculate accurately all dimensions, and make a working drawing of the gear. Use your own judgment for any dimensions not given.

Prob. 6 Make a working drawing of the intermediate pinion shown in Fig. 932. Check the gear dimensions by calculation.

Prob. 7 The same as Prob. 6, but use the intermediate gear shown in Fig. 932.

Prob. 8 The same as Prob. 6, but use the pinion shown in Fig. 945.

Prob. 9 The same as Prob. 6, but use the spur gear shown in Fig. 946.

Prob. 10 A pair of bevel gears have teeth of 3 DP. The pinion has 13 teeth, the gear, 25 teeth. The face width is $1\frac{1}{2}''$. The pinion shaft is $1\frac{3}{16}''$ in diameter, the gear shaft is $1\frac{7}{16}''$ in diameter. Calculate accurately all dimensions, and make a working drawing showing the gears engaged, as in Fig. 969. Make the hub diameters approximately twice the shaft diameters. Select key sizes from table in Appendix 35. The pitch-line backing for the pinion must be $\frac{5}{8}''$; for the gear, $1\frac{7}{8}''$. Use your own judgment for any dimensions not given.

Prob. 11 Make a working drawing of the pinion in Prob. 10.

Prob. 12 The same as Prob. 11, but use the gear described in Prob. 10.

Prob. 13 The same as Prob. 11, but show two views of the pinion.

Prob. 14 The same as Prob. 10, but use 5 DP, 40 and 15 teeth. The face is $1\frac{1}{4}''$: Shafts: pinion, 1″ diam.; gear, $1\frac{1}{2}''$ diam. Pitch-line backing: pinion, $\frac{1}{2}''$; gear, $1\frac{3}{4}''$.

Prob. 15 The same as Prob. 10, but use 4 DP, both gears 20 teeth. Select the correct face. Shafts: $1\frac{3}{8}''$ diam. Pitch-line backing: $\frac{3}{4}''$.

Prob. 16 The worm and worm gear shown in Fig. 970 have a circular pitch of $\frac{5}{8}''$, and the gear has 32 teeth of $14\frac{1}{2}°$ involute form. The worm is double threaded. Make an assembly drawing similar to Fig. 970. The teeth on the gear should be drawn by the approximate method. Calculate dimensions accurately, and use A.G.M.A. proportions. Shafts: worm, $1\frac{1}{4}''$ diam.; gear, $1\frac{5}{8}''$ diam.

Prob. 17 Make a working drawing of the worm in Prob. 16.

Prob. 18 Make a working drawing of the gear in Prob. 16.

Prob. 19 The same as Prob. 17 but the worm is single-threaded.

Prob. 20 A single-thread worm has a lead of $\frac{3}{4}''$. The worm gear has 36 teeth of standard form. Make a working drawing of the worm. The shaft is $1\frac{1}{4}''$ in diameter.

Prob. 21 Make a working drawing of the gear in Prob. 20. Show two views of the gear. The shaft is $1\frac{3}{4}''$ in diameter.

Cams

Prob. 22 Draw the displacement diagram, and determine the cam profile that will give a radial roller follower this motion: up 2″ in 120°, dwell 60°, down in 90°, dwell 90°. Motions are to be in a straight line and of uniform velocity. The roller is $\frac{3}{4}''$ in diameter, and the base circle is 3″ in diameter. The follower has no offset. The cam rotates clockwise.

Prob. 23 The same as Prob. 22, except that the straight-line motions are to be modified by arcs whose radii are equal to one-half the rise of the follower.

Prob. 24　The same as Prob. 22, except that the upward motion is to be harmonic, and the downward motion, parabolic.

Prob. 25　The same as Prob. 24, except that the follower is offset $1''$ to the left of the cam center line.

Prob. 26　Draw the displacement diagram, and determine the cam profile that will give a flat-faced follower this motion: dwell $30°$, up $1\frac{1}{2}''$ on a parabolic curve in $180°$, dwell $30°$, down with harmonic motion in $120°$. The base circle is $4\frac{1}{2}''$ in diameter, and the follower has no offset. After completing the cam profile, determine the necessary width of face of the follower by finding the position of the follower where the point of contact with the cam is farthest from the follower axis. The cam rotates counterclockwise.

Prob. 27　The same as Prob. 26, except that the axis of the follower is offset $1''$ to the right of the cam center line.

Prob. 28　A disc cam operates a pivoted arm roller follower similar to that shown in Fig. 971 (c). The base circle is $3\frac{1}{2}''$ in diameter, and the roller is $1''$ in diameter. In its lowest position the center of the roller is directly over the center of the cam and the straight arm is horizontal. The radius of the arm is $4''$ to the center of the roller. The arm swings up and down with the same motion as prescribed in Prob. 26, except that it swings through an angle of $15°$. The cam rotates counterclockwise. Draw the displacement diagram, and determine the cam profile.

Prob. 29　The same as Prob. 28, except that the motion is to be that given in Probs. 22 and 23.

Prob. 30　The same as Prob. 28, except that the motion is to be that given in Probs. 22 and 24.

CHAPTER 21

Pipe, Fittings, and Valves

498. Introduction. Pipe is used for transporting liquids and gases, and for structural elements such as columns, beams, rails, etc. The choice of the type of pipe is determined by the purpose for which it is to be used.

499. Kinds of Pipe. Pipe is made of aluminum, asbestos, brass, cement, clay, concrete, copper, glass, iron, lead, plastics, rubber, wood, and other materials or combinations of them. Cast-iron, steel, wrought-iron, brass, copper, and lead pipes are most commonly used for transporting water, steam, or gases.

500. Steel and Wrought-Iron Pipe. Steel and wrought-iron pipe is in common use as water, steam, oil, and gas pipe. It is available in three different weights, known as *standard, extra-strong,* and *double-extra-strong* (Fig. 974). See Appendix 10.

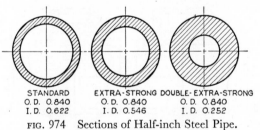

STANDARD   EXTRA-STRONG   DOUBLE-EXTRA-STRONG
O.D. 0.840   O.D. 0.840   O.D. 0.840
I.D. 0.622   I.D. 0.546   I.D. 0.252

FIG. 974   Sections of Half-inch Steel Pipe.

Standard pipe is available in sizes ranging from $\frac{1}{8}''$ to $6''$; larger sizes, up to and including $12''$, being listed as *line pipe* instead of as standard pipe. Extra-strong pipe is available in sizes ranging from $\frac{1}{8}''$ to $12''$ and double-extra-strong pipe in sizes ranging from $\frac{1}{2}''$ to $8''$.

All pipe smaller than $14''$ is listed by its nominal inside diameter which is slightly smaller than the actual inside diameter for standard pipe, and larger for extra-strong and double-extra-strong pipe (Fig. 974). All pipe larger than $12''$ is listed by its outside diameter and its wall thickness, and is known as OD pipe.

611

The smaller pipes, from $\frac{1}{8}''$ to $3''$, are butt welded; the larger pipes are lap welded or are seamless.

It is becoming customary to refer to all pipe by its actual outside diameter and its wall thickness; for example, a $2''$ standard pipe may be referred to as a $2\frac{3}{8}''$ OD pipe with a $0.218''$ wall, or simply as a $2\frac{3}{8}''$ x $0.218''$ pipe.

Steel and wrought-iron pipe is available as *black pipe* and as *galvanized pipe* and in lengths of about 20 feet and about 40 feet.

Some of the physical properties of steel pipe are shown in Appendix 10.

501. Cast-Iron Pipe. Cast-iron pipe is in general use for water pipe, gas pipe, and soil pipe.

For water and gas pipe, it is available in sizes from $3''$ to $60''$ and in standard lengths of 12 feet. The wall thickness varies according to the fluid pressure

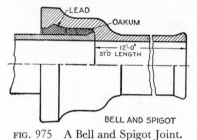

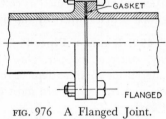

FIG. 975   A Bell and Spigot Joint.   FIG. 976   A Flanged Joint.

which the pipe is to support; this pressure may vary from 50 to 350 lb per sq in.

In general, water and gas pipes have *bell and spigot* joints (Fig. 975) but *flanged* joints (Fig. 976) and other special types of couplings (Fig. 977) are also available.

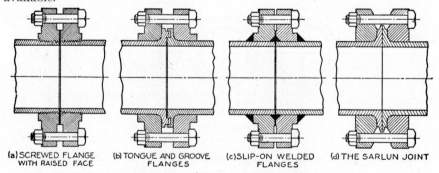

(a) SCREWED FLANGE   (b) TONGUE AND GROOVE   (c) SLIP-ON WELDED   (d) THE SARLUN JOINT
WITH RAISED FACE   FLANGES   FLANGES

FIG. 977   Special Types of Flanged Joints.

For soil pipe, it is available in sizes from $2''$ to $15''$, in standard lengths of 5 feet, as standard and as extra-heavy pipe, and as single-hub and as double-hub pipe. Soil pipe has bell and spigot joints but it is also available with threaded joints for sizes up to $12''$. Threaded soil pipe may have external threads on both ends or an external thread on one end and an internal threaded drainage hub on the other end.

502. Seamless Brass and Copper Pipe. These pipes are suitable for plumbing, including soil, waste, drain, and vent lines, as well as other services. They are available in two weights—*regular pipe* and *extra-strong pipe;* their outside diameters and their threads are the same as those of the corresponding sizes of steel and wrought-iron pipe. The dimensions of $\frac{1}{2}''$ pipe are shown in Fig. 978.

Brass pipe is available as *red brass pipe* containing about 85 per cent of copper and about 15 per cent of zinc. Copper pipe is practically pure copper. The minimum copper content is 99.9 per cent. Brass and copper pipe are available in 12-foot straight lengths.

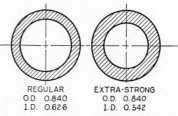

REGULAR
O.D. 0.840
I.D. 0.626

EXTRA-STRONG
O.D. 0.840
I.D. 0.542

FIG. 978   Sections of Half-inch Brass and Copper Pipe.

In an installation of brass or copper pipe, the fittings should be of brass, bronze or other copper base alloys because galvanic corrosion may result where different metals are joined in a pipe line.

Brass fittings are available in the same designs as iron fittings either like malleable iron fittings (Fig. 983) or like cast-iron fittings (Fig. 987).

503. Aluminum Pipe. Standard aluminum pipe is manufactured in lengths of 20 feet and in sizes ranging from $\frac{1}{8}''$ to 12″. The pipe sizes are duplicates of iron pipe sizes with respect to the outside and inside dimensions. Each size is available in three or four alloys and tempers; the strength of the pipe, i.e., its ability to safely sustain internal fluid pressure, varies with the grade of the pipe.

504. Copper Water Tubes. These tubes are suitable for general plumbing, including waste and vent lines as well as heating services. They are available in three weights designated, respectively, *Type K, Type L,* and *Type M.* The sizes and weights of these tubes are shown in Appendixes 11 and 12. The dimensions of half-inch tubes are shown in Fig. 979. Types K and L are available as hard and soft tubes; Type M is available only as hard tube.

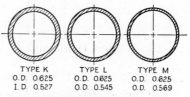

TYPE K
O.D. 0.625
I.D. 0.527

TYPE L
O.D. 0.625
O.D. 0.545

TYPE M
O.D. 0.625
O.D. 0.569

FIG. 979   Sections of Half-inch Copper Tube.

Hard tubes are more rigid than soft tubes and should be used where rigidity is important or desirable. Soft tubes can be easily bent and should be used where the tubes must be bent during assembly.

Tubes are joined to fittings by means of *flared* joints (Fig. 980) or *solder* joints (Fig. 981). There are several types of flared joints but in every case the joint is made by pressing metal against metal as in the case of a ground union.

Solder joints are known also as *capillary* joints because the annular space between the tube and the fitting is so small that the molten solder is drawn

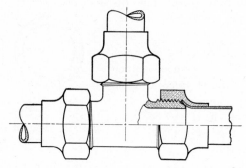

FIG. 980   A Flared Tube Fitting.

into the space by capillary action and not by gravity. In making the solder joint, the solder is introduced either through a hole in the fitting (Fig. 986) or through the outer end of the annular space (Fig. 981).

Copper water tubes can be joined to threaded pipe or fittings by means of *adapters* (Fig. 982) which are soldered to the tube and have either an internal or an external standard pipe thread for the connection.

Copper water tube is available in straight lengths of 12 and 20 feet and in coils in lengths of 60 feet.

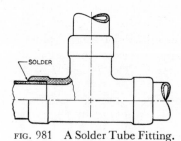

FIG. 981   A Solder Tube Fitting.

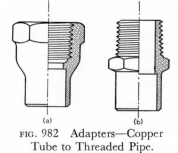

(a)   (b)

FIG. 982   Adapters—Copper Tube to Threaded Pipe.

The name *copper water tube* is derived from its early use as a water pipe; at present this tube is also used for gas, oil, and other liquids.

There is another commercial tube produced in copper which differs from the copper water tube in diameters and wall thicknesses; it is used in refrigeration, automotive and other services.

505. Pipe Fittings. *Fittings* for pipe are generally of cast iron, forged steel, malleable iron, brass, or copper, and are available in various weights corresponding to the weights of the pipe with which they are to be used. They may be threaded, soldered, beveled for welding, or provided with flanges for bolting. The principal types of fittings for screwed connections are shown in Fig. 983, those for welded connections in Fig. 984, those for solder connections in Fig. 986, and for flared copper tubes in Fig. 980.

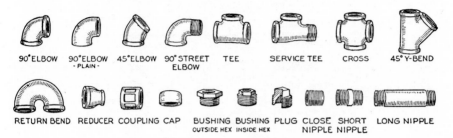

90° ELBOW   90° ELBOW   45° ELBOW   90° STREET   TEE   SERVICE TEE   CROSS   45° Y-BEND
            - PLAIN -   ELBOW

RETURN BEND   REDUCER   COUPLING   CAP   BUSHING   BUSHING   PLUG   CLOSE   SHORT   LONG NIPPLE
                                          OUTSIDE HEX   INSIDE HEX   NIPPLE   NIPPLE

FIG. 983   Screwed Fittings.

In designating the sizes of fittings, the dimensions of the run precede the dimensions of the branches, and the dimension of the larger opening precedes the dimension of the smaller opening, as shown in Fig. 987.

The threads of fittings are tapered (Fig. 771) so as to form a tight joint when a pipe is properly screwed into the fitting; however, a tight joint can be

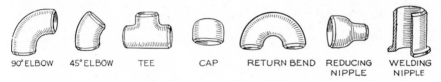

90° ELBOW   45° ELBOW   TEE   CAP   RETURN BEND   REDUCING   WELDING
                                                  NIPPLE   NIPPLE

FIG. 984   Butt-Welded Fittings.

secured more easily by applying a cementing material, commonly referred to as *dope*, to the pipe thread. When dope is used it should be applied to the external thread and not to the internal thread because when applied there a portion of the dope will be forced into the pipe where it will contaminate the liquid flowing in the pipe and form an obstruction to that flow.

506. Pipe Joints. The joints between pipes, fittings, and valves may be *screwed*, *flanged*, *welded*, or *soldered*. The American Standard pipe threads for screwed connections are shown in Fig. 771 and described in § 424.

The standard pipe threads of the American Petroleum Institute (A.P.I.) differ somewhat from the American Standard pipe threads. There are five different types of A.P.I. threads. In general, they are longer than the American Standard thread, have a greater pitch, and the tops and bottoms are truncated.

Several types of flanged connections are shown in Figs. 976 and 977. Several types of welded connections are shown in Fig. 985, and detailed information regarding welding is given in Chapter 22.

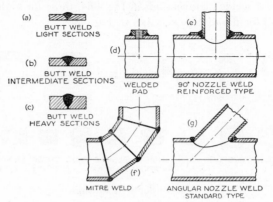

FIG. 985   Welded Joints.

507. Valves. As a means of regulating the flow of fluids in a pipe line, various types of *valves* are available. The most common types are *gate valves, globe valves, check valves, angle valves, needle valves, pressure-reducing valves,* and *safety valves.*

FIG. 986   Solder Fittings.

508. Globe Valves.—Fig. 988 (a). These valves have spherical bodies with the valve opening at right angles to the cross section of the pipe so that the

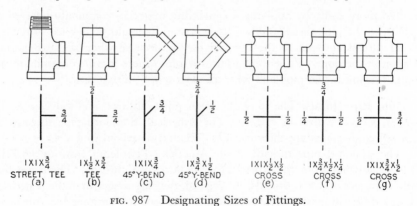

FIG. 987   Designating Sizes of Fittings.

fluid must make two right-angle turns while passing through the valve and thus suffer a considerable loss of head.

509. Check Valves.—Fig. 988 (b). These valves are used to limit the flow of fluids to one direction. The valve disc may be hinged, as shown (b), or it may be attached to a spindle so that it can rise vertically from its seat. The two types are called *swing checks* and *lift checks*, respectively.

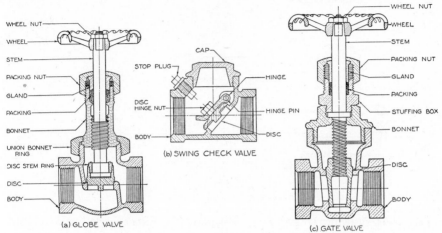

FIG. 988　Globe Valve, Check Valve, and Gate Valve.

510. Gate Valves.—Fig. 988 (c). These valves have full-size straightway openings which offer small resistance to the flow of fluids. The gate, or valve disc, may rise on the stem or the stem may rise with the gate out of the body of the valve. The disc may be solid and wedge-shaped as with the non-rising stem or it may be of two discs with parallel faces which are wedged against the seats by the adjusting wedge between the two discs. In the latter type, the discs are hung loosely on the stem and free of the seats until the adjusting wedge reaches a lug in the bottom of the valve and begins to spread the discs. This makes the parallel faces come into contact with the seats and form a tight joint.

511. Piping Symbols. To simplify the preparation of working drawings of systems of piping the set of symbols shown in Appendix 6 has been developed to represent the various pipes, fittings, and valves in common use. An application of these symbols in a piping drawing is shown in Fig. 989 (b). The symbols in Fig. 989 (b) are standard symbols (Appendix 6) except those for a cap, a plug, and a flange which are suggested as appropriate symbols for those fittings.

512. Piping Drawings. In drawings of power plants, pumping plants, refineries, heating systems, cooling systems, and plumbing systems, the piping layouts and diagrams may be made as *single-line* drawings (Figs. 989 to 992),

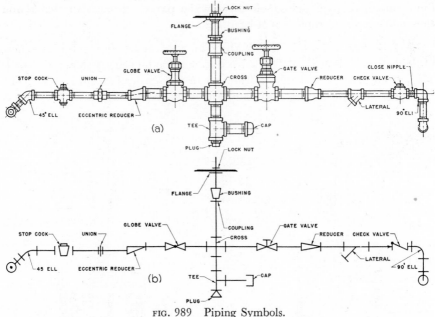

FIG. 989   Piping Symbols.

or *double-line* drawings (Figs. 989 (a), 994, and 995). Either single-line or double-line drawings may be made as multiview projections as shown in Figs. 990 (b), 994, and 996, as axonometric projections (Figs. 990 (a) and 997), or as oblique projections (Figs. 992 and 993). The oblique projection in Fig. 993 is a modi-

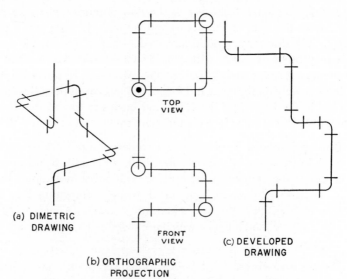

FIG. 990   A Pipe Expansion Joint—Pictorial, Multiview,
and Developed Drawing.

fied form of oblique projection generally used in representing the piping arrangement for heating systems. In these cases, the pipe mains are shown in plan and the risers in oblique projection in various directions so as to make the representation as clear as possible.

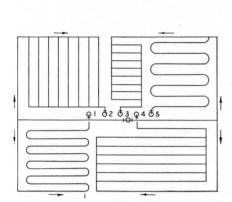

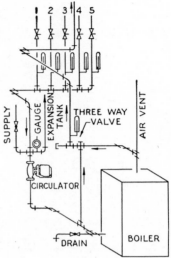

FIG. 991   Pipe Grids and Serpentine Coils for a Panel Radiant Heating System.

FIG. 992   Schematic Drawing of Piping connecting Boiler to Heating Coils.

In most installations some pipes are vertical and some are horizontal. If the vertical pipes are assumed to be revolved into the horizontal plane or the horizontal pipes revolved into the vertical plane by turning some of the fittings (Fig. 990 (c)), the entire installation can be shown in one plane. Such a drawing is a *developed piping drawing.*

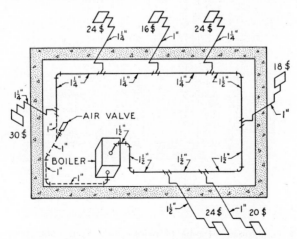

FIG. 993   A One-Pipe Steam Heating System.

513. Dimensioning. In dimensioning a piping drawing, distances should be given from center to center (c to c) of fittings or valves, and the lengths of all straight runs of pipe should be given (Fig. 995). Fully-dimensioned single-

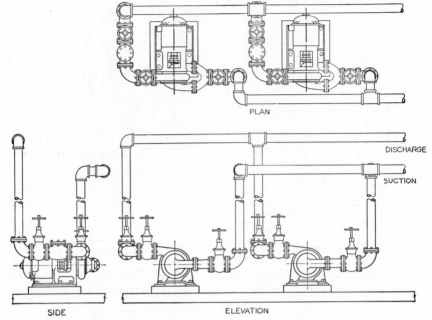

FIG. 994   A Two-Line Piping Drawing for a Pumping Plant.

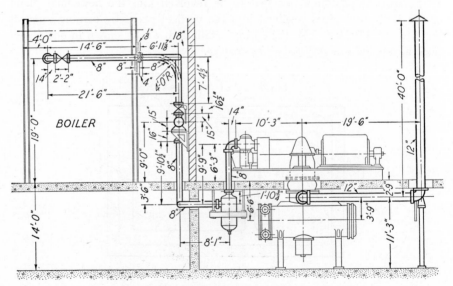

FIG. 995   A Dimensioned Piping Drawing—Side View. (Based upon a design by Crane Co., Chicago.)

line drawings need not be drawn to scale. Allowances in pipe lengths for
make-up in fittings and valves must be made in preparing a bill of materials.
All double-line drawings should have center lines if they are to be dimensioned.
The size of the pipe for each run is shown by a numeral or by a note at the
side of the pipe, with a leader when necessary.

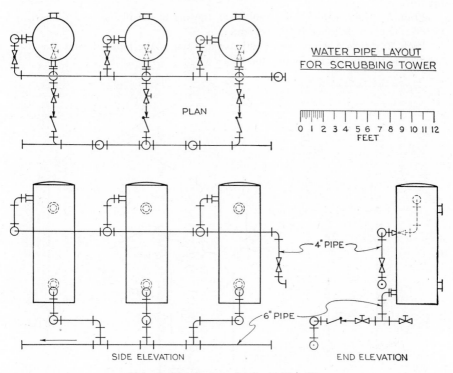

FIG. 996   A Pipe Layout for Scrubbing Towers.

PROBLEMS

514. Piping Drawing. The drawings for the first six problems are to be
three times as large as the corresponding illustrations in the book.

Prob. 1   Make a double-line drawing, similar to Fig. 989 (a) and show a union,
a 45° Y-bend, an eccentric reducer, a globe valve, a tee, a stopcock, and a 45° ell.

Prob. 2   Make a single-line drawing, similar to Fig. 989 (b) and show a 45° ell,
a union, a 45° Y-bend, an eccentric reducer, a tee, a reducer, a gate valve, a plug, a
cap, and a cross.

Prob. 3   Make a single-line drawing of the system of pipe coils and grids shown
in Fig. 991 and show, by their respective standard symbols, the elbows and tees which
must be used to connect pipes meeting at right angles if welding is not used to make
the joints.

Prob. 4 Make an oblique projection, similar to that shown in Fig. 992, of the one-pipe steam heating system shown in Fig. 993. Show the pipes by single lines, the fittings by their standard symbols, and the boiler and radiators as parallelepipeds.

Prob. 5 Make a single-line isometric drawing of the piping layout shown in Fig. 996.

Prob. 6 Make a single-line multiview drawing of the piping layout shown in Fig. 997.

Prob. 7 Make a double-line multiview drawing of the piping layout shown in Fig. 996, to a scale selected by the student.

Prob. 8 Make a double-line multiview drawing of the piping layout shown in Fig. 997, to a scale selected by the student.

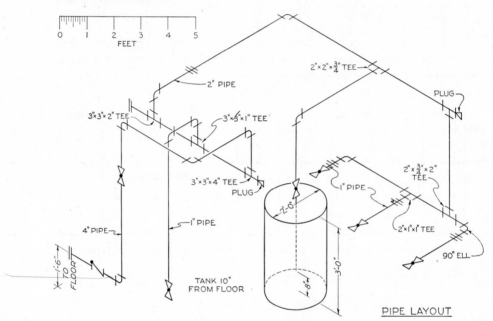

FIG. 997   Isometric Pipe Layout.

CHAPTER 22

Welding

515. Introduction. Two of the principal methods of welding are the oxy-acetylene method, generally known as gas welding, and the electric-arc method, generally known as arc welding.

In gas welding, the flame produced by burning acetylene with oxygen is used since its temperature is high enough to melt metals. If a sheet of metal is to be cut with a gas flame, the metal is heated with an oxyacetylene flame to the ignition temperature, and the metal is then burned away with a stream of oxygen.

Gas welding had its beginning in 1895 when the French chemist, Le Chatelier, discovered that the combustion of acetylene with oxygen produced a flame with a very high temperature. This discovery was soon followed by the development of suitable methods of producing and transporting oxygen and acetylene, and by the construction of suitable torches and welding rods. In arc welding, the heat of an electric arc is used to fuse the metals which are to be welded or cut. The first arc welding was done in 1881 by De Meritens in France. In 1887 Berardos was granted a patent on arc welding in Russia, and in 1892 C. L. Coffin was granted a patent in the United States on a method of heating metals by means of an electric arc. For a number of years the development of arc welding was very slow. During the first world war the Navy used the system to a limited extent for repairing machinery.

Since that time, as the result of intensive research, basic improvements have been made in the manufacture of electrodes and in the mechanical equipment used for welding, so that now arc and gas welding are among the most important and most common operations in industry. Welding is used not only for the repair and construction of machinery, but has practically replaced riveting in the construction of pipe lines and containers for liquids and gases, and is being used to a limited extent in the erection of structural steel frames (Fig. 998).

FIG. 998   Welded Steel Frame of the Hermann
Professional Building, Houston, Texas.

516. Classification of Welding Processes. Welding processes are divided by groups into ARC WELDING, GAS WELDING, RESISTANCE WELDING, THERMIT WELDING, BRAZING, INDUCTION WELDING, and FLOW WELDING. Each of these groups comprises one or more welding processes; for example, RESISTANCE WELDING includes *spot welding*, *seam welding*, *projection welding*, *flash welding*, *upset welding*, and *percussion welding*.

517. Types of Joints. The five basic types of welded joints (**Fig. 999**) are (1) *butt*, (2) *corner*, (3) *tee*, (4) *lap*, and (5) *edge*.

(A) BUTT JOINT   (B) CORNER JOINT   (C) TEE JOINT   (D) LAP JOINT   (E) EDGE JOINT

FIG. 999   The Basic Types of Welded Joints.

518. Types of Welds. The four basic types of arc and gas welds (Fig. 1000) are *bead*, *fillet*, *plug* or *slot*, and *groove*. The groove welds are subdivided as *square*, *V*, *bevel*, *U*, and *J*.

The four basic resistance welds (Fig. 1001) are *spot, projection, seam,* and *flash* or *upset.*

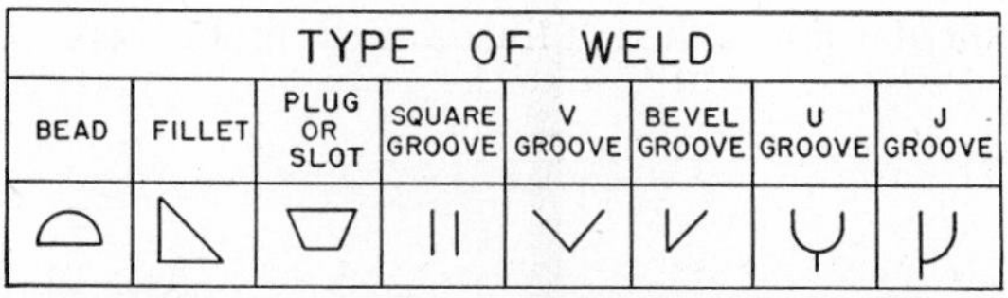

TYPE OF WELD							
BEAD	FILLET	PLUG OR SLOT	SQUARE GROOVE	V GROOVE	BEVEL GROOVE	U GROOVE	J GROOVE
⌒	◣	▽	‖	∨	⌐	⋃	⌡

FIG. 1000 The Basic Arc and Gas Weld Symbols.

519. Welding Drawing. Since welding is used so extensively and for so large a variety of purposes it is essential to have an accurate method of showing, on the working drawings for machines or structures, the exact types and sizes of the welds which are desired by the designer.

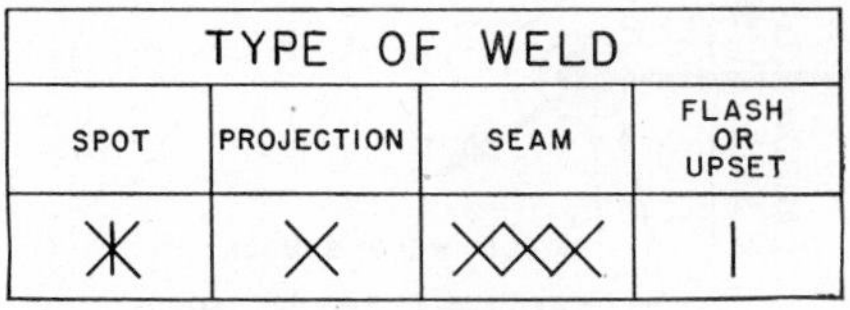

TYPE OF WELD			
SPOT	PROJECTION	SEAM	FLASH OR UPSET
✳	✕	✕✕✕	│

FIG. 1001 The Basic Resistance Weld Symbols.

To make this possible, a system of welding symbols has been developed by the Committee on Symbols of the American Welding Society, and recommended by that committee for adoption as standard by the American Standards Association as a revision of American Standards Z 32.1—1942.

The recommended symbols were published in 1947 by the American Welding Society, 33 West 39th Street, New York 18, N. Y. in a booklet entitled *Standard Welding Symbols* and priced at 50 cents.

520. Welding Symbols. The principal basic directions and explanations for the use of welding symbols on working drawings, recommended in "Standard Welding Symbols," are presented in the following paragraphs.

1. For every welded joint an arrow (Fig. 1002) is drawn, pointing to the joint, and every element of the symbol has a standard location with reference to the arrow.

2. The arrow has a shaft and a barb, and it may have a tail.

3. The shaft is the reference line along which the type and the size of the weld are shown.

4. All welded joints (Fig. 999) have two edges or sides; the side toward which the arrow points is called the *arrow side* of the joint; the opposite side is called the *other side*. Formerly the *arrow side* was called the *near side* and the *other side* was called the *far side*. These designations have been superseded because, when a joint is shown in section, both sides of the joint are equally distant from the reader and the words "near" and "far" are meaningless.

5. When the weld is on the *arrow* side of the joint, the weld symbol is placed below the reference line (Fig. 1004–4).

6. When the weld is on the *other* side of the joint, the weld symbol is placed above the reference line (Fig. 1004–1).

7. When the weld is on both sides of the joint, the weld symbols are placed on both sides of the reference line (Fig. 1004–2).

8. When a weld symbol has a line which is perpendicular to the reference line, the perpendicular line is the left line of the symbol (Figs. 1004–1, 2 and 4).

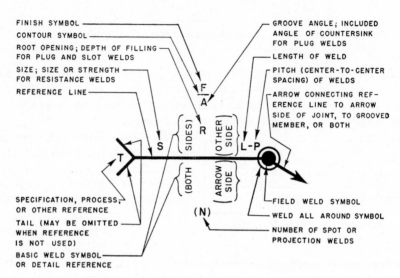

FINISH SYMBOL

CONTOUR SYMBOL

ROOT OPENING; DEPTH OF FILLING FOR PLUG AND SLOT WELDS

SIZE; SIZE OR STRENGTH FOR RESISTANCE WELDS

REFERENCE LINE

GROOVE ANGLE; INCLUDED ANGLE OF COUNTERSINK FOR PLUG WELDS

LENGTH OF WELD

PITCH (CENTER-TO-CENTER SPACING) OF WELDS

ARROW CONNECTING REF- ERENCE LINE TO ARROW SIDE OF JOINT, TO GROOVED MEMBER, OR BOTH

SPECIFICATION, PROCESS, OR OTHER REFERENCE

TAIL (MAY BE OMITTED WHEN REFERENCE IS NOT USED)

BASIC WELD SYMBOL OR DETAIL REFERENCE

FIELD WELD SYMBOL

WELD ALL AROUND SYMBOL

NUMBER OF SPOT OR PROJECTION WELDS

FIG. 1002   The Standard Locations of the Elements of a Welding Symbol.

9. When a joint has more than one weld, a symbol is shown for each weld (Fig. 1004–2).

10. Dimensions of fillet welds are shown on the same side of the reference line as the weld symbol; the size of the fillet is shown on the left and the length,

WELD ALL AROUND	FIELD WELD	FLUSH CONTOUR	CONVEX CONTOUR
◯	●	—	⌒

FIG. 1003   Supplementary Symbols.

on the right of the symbol (Figs. 1008– 19, 20 and 22). When the two legs of a fillet weld are unequal, both dimensions are shown in parenthesis on the left of the weld symbol (Fig. 1009–23).

11. When a bevel or J-groove weld symbol is used, the shaft has a definite break toward the member which is to be chamfered (Fig. 1005–6).

12. Spot and seam weld symbols are placed directly on the drawings at the locations of the desired welds (Figs. 1006–12 and 13).

13. When a specification, a process, or other reference is to be used with a welding symbol, a tail is added to the arrow and the reference is placed in the tail (Figs. 1007–15 and 16).

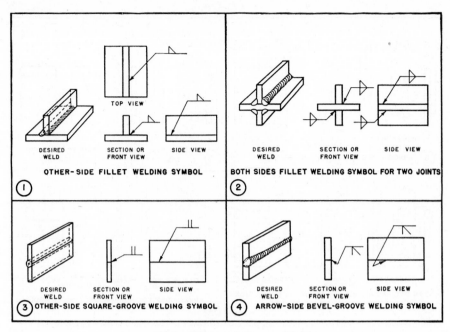

FIG. 1004   Fillet and Groove Welds.

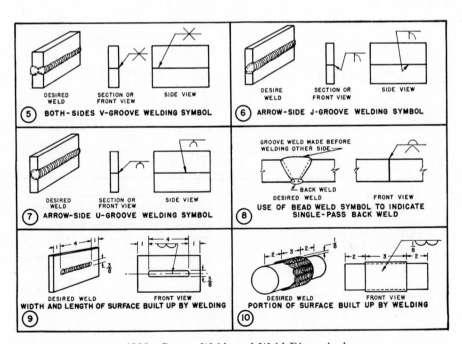

FIG. 1005   Groove Welds and Weld Dimensioning.

627

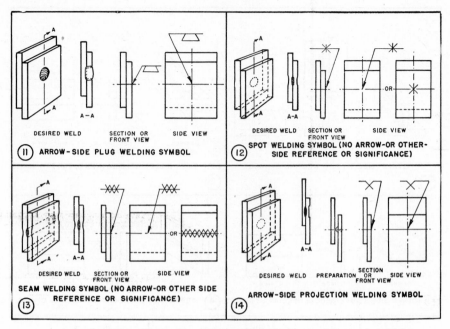

FIG. 1006 Plug Welds, Spot Welds, Seam Welds, and Projection Welds.

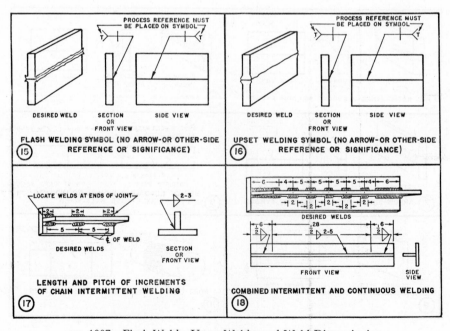

FIG. 1007 Flash Welds, Upset Welds, and Weld Dimensioning.

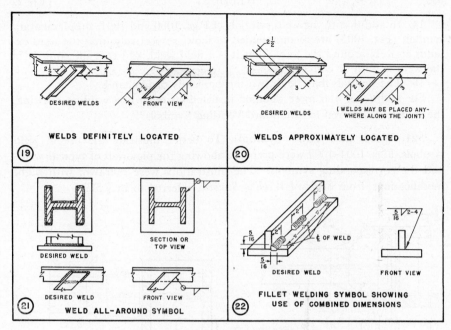

FIG. 1008   Weld Dimensioning.

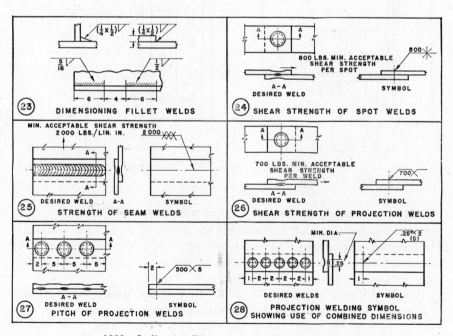

FIG. 1009   Indicating Dimensions and Strengths of Welds.

14. In addition to the weld symbols of Figs. 1000 and 1001, supplementary symbols (Fig. 1003) are recommended to show, respectively, that the weld extends entirely around the joint, that it is a field weld, and that the contour of the weld is flush or convex.

15. The symbols may be drawn mechanically or freehand.

For additional and more detailed instructions regarding welding drawing, the student is referred to "Standard Welding Symbols."

521. Welds and Their Symbols. To better illustrate the use of weld symbols, Figs. 1004–1009 were prepared showing the pictorials of typical welds and the corresponding symbols. The illustrations were redrawn, with slight modifications, from *Standard Welding Symbols*, referred to in § 519.

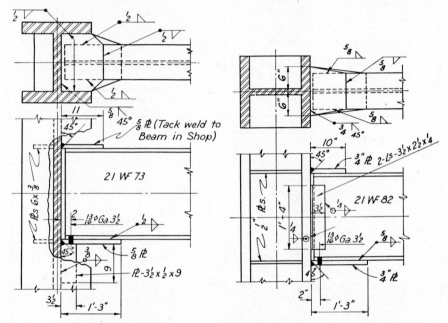

FIG. 1010   Beam Welded to   FIG. 1011   Beam Welded to Face of Column.
Web of Column.

522. Illustrations. Methods of welding beams to columns and preparing working drawings for such connections are shown in Figs. 1010 and 1011. These two detail drawings were redrawn from working drawings prepared by Consolidated Steel Corporation of Texas for the structural frame of the Hermann Professional Building (Fig. 998).

A welded truss is shown in Fig. 1012. In a welded truss it may be easier to place the members so that their center-of-gravity axes coincide with the working lines of the truss than is the case in a riveted truss. The student should compare the welded truss of Fig. 1012 with the riveted truss of Fig. 1088.

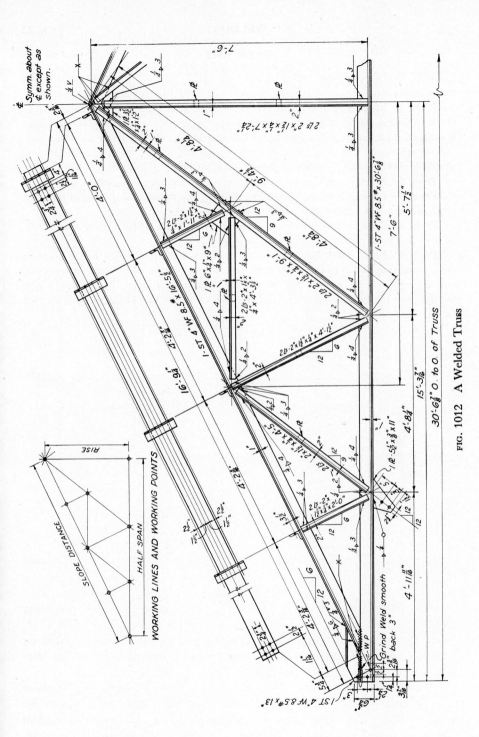

FIG. 1012 A Welded Truss

631

PROBLEMS

523. Welding Drawing. The following problems are given to familiarize the student with the simple welding symbols used in structural drawing.

Prob. 1 Make a half-size drawing of the joint at the center of the lower chord of the truss (Fig. 1012) where the chord is supported by two vertical angles; the chord is a structural tee, cut from an 8 x $5\frac{1}{4}$—17 lb wide-flange shape. Draw the front view and the side view, and show the working lines, the two angles, the structural tee, and all visible welds; draw the welds as shown in Fig. 1012.

Prob. 2 Make an oblique or an axonometric projection of the subject of Prob. 1.

Prob. 3 Draw a half-size front view, showing the welds, of any joint of the truss (Fig. 1012) in which three or four members meet.

Prob. 4 Draw a half-size front view, top view, and left-side view of the end joint of the truss; show the visible welds in each view.

Prob. 5 Make a drawing, three times as large as the illustration in the book, of the construction shown in Fig. 1010 or in Fig. 1011; draw the front view, the top view, and the right-side view, and show all visible welds in each view. The hole shown in the flange of the beam represents two holes, one on either side of the web, to be used for erection bolts.

Shading

524. Introduction. The effect of light can be utilized advantageously in describing the shapes of objects and in the finish and embellishment of such drawings as display drawings, Patent Office drawings (Chapter 24), etc. Ordinary working drawings are not usually shaded.

Figure 1013 illustrates the difference in appearance and clearness produced by the use of shade-lines. The front view of the block at (a) conveys no idea as to whether the pins in the holes are flush with the front face of the block, are countersunk, or project and form a boss on the front face. The front view at (b) shows, by the shade-lines, that one pin is flush with the front face of the block, one is countersunk, and the other projects in front of the face. The sharpness, relief, and realistic effect produced by the shading are obvious.

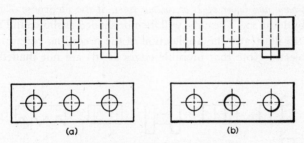

(a)   (b)

FIG. 1013   Effect of Shade Lines.

The conventional source of light for shading drawings is back of, above, and to the left of the draftsman. The rays of light are assumed to be parallel to a diagonal of a cube whose *faces* are parallel to the planes of projection (§ 184); therefore the conventional light rays make angles with the coordinate planes whose tangents are $1/\sqrt{2}$, and the projections of the rays make angles of 45° with the coordinate axes.

There are two systems in use for shading drawings—(a) *shade lines*, and (b) *surface shading*.

525. Shade Lines. Shade lines are the lines which separate illuminated faces or surfaces from those which are not illuminated. Usually the upper, front, and left-hand faces of an object are assumed to receive light from the conventional source, and are illuminated; while the lower, back, and right-hand faces are not illuminated; therefore the right-hand and lower edges of an object are ordinarily the shade lines. By this system of shading, the shade lines are made two or three times as wide as the other object lines of the drawing.

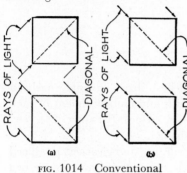

FIG. 1014   Conventional Rays of Light.

Figure 1014 (a) shows the top and front views of a cube, with conventional rays of light parallel to the dotted diagonal of the cube. It is obvious that these rays of light illuminate only the top, front, and left-hand faces of the cube, and therefore three vertical and three horizontal edges separate illuminated from non-illuminated faces. Two of these edges in the front and two others in the top view are *shade lines* and are therefore made wider than the other object lines of the cube.

It is apparent from Fig. 1014 (a), according to the rule stated above, that the right-hand and lower edges of the front view, and the right-hand and upper edges of the top view are shade lines. To simplify the method of shading, it is common practice to *shade all views as if they were front views, to shade lines which separate illuminated surfaces from those which are not illuminated, and to shade the right-hand and lower edges or contour lines*, if the clearness of the drawing is enhanced by doing so. The cube will then be shaded as shown in Fig. 1014 (b).

Figure 1015 illustrates the application of the preceding rule to the shading of various objects. Note that invisible edges at (d) are not shaded.

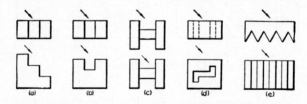

FIG. 1015   Application of Shading.

Surfaces which are parallel to conventional rays of light (Fig. 1016) are regarded as illuminated surfaces.

When two surfaces, inclined to the plane of projection, are located so that one surface is illuminated and the other is not, the edge of the dihedral angle formed by those surfaces is a shade line. If there are a series of such surfaces, all edges of the resulting angles are shade lines. The drawing will be clearer, however, if only alternate edges are shaded, as in Fig. 1015 (e).

Some draftsmen shade the edges of re-entrant dihedral angles, as illustrated in Fig. 1015 (e). Other draftsmen shade only the edges of projecting dihedral angles.

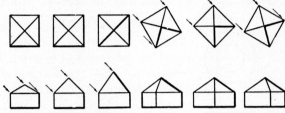

FIG. 1016   Surfaces Parallel to Rays of Light.

Shade lines generally do not add anything to the clearness of a pictorial view of an object but they do improve the appearance of the drawing by adding variety and relief. The method of determining the shade lines on a pictorial view is the same as that explained above.

Figure 1017 shows the shade lines on a cube in isometric and in oblique projection according to this method; however, some draftsmen violate this convention for isometric and shade the edges that intersect at the nearest corner (Fig. 1018).

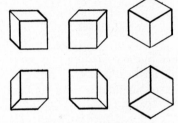

FIG. 1017   Shade Lines in Pictorial Drawings.

Figure 1019 shows the shade lines on cylindrical solids. The circles in the top views and in the end view are shade lines only half-way around, the circle of the hole being shaded on the opposite side from that of the outer surface of the cylinder.

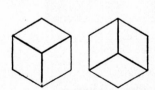

FIG. 1018   Conventional Shading of Isometric Drawings.

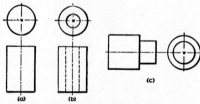

FIG. 1019   Shade Lines on Cylinders.

The shading of circles is done by shifting the center of the compass along a 45° line and drawing a second semicircle with the same radius, as shown.

The additional width necessary to produce a shade line should be applied on the outside of the surface shaded; therefore, in cases like those shown in Fig. 1019 (c), the same center is used for both shade arcs.

Dimension lines on shaded drawings should *read to the original edge of a surface before the shading was added*, as shown at (a), Fig. 1020, and not to the outer edge after the shading is added. It should also be noted that the invisible lines of the hollow cylinder (b) are projected from the original circle in the top view *before the shading was added*, and not from the added shade circle.

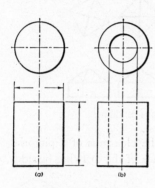

526. Surface Shading. Surface shading is a means of utilizing further the effect of light in describing the shapes of objects. The conventional source of light and the direction of the rays are the same as those described above for shade lines.

A surface of an object appears lighter when the rays of light strike it at a large angle than when they strike at a small angle; therefore, the relative amount of shading applied to the surfaces of objects should depend upon the angle at which the conventional rays of light strike those surfaces. It is

FIG. 1020   Dimensions on Shade Lines.

a general rule that, nearest the eye, plane surfaces in the light are lightest, and plane surfaces in the dark are darkest.

Surface shading may be produced by a wash or tint applied with a brush, or air-brush, or by a series of individual lines drawn with pen or pencil. The latter method is most common in technical drawing.

The relative amount of shade on different surfaces, or the varying amount on a single surface, can be produced in three ways, as illustrated in Fig. 1021.

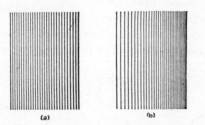

FIG. 1021   Methods of Surface Shading.

(a) By varying the width of the individual lines.
(b) By varying the distance between the individual lines.
(c) By a combination of the first and second methods.

Figure 1022 shows different methods of applying surface shading on some common geometric solids. The gradual blending of the shade on these surfaces requires skill and practice.

When surface shading is used on a drawing, the shade lines (§ 525) should be omitted unless the clearness of the drawing is enhanced by their use. The surface shading on a plane surface, inclined to the plane of projection, should

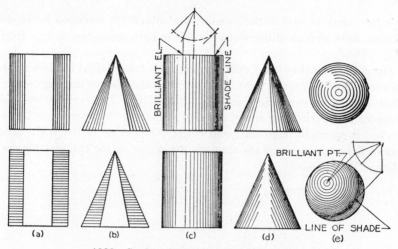

FIG. 1022 Surface Shading on Geometric Solids.

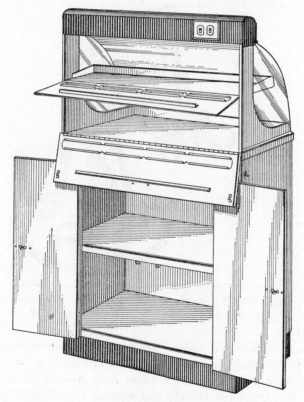

FIG. 1023 Surface Shading Applied to Pictorial Drawing
of Display Case.

grade from dark to light in the receding direction if the surface is in the shade, and from light to dark if the surface is in the light, as shown in Fig. 1022 (a) and (b), (top).

The surface shading on a cylinder and on a cone should be darkest at the element where the rays of light are tangent to the surface and lightest at the *brilliant element*, as shown in Fig. 1022 (c) and (d). The brilliant element of a cylinder is the one from which the rays of light are reflected directly to the observer; it passes through the point where the bisector of the angle between a ray of light and a visual ray through the center of the cylinder pierces the surface of the cylinder.

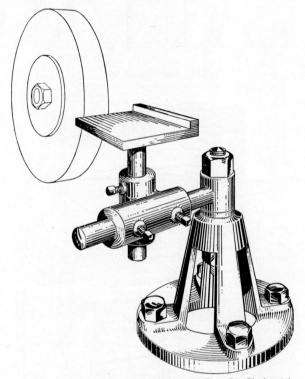

(Reproduced from *A Service Bulletin* of A. M. Byers Co., Pittsburgh.)

FIG. 1024   A Line-Shaded Drawing of an Adjustable
Support for Grinding Pipe-Thread Chasers.

The surface shading of a sphere should be darkest where the rays of light are tangent to the sphere (on the shade line) and lightest at the *brilliant point*. The brilliant point in the surface of a sphere is the point in which the bisector of the angle between a ray of light and a visual ray, through the center of the sphere, pierces the surface of the sphere. The constructions for the determination of the brilliant element and the element of shade on the cylinder, and

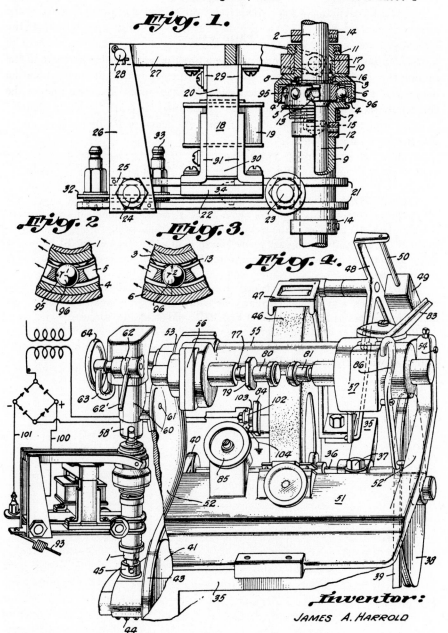

Fig. 1.

Fig. 2. *Fig. 3.*

Fig. 4.

Inventor:

JAMES A. HARROLD

FIG. 1025 A Well Executed Patent Drawing.

639

the brilliant point and the line of shade on the surface of the sphere are shown in (c) and (e), respectively, of Fig. 1022.

Line shading is used extensively in technical illustrations with very satisfactory results as shown in Figs. 1023, 1024, and 1025. See also Figs. 1026–1031.

PROBLEMS

527. Shading. The following problems are given to afford practice in determining the shade lines of objects and in blending gradually the surface shading on curved surfaces. The italicized rules (§ 525) apply to shade lines. The correct methods of surface shading are explained in § 526. Surface shading requires much care and practice. Use Size A sheets for Problems 1, 3, and 4 and layout B3 for Problem 2.

Prob. 1   Draw the two views of Fig. 575 (Prob. 9). Shade the shade lines in both views, making them about twice as heavy as the other object lines. Omit the dimensions.

Prob. 2   Draw the two views of Fig. 687 and shade as in Prob. 1.

Prob. 3   Draw three rectangles about 2″ × 3″ each, the long sides being horizontal. Shade the surfaces of the rectangles similar to those of Fig. 1021, blending the shade of (a) gradually, from dark at the top to light at the bottom, of (b) from dark at the bottom to light at the top, and of (c) from dark at the center to light at the top and bottom.

Prob. 4   Draw a right hexagonal prism, a right hexagonal pyramid, a right circular cylinder, and a right circular cone with the axes horizontal, similar to and about three times as large as those of Fig. 1022, and shade the surfaces.

Prob. 5   Select a part or an assembly from Figs. 575, 901, 904, 905, 907, 908, or 912; draw it in oblique or axonometric projection, and shade it in a manner similar to that shown in Figs. 1023 and 1024.

CHAPTER 24

Patent Drawing

528. Introduction. In view of the importance of properly executed drawings, it is essential that all drawings be mechanically correct and constitute complete illustrations of every feature of the invention claimed. The strict requirements of the Patent Office in this respect serve to facilitate the examination of applications and the interpretation of patents issued thereon.

To aid draftsmen in the preparation of drawings for submission in patent applications, the *Guide for Patent Draftsmen* was prepared and can be obtained from the Commissioner of Patents, Washington, D. C., at a cost of 75 cents per copy. The following instructions and illustrations were reproduced from that publication.

529. Requirements for Patent Drawings. The applicant for patent is required by statute to furnish a drawing of his invention whenever the nature of the case admits of it; this drawing must be filed with the application.

The drawing must either be signed by the applicant in person or have the name of the applicant placed thereon followed by the signature of the attorney or agent as such.

The drawing must show every feature of the invention covered by the claims, and the figures should be consecutively numbered if possible. When the invention consists of an improvement on an old machine the drawing must when possible exhibit, in one or more views, the improved portion itself, disconnected from the old structure, and also in another view, so much only of the old structure as will suffice to show the connection of the invention therewith.

The complete drawing is printed and published when the patent issues, and a copy is attached to the patent. This work is done by the photolithographic process, the sheets of drawings being reduced to a size of about 6 by $9\frac{1}{2}$ inches. In addition, a reduction of a selected portion of each drawing is published in the Official Gazette. It is therefore necessary for these and other reasons that the character of each drawing be brought as nearly as possible to a uniform standard of execution and excellence, suited to the requirements of the reproduction process and of the use of the drawings, to give the best results in the interests of inventors, of the Office, and of the public. The following regulations with respect to drawings are accordingly prescribed:

(a) *Paper and Ink.*—Drawings must be made upon pure white paper of a thickness corresponding to two-ply or three-ply Bristol board. The surface of the paper must be calendered and smooth and of a quality which will permit erasure and correction. India ink alone must be used for pen drawings to secure perfectly black solid lines.

(b) *Size of sheet and margins.*—The size of a sheet on which a drawing is made must be exactly 10 by 15 inches. One inch from its edges a single marginal line is to be drawn, leaving the "sight" precisely 8 by 13 inches. Within this margin all work and signatures must be included. One of the shorter sides of the sheet is regarded as its top, and, measuring downwardly from the marginal line, a space of not less than $1\frac{1}{4}$ inches is to be left blank for the heading of title, name, number, and date, which will be applied subsequently by the Office in a uniform style.

(c) *Character of lines.*—All drawings must be made with drafting instruments or by a photolithographic process which will give them satisfactory reproduction characteristics. Every line and letter (signatures included) must be absolutely black. This direction applies to all lines however fine, to shading, and to lines representing cut surfaces in sectional views. All lines must be clean, sharp, and solid, and fine or crowded lines should be avoided. Solid black should not be used for sectional or surface shading. Free-hand work should be avoided wherever it is possible to do so.

(d) *Hatching and shading.*—Hatching should be made by oblique parallel lines, which may be about one-twentieth inch apart, and should follow the chart for draftsmen in the Appendix.

Heavy lines on the shade side of objects should be used except where they tend to thicken the work and obscure reference characters. The light is supposed to come from the upper left hand corner at an angle of 45°. Surface delineations should be shown by proper shading, which should be open.

(e) *Scale.*—The scale to which a drawing is made ought to be large enough to show the mechanism without crowding when the drawing is reduced in reproduction and views of portions of the mechanism on a larger scale should be used when necessary to show details clearly; two or more sheets should be used if one does not give sufficient room to accomplish this end, but the number of sheets should not be more than is necessary.

(f) *Reference characters.*—The different views should be consecutively numbered figures. Reference numerals (and letters, but numerals are preferred) must be plain, legible and carefully formed, and not be encircled. They should, if possible, measure at least one-eighth of an inch in height so that they may bear reduction to one-twenty-fourth of an inch; and they may be slightly larger when there is sufficient room. They must not be so placed in the close and complex parts of the drawing as to interfere with a thorough comprehension of the same, and therefore should rarely cross or mingle with the lines. When necessarily grouped around a certain part, they should be placed at a little distance, at the closest point where there is available space, and connected by lines with the parts to which they refer. They should not be placed upon hatched or shaded surfaces but when difficult to avoid this, a blank space must be left in the hatching or shading where the character occurs so that it shall appear perfectly distinct and separate from the work. The same part of an invention appearing in more than one view of the drawing must always be designated by the same character, and the same character must never be used to designate different parts.

(g) *Location of signature and names.*—The signature of the applicant, or the name of the applicant and signature of the attorney or agent, should be placed in the lower right hand corner of each sheet within the marginal line. The title of the invention should be written with pencil on the back of the sheet.

(h) *Arrangement of views.*—All views on the same sheet must stand in the same direction and should, if possible, stand so that they can be read with the sheet held in an upright position. If views longer than the width of the sheet are necessary for the clearest illustration of the invention, the sheet may be turned on its side. The space for a heading must then be reserved at the right and the signatures placed at the left, occupying the same space and position on the sheet as in the upright views and being horizontal when the sheet is held in an upright position. One figure must not be placed upon another or within the outline of another.

(i) *Figure for Official Gazette.*—The drawing should, as far as possible, be so planned that one of the views will be suitable for publication in the Official Gazette as the illustration of the invention.

(j) *Transmission of drawings.*—Drawings transmitted to the Office should be sent flat, protected by a sheet of heavy binder's board, or may be rolled for transmission in a suitable mailing tube; but must never be folded. If received creased or mutilated, new drawings will be required.

(k) *Extraneous matter.*—An agent's or attorney's stamp, or address, or other extraneous matter, will not be permitted upon the face of a drawing, within or without the marginal line.

The requirements of the foregoing rule relating to drawings will be strictly enforced. A drawing not executed in conformity thereto may be admitted for purpose of examination, but in such case the drawing must be corrected or a new one furnished, as required. The necessary corrections will be made by the Office upon applicant's request and at his expense.

Applicants are advised to employ competent draftsmen to make their drawings.

The Office may furnish the drawings at cost (with a minimum charge) as promptly as its draftsmen can make them, for applicants who can not otherwise conveniently procure them.

The drawings upon which the original patent was issued may be used in reissue applications if no changes whatsoever are to be made in the drawings.

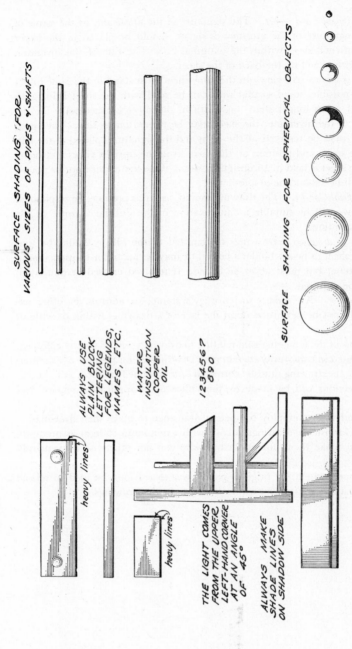

FIG. 1026 Line Shading for Patent Drawings.

Surface delineations should be shown by proper shading. A single heavy line on the shadow side is sufficient shadow for small pipes, rods, and shafts. The amount of shading necessary depends on the diameter of the shaft, etc. When more than one shade line is used on cylindrical surfaces, the shading is blended from the second line; the outer line is a light line. This rule on shading applies to spherical as well as to cylindrical objects.

Heavy lines should be placed on the shade sides of objects because the light is assumed to come from the upper left hand corner at an angle of 45°. These heavy lines should have the same weight throughout the various views on the drawing. All lines should be clear and sharp so that they will reproduce properly.

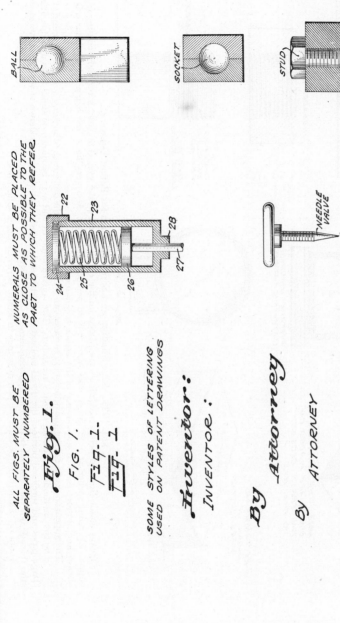

FIG. 1027 Lettering for Patent Drawings.

The different views should be consecutively numbered. Letters and figures of reference must be carefully formed. Several types of lettering and figure marks are shown; however, the draftsman may use any style of lettering he may choose.

Descriptive matter is not permitted on patent drawings. Legends may be applied when necessary, but only plain black lettering should be used.

Reference characters should be placed at a short distance from the parts to which they refer. They should be connected with these parts by a short lead line, never by a long lead line. When necessary, blank spaces must be left on shaded and sectioned areas for applying the numerals.

Convex and concave surfaces are defined by the shading shown in the illustration of the ball and socket.

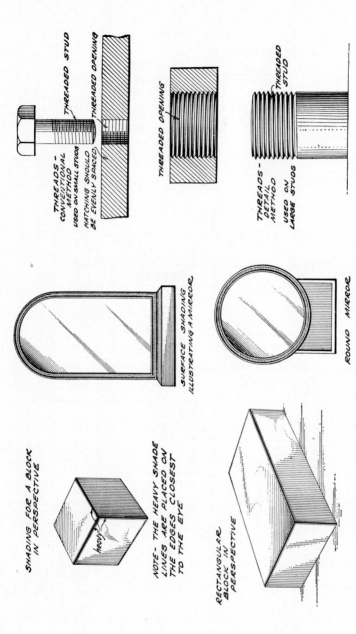

THREADED STUD

THREADS -
CONVENTIONAL
METHOD
USED ON SMALL STUDS

HATCHING SHOULD
BE EVENLY SPACED

THREADED OPENING

THREADED OPENING

THREADED STUD

THREADS -
DETAIL
METHOD
USED ON
LARGE STUDS

SHADING FOR A BLOCK
IN PERSPECTIVE

NOTE- THE HEAVY SHADE
LINES ARE PLACED ON
THE EDGES CLOSEST
TO THE EYE

heavy

SURFACE SHADING
ILLUSTRATING A MIRROR

ROUND MIRROR

RECTANGULAR
BLOCK IN
PERSPECTIVE

FIG. 1028   Line Shading and Screw Threads for Patent Drawings.

Heavy shade lines on perspective views are placed on the edges closest to the eye. The rule of the light coming from the upper left hand corner at a 45° angle does not apply to perspective views. If a very light line is placed on either side of the heavy line, a more finished appearance of the article is obtained.

The appearance of a mirror and other shiny surfaces can be illustrated by the oblique shading shown on the two central views.

The two methods of showing threads are shown. The conventional thread may be shown on small bolts and openings. On large pipes and threaded portions the detail method should be used. Solid black shading as shown is very effective in showing the threads but care should be used in applying same.

India ink alone must be used for pen drawings to secure perfectly black solid lines.

646

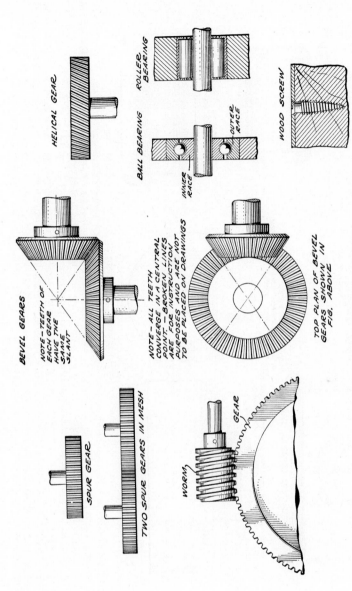

FIG. 1029 Gears and Bearings in Patent Drawings.

Particular care must be given to the correct spacing between the gear teeth and also the weight of the shade lines used. Both must be correctly shown to obtain the desired effect.

The roller bearing is clearly disclosed by the use of the conventional cylindrical shading. The fanciful black shading shown on the ball bearing is very effective in bringing out the idea of an object being shiny as well as round.

Wood graining should be used sparingly on parts of wood in section. Excessive wood graining is objectionable as it blurs the view and is very confusing.

647

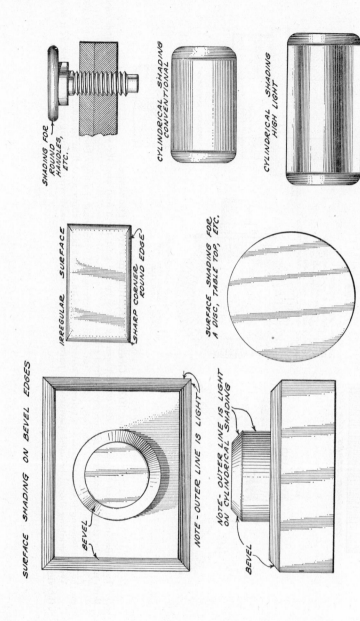

FIG. 1030 Shading Inclined and Curved Surfaces in Patent Drawings.

Inclined surfaces are distinguished from flat surfaces by using the shading shown on the two illustrations. The outer line in the lower plane is always a light line. This gives a slanting effect to the surface as the heavy line is placed on the edge of the upper plane. The surface shading is blended from this heavy line to give the desired appearance. Flat, shiny surfaces may be shown as illustrated in the circular figure.

Highlight shading as shown in the last figure is very effective in creating a shiny appearance on a cylindrical surface. Conventional surface shading should be used by the draftsman until he has obtained enough experience to attempt the more involved types of shading.

The scale to which a drawing is made ought to be large enough to show the mechanism without crowding.

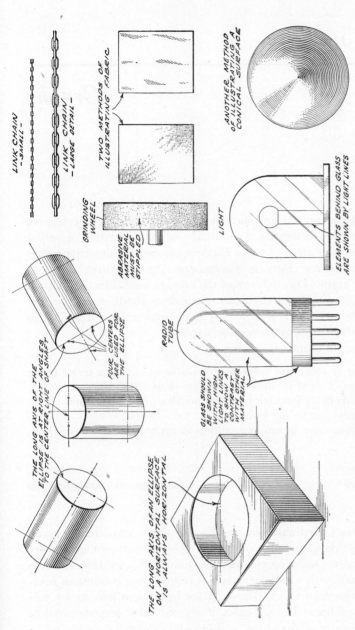

FIG. 1031 Shading Perspective and Other Surfaces in Patent Drawings.

The four figures in perspective clearly explain the fundamental rules of perspective. Center lines are not added on patent drawings. Those above are for instruction purposes only.

Different types of shading are used when it is desired to show a contrast between materials as shown in the illustrations for the radio tube.

The method of showing link chains is determined by the size of the view.

Abrasive material must be stippled as shown in the illustration of the grinding wheel. Irregular surfaces and objects that are impossible to show up properly with line shading must be stippled to bring out the desired effect.

Freehand shading should be used to designate fabric material.

All elements behind glass should be shown in light lines. The light oblique shade lines across the glass give the desired effect.

649

CHAPTER 25

Graphs

530. Graphs. A pictorial or graphical description is more comprehensive and more impressive than a numerical tabulation or than a written or verbal description; hence graphs afford a more effective means of comparing values and expressing mathematical relations. For example, the bar chart (Fig. 1038) and the rectangular graph (Fig. 1039) show the average annual income earned by various groups of professional engineers much more vividly than does the numerical tabulation in Table I, p. 657. These pictorial or graphical descriptions are variously termed *graphs* or *charts* or *diagrams*.

The principal uses of graphical charts are:

(1) To determine or to show the value of a variable quantity in terms of, or with reference to, a fixed or known quantity (Figs. 1032-1035).
(2) To aid in the study of technical or financial problems (Figs. 1036 and 1037).
(3) To convey information to the public (Figs. 1038-1043).
(4) To serve the engineer or technician as tools in his professional work (Figs. 1044-1050).

The principal types of charts are: *rectangular, logarithmic, semilogarithmic, composite, bar, area, circular* or *pie, polar, trilinear, organization,* and *nomographs* or *alignment* charts.

531. Rectangular Coordinate Graphs. For plotting mathematical curves, recording engineering data, and for many other technical purposes, graphs are frequently drawn with the use of rectangular coordinates. Such graphical charts have a distinct advantage over tabular charts in representing continuous functions because such functions will be shown either by straight lines or by uniformly varying curved lines. In such cases, if any one value (experimental or calculated) falls distinctly *off* the curve, it is evidently incorrect, whereas in a tabular chart it is much more difficult to detect incorrect values.

In preparing a coordinate graph, the student should proceed in the following manner:

STEP 1. *Select the type of coordinate paper.*—Of the several types available, those most generally used are ruled with rectangular coordinates, as in Figs.

1032 and 1033, in logarithmic coordinates, as in Figs. 1034 and 1035, or in semilogarithmic coordinates, as in Fig. 1036.

If the dependent variable varies as a constant power of the independent variable, it will be shown by a straight line on logarithmic coordinates; hence, for this case, it is best to use logarithmic coordinates.

STEP 2. *Locate axes, determine the variable for each, and choose appropriate scales.*— The axes should be drawn at the left and at the bottom of the sheet an inch or more inside the border so as to leave ample space for lettering. The intersection of the axes is generally, but not necessarily, the origin of coordinates; i.e., the zero point for vertical and horizontal distances.

The independent variables usually should be plotted as abscissas (parallel to the *x*-axis) and the dependent variables as ordinates (parallel to the *y*-axis). In some cases, for example in stress-strain diagrams, it is customary to plot the independent variables as ordinates. The scales should be chosen so that the entire range of the data to be represented can be shown within the limits of the graph and so that each division on the coordinate paper represents 1, 2, 3, 4, etc. units or some power of ten multiplied by 1, 2, 3, 4, etc.

STEP 3. *Mark the unit values along the axes.*—All figures should be clear and distinct and readable from the bottom, not from the side. If decimal fractions are shown, a zero should precede the decimal point, thus: 0.12 or 0.034.

STEP 4. *Plot the points representing the data.*—Show the points by dots and

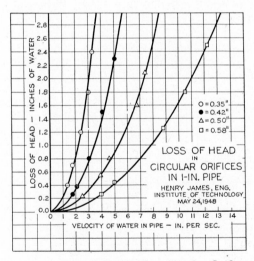

FIG. 1032   The Loss of Head in Circular Orifices.

inclose each dot with a small circle, triangle, or square, giving preference to these symbols in the order shown in Fig. 1032. If more than four curves are shown on the same chart, additional symbols should be used; for example, crosses, double circles, etc.

Step 5. *Draw the curves.*—Draw a uniformly varying curve through the plotted points, as shown in Fig. 1032. If the points vary materially from such a curve, connect them by a broken line and then draw the required curve to intersect the broken line so that the sum of the areas of the triangles formed by the broken line on one side of the curve is approximately equal to the sum of the areas of the triangles formed on the other side of the curve.

Step 6. *Letter the chart.*—The axes and the curves should be lettered so that their use and meaning are clear to the reader. The grid lines should be broken out for all lettering and figures, if possible. When the curves of a chart fall close together, it is best to differentiate between the curves by means of leaders, as shown in Fig. 1034.

Step 7. *Prepare the title.*—The title should be placed at the right side of the chart, near the top or bottom, depending on available space. It should give the name of the subject represented, the name of the engineer or drafts-man or both, the name of the institution, the date, and other relevant informa-tion. When graphical charts are prepared to present data for professional use in lieu of numerical charts, the title may be shown under the diagrams, as in Figs. 1033 and 1035.

Step 8. *Ink in the drawing.*—Check the calculations and the locations of points; if all are correct, ink in the drawing and complete the lettering.

532. Ordinary Coordinate Graphs. The principal advantages of the ordinary coordinate graphs are that they can be easily constructed and easily read. See Figs. 1032 and 1033.

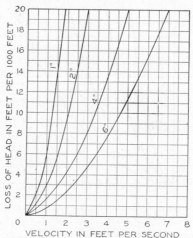

FIG. 1033   The Loss of Head for Water
Flowing in Iron Pipes.

The graph of Fig. 1032 shows the loss of head for water flowing through concentric circular orifices in 1″ pipe as determined by laboratory tests; four different-sized orifices were used and the loss of head determined for five velocities. Smooth curves could be drawn through the four sets of points determined experimentally; this indicates that the laboratory work was accurate. According to the chart, a $\frac{1}{2}''$ orifice in a $1''$ pipe causes a loss of head of $1.3''$ of water, when water is flowing in the pipe with a velocity of 6 inches per second.

The graph of Fig. 1033 records the loss of head when water is flowing through $1''$, $2''$, $4''$, or $6''$ pipe. The curves were plotted according to the formulas:

$$h = 6.50 \, v^{1.88}, \qquad h = 2.73 \, v^{1.83}, \qquad h = 1.16 \, v^{1.78}, \qquad h = 0.69 \, v^{1.75},$$

respectively, for the four pipe sizes, where h is the loss of head, in feet per 1000 feet, and v is the velocity of the water, in feet per second. These values apply when the water is at a temperature of about $70°$ F, and when the pipes are fairly clean, standard black steel or wrought iron pipes.

It is evident from the graphs, for example, that for a $2''$ pipe and a velocity of $2\frac{1}{2}$ ft per second, the loss of head is about 14.3 ft per 1000 ft of pipe. Also, that for a $4''$ pipe and a velocity of 3 ft per second, the loss of head is about 8 ft per 1000 ft of pipe. To plot the curves of this chart, assume a number of values of v, calculate the corresponding values of h from the formulas stated above, locate these values on the chart, and draw smooth curves through the resulting points.

533. Logarithmic Coordinate Graphs. The principal advantages of the logarithmic coordinate graphs (Figs. 1034 and 1035) are that large numbers can be represented by comparatively short distances and that the dependent variable is represented by a straight line when it is proportional to a constant power of the independent variable.

The graph of Fig. 1035 records the same data as the graph of Fig. 1033. To draw any one of the lines of this graph, it is necessary to have either two points of the line or the direction of the line and one of its points. Two points can be calculated and plotted for each line, as is the case of Fig. 1033, and the line drawn through the two points; or one point can be calculated and plotted and the line drawn through this point at the proper inclination.

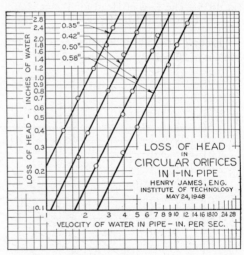

FIG. 1034 The Loss of Head in Circular Orifices.

The inclination of each line is such that the tangent of the angle it makes with the horizontal is equal to the exponent of the independent variable. For example, to plot the line for the $2''$ pipe, the equation of which is $h = 2.73 \, v^{1.83}$, it is evident that when the velocity is 1 ft per second, the loss of head is 2.73

ft; hence, to draw the line, plot the point 2.73 and draw the line through that point and with an upward slope of 183/100.

534. Semilogarithmic Graphs. On semilogarithmic paper, a function is represented by a straight line if its successive values for equal increments of the independent variable, form a geometric progression. For example, if a

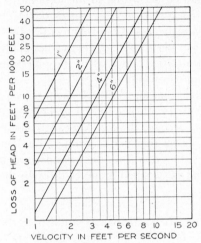

FIG. 1035   The Loss of Head for Water Flowing in Iron Pipes.

sum of money P is invested at compound interest, its successive annual amounts A are represented by the expression $A = P(1 + r)^n$, where r is the rate of interest and n is the number of years. The successive annual amounts form a geometric progression and are represented by straight lines on semilogarithmic diagrams. Figure 1036 is a semilogarithmic graph showing the amount of one dollar invested at various rates of compound interest and for various periods of time. The following types of problems may be easily solved by means of this diagram:

Prob. 1   In how many years will money double itself if invested at 3 per cent compound interest? *Ans.*—About $23\frac{1}{2}$ years.

Prob. 2   If $500 is invested at 4 per cent compound interest, what will be its amount in 20 years? *Ans.*—About $1100.

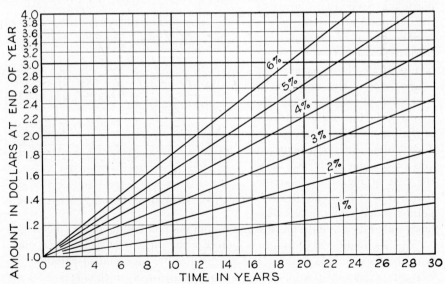

FIG. 1036   The Amount of One Dollar at Compound Interest.

Prob. 3 If an investment of $75.00 amounts to $100 in 10 years, what is the rate of interest, compounded semiannually? *Ans.*—From the graph, slightly less than 3 per cent; more accurately, 2.92 per cent.

Semilogarithmic coordinate diagrams are used in commercial work to study the expansion (or contraction) of the volume of business transacted over a period of years. If a merchant plots his annual sales on semilogarithmic paper and joins the successive points by a line, he can readily determine whether his sales have increased at a regular (percentage) rate each year, and, if so, what that rate is. When used in commercial work, semilogarithmic paper is generally referred to as "ratio-ruled" paper.

Semilogarithmic coordinate diagrams are used in scientific work to study phenomena which can be represented more accurately by that system of coordinates than by any other system; that is, when the successive values of one quantity increase in geometric progression as another quantity increases in arithmetic progression.

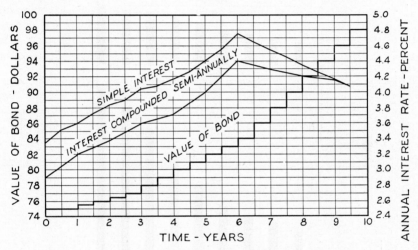

FIG. 1037   A Study of the Value of a $100.00 United States Saving Bond.

535. Composite Graphs. The chart of Fig. 1037 shows the results of a study to determine the economic value of an investment in a $100 United States Savings Bond. The diagram is a combination of three graphs: one shows the gradually increasing value of the bond, with time; the others show the varying rates of interest which the bond will earn during its unexpired term. For example, when the bond has been held for 6 years it can be cashed for $84.00, but if it is held till maturity, it will earn $16.00 in interest; this earning corresponds to a rate of about 4.75 per cent simple interest or 4.4 per cent interest, compounded semiannually.

Prob. 1 When a $100 bond has been held for 3 years, what is its cash value? *Ans.*—$80.00.

Prob. 2 When a $100 bond has been held for 3 years, what rate of interest will it earn during the remaining 7 years, if held till maturity? *Ans.*—About 4.05 per cent simple interest or about 3.6 per cent interest, compounded semiannually.

536. Bar Charts. The bar chart is effective for common or nontechnical use because it is most easily read and understood. It is therefore used extensively by newspapers, magazines, and similar publications.

In this form of chart, quantities, values, relations, etc., are represented by bars; the lengths of the bars indicate quantities or values. The bars may be vertical or horizontal; in either case, they should extend from the same initial line.

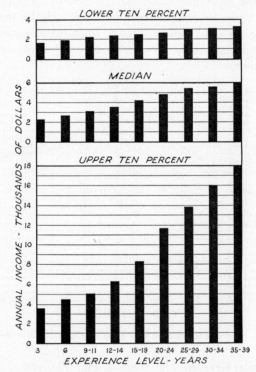

FIG. 1038   The Annual Income of Three Groups
of Professional Engineers.

The length of a bar that represents a quantity or a value should be drawn to a definite scale, and the quantity or value should be written in numerals either on the bar or on the margin of the chart. Figure 1038 is a triple bar chart; it shows, by the lengths of the respective bars, the annual income of three groups of professional engineers for various experience levels. This chart conveys the same information which is conveyed by the chart of Fig. 1039 and by Table I on the next page.

TABLE I

Three Levels of Annual Income of Professional Engineers,
by Experience Level in 1939

Experience level in years	Lower 10 per cent	Median	Upper 10 per cent
3........................	$1,609	$2,187	$3,359
6........................	1,913	2,683	4,515
9–11.....................	2,158	3,137	5,083
12–14....................	2,416	3,548	6,311
15–19....................	2,648	4,162	8,340
20–24....................	2,709	4,893	11,597
25–29....................	3,103	5,353	13,672
30–34....................	3,083	5,563	15,929
35–39....................	3,161	6,017	18,051
40 or more...............	2,695	5,867	h

This table is the basis for the bar chart of Fig. 1038 and for the rectangular coordinate chart of Fig. 1039. The student should note the differences between the three methods of presenting data to the public and compare their respective values.

The data of this table are from *The Engineering Profession in Transition*, published by the Engineers Joint Council, 39 W. 39th St., New York, 1947.

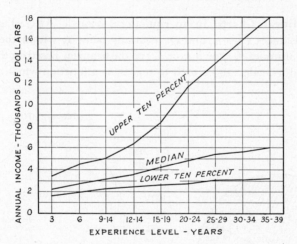

FIG. 1039   The Annual Income of Three Groups of
Professional Engineers.

537. Area Charts. Data can be represented by the areas of rectangles, trapezoids, circular sectors, and other geometrical figures; the resulting charts can be understood as easily as bar charts and are more pleasing in appearance. This is illustrated by Fig. 1040 which shows the numbers of passenger-train cars of various ages of Class I railroads in the United States on January 1, 1947.

538. Circular or Pie Charts. When the areas of circular sectors are used to represent data, the resulting area charts are generally called circular charts or pie charts. Figure 1041 is such a chart; it shows how the annual income of a system of railways was distributed among six major accounts.

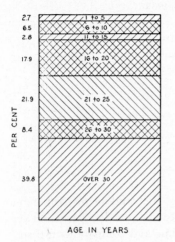

FIG. 1040 The Relative Numbers of Railway Cars of Various Ages.

539. Polar Charts. When a function which varies as its distance from a central point is represented graphically, the resulting graph is called a polar chart. Such charts are in common use to represent the varying intensity, with distance and direction, of the illumination produced by electric lamps, with or without enclosures or reflectors. Figure 1042 shows the candlepower distribution for a typical bare 200-watt filament lamp at a distance of 10 feet from the source. Since the light emitted by the lamp is radiated in all directions, the curve of Fig. 1042 may be considered to be the line of intersection of a double curved surface of revolution with a plane passing through the axis of the lamp.

540. Trilinear Charts. In an equilateral triangle ABC (Fig. 1043) the sum of the distances $x\,l$, $x\,m$, and $x\,n$ from any point x, within the triangle, is equal to the altitudes $A\,r$, or $B\,s$, or $C\,t$ of the triangle. Based on this principle, an equilateral triangle can be used to represent a function which is the sum of

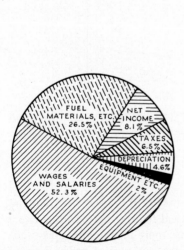

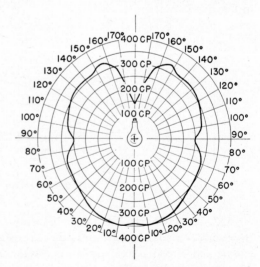

FIG. 1041   The Distribution of the Annual Income of a System of Railways.

FIG. 1042   The Candlepower Distribution of an Electric Lamp.

three variables or the result of the combined actions of three forces. For example, if the distances x *l*, x *m*, and x *n* are, respectively, 20, 50, and 30 units, the altitude of the triangle is 100 units, and the point x will represent the function composed of, or resulting from, 20 parts of C, 50 parts of A, and 30 parts of C, if A, B, and C are the three variables whose functions are to be

charted. The resulting chart is a *trilinear chart;* such a chart is shown in Fig. 1044; in this chart the various freezing temperatures of mixtures, in various proportions, by volume, of water, methanol, and ethanol are shown. For example, a freezing temperature of −40 F can be obtained by mixing 50 parts of water, by volume, with 10 parts of ethanol and 40 parts of methanol.

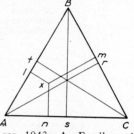

Prob. 1 What mixture will have a freezing temperature of 0 F? *Ans.*—70 parts water, 15 parts methanol, and 15 parts ethanol, by volume.

FIG. 1043   An Equilateral Triangle—the Basis of a Triangular Chart.

541. Organization Charts and Flow Charts. In every industrial, commercial, educational, or other organization, it is important to specify clearly and distinctly how the authority, duty, and responsibility of the several officers are related, one to the other, and to communicate this information to all who must be guided and governed by it. This is accomplished by means of an *organization chart* which is delivered to all concerned and posted where useful. Figure 1045 is a slightly modified form of the chart showing the Engineering Division Organization of the Boeing Airplane Company. The names of the several officials, which are usually shown on organization charts, were omitted in Fig. 1045.

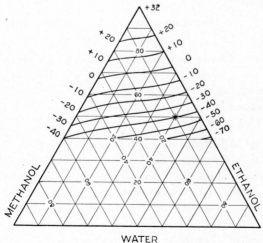

FIG. 1044   The Freezing Temperatures of Mixtures of Water, Methanol, and Ethanol.

In addition to the organization charts which refer to the officials of the corporation, it is necessary to prepare charts which show how the designing and the manufacturing operations proceed orderly, step by step. These charts are similar to the organization charts and are known as *flow charts*.

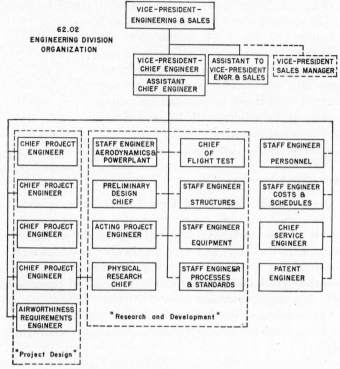

FIG. 1045   The Organization Chart of the Engineering Division of the Boeing Airplane Company.

542. Alignment Charts or Nomograms. These charts are intended to simplify or eliminate mathematical calculations. They are very useful in commercial, engineering, and scientific fields, and they vary from very simple to extremely complicated forms. A few examples will be shown, as follows, to explain fundamental principles.

543. Graphical Addition or Subtraction.—Fig. 1046. To construct a diagram for addition or subtraction, draw three parallel lines *A*, *B*, and *X* at equal distances apart and intersect them with a datum line from which measurements are to be made. The datum line need not be at right angles to the other lines. Set off from the datum line a series of equal distances along the three lines, the divisions of the middle line being half as large as those of the two outer lines, and number the divisions as shown.

Draw any straight line, as *JK*, to intersect the lines *A*, *B*, and *X*. The line *JK* and the datum line form a trapezoid *LMNO* with the segments of the lines A and B. The line X is halfway between the bases of the trapezoid; its segment PQ, within the trapezoid, is equal in length to half the sum of the

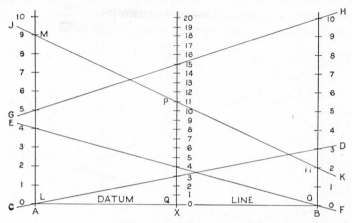

FIG. 1046   Graphical Addition and Subtraction.

lengths of the two bases LM and NO. Since the divisions on X are half as long as those on A and B, the number of divisions on the segment of X is equal to the sum of the number of divisions on the segments of A and B.

If the line JK is moved so that it passes through the lower end of either the line A or the line B, as do the lines CD and EF, the trapezoid becomes a triangle, but the same relation still exists, namely, that the number of divisions of the segment of the line X is equal to the sum of the number of divisions of the segments of the lines A and B. It is evident, therefore, that every straight line will intersect the three given lines A, B, and X so that the number of divisions on the line X is equal to the sum of the number of divisions on the lines A and B.

To use the diagram for addition, for example, to add 5 and 10, draw the line GH through the points 5 and 10 of the lines A and B; its intersection with the line X, the point 15, is the sum of 5 and 10.

To use the diagram for subtraction, for example, to subtract 2 from 11, draw the line JK through the points 11 of X and 2 of B; its intersection with the line A, the point 9, shows the difference between 11 and 2.

The operations of addition and subtraction are so simple that no graphical diagram is needed and Fig. 1046 is introduced here primarily to explain the use of Fig. 1047.

544. Graphical Multiplication or Division.—Fig. 1047. If three lines A, B, and X are drawn as in Fig. 1046, but divided according to logarithmic scales as shown in Fig. 1047, instead of according to ordinary scales, as shown in Fig. 1046, the geometric relations will be the same, but the divisions on the line X will represent the products of the divisions on the lines A and B

instead of their sums. For example, the line CD shows that $1 \times 3 = 3$, and
the line EF shows that $4 \times 1 = 4$. The line GH shows that $5 \times 10 = 50$, or
that $50 \div 10 = 5$, or that $50 \div 5 = 10$, etc. A diagram of this type may be
used to advantage to determine the cost of any product which is sold at a
given price per square inch or per square foot, simply by using the scales on

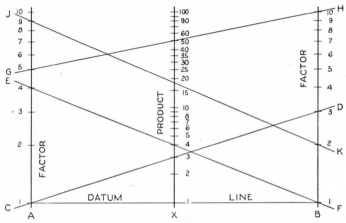

FIG. 1047   Graphical Multiplication and Division.

the lines A and B to represent inches or feet, and the scale on the line X to
represent dollars and cents. In that case, the divisions of the line X must be
changed so that they represent the product of the divisions of the lines A
and B in square inches or square feet, multiplied by the corresponding cost
in dollars or cents per square inch or per square foot, in order that the reading may be directly in dollars or cents instead of in square inches or square
feet. Obviously this type of graph has many other practical applications.

545. Extended Multiplications.—Fig. 1048. The construction of Fig.
1047 can be expanded to embody more than two factors and the resulting
chart may become quite complicated. As an illustration, let it be required to
prepare a chart to determine the loss of head of water flowing in a $2''$ pipe
of any desired length. The required loss of head is given by the equation
$h = 2.73 \, Lv^{1.83}$, where h is the loss of head in feet divided by 1000, L the
length of the pipe in feet, and v the velocity of the water in feet per second.
To construct the diagram, draw the datum line as in Fig. 1047, and draw
three parallel lines L, H, and V, corresponding to the lines A, X, and B in Fig.
1047. Select any desired logarithmic scale and set off, on the line L, the logarithm of 2.73 to this scale. Beginning at this point, set off the logarithmic
scale as shown, so that the distance from the datum line to any point in the
line L will be equal to the logarithm of 2.73 plus the logarithm of the desired
length of pipe. On the line H, beginning at the datum line, set off divisions
according to a logarithmic scale half as large as that used for the line L. On
the line V, beginning at the datum line, set off a logarithmic scale with divisions

equal to those on line L multiplied by 1.83, as shown. This scale can be easily constructed graphically from the scale of the line L by similar triangles, as explained in § 86.

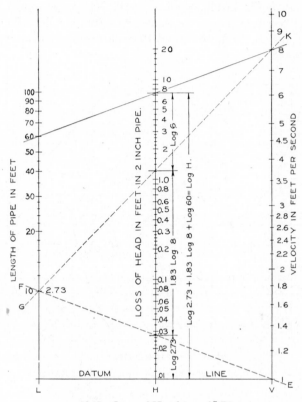

FIG. 1048   Loss of Head in a 2″ Pipe.

To apply this diagram, let it be required to find the loss of head in a 2″ pipe 60 ft long when the water has a velocity of 8 ft per second. Draw a line through the point 60 of line L and the point 8 of line V. Its intersection with the line H (about 7.3) is the required loss of head. If the length of the pipe were 600 ft, the loss of head would be 73 ft, and if the length of the pipe were 6 ft, the loss of head would be 0.73 ft.

In all cases, the loss of head is directly proportional to the length of pipe. This, however, is not true with the velocity, since the loss of head is proportional to $v^{1.83}$. Therefore, to find the loss of head for a pipe 60 ft long and with a velocity of 0.8 ft per second, the loss of head would be 7.3 divided by $10^{1.83}$, or by 67.6. The loss of head would therefore be 0.108 ft.

To understand the construction and operation of this diagram, note that the two dashed lines, FE and GK, intersect the line H and determine three segments which are, respectively, the logarithm of 2.73, the logarithm of 8 multiplied by 1.83, and the logarithm of 60. The sum of these three logarithms is the logarithm of the required loss of head, *h*.

546. Practical Use of Charts in Engineering. Graphs, charts, and diagrams are very useful in all technical work. They save much time to the designing engineer and reduce the danger of errors in calculations. The diagrams shown in Figs. 1034, 1035, and 1048 illustrate practical applications as explained above.

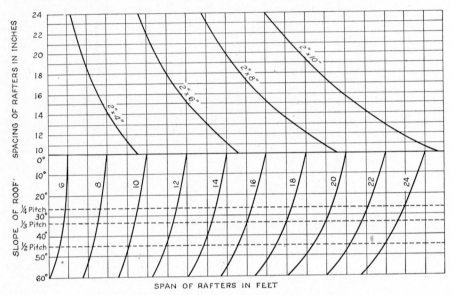

FIG. 1049   Sizes, Spacing, and Spans of Rafters.

The chart shown in Fig. 1049 was prepared to determine the correct sizes, spacings, and spans of yellow pine rafters for roofs weighing about $7\frac{1}{2}$ lb per sq ft not including the weight of the rafters, and for a wind pressure of about 25 lb per sq ft normal to the roof for sloping roofs, and a live load of about 30 lb per sq ft for flat roofs.

To illustrate the use of the chart, assume a roof having a $\frac{1}{3}$ pitch with rafters having a span of 16 ft and find that 2 × 8 rafters, spaced 16 in. c. to c., should be used, as follows: Enter the lower part of the chart on the 16-ft line, follow this line to its intersection with the horizontal, the $\frac{1}{3}$ pitch line, thence vertically upward to the intersection of the 2 × 8 rafter line, and thence horizontally to the left, and read the spacing, 16.

In a similar manner, it may be found that, for an 18-ft span and a 30° roof, the rafters should be 2 × 8 spaced 13 in. or 2 × 10 spaced 21 in. c. to c.; also, that if 2 × 4 rafters spaced 24 in. c. to c. are to be used, the span should be about 6 ft for a flat roof and about 7 ft for a steep roof.

The chart may be used with sufficient accuracy for roofs weighing more than $7\frac{1}{2}$ lb per sq ft as follows: if the roof weighs w lb per sq ft, select the spacing as described above, multiply by $7\frac{1}{2}$ plus 25, and divide by w plus 25 to secure the correct spacing.

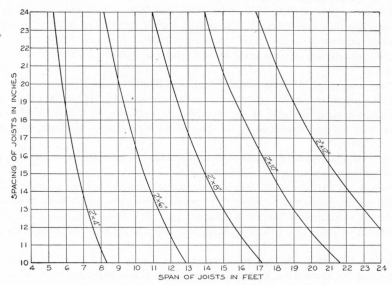

FIG. 1050   Sizes, Spacings, and Spans of Joints.

The chart shown in Fig. 1050 was prepared to determine the correct sizes, spacings, and spans of yellow pine floor joists for a live load of 50 pounds per square foot, and an extreme fiber stress of 1200 lb per sq in.

It is evident from the diagram that, for a span of 12 ft, the joists should be either 2 × 6 spaced 11 in. or 2 × 8 spaced 20 in. c. to c.; also, that if the spacing is to be 18 in., the joists should be 2 × 4 for a 6-ft span, 2 × 6 for a 9-ft span, etc.

PROBLEMS

547. The following problems are given to familiarize the student with the methods of constructing graphs and the relative advantages of the several types of graphs and charts.

Prob. 1 A semifireproof dormitory of 276 rooms built of brick, with reinforced concrete frame, cost $239,800. The cost was subdivided as follows: Earth and concrete work, $50,600; masonry, $64,100; lath and plaster, $15,500; mill work and carpentry, $15,800; mechanical equipment, $30,900; roofing, $2,750; finish floors, $15,500; painting, $8,050; miscellaneous, $11,100; equipment and supervision, $12,000; architectural and engineering fees, $13,500. Draw a bar chart similar to the lower chart in Fig. 1038 using a scale of 1 in. = 10,000 dollars, arranging the bars in the order of length.

Prob. 2 With the data of Prob. 1, draw a circular, or pie, chart similar to that of Fig. 1041.

Prob. 3 In testing a piece of timber in compression it was found that for a load causing a stress of 500 pounds per square inch the shortening, or compression, or strain was 0.0003 of the original length; i.e., 0.0003 inches per inch or 0.0003 feet per foot; similarly for stresses of 1000, 1500, 2000, 2500, and 3000 pounds per square inch the corresponding unit strains were 0.0006, 0.0010, 0.0013, 0.0017, and 0.0020. In testing a piece of concrete in compression, it was found that unit stresses of 500, 1000, 1500, and 2000 pounds were accompanied by unit strains of 0.00025, 0.00050, 0.00082, and 0.00180.

Draw a rectangle $5''$ wide and $7\frac{1}{2}''$ high and divide it into $\frac{1}{4}''$ squares. Use this figure as a set of rectangular coordinates similar to that of Fig. 1032. Set off the unit stresses above along the side of the rectangle, as ordinates, to a scale of $\frac{1}{4}'' = 100$ pounds, and the unit strains along the base of the rectangle, as abscissas, to a scale of $\frac{1}{4}'' = 0.0001$.

Using the data above, draw the stress-strain diagrams for timber and concrete, and letter the diagrams in an appropriate manner.

Prob. 4 It has been found that in industrial plants which are not properly heated and lighted the number of accidents per month is greater in winter than in summer and that it varies approximately as follows: Jan., 295; Feb., 200; Mar., 145; Apr., 135; May, 130; June, 115; July, 100; Aug., 160; Sept., 175; Oct., 215; Nov., 295; and Dec., 335.

Draw a bar chart, the bars being vertical, to a scale of 1 inch to 100 accidents, representing the above data, arranged chronologically, and beginning with the month of July. Letter the chart appropriately.

Prob. 5 For a frame dwelling with an attic which was not well ventilated, the following attic temperatures, indoor temperatures, and outdoor temperatures were recorded for a 24-hour period, at two-hour intervals, beginning at midnight.

Hour......	12	2	4	6	8	10	12	2	4	6	8	10	12
Attic......	81	79	77	76	79	87	94	99	100	97	91	87	83
Indoor......	77	76	76	77	78	82	83	84	84	83	82	80	79
Outdoor......	74	71	70	72	80	86	89	91	92	90	82	79	76

Draw a rectangle $4''$ wide and $5''$ high. Divide the base into 12 equal parts and the altitude into 50 equal parts and draw vertical and horizontal lines through the division points to form a set of rectangular coordinates. Let the horizontal divisions represent 2-hour periods and number them from left to right beginning at 12. Let the vertical divisions represent degrees and number them upward from 60 to 110, in 5-degree intervals.

On these coordinates, plot the temperature curves from the data given above for the attic temperatures, the indoor temperatures, and the outdoor temperatures (all in degrees Fahrenheit), and letter the diagram properly.

Prob. 6 The loss of head for water flowing in an iron pipe depends upon the diameter of the pipe, the velocity of the water, the temperature of the water, and the character of the inner surface of the pipe.

For fairly clean iron pipe and water at a temperature of about 70° F, the following losses of head were calculated by formula for pipe sizes ranging from $\frac{3}{4}''$ to $2''$, and for water velocity ranging from $6''$ per second to $30''$ per second as listed below. The losses of head shown are expressed in inches per 1000 feet of pipe.

	$\frac{3}{4}''$	$1''$	$1\frac{1}{4}''$	$1\frac{1}{2}''$	$2''$
$6''$	30	20	12	13	9
$12''$	105	80	55	45	32
$18''$	230	180	115	93	68
$24''$	400	300	200	160	115
$30''$	600	440	300	240	175

Draw a rectangle $5''$ wide and $8''$ high. Divide the base into 30 equal parts and the altitude into 400 parts. Through the division points draw vertical and horizontal lines to form a set of coordinates. Let the horizontal divisions represent velocities, in inches per second, number them from 0 to 30 in intervals of 6, and draw the corresponding lines heavier than the others. Let the vertical divisions represent losses of head, in inches per 1000 feet, number them from 0 to 400 in intervals of 50, and draw the corresponding lines heavier.

On these coordinates plot curves showing the losses of head for the several pipe sizes according to the data above and in a manner similar to that used for Fig. 1033, and letter the diagram properly.

Prob. 7   With the data of Prob. 6, draw a logarithmic coordinate diagram similar to that of Fig. 1035. Number the divisions of the base from 1 to 30, and those of the altitude from 1 to 400. To secure the divisions, use a table of logarithms and note that the logarithm of 30 is 1.4771.

Set off this number by means of an engineers' scale (Fig. 20), using any convenient scale, for example, $\frac{1}{30}$ of an inch. The distance on this scale from 0 to 1477 is about 4.92 inches, and is a convenient dimension for the diagram. Similarly, the altitude of the diagram is proportional to the logarithm of 400 or to 2.6021, and this, to the same scale, is about 7.81 inches.

The remaining division points can be calculated in a similar manner, and the diagram may be completed and lettered in a manner similar to that shown in Fig. 1035. If the data for the problem are accurate, the graphs in the diagram will be straight lines.

Instead of calculating the logarithmic divisions, they may be taken from a slide rule or from logarithmic paper.

Architectural Drawing

548. Introduction. Architectural drawing is that branch of technical drawing which is devoted to the representation of buildings and similar structures. The drawings for an architectural structure include plans, elevations, sections, and details sufficient to define adequately, in graphic forms, the entire construction, so that it can be executed in complete accord with the architect's ideas.

To become an efficient architect or architectural draftsman, the student must have natural ability and a thorough training in the arts and sciences related to his work, as offered in the leading schools of architecture. The curricula in these institutions include general educational courses to help the student understand the best use and purpose of buildings from economic and social points of view; engineering courses to teach him the construction, sanitation, illumination, and other engineering features of building construction which have such an important bearing on the safety, durability, and comfort of buildings; courses in business administration to acquaint the student with the fundamental principles of accounting and law so that he may thoroughly understand the financial and legal transactions incident to modern building construction; and courses in art and in architectural composition and design which offer training intended to enable the student to provide his designs with pleasing form, proportion, and color—to give them aesthetic appeal or beauty.

Architecture should be chosen as a profession only by those who have a distinct love of beauty as applied to structural forms or a special liking for the sciences which relate to building construction or building equipment.

549. Office Practice. When an architect has been commissioned to prepare plans for a building, his first step is to study the owner's requirements, to analyze them thoroughly, and to set up a tentative program of minimum needs, with cost allotments. With these as a basis, he prepares a series of preliminary sketches, specifications, and cost estimates covering only the major or general elements of the problem, for discussion with the owner. Having secured the owner's approval of a preliminary design with specifications and cost estimate, the architect proceeds with the preparation of the final working drawings and specifications which describe the building in all its details. After their approval by the owner, the architect or the owner secures construction bids from approved building contractors. After a contract has been entered into by the owner and the contractor, the construction of the building proceeds under the supervision and direction of the architect.

550. Preliminary Sketches, Perspective Drawings, and Models. A preliminary sketch of a building project is intended to show the owner the general arrangement and appearance of the proposed building, and to help him to develop the plan, with the architect's assistance, so that it will best meet his needs and his wishes.

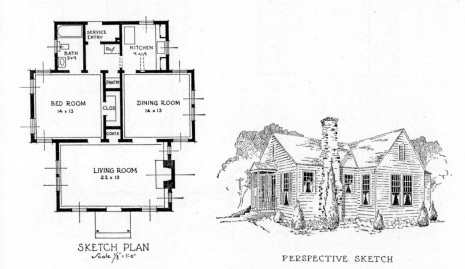

SKETCH PLAN
Scale ⅛" = 1'-0"

PERSPECTIVE SKETCH

FIG. 1051   A Preliminary Sketch
Plan for a Residence.

FIG. 1052   A Preliminary Perspective Sketch
for a Residence.

Preliminary sketches of a small cottage, such as an architect would prepare for submission to and discussion with the owner, are shown in Figs. 1051 and 1052. Four additional preliminary sketches of small cottages are shown in Fig. 1053. These sketches were redrawn, in a modified form, from designs published in *Small Homes of Architectural Distinction*, Harper and Brothers, to which the student is referred for many other good cottage plans and details. The designs of Fig. 1053 are presented to acquaint the student with the technique of preparing preliminary sketches and with a few of the large number of variations in cottage design.

For a building of considerable size and importance, for example, a school, a church, a city hall, an auditorium, or a post office, it is customary to supplement the preliminary sketches and specifications with a perspective drawing (§ 304), because such a drawing enables the owner and the architect to visual-

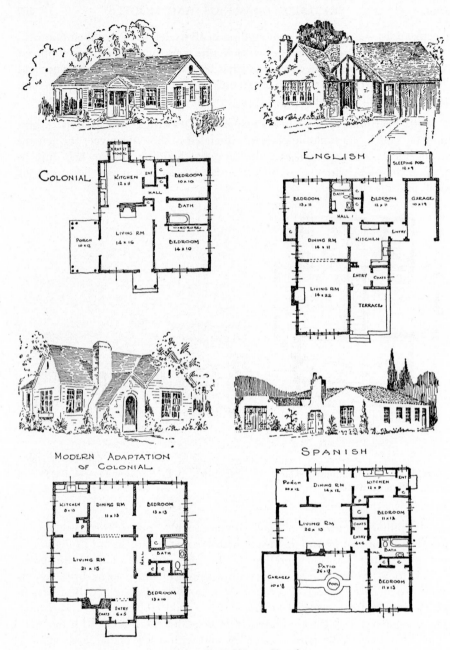

FIG. 1053 Preliminary Sketches.

ize the final appearance of the proposed building much more clearly and accurately than do the ordinary sketch, elevation, and plan. A perspective drawing of a post office is shown in Fig. 1054. This illustration was reproduced from a perspective drawing of a typical post office building supplied by the Public Works Branch of the Treasury Department.

For very monumental structures, it is customary to supplement preliminary sketches and perspective drawings with models, either full size or to a reduced

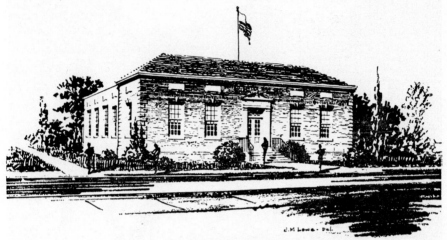

FIG. 1054   A Perspective of a Post Office Building.

scale, of the proposed structures or of parts of them, because a model affords the best possible opportunity for judging the appearance of a proposed structure and, in addition, for changing the design so as to make it more pleasing in appearance and better suited for its purpose.

A picture of a model to a reduced scale of a design for a residence is shown in Fig. 1055.

The practice of studying designs for structures by means of models is growing rapidly. At the present time it is being applied to the design of buildings, bridges, dams, road intersections, automobiles, airplanes, etc.

During the period of the Italian Renaissance, full size models were made of balustrades and other details, and were installed on monumental buildings for examination and criticism before the final execution was made in marble.

Permission to build a bridge across a street to connect two buildings in a European city was granted only after a wooden model, covered with canvas painted to represent the proposed structure, had been constructed to enable the city officials to judge the effect of the proposed bridge on the traffic, light, and ventilation and appearance of the street.

551. Architectural Design. The construction and equipment of a modern building are so complicated that no one person can design such a building in all its details. The *architect*, as a rule, has associated with him an *architectural engineer* to design the framework of the building and its structural details, and, for small and simple buildings, also the lighting system, and the plumbing, heating, and air conditioning systems. For large and complicated buildings,

FIG. 1055   A Model for a Residence.

electrical and mechanical engineers are employed to design the electrical and the mechanical equipment. The portion of the design which is prepared by the *architect* is the arrangement of the building, as to plan, elevation, and decoration, including selection of materials, so that the building will best suit its purpose and will present a pleasing appearance as a whole and in all of its details. This branch of building design is called *architectural design*.

To become proficient in architectural design, the student must know the requirements of the building he is to design—a school, a church, a theater, etc.—he must be familiar with the historical development of the several styles of architecture and of architectural ornament, and he must be well trained in architectural design and composition.

The style of architecture in vogue during a certain period represents and reflects the civilization of that period. As civilizations change, styles of architecture also change. The most important styles which influence modern

American architecture and the approximate periods during which they pre-vailed are: Egyptian (4000 to 200 B.C.), Greek (800 B.C. to A.D. 200), Roman (200 B.C. to A.D. 400), Romanesque (A.D. 900 to 1200), Gothic (A.D. 1300 to 1500), Renaissance (A.D. 1500 to 1800), Modern (A.D. 1800 to the present time). The most recent phase of modern architecture, beginning about 1900, is known as the International style, or Modern.

Greek architecture is perhaps the most important of the historical styles, since it forms the basis for Roman and for Renaissance architecture. Greek architecture evidently began its development very early with wooden columns decorated with natural foliage during festive occasions. From this simple be-ginning the art advanced to the use of stone columns decorated with conven-tionalized forms, and reached its zenith about 454–438 B.C. with the creation of one of the most beautiful buildings ever erected—the Parthenon.

Greek architecture was a living art, dedicated almost exclusively to the erection of temples. No two temples were alike. Each was better and more beautiful than its predecessor. The end of this development came when Greece was subdued by Rome, about 150 B.C. Thereafter, Greek art and Greek artists were transported from Greece to Rome, and the influence of Greek art was distributed over the leading Roman provinces.

During the Renaissance period, a noted architect, Giacomo Barocchio (1507–1573) living in Vignola, Italy, made careful studies and accurate measurements of Greek and Roman buildings and described his findings in a book on The Five Orders of Architecture, Tuscan, Doric, Ionic, Corinthian, and Composite. This book is still the authority on the orders of architecture; the four orders shown in Fig. 1056 were reproduced from it. The Composite order was omitted because it is less important than the other four. The Doric, Ionic, and Corinthian orders are of Greek origin; the Tuscan and Composite are of Roman origin. Giacomo Barocchio is generally known and referred to as Vignola. He succeeded Michelangelo as architect of St. Peter's Cathedral in Rome after the latter's death in 1564.

Students who wish to apply the orders of Fig. 1056 in their designs may safely copy the proportions exactly as shown; they may also make minor alterations; but if they make major changes, the results may be decidedly inferior.

For additional information relating to architectural design, the student should consult modern texts on the history of architecture, on architectural design and composition, and on architectural ornament (Appendix 44).

552. Working Drawings and Specifications. Having decided on the general plan of the proposed building, the architect prepares the working drawings. These drawings and the accompanying specifications should be prepared in such detail and with such accuracy that the building contractor can prepare an accurate estimate of all materials and labor necessary for the construction of the building. The specifications should be very carefully pre-

FIG. 1056   The Orders of Architecture.

pared, so that they give all information necessary, and so that they permit of only one interpretation.

The beginner can secure much help from standard texts on contracts and specifications and from publications by manufacturers of the materials or appliances to be specified (Appendix 44).

Since many drawings are needed for the erection of a building, it is generally not practicable to arrange the several views with reference to each other as explained for multiview projections and for general working drawings. It is quite common to use a separate sheet for each plan or elevation or section, together with such special details as apply to the particular drawing.

553. General Drawings. The drawings which give general information about a building and which are usually the first in the series to be prepared are the *general drawings*. They include the floor plan (Fig. 1057), two or more elevations (Figs. 1058 and 1059), the foundation and floor-framing plan (Fig. 1060), the roof-framing plan (Fig. 1061), and the wall section (Fig. 1062). When necessary, ceiling plans and roof plans are prepared and included in the general drawings. In some cases, it is best to have separate foundation plans and floor-framing plans instead of combining the two in one drawing as shown in Fig. 1060. When desirable, the general drawings include a section of the entire building instead of a section of only one wall as shown in Fig. 1062.

The general drawings are prepared to scales of $\frac{1}{4}$ in. = 1 ft, $\frac{1}{8}$ in. = 1 ft, or $\frac{1}{16}$ in. = 1 ft, depending on the size of the building and the size of the drawing.

It may seem unnecessary to provide plans like those of Figs. 1060 and 1061, in which the joists, rafters, etc., are shown in detail. The preparation of such drawings should never be omitted, because the information conveyed by them must be determined by somebody before the material can be ordered and the building erected, and that can be done most efficiently and most economically in the architect's office before the erection of the building is begun.

The student should examine Figs. 1060–1069 carefully to see the character of the information conveyed by them, and to learn the names of the several parts of the structure.

554. Dimensioning. The general principles of dimensioning given in Chapter 16 apply to architectural drawing with the following modifications.

Dimension lines are continuous, and the figures are written above the dimension lines.

The dimensions are shown in feet and inches, and are so marked.

Some architects use dots or very small circles, instead of arrowheads, to terminate dimension lines.

Practice regarding extension lines varies with draftsmen and with subject matter. In some cases, extension lines are allowed to touch the object; in others, a gap is left, as in machine drawing.

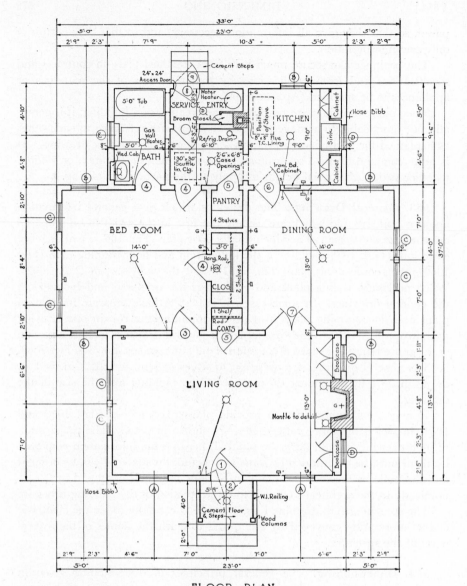

FLOOR PLAN

Scale ¼" = 1'-0"

FIG. 1057 Floor Plan.

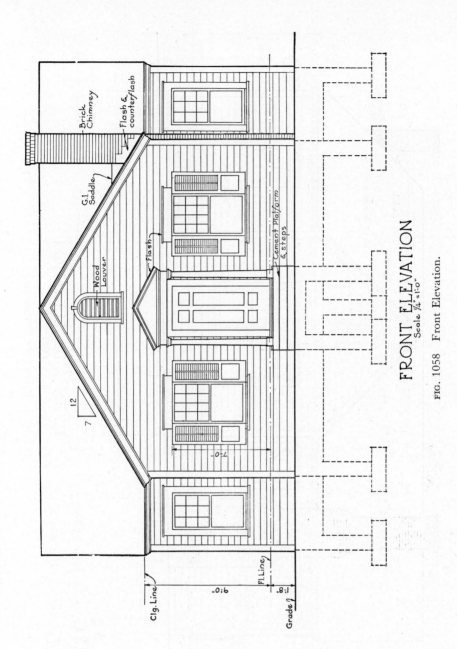

FRONT ELEVATION
Scale 1/4" = 1'-0"

FIG. 1058   Front Elevation.

Brick Chimney

Flash & counterflash

G.I. Saddle

Wood Louver

Flash

Cement Platform & steps

12
7

7'-0"

Clg. Line

9'-0"

Fl. Line

1'-8"

Grade

677

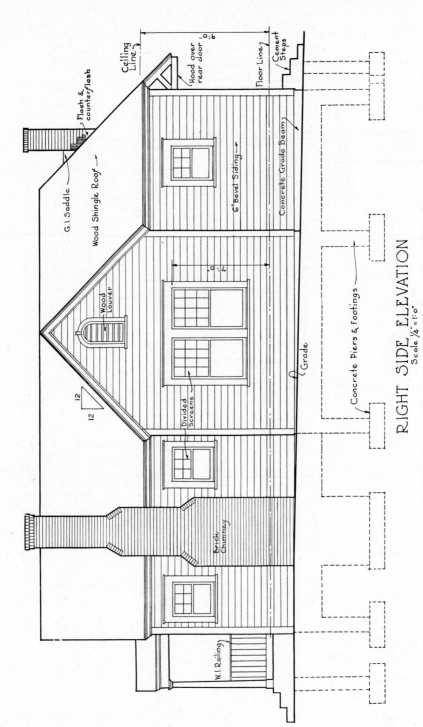

RIGHT SIDE ELEVATION
Scale 1/4" = 1'0"

FIG. 1059 Right Side Elevation.

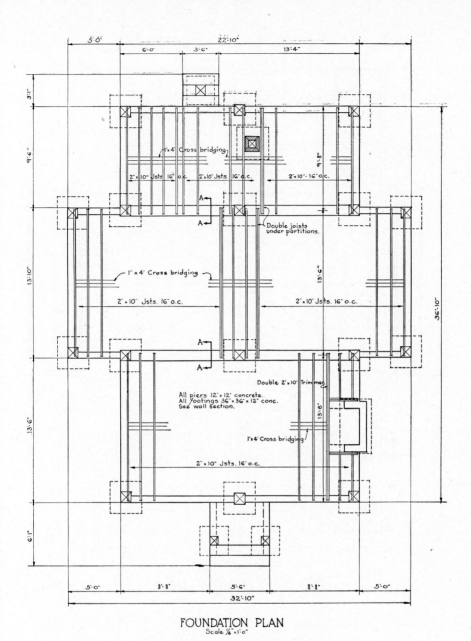

FOUNDATION PLAN
Scale ¼"=1'·0"

FIG. 1060 Foundation and Floor Framing Plan.

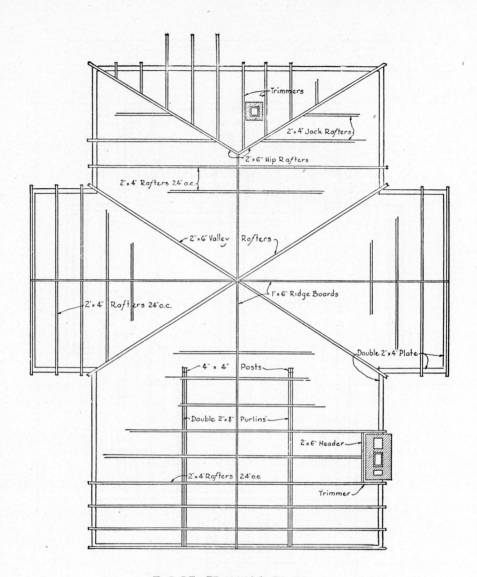

Trimmers

2″x 4″ Jack Rafters

2″x 6″ Hip Rafters

2″x 4″ Rafters 24″ o.c.

2″x 6″ Valley Rafters

2″x 4″ Rafters 24″ o.c.

1″x 6″ Ridge Boards

Double 2″x 4″ Plate

4″ x 4″ Posts

Double 2″x 8″ Purlins

2″x 6″ Header

2″x 4″ Rafters 24″ o.c.

Trimmer

ROOF FRAMING PLAN
Scale ¼″=1′0″

FIG. 1061   Roof Framing Plan:

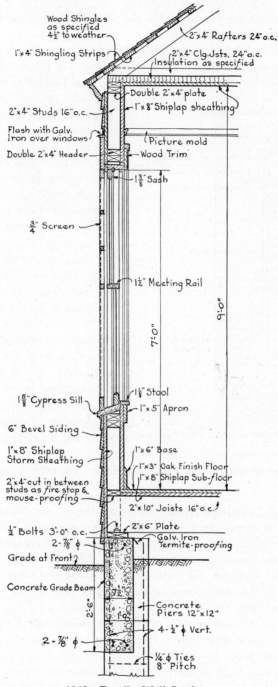

Wood Shingles
as specified
4½" to weather

2"x4" Rafters 24" o.c.

1"x4" Shingling Strips

2"x4" Clg. Jsts. 24" o.c.
Insulation as specified

Double 2"x4" plate

2"x4" Studs 16" o.c.

1"x8" Shiplap sheathing

Flash with Galv.
Iron over windows

Picture mold

Double 2"x4" Header

Wood Trim

1⅜" Sash

¾" Screen

1½" Meeting Rail

9'-0"

7'-0"

1⅜" Stool

1⅝" Cypress Sill

1"x5" Apron

6" Bevel Siding

1"x6" Base

1"x8" Shiplap
Storm Sheathing

1"x3" Oak Finish Floor
1"x8" Shiplap Sub-floor

2"x4" cut in between
studs as fire stop &
mouse-proofing

2"x10" Joists 16" o.c.

½" Bolts 3'-0" o.c.

2"x6" Plate

2-⅞" φ

Galv. Iron
Termite-proofing

Grade at Front

Concrete Grade Beam

2'-6"

Concrete
Piers 12"x12"

4-½" φ Vert.

2-⅞" φ

¼" φ Ties
8" Pitch

FIG. 1062   Details, Wall Section.

681

The dimensions are placed within the views if that improves the clearness or the appearance of the drawing.

The figures and letters are of an architectural type (Fig. 217, p. 135).

The dimensions are always given to those parts of the structure which are in position when the dimensions are needed by the builder or the owner. For example, on the foundation plan (Fig. 1060), the dimensions fix the locations of the sills and studs and therefore also those of the walls. On the floor plan (Fig. 1057), the figures give the outside dimensions of the building and the inside dimensions of the rooms, since the owner usually desires to know them.

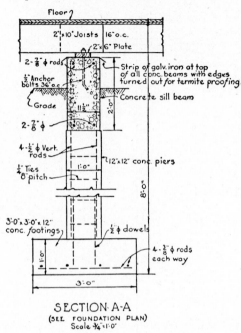

SECTION A-A
(SEE FOUNDATION PLAN)
Scale ¾"=1'-0"

FIG. 1063   Interior Sill and Other Details.

In some cases, it may be well to show the center lines of the walls; however, if these center lines are not definitely marked in the building, it is safer for the builder to make his measurements from the side of a wall which is in existence than from the center of the wall which must be determined by measurement or by calculation.

In certain cases, for example, the spacing of columns, windows, recurring ornaments, etc., it is better to give dimensions from center to center.

In modular design (§ 557) dimension lines terminate in grid lines where possible.

555. Detail Drawings. Having completed the general drawings, the architect prepares as many detail drawings as seem necessary. For a one-story cottage, it is generally sufficient to prepare a detail drawing showing the framing of the floors, the roof, and the walls (Figs. 1060, 1061, and 1062), the construction of the windows and doors and a window and door schedule (Figs. 1064 and 1065), the construction of the fireplace (Fig. 1066), and that of the kitchen cabinet (Fig. 1067).

For a two-story building, it is desirable to prepare detail drawings also of the stair construction (Fig. 1068). In planning stairs, it is important to secure correct proportions for the rise and the run of the stairs. Good results are secured if stairs are built so that the run plus twice the rise equals $24\frac{1}{2}''$.

For larger and more complicated buildings than the cottage represented in Figs. 1057 to 1067, many additional detail drawings must be prepared, as illustrated in Fig. 1069. To be able to prepare good detail drawings, the draftsman needs much ingenuity, a wide experience, and access to books and magazines dealing with construction details.

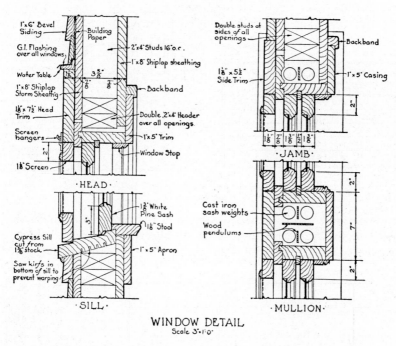

FIG. 1064　Detail Showing Construction of Window Frames.

Detail drawings are generally prepared to scales of one-sixteenth ($\frac{3}{4}$ in. = 1 ft), one-eighth ($1\frac{1}{2}$ in. = 1 ft), one-fourth (3 in. = 1 ft), one-half (6 in. = 1 ft), or full size.

556. Shop Drawings. After the contract for the construction of the building has been awarded, the contractor or the respective subcontractors prepare full-size detail or shop drawings of the particular parts of the structure which they are to supply. The shop drawings are submitted to the architect for his approval or rejection before the production of the part represented is begun.

Shop drawings relate principally to the installation of interior finish, such as tile and marble work, special doors and windows, cabinet work, lighting fixtures, elevators, heaters, refrigerators, and pipe lines. These details belong more properly to the various fields of engineering than to that of architecture, and cannot be considered further in this brief treatment of architectural drawing.

557. Dimensional or Modular Coordination. Every building is composed of a large number of small parts. If these small parts are of a size and shape so that they can be fitted together without cutting on the job the cost of construction and the cost of planning such construction is lower than it would be otherwise. To bring this condition about, a committee of the Amer-

DOOR SCHEDULE

MK	SIZE	DESCRIPTION
1	3'-0" x 7'-0 x 1¾"	6 Pan. W.P.
2	3'-0" x 7'-0"x 1⅛"	1 Pan. Screen
3	2'-8" x 6'-8"x 1⅜"	1 Pan. W.P.
4	2'-6" x 6'-8"x 1⅜"	" " "
5	2'-0" x 6'-8"x 1⅜"	" " '
6	2'-6" x 6'-8"x 1⅜"	" " " D. Acting
7	PR.2'-6"x6'-8"x1⅜"	15 Lt. French
8	2'-6" x 6'-8"x 1⅜"	Upper pan. Glass
9	2'-6" x 6'-8"x 1⅛"	2 pan. Screen

WINDOW SCHEDULE

MK	SIZE OF GLASS	DESCRIPTION
A	30" x 28"	2Lt. Check Rail
B	26" x 28"	" " "
C	28" x 28"	" " "
D	24" x 14"	" " "
E	24" x 16"	" " "

FIG. 1065   Door and Window Schedules.

ican Standards Association was organized in 1939 and, acting under the sponsorship of the American Institute of Architects and the Producers Council Inc., the committee adopted 4″ as the spacing for a three-dimensional grid

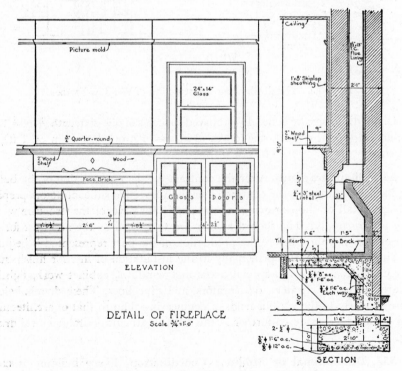

ELEVATION

DETAIL OF FIREPLACE
Scale ¾"=1'-0"

SECTION

FIG. 1066   Detail Showing Construction of Fireplace.

(Fig. 1070). This grid has been approved as the American Standard basis for the coordination of building materials and equipment. The 4″ spacing of the grid is known as the American Standard module.

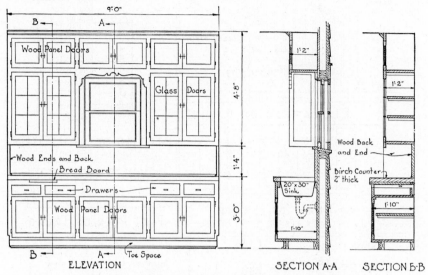

FIG. 1067   Detail Showing Construction of Kitchen Cabinet.

In classic architecture, the module was used as a unit of measurement and equaled one-half the diameter of the column at the base of the shaft. This module was subdivided into thirty equal parts so that all the elements of the orders could be dimensioned in terms of the module and its parts (Fig. 1056).

In modular coordination the module is used *only as the unit of measurement for the standard grid.* Since building parts are related to this grid *only* in order to effect their coordination with each other and since they must generally be joined by mortar or nails or bolts, or must overlap, as in the case of shingles and clapboards, the building parts are only rarely equal to some multiple of the module.

Thus, as shown in Figs. 1071 and 1072, brick widths, heights, and lengths are related to the module and the grid so that the brick size *plus* the joint may be expressed in terms of 4″. Brick sizes are given in nominal dimensions very much like lumber sizes. For example, a 4″ × 6″ beam is actually $3\frac{5}{8}″ \times 5\frac{5}{8}″$; a 4″ × 4″ × 8″ brick, to be laid with $\frac{3}{8}″$ mortar joints (Fig. 1071), is actually $3\frac{5}{8}″ \times 3\frac{5}{8}″ \times 7\frac{5}{8}″$; and a 4″ × $2\frac{2}{3}″$ × 8″ brick, to be laid with $\frac{3}{8}″$ mortar joints, is actually $3\frac{5}{8}″ \times 2\frac{7}{24}″ \times 7\frac{5}{8}″$. If the mortar joints are to be $\frac{1}{2}″$ instead of $\frac{3}{8}″$, the brick sizes are correspondingly smaller and the actual thickness of a nominal 8″ wall is $7\frac{1}{2}″$. The designing architect must determine which sizes of brick are available in the territory where the building is to be erected.

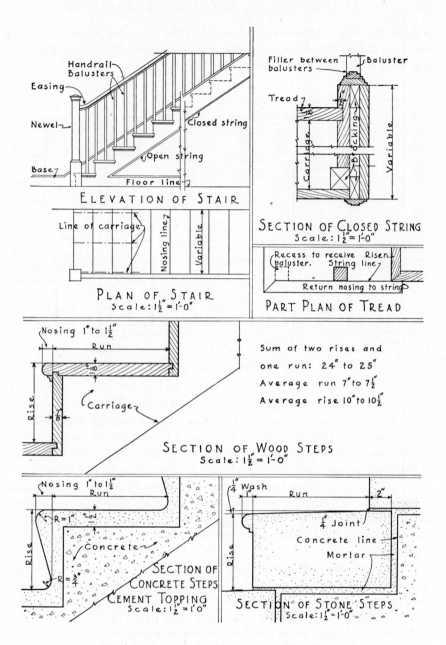

Handrail
Balusters
Easing
Newel
Base
Open string
Closed string
Floor line

ELEVATION OF STAIR

Line of carriage
Nosing line
Variable

PLAN OF STAIR
Scale: $1\frac{1}{2}'' = 1'\text{-}0''$

Filler between balusters
Baluster
Tread
Carriage
Blocking
Variable

SECTION OF CLOSED STRING
Scale: $1\frac{1}{2}'' = 1'\text{-}0''$

Recess to receive Riser
baluster.
String line
Return nosing to string

PART PLAN OF TREAD

Nosing 1" to $1\frac{1}{2}''$
Run
$\frac{1}{100}$
Rise
$\frac{1}{8}$
Carriage

Sum of two rises and
one run: 24" to 25"
Average run 7" to $7\frac{1}{2}''$
Average rise 10" to $10\frac{1}{2}''$

SECTION OF WOOD STEPS
Scale: $1\frac{1}{2}'' = 1'\text{-}0''$

Nosing 1" to $1\frac{1}{2}''$
Run
R = 1"
Rise
Concrete
R = $\frac{3}{4}''$

SECTION OF
CONCRETE STEPS
CEMENT TOPPING
Scale: $1\frac{1}{2}'' = 1'\text{-}0''$

$\frac{1}{4}''$ Wash
Run
2"
$\frac{1}{4}''$ Joint
Concrete line
Mortar
Rise

SECTION OF STONE STEPS
Scale: $1\frac{1}{2}'' = 1'\text{-}0''$

FIG. 1068 Detail Showing Stair Construction.

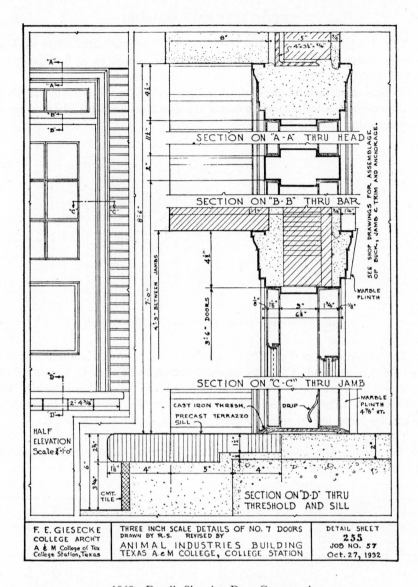

SECTION ON "A-A" THRU HEAD

SECTION ON "B-B" THRU BAR

MARBLE PLINTH

SECTION ON "C-C" THRU JAMB

MARBLE PLINTH 4⅞" HT.

CAST IRON THRESH,
PRECAST TERRAZZO SILL

DRIP

HALF ELEVATION
Scale ¾"=1'-0"

SECTION ON "D-D" THRU THRESHOLD AND SILL

CMT. TILE

7'-0"
4'-3" BETWEEN JAMBS
8'-6"
3'-6" DOORS

F. E. GIESECKE
COLLEGE ARCH'T
A & M College of Tex
College Station, Texas

THREE INCH SCALE DETAILS OF NO. 7 DOORS
DRAWN BY R.S.   REVISED BY
ANIMAL INDUSTRIES BUILDING
TEXAS A. & M. COLLEGE, COLLEGE STATION

DETAIL SHEET
255
JOB NO. 57
Oct. 27, 1932

FIG. 1069   Detail Showing Door Construction.

687

The standard 4″ module and the standard 4″ grid are applied to working drawings, plans, elevations, sections, and details as well as to building parts and to equipment items.

In dimensioning modular designs, it is customary to use arrowheads where the dimension line terminates on one of the grid lines and dots where it terminates on other than grid lines.

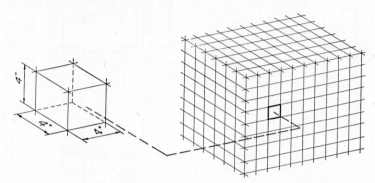

FIG. 1070   The Standard 4″ Module and 4″ Grid.

The illustrations of Figs. 1073 and 1074 show how a window opening is referenced to the grid. The dimensions R, shown in Fig. 1074, depend on the construction of the frame which is to be fitted into the window opening. The grid lines to which window and door openings are referenced in modular design are indicated by semibracket symbols as shown in Fig. 1074.

The illustration of Fig. 1075 shows a small building plan on a modular grid but the module is 16 times 4″ or 5′–4″ and is called a *large planning module*. In this case the center lines of the walls coincide with the grid lines.

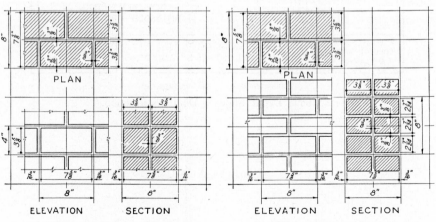

FIG. 1071   A Modular Detail of a
Brick Wall with 4″ Courses.

FIG. 1072   A Modular Detail of a
Brick Wall with $2\frac{2}{3}$″ Courses.

Modular sizes of brick, structural tile, glazed tile, concrete masonry, glass block, metal and wood windows and doors, and many other building materials and equipment are now available throughout the country. This availability

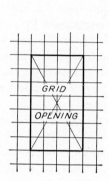

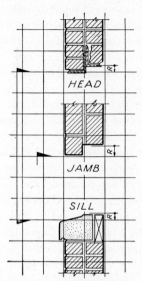

FIG. 1073   A Grid
Opening in a Wall.

FIG. 1074   A Modular De-
tail of a Window Opening.

has encouraged architects and builders to apply the principles of modular coordination and thereby derive the benefits resulting from the use of these modular products.

Additional information can be secured from the *A 62 Guide for Modular Coordination* published by the Modular Service Association, 110 Arlington St., Boston, Mass.

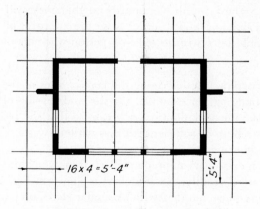

FIG. 1075   A Large Planning Module.

558. Federal Housing Administration. The Federal Housing Administration (FHA) was established in 1934 to encourage improvements in housing standards and conditions, and to guide the creation of a sound mortgage market. The powers of the Administration are exercised by the Federal Housing Administrator who has offices in the several states and territories. If a person wishes to buy or build or improve a house and needs financial aid, he can secure that aid from FHA provided that the site of the building and the proposed construction of the building meet the standards prescribed by the administrator.

To secure this financial aid, an application must be made through an approved lending institution and must be accompanied by a description of the building site and by plans and specifications for the proposed building. If the application is approved, FHA will guarantee the mortgage loan and the loan will be made by one of the approved institutions if the borrower makes the required initial payment and agrees to pay the remainder in monthly installments which are based on his ability to pay.

The importance of good planning and good construction are constantly emphasized by FHA, and its architectural staff is frequently able to offer suggestions for improving proposed designs. During the construction of the building FHA makes at least three inspections to see that the construction of the building is in accordance with the plans and specifications.

The standards prescribed for building sites and buildings by the Administrator are described in FHA publications which are available to architects and to prospective builders. The prescribed standards vary with the climatic conditions of the district in which the building is to be located; for example, the standards for a building in Minnesota differ from those for a building in Florida.

Several of the construction details suggested by FHA were redrawn from one of the FHA publications and are shown in Fig. 1076.

Many persons who do not need financial aid for building comply with FHA standards. They comply voluntarily so that they will be assured of a well-constructed building and in order to secure approval of the building by FHA if they should later wish to sell to a person who cannot buy without an FHA loan.

559. Construction. To determine the correct sizes of the several parts of the frame of a building, for example, the size and spacing of floor joists, it is necessary to make a calculation for each case so that the resulting floors will have sufficient strength or sufficient stiffness without waste of material. Since an architect or his engineer has to make many such calculations during his routine work, it is customary to prepare charts from which the desired information can be obtained readily. Such a chart is shown in Fig. 1050, and its use fully explained in connection therewith. A similar chart, prepared for the determination of the correct size, span, and spacing of rafters, is shown in Fig. 1049.

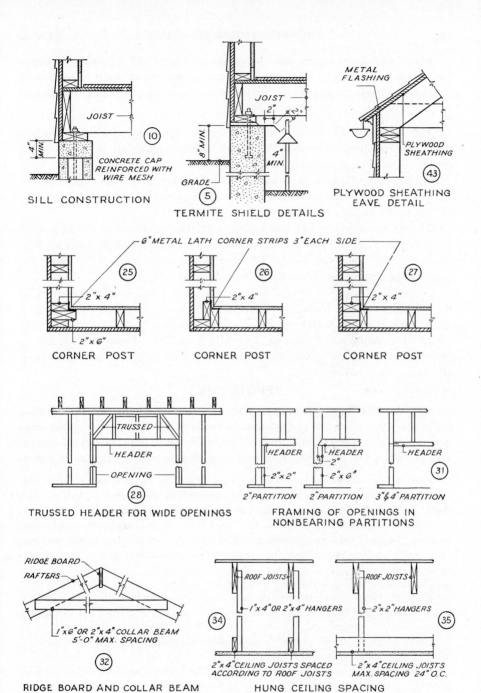

FIG. 1076   Some of the Construction Details Suggested by FHA.

691

Many additional charts may be prepared which will materially simplify the design of constructional elements formed of steel or of plain or reinforced concrete, as well as the design of foundations, heating systems, ventilating systems, etc.

560. Symbols. To simplify the construction of working drawings, symbols have been adopted to represent certain building materials or to represent certain fixtures or appliances. However, since these symbols have not been universally adopted, it is important to include a key to the symbols either in the plans or in the specifications, and to call especial attention in the specifications to the various materials to be employed.

The ASA symbols to indicate various materials in elevation and in section are shown in Figs. 405 and 406. If drawings are to a large scale, more specific symbols should be used instead of those in Figs. 405 and 406. These are available in architectural handbooks (see Appendix 44).

A system of symbols to represent various pipe lines and fixtures used in the plumbing and heating equipment of buildings is shown in Appendixes 6 and 7, pp. 785-786. A system of symbols to represent details of the electric wiring of a building is shown in Appendix 9, p. 788. These symbols are in general use by architects and engineers, and the majority of them have been adopted as standard by ASA.

PROBLEMS

561. Architectural Drawing. The following problems are intended to guide the student in the preparation of working drawings for building construction, and to present an introduction to the study of architectural design. The problems are to be modified and amplified by the teacher as required.

Prob. 1 Draw a plan of a small residence similar to one of those shown in Fig. 1053, with such modifications as the student may wish to make, or of a residence with which the student is familiar and which he can examine and measure.

The drawing should be to a scale of $\frac{1}{4}'' = 1$ ft ($\S$ 54), and walls, doors, windows, shelving, fireplace, cabinets, plumbing and heating fixtures, electric lights, switches, convenience outlets, etc., should be represented as shown in Fig. 1057 and in Appendixes 7-9.

The drawing should be fully dimensioned and lettered.

Prob. 2 Draw one or more of the four orders shown in Fig. 1056 to a scale not smaller than $\frac{1}{2}'' = 1$ module, and name the several parts as shown for the Corinthian order.

Prob. 3 Draw details of one or more of the following: window, door, cornice, fireplace, kitchen cabinet, and book case.

In this problem the student's drawings should be from measurement of actual construction or according to Figs. 1064-1067 with such modifications as the student may wish to make.

The scales for these details should be $\frac{3}{4}''$ or $1\frac{1}{2}'' = 1$ ft.

Prob. 4 Draw a section, similar to that shown in Fig. 1062, of the building of Prob. 1 to a scale of $\frac{1}{4}'' = 1$ ft.

Prob. 5 Draw the front elevation of the building of Prob. 1 to a scale of $\frac{1}{4}'' = 1$ ft. This assignment may be enlarged by including a side elevation and the rear elevation.

Prob. 6 Draw a combination foundation and floor-framing plan, similar to that shown in Fig. 1060, of the building of Prob. 1.

The roof-framing plan, the ceiling-framing plan, and one of the wall-framing plans should also be drawn.

Prob. 7 Draw a perspective of the building of Prob. 1 similar to one of those shown in Fig. 1053 or to that in Fig. 610, p. 326, choosing the station point, the center of vision, and the position of the building with respect to the picture plane so that the best appearance of the building will result.

Prob. 8 Make a modular drawing, similar to Fig. 1072, of a 12″ wall, built of hollow tile, nominal size $6'' \times 5\frac{1}{3}'' \times 12''$, with $\frac{1}{2}''$ mortar joints. What is the actual size of the tile?

Prob. 9 Make a modular drawing, showing the elevation and vertical section, of a portion of an 8″ wall with a window opening 3 ft wide and 5 ft high, using brick courses $2\frac{2}{3}''$ high and the structural details shown in Fig. 1074.

CHAPTER 27

Structural Drawing

562. Wood Construction. The principal woods employed in construction are yellow pine, white pine, fir, cypress, and oak. A *Manual of Standard Wood Construction* is issued by the Southern Pine Association, which gives the standard dimensions, physical properties, rules for grading timber, and other information of value to the structural draftsman.

Wood is in common use in building construction for sills, columns, joists, studs, and rafters. Typical drawings of wood structures are shown in Chapter 26, and in Figs. 1077–1082. Additional construction details may be seen in a bulletin on *House Framing Details* issued by the National Lumber Manufacturers' Association.

Wood is in common use in the construction of roof trusses and sometimes in the construction of bridge trusses. In these cases, wood is generally used in

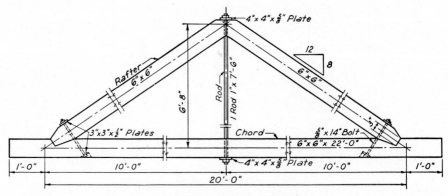

FIG. 1077　A King-Rod Truss.

conjunction with steel plates and rods, arranged so that the latter take the tensile stresses, because it is difficult to connect wooden members so that their tensile strengths can be developed to a satisfactory degree. A king-rod truss is shown in Fig. 1077, and a Howe truss is shown in Fig. 1078. Either truss

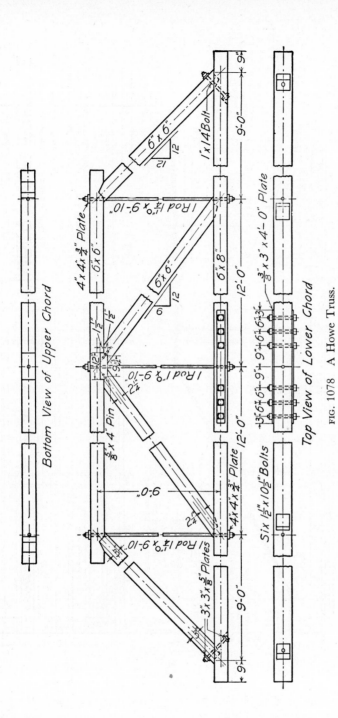

FIG. 1078   A Howe Truss.

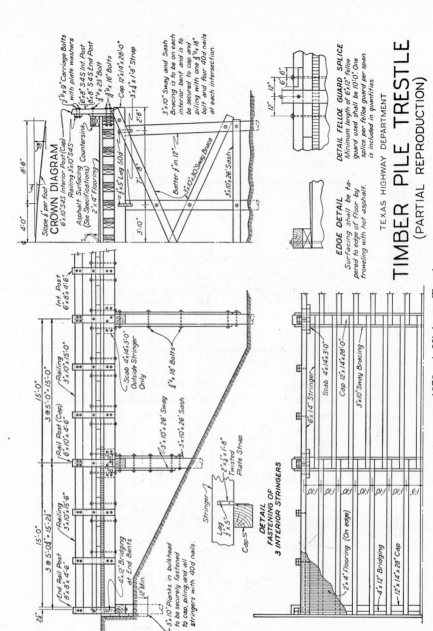

TIMBER PILE TRESTLE
(PARTIAL REPRODUCTION)

TEXAS HIGHWAY DEPARTMENT

FIG. 1079 A Highway Trestle.

(Based on a Design by the Texas Highway Department, Austin.)

can be used to support a roof and a suspended ceiling. The method of preparing a drawing of such a structure is illustrated in the two figures. It should be noted that the drawings are constructed on the center lines of the truss members, that the overall length of a wooden member is not given if its ends are not square, and that two scales are used, one for the center lines of the truss and the other, generally twice as large, for the truss members. It should be noted also that it is customary, in structural drawings, not to break the dimension line but to letter the dimension above the line.

Wood is sometimes used in the construction of trestles for highways and for railways; an example of such structures is illustrated in Fig. 1079, in which an assembly drawing of the structure and a detail drawing of some of the parts are shown.

In preparing drawings, especially detail drawings, of wooden structures, the student must keep in mind that commercial timbers are not "full size"; for example, a joist which has a *nominal* size of $2'' \times 10''$ has an *actual* size of $1\frac{5}{8}'' \times 9\frac{1}{2}''$, and a flooring board which has a *nominal* size of $1'' \times 4''$ has an *actual* size of $\frac{25}{32}'' \times 3\frac{1}{4}''$.

563. Metal-Ring Connectors. A novel method of connecting timbers in structures (Figs. 1080 and 1081) was recently developed in Europe and intro-

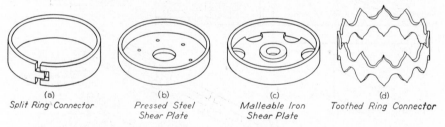

(a)   (b)   (c)   (d)
Split Ring Connector   Pressed Steel   Malleable Iron   Toothed Ring Connector
                       Shear Plate   Shear Plate

FIG. 1080   Metal Connectors for Timber Structures.

duced into the United States by the U. S. Department of Commerce, and is being developed by the Timber Engineering Company of Washington, D. C. The method consists of using either a toothed ring, called an alligator, or a split ring (Fig. 1080). If the toothed ring is used, it is placed between the two members to be connected and these are drawn together by a bolt so that the teeth of the ring are forced into the two members and the ring thus assists in transmitting stress from one member to the other. If the split ring is used, a groove is cut into each of the two members to be connected, the ring is placed in the grooves, and the two members are held together by means of a bolt, as shown in Fig. 1081. The open joint of the ring should be in a direction at right angles to that of the stress, so that as the stress is applied the ring is deformed slightly and transmits the pressure to the wood within the ring as well as to that without. With this connection, the tensile and shearing strengths of wood are more developed than by the ordinary methods of connec-

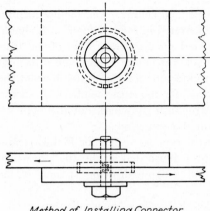

Method of Installing Connector

FIG. 1081   Method of Installing Split-Ring Connectors.

tion, and it is possible to use timber in tension much more economically.

The use of these connectors is shown in Fig. 1082. A wooden highway bridge having a span of 180 feet was constructed in California (*Engineering News Record*, Jan. 31, 1935) and a series of roof trusses having a span of 150 feet were erected for an aircraft plant; the roof trusses were supported by columns 54 feet high made of laminated wood. Every column was made of two posts bolted together, each post measuring $17\frac{1}{2}'' \times 34\frac{3}{8}''$ in cross section (*Engineering News Record*, Oct. 21, 1943).

LUMBER			
No.	Size	Length	F.B.M.
4	3″x8″	20'-0″	160
1	2″x6″	8'-0″	11
4	2″x6″	10'-0″	40
2	2″x6″	12'-0″	24
2	3″x6″	10'-0″	30
2	3″x6″	12'-0″	36
2	3″x6″	16'-0″	48
		Total F.B.M. =	349

HARDWARE		
No.	Item	Size
40	Split Rings	4″
14	Machine Bolts	$\frac{3}{4}$″x 13″
28	Washers	$\frac{2}{3}$″x3$\frac{1}{2}$x2$\frac{1}{4}$

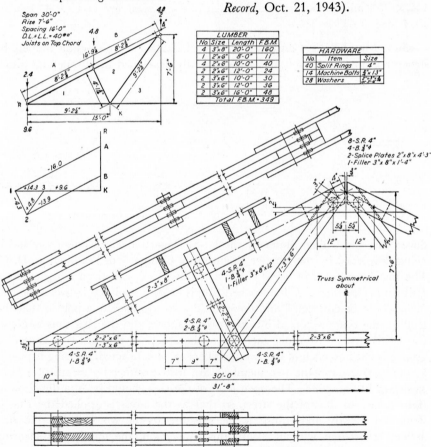

FIG. 1082 A Roof Truss.   (Based on a Design by Timber Engineering Company, Washington.)

564. Steel and Iron Construction. Cast iron, wrought iron, steel, aluminum, and many other metals are used in construction, but only steel structures can be considered in this brief chapter. Structural steel is available in many standard shapes. The principal shapes—*square bar, round bar, plate, equal-leg angle, unequal-leg angle, bulb angle, channel, standard beam, wide-flange shape, structural tee, tee, zee, crane rail,* and *pipe column*—are shown in Fig. 1083.

Structural tees are obtained, as indicated in Fig. 1083, by cutting the webs of wide-flanged shapes, or other beams, in two.

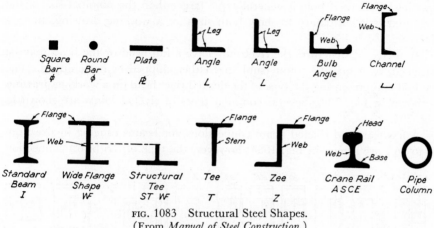

FIG. 1083   Structural Steel Shapes.
(From *Manual of Steel Construction.*)

565. Abbreviated Shape Designations. In preparing a working drawing using structural steel shapes, it is desirable to have a system of standard abbreviations for designating the several steel shapes without the use of inch and pound marks. The following system, based largely on the *Manual of Steel Construction*, (§ 567) is recommended.

A SYSTEM OF ABBREVIATED SHAPE DESIGNATIONS

Square Bar	Size–symbol–length	$\frac{3}{4}$ ⬜ 6′–4
Round Bar	Size–symbol–length	$\frac{7}{8}$ ⬤ 8′–6
Plate	Symbol–width–thickness–length	Pl 6 × $\frac{1}{4}$ × 9
Equal Leg Angle	Symbol–leg–leg–thickness–length	L 3 × 3 × $\frac{3}{8}$ × 12′–0
Unequal Leg Angle	Symbol–long leg–short leg– thickness–length	L 2 × $1\frac{1}{2}$ × $\frac{1}{4}$ × 9′–1
Bulb Angle	Symbol–web–flange–weight–length	Bulb L 5 × $2\frac{1}{2}$ × 7.3 × 8′–3
Channel	Height–symbol–weight–length	6 ⌐ 10.5 × 15′–4
Standard Beam	Height–symbol–weight–length	12 I 31.8 × 10′–2
Wide Flange Shape	Height–symbol–weight–length	8 WF 17 × 30′–6$\frac{7}{8}$
Structural Tee	Symbol–height–weight–length	ST4 WF 8.5 × 30′–6$\frac{7}{8}$
Tee	Symbol–flange–stem–weight–length	T 5 × 3 × 11.5 × 11′–5
Zee	Symbol–web–flange–weight–length	Z 5 × $3\frac{1}{4}$ × 14.0 × 7′–11
Rail	Weight per yard–name	80 lb rail
Pipe	Nominal diameter–name	4″ extra strong pipe

566. Rivets and Riveting. Structural rivets are made of soft carbon steel and are available in sizes ranging from $\frac{1}{2}''$ to $1\frac{1}{2}''$. Rivets which are driven in the shop are called *shop rivets* and those which are driven in the field are called *field rivets*.

In a working drawing field rivets are shown by black circles equal in diameter to the diameter of the rivet hole and shop rivets are shown by circles equal in diameter to the diameter of the rivet head. The size of the rivet-head drawing is approximately one and one-half times the size of the rivet hole drawing. The rivet hole is generally $\frac{1}{16}''$ larger than the nominal size of the rivet and it is customary to show both sizes on a working drawing, thus: $\frac{3}{4}$ rivets and $\frac{13}{16}$ holes.

In a riveted structure, the rivet may have a full head or the head may be flattened, or it may be countersunk and either chipped or not chipped. The method of representing the type of the desired rivet head on a working drawing is shown in Fig. 795. Several common types of riveted joints are shown in Fig. 794.

A few standard riveted beam connections, for beams ranging in size from 5″ to 36″, are shown in Fig. 1084; however, the type of the beam connection

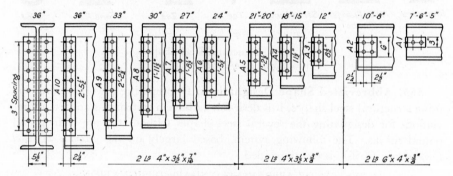

FIG. 1084   Riveted Beam Connections.
(From *Manual of Steel Construction.*)

depends not only on the size of the beam but also on the load which the connection must transmit. Detailed information regarding these connections is given in the *Manual of Steel Construction* (§ 567).

When a beam is to be placed between two other structural members and riveted thereto, the beam is cut $\frac{1}{2}''$ shorter than its span and the back of the angle projects $\frac{1}{4}''$ beyond the end of the beam.

The *gage* of a line of rivets is the distance from the back of an angle, or other shape, to the line of rivets, or the distance between two parallel lines of rivets. The *pitch* of a line of rivets is the distance between the centers of consecutive rivets in the line of rivets.

In aircraft and other similar construction it is sometimes difficult or impossible to reach both ends of a rivet so that the rivet cannot be driven in the ordinary way and it becomes necessary to use rivets which are constructed so that after the shank of the rivet has been inserted in the rivet hole, the shank can be expanded so that its lower end will serve the purpose of a rivet head; these rivets are called *blind rivets*.

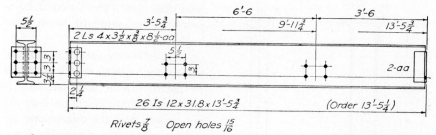

FIG. 1085 A Floor Joist. (Based on a Design by American Bridge Company.)

567. Steel Construction Manual. The American Institute of Steel Construction, New York, N.Y., publishes a manual which gives detailed information about (a) the dimensions, weights, and properties of rolled steel structural shapes, (b) the preparation of working drawings, (c) the allowable loads on structures under stipulated conditions, (d) specifications and codes applicable to steel buildings, and (e) many other subjects of importance to draftsmen and to engineers.

The fifth edition of the manual was published in 1947. The student is referred to this manual for detailed information.

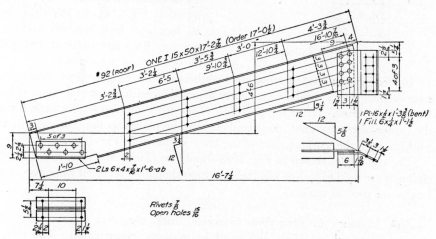

FIG. 1086 A Rafter. (Based on a Design by American Bridge Company.)

568. Steel Structures. Steel structures are fabricated by riveting (Figs. 1085–1088) or welding (Figs. 1010–1012) the several shapes into structural members and then the members into complete structural frames.

The method of preparing working drawings of simple structural members is illustrated in Figs. 1085, 1086, and 1087, which show, respectively, a floor joist composed of a standard beam and four angles; a rafter composed of a standard beam, two angles, and one bent plate; and a short column composed of one standard beam, four angles and a base plate.

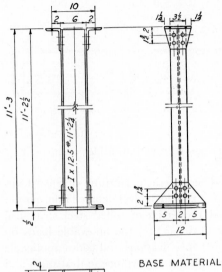

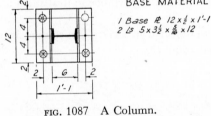

BASE MATERIAL

1 Base ℞ 12 x ½ x 1'-1
2 ℄s 5 x 3½ x ⅝ x 12

FIG. 1087   A Column.

The following special features of these three working drawings should be noted: (a) the inch symbol ″ is omitted, (b) the dimension lines are not broken and the dimensions are written above the dimension lines, (c) when progressive dimensions are given from one origin (Fig. 1085), the dimension line is broken and the progressive dimensions are written near the outer arrowhead and (d) the inclination of a member is given by drawing a right triangle and expressing the inclination by the tangent of the angle whose base is 12.

The method of preparing a working drawing of a riveted truss is illustrated in Fig. 1088. In this drawing all foot and inch symbols and all fraction lines are omitted and yet all dimensions are clear.

In designing a riveted truss, all members should be placed so that their *center-of-gravity* lines coincide, as nearly as possible, with the *working* lines (Fig. 1082) of the truss. When the *gage lines* of the truss members differ little from the center-of-gravity lines, the members may be placed so that the gage lines coincide with the working lines of the truss as shown in Fig. 1088.

The *clip* angles shown in Fig. 1088 should be placed as shown there when channels are used as *purlins*, but their position should be reversed when wooden beams are used as purlins.

569. Masonry Construction. Concrete, brick, tile, terra cotta, and stone are the principal materials employed in masonry construction. The component parts of a masonry structure are cemented to each other with mortar and, when necessary, attached with metal ties so that all will act as a unit in resisting the forces to which the structure is subjected. In addition to this, the individual parts are shaped and laid so that they are bonded to each other by their respective forms and positions.

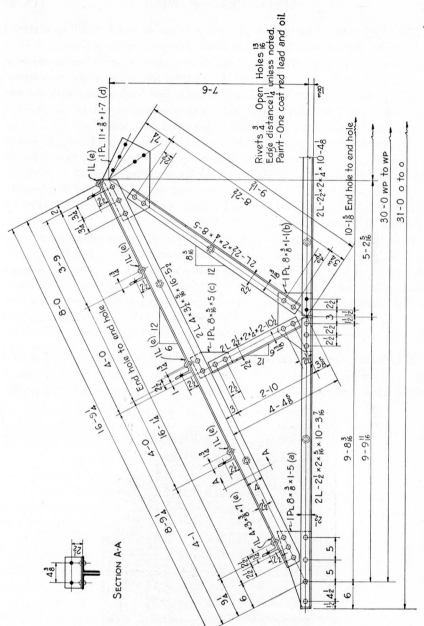

FIG. 1088   A Riveted Truss.   (Based on a Design by Fort Worth Structural Steel Company.)

703

570. Concrete Construction. Concrete is an artificial building material made by mixing sand and gravel or other fine and coarse aggregate with a cementing material, generally portland cement and water. The strength of concrete varies with the quality and the relative quantities of the constituent materials, with the manner of mixing, placing, and curing, and with the age of the concrete. The compressive strength of concrete, at the age of 28 days, varies from about 1500 to about 4500 lb per sq in. The tensile strength of concrete is about one-twelfth that of the compressive strength. Portland cement is an artificial hydraulic cement in distinction from the natural hydraulic cements found in many localities; it derived its name from its color which resembles that of a famous building stone found on the island of Portland in southern England. The first portland cement was manufactured in 1824 by J. Aspden in Leeds, England.

Since the tensile strength of concrete is very low, the usefulness of concrete as a building material can be materially improved by combining it with steel rods in such a way that the two materials cooperate in resisting the stresses produced in the structure. Concrete, combined in this manner with steel rods, is called *reinforced concrete;* without the addition of steel rods or wires, it is called *concrete* or, sometimes, *plain concrete.* Concrete with little or no reinforcement is used in pavements, massive foundations, and similar structures.

571. Reinforced Concrete Construction. The method of reinforcing concrete with metal had its origin in France where, about 1850, Lambot built a boat of reinforced mortar and, about 1861, Monier constructed flower pots of

FIG. 1089   Reinforced Concrete Frame.
(John Lovejoy Elliott Houses, New York City Housing Administration.)

wire frames enclosed in cement mortar. A patent on this method of constructing vessels was granted Monier in 1867 and later other patents were granted him on the construction of straight and curved beams and other structural elements. The Monier patents were sold to German and Austrian engineers in 1884 and a publication by G. A. Waysz, titled *The Monier System, Iron Frames Enclosed in Cement* was issued in 1887. Since then intensive research has been conducted in Europe and in America to determine the best method of manufacturing portland cement, of making, placing, and curing concrete, and of designing and placing metal reinforcement in concrete. As the result of this

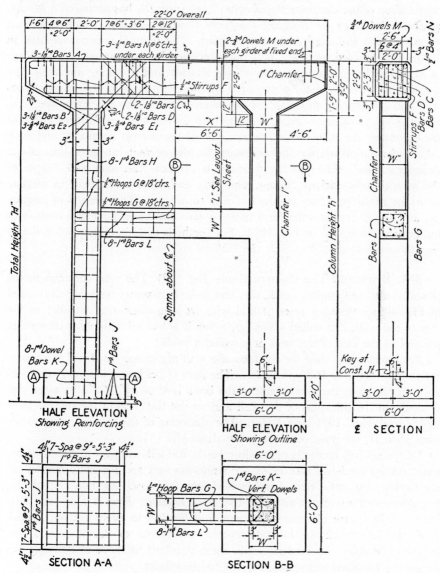

FIG. 1090   An Interior Bent of a Highway Bridge.
(Based on a Design by the Texas Highway Department, Austin.)

extensive research it is now possible to construct large and complicated structures of reinforced concrete, as illustrated in Figs. 1089 and 1090.

572. Reinforced Concrete Drawing. The design of the reinforcing for a reinforced concrete structure and the preparation of the corresponding drawings is complicated. In order to simplify this work and to secure uniformity in the many engineering offices, the American Concrete Institute, with the cooperation of the Concrete Reinforcing Steel Institute, has prepared a *Manual of Standard Practice for Detailing Reinforced Concrete Structures* which has been approved as a Proposed A. C. I. Standard. The manual was copyrighted in 1944 and reprinted in 1947. It is recommended in the manual that two sets of drawings be prepared, an *engineering drawing* and a *placing drawing*. The engineering drawing is to be prepared by the engineer who designs the structure and the placing drawing, by the manufacturer who fabricates the reinforcing steel. The engineering drawing is to show the general arrangement of the structure, the sizes and reinforcements of the several members, and such other information as may be necessary for the correct interpretation of the designer's ideas. The placing drawing is to show the sizes and shapes of the several rods, stirrups, hoops, ties, etc., and to arrange them in tabular forms for ready reference by the building contractor. The method of preparing an engineering drawing for a two-way slab and beam floor of a multistory building is illustrated in Fig. 1092. For methods of preparing placing drawings the student should consult the manual referred to above.

573. Brick and Tile Construction.—Fig. 1091. The most common methods of laying and bonding brick, tile, and stone in masonry walls are illustrated in Fig. 1091. When a brick is laid with its long dimension parallel to the face of the wall, it is called a *stretcher;* when it is laid with its short dimension parallel to the face of the wall, it is called a *header.*

Brick which are used for the face of a wall are called *face brick;* the others are called *common* or *backing-up brick.* The sizes of brick and tile vary considerably; in one case, the *nominal* size of the brick is $4'' \times 2\frac{2}{3}'' \times 8''$; its *actual* size depends on the thickness of the wall and on the thickness of the mortar joint (§ 557 and Figs. 1071 and 1072). The thickness of the mortar joint varies from $\frac{1}{8}''$ to $1''$; the most common being about $\frac{1}{2}''$.

Of the several methods of bonding brick, the following are the most common: *running bond*—all face brick are stretchers and are generally bonded to the backing by metal ties; *American bond*—the face brick are laid alternately, five courses of stretchers and one course of headers; *Flemish bond*—the face brick are laid with alternate stretchers and headers in every course; *English bond*—the face brick are laid alternately, one course of stretchers and one course of headers. In modern work, these standard methods of bonding are frequently modified to produce various artistic effects.

When brick are laid on edge so that the ends are in the face of the wall, the resulting course is called a *rowlock course;* when they are laid on end so that the edges are in the face of the wall, the resulting course is called a *soldier course*.

The mortar joints in brick walls are finished in various ways; the principal methods are illustrated in Fig. 1091.

Structural clay tile are manufactured of different forms and sizes. Some of the *nominal* sizes are $4 \times 8 \times 12$, $6 \times 8 \times 12$, $8 \times 4 \times 8$, and $12 \times 8 \times 12$ inches; all are hollow and divided into several cells.

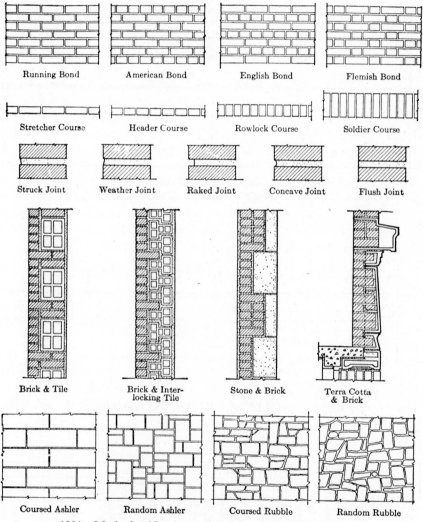

FIG. 1091   Methods of Laying and Bonding Brick, Tile, and Stone.

574. Stone Construction.—Fig. 1091. *Natural stone*, used in masonry construction, is generally limestone, marble, sandstone, or granite.

Ashlar (or *ashler*) masonry is formed of stones cut accurately to rectangular faces and laid in regular courses or at random with thin mortar joints.

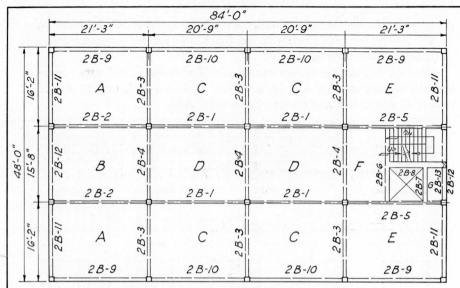

SECOND FLOOR FRAMING PLAN
ALL SLABS 5" THICK. DESIGN LIVE LOAD = 75 #/□'

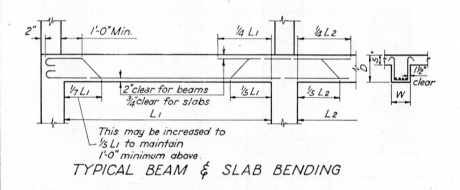

TYPICAL BEAM & SLAB BENDING

BEAM SCHEDULE - (INCOMPLETE)									
BEAM MARK	SIZE		STRAIGHT		TRUSSED		STIRRUPS		REMARKS
	W	D	NO.	SIZE	NO.	SIZE	NO.	SIZE	SPACING EACH END	

BEAM MARK	W	D	NO.	SIZE	NO.	SIZE	NO.	SIZE	SPACING EACH END	REMARKS
2B-1	11½	22	2	⅝φ	2	1φ	14	⅜φ	3-6-6-9-9-9-9	
2B-2	11½	22	2	¾φ	2	1φ	14	⅜φ	3-6-6-9-9-9-9	
2B-3	11½	16	2	¾φ	2	⅞φ	14	⅜φ	3-6-6-6-6-6-6	
2B-4	11½	16	2	⅝φ	2	¾φ	14	⅜φ	3-6-6-6-6-6-6	

FIG. 1092   The Engineering Drawing for a Two-Way Slab and Beam Floor.
(Based on the *Manual of the American Concrete Institute*.)

SLAB SCHEDULE - (INCOMPLETE)

SLAB MARK	DIRECTION	BAR SIZE	BAR SPACING			REMARKS
			BAND "a"	BAND "b"	BAND "c"	
A	N-S	½ ø	7½ W	7½	10	
	E-W	½ ø	9 W	9	12	
B	N-S	½ ø	9 W	9	12	
	E-W	½ ø	15	11½	15	
C	N-S	½ ø	12	9	12	
	E-W	½ ø	11½ W	11½	15	
D	N-S	½ ø	13	10	13	
	E-W	½ ø	15	11½	15	

NOTE: Suffix "W" after bar spacing denotes band adjacent to wall. OTHER SLABS NOT SHOWN.

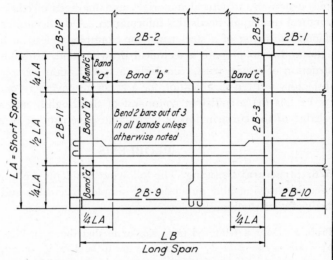

TYPICAL PLAN OF SLAB "A"

ENGINEERING DRAWING
SECOND FLOOR FRAMING PLAN
OFFICE BUILDING
FOR
TEXAS WELDING CO.
AUSTIN, TEXAS

BROWN & JONES - ARCHITECTS
WILSON & COTTINGHAM - ENGINEERS
AUSTIN, TEXAS

Rubble masonry is formed of stones of irregular shapes and laid in courses or at random with mortar joints of varying thickness.

Manufactured stone is concrete made of fine aggregate for the facing and coarse aggregate for the backing. The fine aggregate consists of screenings of limestone, marble, sandstone, or granite, so that the manufactured stone presents an appearance similar to that of natural stone. Manufactured stone is made of any desired shape, with or without architectural ornament.

Architectural terra cotta is a hard burned clay product and is used primarily for architectural decoration and for wall facing and wall coping.

Brick, stone, tile, and terra cotta are combined in many different ways in masonry construction. A few examples are shown in Figs. 1069 and 1091.

575. Conclusion. Considerable space has been given to descriptions of various structures, structural materials, and methods of construction because a structural draftsman needs this information. A draftsman cannot prepare a satisfactory drawing of a steel truss, for example, unless he has (a) the skill and the ability to prepare a technical drawing and (b) a knowledge of the construction of a steel truss. Similarly, a specification writer cannot prepare a satisfactory written specification for a concrete pavement or for a slate roof unless he has (a) a sufficient command of the English language and (b) a knowledge of the construction of a concrete pavement or of a slate roof.

PROBLEMS

576. Structural Drawing. The following problems are intended to afford practice in drawing and dimensioning simple structures, and in illustrating methods of construction.

Prob. 1   Draw a King-rod truss, similar to that shown in Fig. 1077, for a span of 16'–0" and a rise of 5'–4". The timbers are to be 4" × 6", on edge, and the rods, bolts, and plates similar in size to those shown in the figure.

Prob. 2   Draw a detail of a joint illustrating the use of the split-ring connector similar to one of the truss joints shown in Fig. 1082.

Prob. 3   With the dimensions taken from any structural-steel shape book, draw, half size, the heaviest and the lightest sections of the following shapes: 12" I, 12" channel, 8" angle, $6\frac{1}{2}$" tee, and 6" Z.

Prob. 4   Draw, half size, front views and sectional views of the double-riveted butt joint and the single-riveted lap joint shown in Fig. 794, using $\frac{1}{2}$" plates, $\frac{3}{8}$" cover plates, and $\frac{3}{4}$" rivets spaced approximately as shown in the figure. Also draw, to as large a scale as practicable, the conventional rivet symbols shown in Fig. 795.

Prob. 5   Draw a steel floor joist similar to that of Fig. 1085, or a steel rafter similar to that of Fig. 1086, and dimension as shown.

Note that the length of the joist and the distances from the end of the joist to the centers of the riveted connections are not to scale; whereas all detail dimensions are to scale. These variations from standard methods economize space and time.

Prob. 6 Draw front, side, and top views of the base of a steel column, similar to that shown in the upper part of Fig. 1087, the column to be 8 $W\!F$ 17 × 10′–6 resting on a 16 × 16 × $\frac{3}{4}$ base plate and attached thereto by means of two 6 × 6 × $\frac{1}{2}$ angles.

Prob. 7 Draw and dimension, as shown, the right-hand half of the roof truss of Fig. 1088. Draw the center lines of the truss to a scale of $\frac{3}{4}''$ = 1 ft and the truss members and details to a scale of $1\frac{1}{2}''$ = 1 ft.

Prob. 8 Draw to a scale of $\frac{1}{2}''$ = 1 ft and dimension as shown, the bridge bent of Fig. 1090, using $H = 18'-0''$, $L = 9'-0''$, and $W = 1'-9''$; all other dimensions as shown.

CHAPTER 28

Topographic Drawing

577. General Statement. A map is a drawing of a part or the whole of the earth's surface or of the celestial sphere. A bound collection of maps is

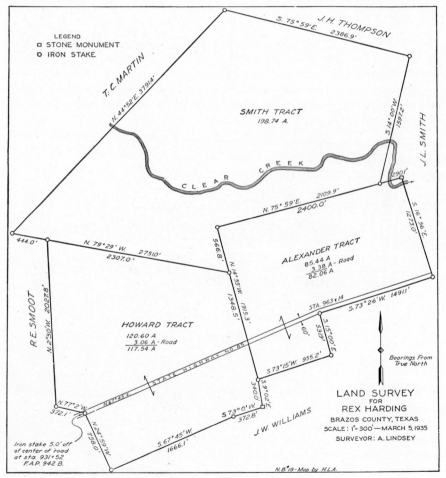

FIG. 1093 Land Survey.

712

called an *atlas*. If a map is prepared primarily for the use of seamen, it is generally known as a *chart*. A map of a small piece of land is called a *plot* or a *plat*. Figure 1093 is a plot of a farm which includes several tracts of land.

To show the bearing of a line, some engineers place a hyphen between the degrees and the minutes, thus: S 75°-35′ E; the hyphen is not necessary because the degree symbol (°) is sufficient to separate the degrees from the

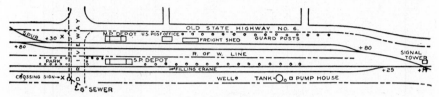

FIG. 1094   Railroad Yard.

minutes. When the bearing is in even degrees, it may be written S 75° E or S 75° 0′ E. The latter form is the better because it shows definitely that there are no *minutes* involved in the bearing.

If a map is drawn to a large scale, it is called a *plan*. Figure 1094 is a plan of a railroad yard. Figure 1095 is a plan or map of a portion of a city. Figure 1096 is a plan or map of a highway.

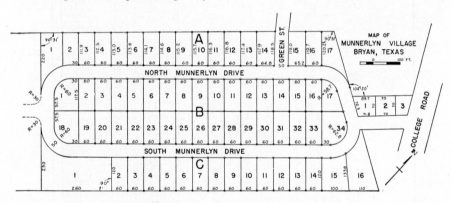

FIG. 1095   A Partial City Map.

If a map includes graphical representations of the principal natural and artificial features of the area represented, it is called a *topographic* map. The features represented include lakes, streams, canals, etc.; communication and transportation lines; buildings, bridges, and other structures; timber, standing and cut-over; fields, meadows, and marshes; and any other surface features of sufficient importance to be included. Generally, the elevations of the several portions of the area are represented by means of *contour lines*. Figure 1097 is a topographic map of a country estate.

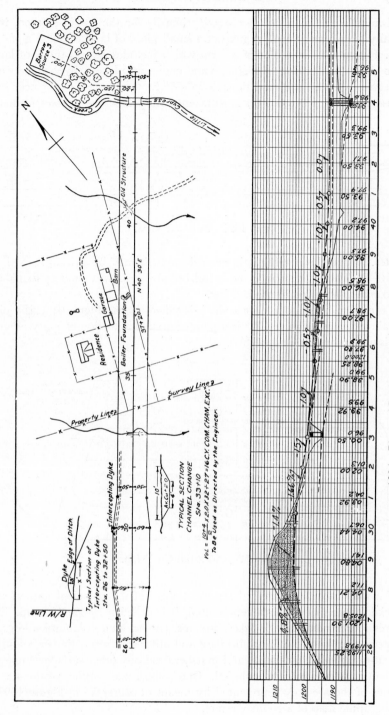

FIG. 1096 Plans of Proposed State Highway Improvement.

714

The purpose for which a map is to be used determines what features should be represented and how much detail should be included.

Topographic maps of large areas, such as townships, counties, or states, do not show the surface features with as much detail as do maps of smaller areas, such as city additions, parks, camp sites, etc.

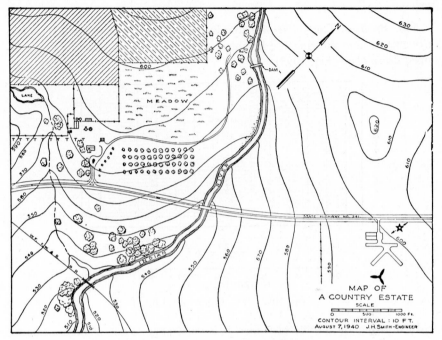

FIG. 1097   A Topographic Map.

578. Scale. The scale to which a map is drawn should be determined by the extent of the area to be described and the minuteness of detail necessary. A map of a large area may be drawn to a small scale and one of a small area to a large scale.

Maps of the United States Geological Survey are generally drawn to a scale of 1 : 62 500, very nearly one inch to a mile; sometimes, to a scale of 1 : 125 000 or 1 : 250 000. In Great Britain and Ireland, the common scale is 1 : 63 360, or one inch to a mile. In other European countries, the common scales are 1 to 25 000, or to multiples of 25 000.

579. Conventional Topographic Symbols. Topographic features are represented by certain conventional signs, or symbols, which are pictorial representations of the features so far as practicable, and which have become more or less standardized by general use.

The Federal Board of Maps and Surveys and the American Railway Engineering Association have adopted standard conventions which are in very general use. Some of the more common of these are shown in the Appendixes 4 and |5. The correct execution of these symbols requires much care and practice.   Colors are occasionally used for symbols of topographic features, but the practice is not common with engineers. Symbols on engineering maps are generally drawn with India ink and are rendered, entirely or partially, freehand.

580. Profiles. The *profile* of a line is a side view of, or a vertical section through, the line showing the height of every point of the line above an assumed *datum plane* (Fig. 1098).

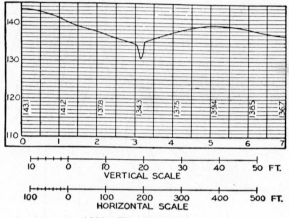

FIG. 1098   The Profile of a Line.

In drawing the profile of a line, it is customary to use a larger scale for the vertical distances than for the horizontal distances in order to exaggerate the surface irregularities. For example, the vertical scale may be 10 feet to 1 inch, and the horizontal scale 100 feet to 1 inch (Figs. 1096 and 1098).

The sea level is the datum from which elevations are reckoned whenever possible, but any other horizontal plane may be assumed as the datum plane. If the elevation of the datum plane is assumed to be 100 ft below the lowest point of a survey, the elevation of any other point of the survey would be 100 ft plus the height of that point above the lowest point. The elevations of points along a survey line are ascertained by a level party in the field. The profile of the line is plotted from the level notes. The profile of a highway line plotted from level notes is shown in Fig. 1096.

581. Contours, Contour Lines, and Contour Intervals. A *contour* is an imaginary line on the surface of the earth passing through points of equal elevation; that is, through points equally distant from mean sea level. The surface of the sea is a curved surface and hence every *level surface* is a *curved surface* and not a *plane surface;* however, the surfaces with which engineers and architects deal are so small compared with the surface of the earth that they are always considered to be *plane surfaces* tangent to the true curved surface at that elevation, and they are referred to as *level planes*.

For example, if the line *KL* in Fig. 1099, which is drawn to represent a level plane, were to be drawn to represent the true curved surface at that elevation, as indicated by the dashed line *KML*, the ordinate *MN* of the curve would be 1 inch divided by about 20,000,000, if the length of the line *KL* were 10 inches and the diameter of the earth, about 8000 miles; the curvature of the line *KML* is entirely too small to be represented on an ordinary drawing.

A *contour line* is a line on a map representing a contour.

A *contour interval* is the vertical distance between planes passing through successive contours. On a topographic map, the elevations of points of the earth's surface above mean sea level, or above some other datum plane, are shown by contour lines (Fig. 1099). Contour lines form closed figures if ex-

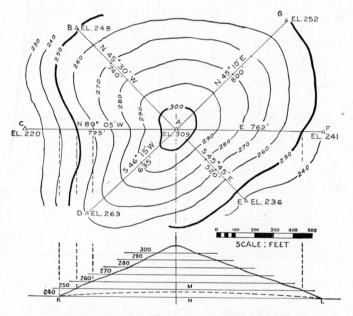

FIG. 1099   Contours Determined from Control Points.

tended far enough. Contour intervals are equal for any one map. The contour interval for a map should depend entirely upon the purpose of the map and the undulations of the surface mapped. If the area is extensive and the surface is rugged, the contour interval may be as great as 100 ft; while for a small area such as a garden, a small park, or a building site, if the surface has a gentle slope, the contour interval may be less than one foot.

The legibility of a topographic map is improved if every fifth or every tenth contour line is heavier than the others (Fig. 1099).

582. Plotting Contours. *Contour lines* may be plotted from elevations of *control points* of a stadia survey, as illustrated in Fig. 1099, or from level readings, taken at regular intervals, as illustrated in Fig. 1100. The control points of the stadia survey should be summits of hills, lowest points of depressions, divides,

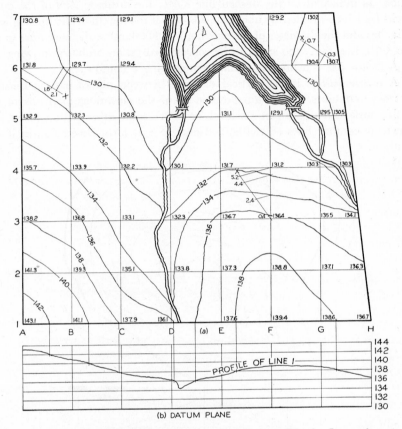

FIG. 1100   Contours Determined from Readings at Regular Intervals.

bends of streams, intersections of streams, road crossings, etc. Locations of points on contour lines, between control points, are determined by *interpolation*.

The topographic map of Fig. 1099 is based on a stadia survey by means of which the locations and the elevations of seven points were determined, and on the assumption that the slope of the surface of the ground is uniform between station *A* and the six adjacent stations. To draw the contour lines, a contour interval of 10 ft was adopted and the locations of the points of intersection of the contour lines with the straight lines, joining the point *A* and the six adjacent points, calculated as follows.

The horizontal distance between stations *A* and *B* is 740 ft. The difference in elevation of those stations is 61 ft. The difference in elevation of station *A* and contour 300 is 9 ft; therefore, contour 300 crosses the line AB at a distance from station A of $\frac{9}{61}$ of 740, or 109.1 ft. Contour 290 crosses the line AB at a distance from contour 300 of $\frac{10}{61}$ of 740, or 121.3 ft. This 121.3 ft distance between contour lines is constant along the line AB and can be set off without further calculation.

In the same way, points in which the contours cross the other lines of the survey can be interpolated.

After this process is finished, the several contour lines can be drawn through points of equal elevation, as shown. When contour lines cross a stream, they follow upstream for the crossing (Fig. 1100).

The front view of the terrain (Fig. 1099) was determined by projection from the plan and drawn to a larger vertical scale than that of the plan to show the varying slope of the ground more clearly.

Figure 1100 (a) shows a survey of a small area where lines are run at right angles to each other dividing the survey into 100-ft squares, and where elevations were taken at the corners of the squares. The contour interval is taken as 2 ft and the slope of the ground between adjacent stations is assumed to be uniform.

The points in which the contour lines cross the survey lines can be located, approximately, by inspection and, accurately, by the graphical method shown in Fig. 115 (a) or by the numerical method explained for Fig. 1099.

The points of intersection of contour lines with survey lines may also be found by constructing a profile of each line of the survey, as shown for line 1 in Fig. 1100 (b). Horizontal lines are drawn at elevations at which it is desired to show contours. The points in which the profile line intersects these horizontal lines indicate the elevations of points in which corresponding contour lines cross the survey line 1, and therefore can be projected upward, as shown, to locate these points.

It is obvious that the profile of any line can be constructed from the contour map by the converse of the process just described.

583. Maps. Topographic maps are usually made from transit notes and level notes, plane table sketches, or aerial photographs.

If the map is to represent correctly the surface features of an area, the relative locations of those features must be shown on the map by the correct conventional symbols. See Appendixes 4 and 5.

PROBLEMS

584. Topographic Drawing. The following problems are given to afford practice in topographic drawing. The exercises are designed for a sheet 11″ × 17″ (Size B, Fig. 1130). The position and arrangement of the titles should conform approximately to that of Fig. 1093.

Prob. 1 Draw symbols of six of the common natural surface features (streams, lakes, etc.), and six of the common development features (roads, buildings, etc.) shown in Appendix 4.

Prob. 2 Draw, to assigned horizontal and vertical scales, profiles of any three of the six lines shown in Fig. 1099.

Prob. 3 Assuming the slope of the ground to be uniform, and assuming a horizontal scale of 1″ = 200 ft and a contour interval (§ 581) of 5 ft, plot, by interpolation, the contours of Fig. 1099.

Prob. 4 Using the elevations shown in Fig. 1100 (a) and a contour interval of 1 ft, plot, to any convenient horizontal and vertical scales, the contours, and draw profiles of lines 3 and 5 and of any two lines perpendicular to them; check, graphically, the points in which the contours cross these lines.

Prob. 5 Using a contour interval of 1 ft and a horizontal scale of 1″ = 100 ft, plot the contours from the elevations given (Fig. 1101) at 100-ft stations, check, graphi-

144.7	139.2	143.1	144.6	144.3	143.5	142.2
142.5	138.0	139.0	141.3	142.7	139.3	139.1
140.7	137.5	136.1	138.6	138.0	136.1	137.2
138.8	136.5	135.0	136.2	135.7	135.9	136.1
139.1	136.4	134.6	133.5	133.7	134.1	135.8
135.3	134.5	133.0	132.7	132.0	131.9	132.3
135.9	134.0	132.7	131.3	130.8	129.6	131.5

FIG. 1101 (Problem 5). To Draw Contours.

cally, the points in which the contours cross one of the horizontal lines and one of the vertical lines, using a vertical scale of 1″ = 10 ft; sketch, approximately, the drainage channels.

Prob. 6 Draw a plat of the survey shown in Fig. 1093 to as large a scale as practicable; use an engineer's scale to set off distances and a protractor to set off bearings; if the drawing is accurate, the plat will close.

Prob. 7 Draw a topographic map of a country estate, similar to that shown in Fig. 1097.

CHAPTER 29

Aeronautical Drafting

By WILLIAM N. WRIGHT[*]

585. Airplane Development. The aircraft industry is composed of a large number of professions and skills, each of which is integrated as nearly intact as possible into a single major operation which has suddenly become the most strategic of modern developments. The aircraft industry, of course, includes many supporting industries from which a vast amount of raw materials and equipment is drawn. Aeronautical drafting is a composite of mechanical, structural, electrical, and sheet-metal drafting, in which some deviations are made from each in order to establish uniformity as a single basic system. Individual drafting systems, while distinct in themselves, must also serve the supporting industries, and are thus built upon the basic principles of drafting as set forth in earlier chapters.

An example of the magnitude of the aircraft industry is afforded in the development of a single heavy bomber during the recent war. The combined efforts of over 2000 engineers and draftsmen, expending 3,000,000 man hours in the preparation of 17,000 drawings containing designs for 90,000 different parts, were required to put this one airplane into production on a scale sufficient for the needs of our armed forces. This operation required not only accurate and workable designs but also a systematic accounting for the use of each part. A distinctive feature of aeronautical drafting is the planning of logical assembly and installation sequences as well as designing for maximum strength with minimum weight. The "exploded assembly" in Fig. 1103 shows the production breakdown for the Boeing Stratocruiser and illustrates the need for careful planning.

Inasmuch as peace treaties do not end military activity, it is to be expected that both military and commercial aircraft will be developed simultaneously and thus assure a continued demand for capable engineers and draftsmen. A recent development in military aircraft is shown in Fig. 1102.

[*] *Aeronautical Engineer*, Boeing Airplane Co., Seattle, Wash. Illustrations in this chapter are reproduced through the courtesy of The Boeing Airplane Co.

721

FIG. 1102 Boeing XB-47 in Takeoff.

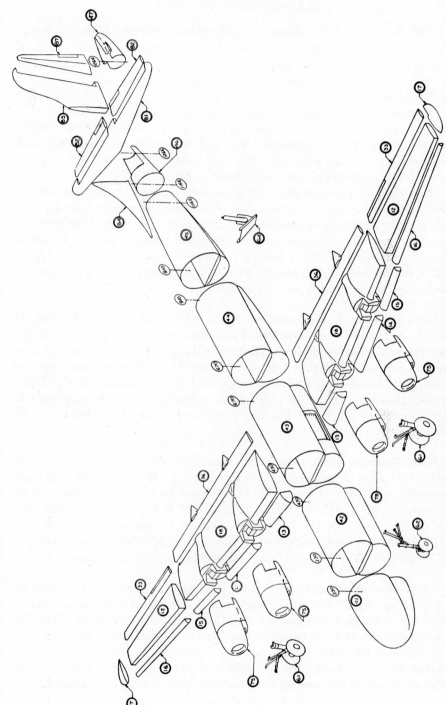

FIG. 1103   Production Breakdown of Boeing Stratocruiser.

586. Requisites for an Aeronautical Engineer. The most important requisites in aeronautical drafting are accuracy and attention to detail. Lack of care in either will result in expensive revisions, waste of time and material in the shop, and, in many cases, serious consequences during actual operation of the aircraft.

A good engineer is one who can design and complete the drawing of a part to meet shop production conditions—a drawing which is well thought out and properly part-numbered. The task of keeping part numbers and dimensions in order on related drawings and seeing that all parts will properly match is one requiring patience and ability to handle details.

Less than 10 per cent of the total engineering work in airplane design involves the use of higher mathematics, performance calculations, model testing, etc.; the remainder is careful attention to basic drafting practice in detail design. *A good aircraft engineer must know projections thoroughly and will find that a thorough knowledge of descriptive geometry is even more useful than the calculus. Neatness in drafting and lettering, plus the ability to make pencil drawings whose lines are dark enough to print sharply, are much in demand.*

587. Drafting Equipment. Practically all aircraft drafting is done in pencil. A draftsman needs one small and one large sturdy bow compass, an assortment of triangles, decimal and fractional scales, French curves, and ship curves. Ink work is required at plants where U. S. Navy contracts are on hand, since inked cloth tracings are specified for preparation of Van Dyke prints. However, the use of pencil cloth is growing and may supplant the tedious effort of ink work. Drafting machines have been adopted by many large plants.

588. Drawing Sizes. Drawing sizes vary with different companies but in general they are determined so that the drawing will fold accordion-fashion to an $8\frac{1}{2}'' \times 11''$ size. A sample list of sizes used for one major company is as follows: (1) $8\frac{1}{2}'' \times 11''$, (2) $11'' \times 17''$, (3) $11'' \times 25\frac{1}{2}''$, (4) $17'' \times 22''$, (5) $17'' \times 33''$, (6) $17'' \times 44''$ (or any multiple of $11''$ longer), (7) $22'' \times 34''$, (8) $25\frac{1}{2}'' \times 44''$ (or any multiple of $11''$ longer), (9) $34'' \times 44''$ (or any multiple of $11''$ longer). The $8\frac{1}{2}'' \times 11''$ size is desirable for filing or mailing.

589. Dimensioning. In general the principles of dimensioning outlined in Chap. 16, pp. 384-429, apply to aircraft drawings. With a few exceptions dimensions are given in inches instead of in feet and inches. Practice differs in various factories as to the use of the fractional or decimal system of dimensioning, although the trend seems to be toward complete adoption of the decimal system, which has been quite successful and efficient wherever used. On all dimensions where feet are not expressed, the inch symbol is eliminated.

Many aircraft standards include the use of the unidirectional system of dimension figures, as shown in Fig. 691 (b).

590. Lettering. Lettering is usually of the vertical Gothic style shown in Fig. 182, but some firms use upper-case and lower-case inclined letters, as shown in Figs. 200–203. Upper-case lettering only is usually preferred on drawings, and the lettering is not underlined in most factories since simplicity and elimination of frills is desired. For dimensions and notes, lettering ranges from $\frac{3}{32}''$ to $\frac{1}{8}''$ in height; titles of special views are $\frac{3}{16}''$ or $\frac{1}{4}''$ high. The minimum height of letters on master layouts (Fig. 1109) is $\frac{3}{16}''$ to allow for one-half size reduction in the photographic process.

591. Scale of Drawings. Wherever possible it is desirable to make all layout and shop drawings full size. However, when this is not practicable the drawings may range fractionally to half, quarter, or eighth sizes. General arrangement drawings (Fig. 1104) and proposal drawings (§ 595) are made to a decimal fraction scale, as 1/10, 1/20, 1/40, etc.

592. Placing of Views. Wherever practicable the principal view of any part or assembly on a drawing is taken from the left side of the airplane with the nose pointing toward the left border. Sections are taken as projected views when possible, but, if removed, care must be exercised to maintain the direction of sight.

593. Design Practice. The design of an airplane is based on a carefully prepared set of *specifications*. These are supplied by the military air forces, commercial air lines, or other agencies who are the prospective customers. These specifications set out in great detail all items of performance, general construction, power plants, servicing, etc. They are turned over by the company officials to the preliminary design section of the engineering department where gross weights, pay loads, over-all dimensions and areas, together with required performance, are determined in conjunction with the flight and aerodynamics department. During the course of this preliminary study, the original conception of the design may be changed in some respects in order to assure more satisfactory performance, as determined by the wind tunnel or towing basin tests, as the case may be. A scale model of the proposed airplane is built and tested under conditions which simulate actual flight conditions, and from these tests the designers determine whether their calculations have or have not been correct. These models are very expensive, but they represent an effort to detect and correct basic errors before actual construction is begun. When this information has been determined and compiled, it is turned over to the engineering department for complete development of the design.

A project engineer is appointed to assume the responsibility for development of the detail design and the engineering personnel assigned to assist him in this work is divided into groups, each group being controlled by a group engineer. Thus, the airplane is developed in sections, such as wings, landing gear, fuselage or hull, power plant, etc., but all sections are developed simultaneously, thus requiring the closest possible cooperation among all of the engineers as-

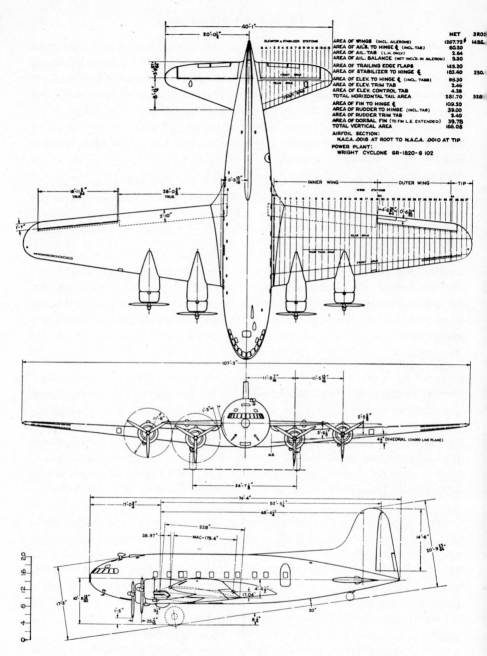

The table and labels within the drawing:

	NET	3 ROS
AREA OF WINGS (INCL. AILERONS)	1267.72	1485.
AREA OF AILS. TO HINGE ℄ (INCL. TAB)	60.20	
AREA OF AIL. TAB (L.H. ONLY)	2.64	
AREA OF AIL. BALANCE (NOT INCL'D. IN AILERON)	9.30	
AREA OF TRAILING EDGE FLAPS	149.20	
AREA OF STABILIZER TO HINGE ℄	183.40	230.
AREA OF ELEV. TO HINGE ℄ (INCL. TABS)	98.30	
AREA OF ELEV. TRIM TAB	2.46	
AREA OF ELEV. CONTROL TAB	4.28	
TOTAL HORIZONTAL TAIL AREA	281.70	328
AREA OF FIN TO HINGE ℄	109.30	
AREA OF RUDDER TO HINGE (INCL. TAB)	39.00	
AREA OF RUDDER TRIM TAB	3.40	
AREA OF DORSAL FIN (TO FIN L.E. EXTENDED)	39.78	
TOTAL VERTICAL AREA	188.08	

AIRFOIL SECTION:
N.A.C.A. .0018 AT ROOT TO N.A.C.A. .0010 AT TIP
POWER PLANT:
WRIGHT CYCLONE GR-1820-G 102

FIG. 1104 General Arrangement Drawing, Model S-307.

726

signed to the project. Of course, the airplane is not yet in existence, and therefore no measurements can be made on the actual airplane. Therefore, it is imperative that the drawings which are produced by one group be available to all other groups in order that no duplication or interference will result. In addition to the cross-checking among the groups, a careful check is also kept on the weight and strength of each part designed in order to prevent the design development from getting out of control. A weight budget is assigned to each group and definite strength requirements, as determined by the structures unit of the engineering department, must be met and kept within the weight budget. Thus, the weight department knows in advance the trend of the design development and can predict an increase or a decrease in the estimated weight of the finished airplane. Many contracts require the payment of penalties for overweight airplanes, such as $100.00 per pound. Thus, an airplane manufacturer could not continue long in business without a system whereby he could predict and control weights.

It is evident that the problem of the designer is exceedingly complex in that he must not delay the design through his inability to make basic decisions quickly and to efficiently carry out those decisions. He cannot sacrifice strength in order to save weight, or add excessive weight to obtain adequate strength. An airplane design must always be a compromise in which the maximum strength must be obtained with the minimum weight.

594. Preliminary Drawings. Once the general features of the new design are determined, the preliminary design engineers prepare a *general arrangement drawing* (Fig. 1104), showing the shape and appearance of the airplane. All principal dimensions are indicated, together with a table of general data which lists the areas of various components of the airplane as well as the wing sections used and power plant required. This is the basic drawing of the airplane, and all other drawings are additional drawings of it. It is used to plan hangers, jacks, towing equipment, and other related ground-handling equipment.

Usually three views are shown, a front view (which shows propeller clearances), top view with nose pointed downward, and a right side view (left side of airplane). Additional views may be needed to show details on both sides, top, bottom, front, and rear of the airplane. In Fig. 1104 the side view has been moved from its normal position at the right of the front view so that it could be included on this page.

The general arrangement drawing is usually drawn in pencil, and, depending upon the size of the airplane, to reduced scales of 1/10th to 1/40th size.

A perspective drawing is usually prepared to show more adequately the appearance of the finished airplane. Sometimes this is accompanied by a small-scale wood model to illustrate the finished appearance.

Additional drawings are then made which show interior arrangements of the airplane, including location of the crew, passengers, guns, bombs, fuel, baggage, etc., as shown in Fig. 1105. The lower view, which is a longitudinal

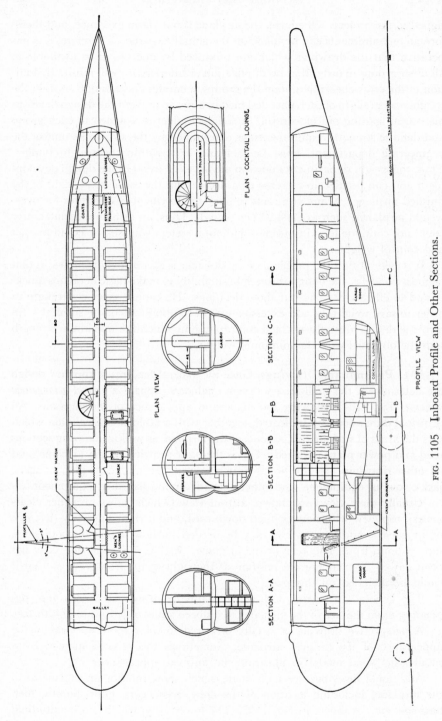

PLAN - COCKTAIL LOUNGE

PLAN VIEW

SECTION A-A

SECTION B-B

SECTION C-C

PROFILE VIEW

FIG. 1105 Inboard Profile and Other Sections.

section, is known as an *inboard profile*. These drawings are usually drawn in pencil to a scale at least double that of the general arrangement drawings in order to show more detail. For large airplanes, many such drawings may be required to show different interior features, each of which would be so complicated that a single inboard profile would be unintelligible.

Functional diagrams are prepared early in the design because they constitute the actual proving ground for the basic design. They are made in rough pencil form at first and are revised and refined as the design progresses.

595. Proposal Drawings. At this stage the airplane design is turned over to layout engineers for the preparation of *proposal drawings*. These drawings are used entirely for developing the general scheme of the airplane structure, controls, equipment, heating, plumbing, fuel tankage, gun turrets, etc. They are laid out with an eye to giving the prospective customer as much information about the plane as possible without excessive effort. Once the general details of the airplane have been approved, the work will all be redesigned in more detail and with greater care.

596. Model Drawings. *Model drawings* are prepared at the same time from which test specimens will be prepared for wind-tunnel and tank tests. These tests must be carried out along with the preparation of proposal drawings to obtain data that will enable the manufacturer to guarantee performance figures demanded by the specifications. These guarantees cannot be made by computation alone nor by guesswork, for a manufacturer will lose heavily financially and in reputation if his product fails to measure up on performance flight tests.

Draftsmen doing model drafting are usually assigned to the testing department. They design model structures and test equipment of all sorts. With many models now being built of hollow metal structures and filled with a maze of controls and gadgets, the work often becomes quite involved. Tank models are used for flying boats where testing is required by water towing and for buoyancy.

597. Mock-up Drawings. *Mock-up drawings* are prepared for the construction of full-size wood dummy models of various important parts of the airplane. Often all but the outer portions of the wing and vertical tail are included in one large *mock-up* of the entire airplane. Great attention is paid to the control compartment, passenger accommodations, bomb and gun installations, engine compartments, etc. The mock-up is revised as the design progresses and, though expensive to set up, it is the only way to insure against serious undesirable features in the finished airplane.

It is customary to have the customer inspect and approve the mock-up before the final design is determined.

598. Design Layouts. Once the airplane design is ready for the *general design layout* and *detail drafting*, the various components are parceled out to

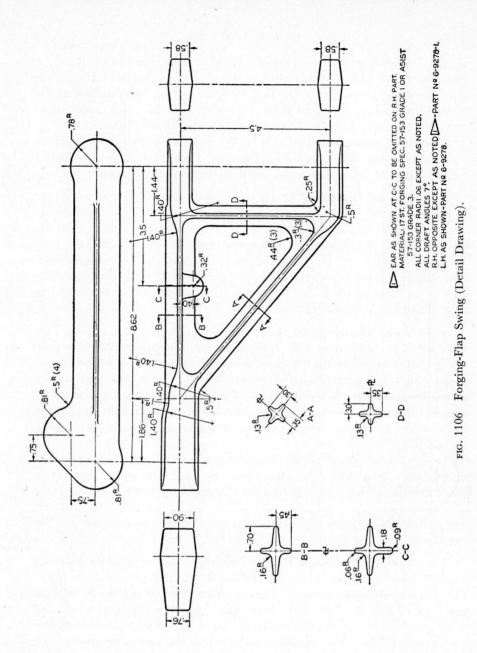

△ EAR AS SHOWN AT C-C TO BE OMITTED ON R.H. PART
MATERIAL: 17 ST. FORGING SPEC. 57-153 GRADE 1 OR A5IST
57-153 GRADE 3.
ALL CORNER RADII .06 EXCEPT AS NOTED.
ALL DRAFT ANGLES 7°.
R.H. OPPOSITE EXCEPT AS NOTED △—PART N⁰ 6-9278-1.
L.H. AS SHOWN—PART N⁰ 6-9278.

FIG. 1106 Forging-Flap Swing (Detail Drawing).

730

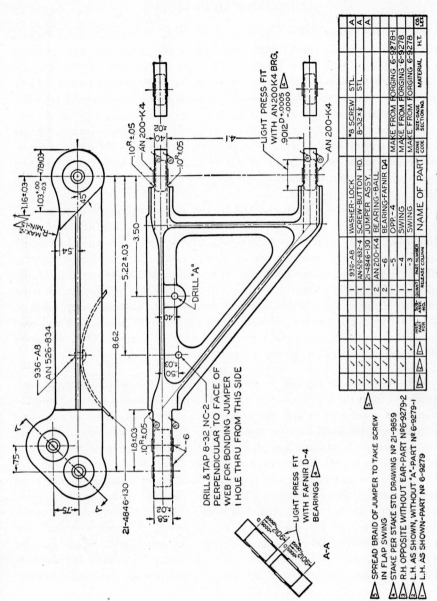

FIG. 1107 Swing Assembly—Flap Support (Assembly Drawing).

731

the engineering groups designated to work on them. These elements are some-what as follows: wing, body, control surfaces, power plant, mechanical equip-ment, plumbing, etc. Each group has a separate *head* and under him are placed *assistants, major layout engineers, minor layout engineers,* and *detailers*. Over the entire design a *project engineer* supervises, and he in turn consults with the *chief engineer* and assistants.

With the general design already established, the major layout engineers set about carrying on the detail designs, and pencil layouts are made of these. Sample jobs might be the layout of a fuselage bulkhead, wing tip, or the ele-vator control system. Minor layout engineers proceed with the design of pulley brackets, fittings, etc.

Once the layout has been checked by the group engineer, and sometimes the project engineer, it is turned over to the detailer with instructions for de-tailing *production drawings* of the parts which may be desired on individual draw-ings. The layouts are usually made on high-quality vellum because of the ease with which it may be drawn upon and because of the small amount of shrinking and stretching of the vellum that will result from changes in humidity or from handling. Pencils of 4H to 6H hardness are used and accuracy must be to at least $\pm$ 0.015″. The layouts are made full scale wherever practicable and con-tain no dimensions since they are meant to be scaled directly. Only necessary notes describing materials, rivets, bolts, etc., are included.

599. Working Drawings. There are several ways in which information is transferred from the layouts to the shop. The first of these is the conventional detailing of various parts and assemblies by detailers. The separate drawings are made so the parts can be conveniently fabricated, and then assembly drawings are made to show how they are put together. A typical detail draw-ing is shown in Fig. 1106, entitled *Forging-Flap Swing*. The same part is shown in Fig. 1107 in machined form plus the insertion of bearings to make an assembly entitled *Swing Assembly—Flap Support*. In Fig. 1108 a bracket assem-bly is shown together with installation details. Assembly drawings are made primarily for use in the assembly shop. However, in order to reduce the number of drawings (as many as 3,000 or 4,000 working drawings may be needed for one large airplane), it is common practice, in many instances, to include completely-dimensioned details of parts directly on the assembly drawing.

These drawings are made on standard-size vellum sheets (see § 588) using H and 2H pencils. They are completely dimensioned and part-numbered (see §§ 589 and 604).

When these drawings are released, the production department makes necessary accurate *master layouts* of parts and assemblies that must fit curved contours, and of all key or important assemblies in the airplane. The layouts are made on 0.040″ duraluminum sheets which have been treated with three coats of white *Preparakote* finish. This is done to provide the shop with accurate

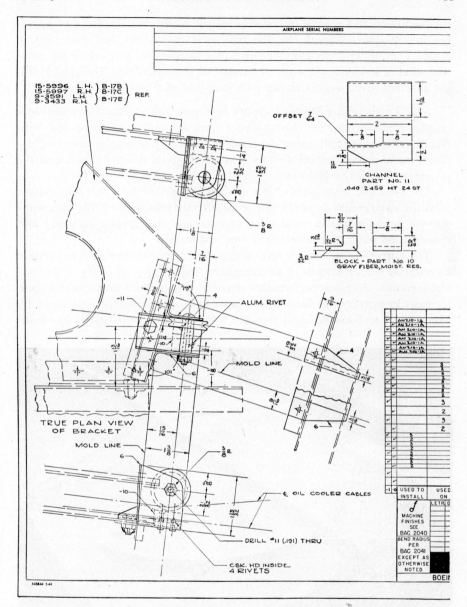

FIG. 1110   Portion of an Installation Drawing.

reference layouts which are full scale and which will not shrink or change scale. From these layouts patterns on unfinished steel are made for shop use. (See §§ 600–602 for Layout, Lofting, and Photo Templates.)

Installation drawings show the mechanic what to do with finished parts and subassemblies, and are not intended primarily to show either detail or assembly information, although, for the reasons stated above, they may contain both. They differ from assembly drawings in that the latter show all parts with solid or hidden lines, while in installation drawings (Figs. 1108 and 1110). the adjacent structures are shown with long-dashed ("phantom") lines.

600. Engineering Master Layouts. Because of recent innovations in photographic reproduction, the master layout work in many large plants has been transferred to the engineering department. Under this plan engineering detailers make master layouts directly from the original design layouts, and the procedure is closely coordinated.

The principal advantages of this method include the facts that information from the engineering department can be directly presented to the shop without the need for further production layouts, and that greater accuracy and coordination result, plus a saving of time and money.

The purpose of the master layouts department in engineering is to prepare sheet-metal master layouts of all assemblies desired plus all *lofting* of sections and contours. Airplane performance depends upon smooth contours and these contours in turn control basic structural design. The contours determined by wind-tunnel and towing-basin tests are translated into actual parts by means

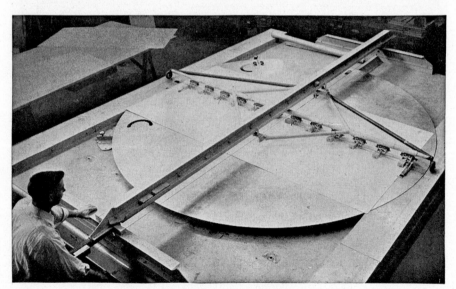

FIG. 1111   Use of Grid Machine.

of layout and lofting procedures, the latter being the means by which smooth outer surfaces are obtained. Master layouts of frames, bulkheads, plating, flooring, etc., are then made to fit the lofted contours. For further discussion of lofting, see § 601.

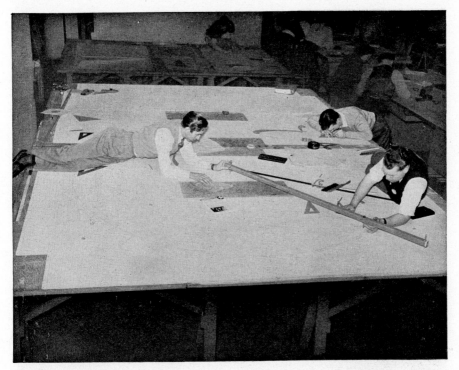

FIG. 1112 Starting a Master Layout.

Under this arrangement many of the vellum detail drawings are eliminated. All forgings and machined parts are detailed, but brackets and fittings that are fitted on a contour are laid down only on the master layout of the assembly affected. *Parts that can be conveniently shown on master layout assemblies are not detailed on separate sheets.*

The duraluminum sheets, upon which the master layouts are drawn, are first painted white as described in § 599. Horizontal and vertical grid lines, spaced accurately at 10″ intervals, are then scribed upon the sheets by means of a special grid machine (Fig. 1111). These lines provide accurate bases for buttock, section, and water lines (§ 601) as well as zones for cross reference between views. The starting of a master layout is shown in Fig. 1112, and the finishing of it is illustrated in Fig. 1113. The master layouts are complete as to notes, part numbers, and designations, but differ from detail drawings in that no dimensions are included; the master layouts are meant to be scaled directly. An example of a master layout is shown in Fig. 1109. Lines are drawn with an 8H or 9H pencil or brass stylus. Accuracy required is ±0.01″. India ink is used for lettering and for some of the parts which are blocked in. These sheets are numbered similarly to the vellum assembly drawings.

FIG. 1113   Finishing a Master Layout.

601. Lofting. The *lofting* department is ordinarily a division of the master layout unit and is concerned with the development of the lines, contours, and cross sections of the airplane. As shown in Fig. 1114, the work is done on large treated duraluminum sheets placed on wooden platforms about six inches above the floor. The engineers remove their shoes and wear special oversocks while working on the large surfaces.

It is customary to develop all contours and cross sections to full size where

FIG. 1114 Lofting.

possible, although on large airplanes the body or.hull will often have to be developed one-half size.

The same kinds of drawing tools are used in lofting as are used in master layouts except that more extensive use is made of *ship curves*, *splines*, and *ducks* for layout of *faired lines*. The spline may be any flexible wood or plastic strip varying from 0.094″ thickness and 0.25″ width up to 1.00″ thick by 1.50″ width, depending on how much curvature is involved. The ducks are peculiarly shaped lead weights fitted with brass or steel prongs which rest on the splines and hold them firmly in place.

To loft a set of faired lines (Fig. 1115) of a hull, for instance, plan and elevation views of the object are laid out in proper relationship. The two views are then divided up into stations which slice through the body at given intervals. The plan view is divided by *buttock lines* spaced at given distances from and parallel to the longitudinal center line. The elevation view is divided by *water lines* spaced at equal intervals above and parallel to the keel line. Cross sections at certain stations where the shape is definitely known are laid out first as starting points. For example, a cross section might be laid out for the hull at the control compartment and another at the trailing edge of the wing plus an additional one at the tail end of the body where space would be needed for a gunner. The problem then would be to provide smooth contours for the hull and to develop suitable cross sections between the known points.

Figure 1115 is an end view of the airplane hull showing cross sections through the hull at various stations. The planes of these sections are perpendicular to the longitudinal center line or base line.

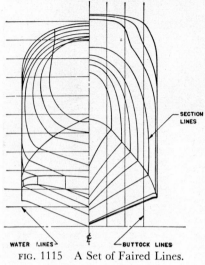

FIG. 1115   A Set of Faired Lines.

When the hull is properly lofted or faired, it may be sliced through along any water line or buttock line and the result will be a smooth curve. When a few points are known on a curve and it is desired to develop a smooth pleasing shape, the spline is often used. As shown in Fig. 1114, the flexible strip is laid down with ducks holding it where points have been definitely located. It the spline lies on all the points without being forced, the line is considered faired. A true test is to lift any duck placed on the spline except the end one. If the spline does not spring back from its position, it is following a faired curve. Conversely, if it must be held in place by force, the points will have to be adjusted to bring them on a faired line.

Contours and sections developed by the loftsmen are used by the master layout and engineering groups for carrying out their work, and photo templates (§ 602) of the contours are made where frequent reference will be necessary and whenever the production department requests a contour template.

602. Photo Templates. Upon completion and after being checked, the above-described master layouts go to the *photo template unit*. Here they are accurately photographed by a special large camera (Fig. 1116) fitted with sensitized glass plates. Glass negatives are required to prevent shrinking or stretching.

From this negative, by an enlargement process, other sensitized dural sheets are made to duplicate the original master layouts in the original full size. Metal sheets are also printed to be used as patterns.

If *mock-up patterns* are needed, sensitized plywood is printed to duplicate the master layout, and the shop then saws the wood to shape. Plywood reproductions are also placed on the shop bench, and the assembly is built up on them from the individual parts. Reproductions are also made of steel, aluminum, and masonite for various uses in the shop. For example, steel reproductions are used for drill and router templates, jig bases, and form templates; aluminum for reference and assembly table templates; and masonite for form blocks.

The photo template process is further employed to provide blueprints for reference in shop assembly work. Sensitized cloth is exposed from the negative of the master template. This results in a photo tracing which is one-half full size. This tracing is then sent to the blueprint department for reproduction of all needed prints for shop use and for the engineering file.

Since the enlargement made from the glass negative can be made to any desired fractional size, the photo process is often employed to make model drawings and patterns which may be made to a decimal-fraction scale.

FIG. 1116   Making a Photo Template.

Photo templates provide an additional advantage in the case of symmetrical and opposite-hand parts. It is necessary to draw only one side as an original master layout as the opposite side can be produced by merely reversing the negative in the printing step. In a similar manner, intermediate wing ribs need not be drawn separately if the thickness ratio remains constant. All such ribs can be produced photographically from a drawing of only one rib by making the size of each successive copy in the proper proportion to its location in the plan form.

The prime advantage of the master layout photo template system is that it eliminates time usually lost in getting engineering information to the shop in the proper form. With this setup the production department need not spend valuable months working up templates and data for shop use. The material is available just as fast as the photo unit can turn it out. This is important in getting new airplane designs into the air in the shortest possible time.

The system also promotes efficiency and eliminates duplication of effort with consequent errors and delays. The Glenn L. Martin Co., a major aircraft concern responsible for development of the process, estimates that it saved $80,000 *plus time gained* in production in one year.

603. Zone Marking. Figure 1108 is an example of *zone-marking* a drawing to provide an easy reference for locating parts, sections, and special views. The drawing is divided into zones 11″ in length which are marked off from right to left along the lower border and numbered consecutively, with the title block section being zone *1*. In the figure the zone numbers are encircled. After each part in the parts list column, the zone in which it is detailed is indicated and each section or view is "zone cross-referenced" as to where it was taken and where located. For example, in Fig. 1108, note that the removed view $A-A_2$ (upper left of drawing), is taken from zone *2*. Likewise, note in zone *2* this same view is indicated $A-A_3$, thus indicating that the removed view is shown in zone *3*.

604. Part Numbering. On a drawing where only one part is shown, the drawing number is the part number. However, when more than one part is shown, *dash numbers* are employed as suffixes to the drawing number. Where left- and right-hand parts exist which are direct opposites of each other, the left-hand part is the one shown. In Fig. 1108 it will be noted in the part number column that the left-hand parts are given odd dash numbers while right-hand parts take the next even number. It will be seen also that the individual parts on the drawing are identified by dash numbers and arrows which point to the part in question.

The term DASH NUMBER is used to identify a portion of a part number, an assembly number, or an installation number. Thus, in the composite number 15–3601–10, the 10 is a dash number and indicates that on Drawing No. 15–3601 there are several component parts completely detailed and that the complete part number of one of them is 15–3601–10, but it is commonly called –10 for the sake of simplicity. Obviously, each of the other parts which is detailed on that same drawing is assigned a dash number for the same reason. If this practice were not followed, there could be no means of identifying any of the component parts detailed on a given drawing, and for this reason the complete part number must consist of the drawing number and the dash number together.

The system of numbering varies among the various aircraft companies, but the above indicates the basic scheme generally in use.

605. Standard Parts. Standard parts which are carried in stock are used frequently in the design of airplanes. Such parts include bolts, turnbuckles, pulleys, spacers, cotter pins, etc. One group of these parts is included in the Army-Navy Standards and is termed *AN parts*. Navy Standard parts include parts approved for naval aircraft only and have an *NAF* (Naval Aircraft Factory) prefix provided.

Most aircraft factories have in addition standard parts of their own which are catalogued for use by the engineer. A similar system is used as for *AN* standards; however, the factory abbreviation is used for a prefix. Examples of some standard part listings are shown in the part number column of Fig. 1107.

606. Bend Radii. Considerable care must be taken in the forming of metal parts on airplanes so that no cracking or surface gouging occurs. Most important in this regard is the provision of an ample *bend radius*. In general, it may be stated that the bend radius for annealed dural is double the gage, while for other metal sheets the radius is equal to the gage.

The developed length of material to make the bend is computed from the empirical formula $(0.01745\ R + 0.0078\ T)$ (no. of degrees). See Figs. 732 and 733.

607. Joggling. When structural shapes overlap the edges of other material, the overlap portion is bent up, or *joggled*, to produce a flat bearing area on both the material and the seam. When joggling is required, it is done over a minimum distance of six times the joggle. The required flat section is dimensioned and the joggle dimensions given as in Fig. 1117.

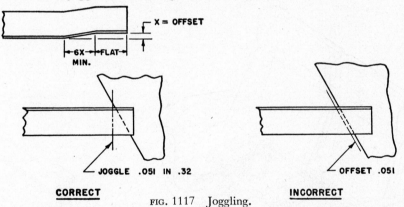

FIG. 1117 Joggling.

608. Screw Threads. Threads specified on aircraft drawings include the American National Screw Threads and the Acme Thread (pp. 440–448). Methods of showing threads according to aircraft practice are illustrated on pp. 442–447.

609. Production Illustration. In August 1939, the Douglas Aircraft Company first used perspective drawings to provide a complete picturization of the "manufacturing breakdown" of a proposed plane for a military bid. So useful were these drawings that the process was not only continued in the Douglas plant but has been adopted throughout the country. Briefly, *production illustrations* are pictorial drawings (axonometric, oblique, or perspective), either in pencil or ink, of complete airplanes (cut-away, if necessary), mechanical systems of the airplane (such as the wiring or fueling systems), subassemblies (as "Nose Wheel Assembly"), or of details (as a "Hinge Bracket"). These drawings, usually in blueprint form, are employed in every way possible to clarify and amplify the working drawings. Their chief value is in enabling the large number of workers who cannot read blueprints to obtain a clear understanding of their work. Production illustrations are therefore keyed closely to the production line so that each step in the fabrication of the plane is clearly shown.

The principles of pictorial representation used in production illustration are explained in Chapters 11, 12, and 13, and should be carefully studied by those who are entering this type of work. A thorough training in perspective is especially important to the production illustrator, particularly if he expects to be employed in a company where true perspective drawings are required.

An unshaded production illustration drawn in isometric is shown in Fig. 1118, and a pencil-shaded illustration is shown in Fig. 1119. An illustration showing how the airplane is divided into sections so that each section may be completed independently of the others and then assembled later into a complete airplane is shown in Fig. 1103.

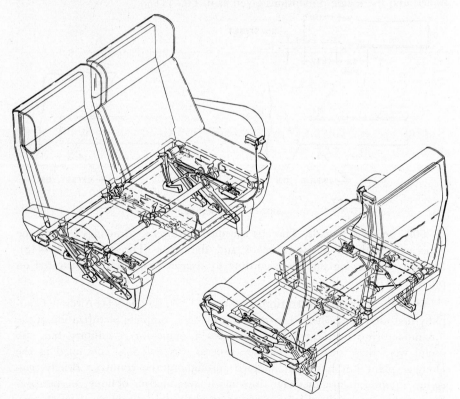

FIG. 1118   Production Illustration Showing Seat Mechanism.

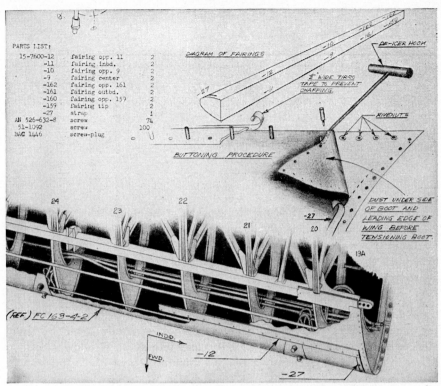

PARTS LIST:

15-7600-12	fairing opp. 11	2
-11	fairing inbd.	2
-10	fairing opp. 9	2
-9	fairing center	2
-162	fairing opp. 161	2
-161	fairing outbd.	2
-160	fairing opp. 157	2
-159	fairing tip	2
-27	strap	1
AN 526-632-8	screw	74
51-1092	screw	100
BAC 1446	screw-plug	

FIG. 1119   Production Illustration Showing Deicer Installation.

PROBLEMS

610. Aeronautical Drafting Problems. The following problems will afford the student some practice in problems which are typical of the aircraft industry.

Prob. 1   Draw to a full-size scale the *Forging-Flap Swing* shown in Fig. 1106. Rearrange as necessary to fit a size B sheet (Appendix 1, Fig. 1130).

Prob. 2   Draw to a full-size scale the *Swing Assembly–Flap Support* shown in Fig. 1107. Rearrange as necessary to fit a size B sheet (Appendix 1, Fig. 1130). To obtain dimensions not given, refer to the corresponding forging drawing in Fig. 1106.

Prob. 3   Draw to a full-size scale the *Terminal Assembly–Upper Drag Strut* shown in Fig. 843.   Use size B sheet (Appendix 1, Fig. 1130), and prepare title strip similar to that shown.

Prob. 4   Draw to a full-size scale the *Bracket* shown in Fig. 1108.   Select the size of sheet and rearrange views where necessary.   Design similar title and parts list.   To obtain dimensions not given, use the dividers and apply to the scale shown, but omit this scale from your drawing.

Prob. 5   Make general arrangement drawing of Model S-307 in Fig. 1104 to any chosen scale.   To obtain dimensions not given, use the dividers and apply to the scale shown.   (This scale should not appear on the general arrangement drawing, and is given here only to assist the student in obtaining some minor dimensions.)   Select the necessary size of sheet and, if space permits, draw the side view of the airplane to the right of the front view.

CHAPTER 30

Reproduction of Drawings

611. Introduction. After the drawings of a machine or other structure have been completed, it is usually necessary to preserve one or more copies for future reference and to supply copies to many different individuals and firms; it is therefore obvious that some means of exact, rapid, and economical reproduction must be employed.

612. Blueprint Process. Of the several processes in use for reproduction, the blueprint process is still probably the most generally used. Sir John Herschel discovered the process in 1840, and introduced it into the United States in 1876. It is essentially a photographic process in which the original tracing is the negative.

In all methods of reproducing drawings, the paper or cloth upon which the drawing is to be printed is coated or sensitized with a chemical preparation which is affected by the action of light. When such paper or cloth is exposed to light in a printing frame with the tracing so that the light must pass through the tracing to reach the sensitized paper, a chemical reaction is produced in all parts of the print except those which are protected by the opaque lines of the drawing.

FIG. 1120   Sun Frame.

After the paper has been exposed a sufficient length of time, it is removed from the frame, or the blueprint machine, and subjected to a developing bath and a fixing bath, or to a fixing bath only, according to the method employed.

When this process of printing was first employed, a *sun frame* was used, as shown in Fig. 1120.

In sunlight printing, the printing surface should be at right angles to the rays of light in order that the surface may receive the greatest amount

of light and in order that the light may be diffused least under the lines of
the drawing.

When only a small number of prints are required and better facilities
are not available, prints can be made by exposing the tracing and print paper
to sunlight while it is held against a window pane or under a piece of glass.
The tracing must be against the glass with its face toward the light and the
sensitized surface of the print paper against the tracing.

Modern blueprint machines are available in *non-continuous* types in which
cut sheets are fed through the blueprint machine for exposure only and then
washed in a separate washer. The *continuous* blueprint machine (Fig. 1121)
combines exposure, washing and drying in one continuous operation.

FIG. 1121   Automatic Blueprinting Machine (Revolute).

Blueprint papers are made by applying a coating of a solution of potassium ferricyanide and ferric ammonium citrate. In the old days, draftsmen
often made their own blueprint paper, applying the solutions with a brush.
Now blueprint papers are purchased in any desired quantity from manufacturers or dealers. They are available in various speeds and in rolls of various
widths, or may be supplied in sheets of specified size. The coated side of fresh
paper is a light greenish-yellow color. It will gradually turn to a grey-bluish
color if not kept carefully away from light, and may eventually be rendered
useless.

The length of exposure necessary depends not only upon the kind of paper
used and the intensity of the light, but also upon the age of the paper. "The
older the paper the quicker it prints and the longer to wash; the fresher the
paper the slower it prints and the quicker to wash."

A print apparently ruined by overexposure may be saved by being washed
in a solution of potassium dichromate. Hydrogen peroxide may be used for
the same purpose.

Notations and alterations can be made on blueprints with any alkaline solution of sufficient strength to destroy the blue compound; for instance, with a 1.5 per cent solution of caustic soda.

Blueprints can be made from a typewritten sheet if carbon paper has been used with the carbon side turned over, so as to produce black imprints on both sides of the sheet.

Although best results are obtained when the original tracing is drawn in ink on cloth or vellum, excellent prints may be made from penciled drawings or tracings if the tracing paper or pencil tracing cloth is of good quality and if the draftsman has made all required lines and lettering jet black.

613. Vandyke Prints and Blue-Line Blueprints. A *negative* Vandyke print is composed of white lines on a dark brown background made by printing, in the same manner as for blueprinting, upon a special thin Vandyke paper from an original pencil or ink tracing. This negative Vandyke is then used as an original to make positive blueprints or "blue-line blueprints." In this way the Vandyke print replaces the original tracing as the negative and the original is not subjected to wear each time a run of prints is made. The blue-line blueprints have blue lines on white backgrounds and are often preferred because they can be easily marked upon with an ordinary pencil or pen. They have the disadvantage of soiling easily in the shop.

614. Black and White and Colored-Line Prints. A black and white print is composed of nearly black lines on a white background and may be made from ordinary pencil or ink tracings by exposure in the same manner as for blueprints, directly upon special black-print paper, cloth, or film.

Exposure may be made in a blueprint machine or any machine using light in a similar way. However, the prints are not washed, as in blueprinting, but must be fed through a special developer which dampens the coated side of the paper with a developing solution.

A popular combination printer (exposer) and developer is shown in Fig. 1122. Two operations are involved: the tracing and *BW* paper are fed into the printer slot and when they emerge the *BW* paper is then fed through the developer slot. Within a minute or two after developing, the prints are practically dry and are ready for use.

BW colored-line prints in red, brown, or blue lines on white backgrounds may be made on the same machine simply by using the appropriate paper in each case.

These prints, together with Ozalid prints (§ 615), are coming into greater use and undoubtedly will largely replace the more cumbersome blueprint process.

615. The Ozalid Process. The Ozalid reproduction process is founded on the sensitivity to light of certain dyestuff intermediates which have the characteristic of decomposing into colorless substances if exposed to actinic light

and of reacting with coupling components to form an azo dyestuff upon
exposure to ammonia vapors. It is a contact method of reproduction and is
based upon the transmission of light through the original for the reproduction
of positive prints. The subject matter may be pen or pencil lines, typewritten
or printed matter, or any opaque image. There is no negative step involved;
positives are used to obtain positive prints. Ozalid sensitized materials can
be handled under normal indoor illumination.

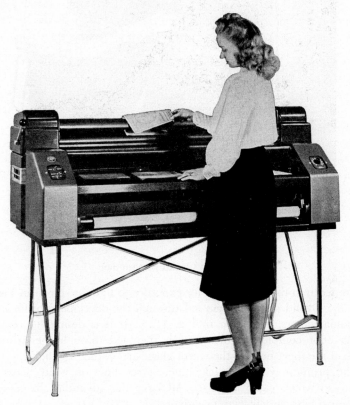

FIG. 1122   Bruning BW Whiteprinter.

The Ozalid method of reproduction consists of two simple steps—expo
sure and dry development by means of ammonia vapors. Exposure is made
in a printer equipped with a source of ultraviolet light, a mercury vapor
lamp, or carbon arc, or even by sunlight. The light emitted by these light
sources brings about a photochemical decomposition of the light-sensitive
yellow coating of the Ozalid material except in those places where the surface
is protected by the opaque lines of the original. The exposed print is developed dry in a few seconds in an Ozalid dry-developing machine by the
alkaline medium produced by ammonia vapors.

A popular exposer and developer combined in one machine is shown in Fig. 1123. Two operations are involved: (1) the tracing and the Ozalid

FIG. 1123 Ozalid Streamliner.

paper are fed into the printer slot for exposure to light as shown in Fig. 1124; and (2) the Ozalid paper is then fed through the developer slot for exposure to ammonia vapors, as shown in Fig. 1125. If it is desired to remove the ammonia odor completely, the print is then fed through the printer with the back of the sheet next to the warm glass surrounding the light.

Ozalid prints may have black, blue, or red lines on white backgrounds, according to which paper is used. All have the advantage of being easily marked upon with pencil, pen, or crayon.

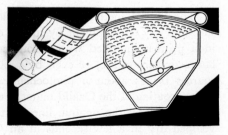

FIG. 1124 Exposure.   FIG. 1125 Ammonia Development.

Ozalid "intermediates" are made in the same manner as regular prints, but upon special translucent paper, cloth, or foil (transparent cellulose acetates). These are used in place of the original to produce Ozalid prints. They may be used to save wear on the original or to permit changes to be made. Changes may be made by painting out parts with correction solution, and then drawing the new lines or lettering directly on the intermediate in pencil or ink. Special masking and cut-out techniques can also be used.

Several types of Ozalid foil intermediates are available, including matte surfaces to facilitate pen and pencil additions. By means of foils, many new procedures are possible, such as a composite print in which a wiring system is superimposed over a drawing.

616. Photographic Contact Prints. Either transparent or opaque drawings may be reproduced the same size as the original by means of contact printing. The original is pressed tightly against a sheet of special photographic paper, either by mechanical spring pressure or by means of suction as in the "vacuum printer." The paper is exposed by the action of the transmitted or reflected light, and the print is developed in the manner of a photograph in a dark or semi-dark room. To give a negative, a positive print is made from the negative by again contact printing on the equipment.

The *Portograph*, manufactured by Remington Rand Inc., is a popular machine for making contact prints of this type. The Portograph is available in various sizes with copying areas from $10'' \times 15''$ up to $40'' \times 60''$.

Excellent duplicate tracings can be made on paper, on film, and on either opaque map cloth or transparent tracing cloth through this process. Poor pencil drawings or tracings can be duplicated and improved by intensifying the lines so as to be much better than the original. Pencil drawings can be transformed into "ink-like" tracings. Also, by this process, a reproduction can be made directly from a blueprint.

The Eastman Kodak Company has developed a new "Kodagraph Auto-positive" paper by means of which an excellent positive print can be made directly *from either a transparent or opaque original on an ordinary blueprint machine, Ozalid machine, BW machine, or any similar machine, without use of a darkroom or costly photographic equipment.*

617. Duplicate Tracings on Cloth. Specially-prepared tracing cloth is available upon which a drawing may be reproduced from a negative Vandyke print of the original. Exposure of the duplicate tracing cloth may be made in a regular blueprint machine or in any machine employing light in the same way.

Excellent duplicate tracings can also be produced on the Ozalid machine with special Ozalid materials, on the Bruning machine with special Bruning materials, or on any of the several types of photographic copying machines.

618. Photostats. The *Photostat* machine (Fig. 1126) is essentially a specialized camera. A photostat print may be the same size, or larger or smaller than the original, while photographic contact prints (§ 616) must be the same size.

The original may be transparent or opaque. It is simply fastened in place, the camera is adjusted to obtain the desired size of print, and the print is made, developed, and dried in the machine (no darkroom is required). The result is a negative print with white lines on a near-black background. A positive print having near-black lines on a white background is made by photostating the negative print.

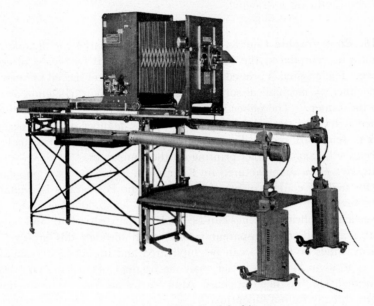

FIG. 1126   Photostat Machine.

619. Line Etching. Line etching is a photographic method of reproduction. The drawing, in black lines on white paper or on tracing cloth, is placed in a frame behind a glass and photographed. This photographic negative is then mounted on a pane of glass and is printed upon a sheet of planished zinc or copper. After the print has been specially treated to render the lines acid-resisting, the plate is washed in a nitric acid solution, which eats away the metal between the lines, leaving them standing above the surface of the plate, like type. The plate is then mounted upon a hardwood base, which can be used in any printing press as are other blocks of type. All of the line drawings in this book were reproduced by this process.

620. Mimeographing and Hectographing. While mimeographing is especially adaptable for reproducing typed material, it can also be very satisfactory in reproducing small and fairly simple drawings. The excellence of the reproduction of such drawings will depend upon the skill of the draftsman in drawing upon the stencil. The A. B. Dick Company, of Chicago, manufacturers of the Mimeograph, have now developed a photochemical process by means of which a complicated drawing may be reduced and incorporated into the stencil, which is then used to produce very satisfactory prints.

In the hectographing process an original is produced by typing on plain paper through a special carbon paper or drawing with a special pencil or ink. This sheet is then brought into contact with a gelatin pad which absorbs the coloring from the lines of the original. The original is then removed and prints are produced by bringing sheets of blank paper in contact with the gelatin. A number of different machines using this basic principle are available.

621. Other Processes. Line drawings may be reproduced by the wax process, which consists of photographing the drawings or transferring them by "rubbing down" from a tracing upon a waxed copper plate. The lines are then cut into the wax and an electrotype made from this mold.

By the lithographic process, drawings are reproduced on lithographic stone, and prints are made from this surface. Maps are the only type of technical drawings which are reproduced by this process.

The *photolithographic process* is used by the United States Patent Office in reproduction of patent drawings (see § 529).

The *photolithoprint process* employs an aluminum sheet upon which the imprint is made and from which, by the offset method, several thousand prints may be made. These have the appearance of prints made from zinc etchings, and for relatively small numbers, are much cheaper. *Planographing* is a similar process.

CONTENTS OF APPENDIX

APPENDIX

1. SHEET LAYOUTS

A convenient code to identify sheet sizes and shapes, for use of instructors in making assignments, is adopted here.

Three *sizes* of sheets are adopted: *Size A* (Fig. 1127), *Size B* (Fig. 1130), and *Size C* (Fig. 1132).

Nine *forms* of lettering arrangements are adopted, known as *Forms 1, 2, 3, 4, 5, 6, 7, 8,* and *9* (Figs. 1128, 1129, 1131, and 1133 to 1138 inclusive).

The term *layout* designates a sheet of certain size plus a certain arrangement of lettering. Thus *Layout A1* is a combination of *Size A* (Fig. 1127) and *Form 1* (Fig. 1128). *Layout C789* is a combination of *Size C* (Fig. 1132) and *Forms 7, 8,* and *9* (Figs. 1136 to 1138 inclusive). Any other combinations may be employed as assigned by the instructor.

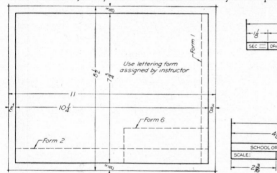

FIG. 1127   Size A (American Standard).

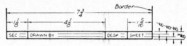

FIG. 1128   Form 1.

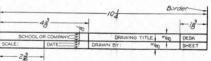

FIG. 1129   Form 2.

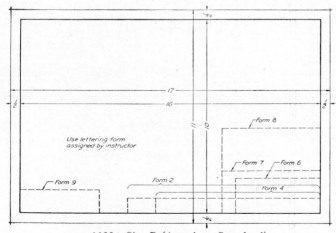

FIG. 1130   Size B (American Standard).

755

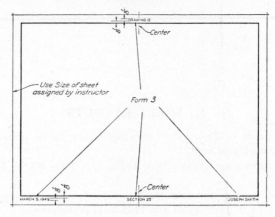

FIG. 1131   Form 3.

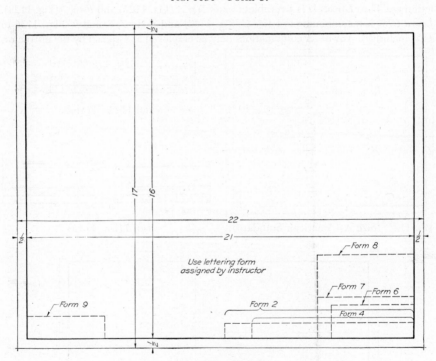

FIG. 1132   Size C.

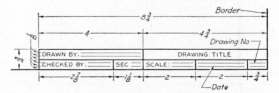

FIG. 1133   Form 4.

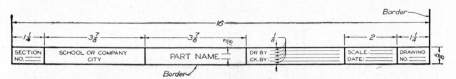

FIG. 1134   Form 5.

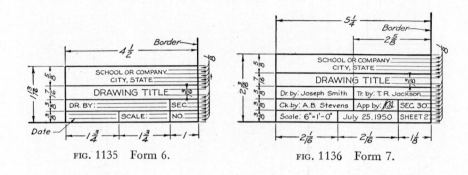

FIG. 1135   Form 6.

FIG. 1136   Form 7.

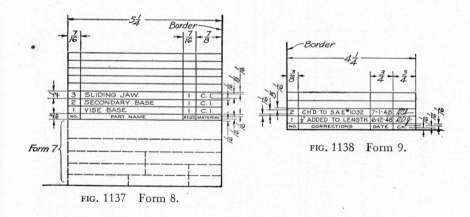

FIG. 1137   Form 8.

FIG. 1138   Form 9.

2. (ASA Z14.1—1946)

American Standard

Drawings and Drafting Room Practice

SECTION 1—ARRANGEMENT OF VIEWS

1 *Based on Third Angle Orthographic Projection*

For drawings in orthographic projection the third angle system (known in Europe as "American Projection") has been in practically universal use in the United States for many years and is continued as the American Standard. A brief discussion of this practice based on sketches of the object shown in Fig. 1 follows.

April, 1946

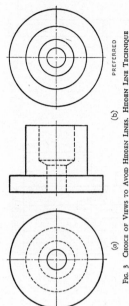

FIG. 1 PICTORIAL VIEW OF OBJECT SHOWN IN FIG. 2

2 *The Six Possible Principal Views*

In third angle projections the six views, top, front, bottom, right side, left side and rear, will be arranged as shown in Fig. 2. The plane of projection is between the observer and the object, and in all cases except for the rear view will be hinged to the vertical plane and be revolved into coincidence with it, in a direction away from the object. The rear view may appear at the extreme right in reverse position to that shown in Fig. 2.

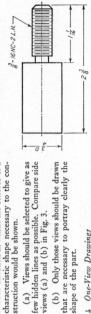

TOP VIEW

RIGHT SIDE VIEW

FRONT VIEW

BOTTOM VIEW

LEFT SIDE VIEW

REAR VIEW

FIG. 2 THE SIX POSSIBLE PRINCIPAL VIEWS OF AN OBJECT

3 *Choice of Views*

As a general rule a view should be made in each direction in which the contour of a characteristic shape necessary to the construction would be shown.

(a) Views should be selected to give as few hidden lines as possible. Compare side views (a) and (b) in Fig. 3.

(b) Only those views should be drawn that are necessary to portray clearly the shape of the part.

4 *One-View Drawings*

In general, two views are necessary as a minimum for the description of the shape of a simple object, but many cylindrical parts may be portrayed adequately by one view, if the necessary dimensions are indicated as diameters. See Fig. 4.* Thin pieces of uniform thickness such as shims, gaskets and plates may also be shown by one view with a note giving the thickness.

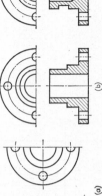

(a)

(b)

PREFERRED

FIG. 3 CHOICE OF VIEWS TO AVOID HIDDEN LINES. HIDDEN LINE TECHNIQUE

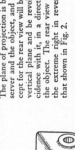

3/8 - 16 NC - 2 L.H.

1/16

2 3/8

D

FIG. 4 ONE VIEW DRAWING ✱

✱ In examining the illustrations it should be kept in mind that these drawings are not necessarily complete in themselves but have been designed to illustrate principles stated in the text matter. In so far as they are complete they conform to standards recommended herein; frequently in the interest of simplicity they are fragmentary.

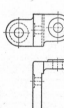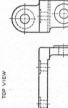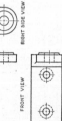

(a)

(b)

(c)

FIG. 5 ARRANGEMENT OF HALF VIEW DRAWINGS

5 Two-View Drawings

Two-view drawings may be arranged as any two adjacent views in the relation shown in Fig. 2.

6 Two-View Drawings—One View a Half View

When space is limited, it is permissible to represent symmetrical objects by half views. If the adjacent view is an exterior view, the near half of the symmetrical view should be drawn, see Fig. 5(a). If the adjacent view is a full or half section, the far half of the symmetrical view should be drawn, see Fig. 5(b) and 5(c).

7 Three-View Drawings

Any three adjacent views in the relation to each other as illustrated in Fig. 2 may be used.

8 Three-View Drawings—Alternate Positions

When space limitations require, the side view may be placed across from the top view as in Fig. 6.

9 Three-View Drawings

FRONT AND TWO SIDE VIEWS. For objects where two side views can be used to better advantage than one, these need not be complete views of the entire object, if together they describe the shape of the object, Fig. 7. In this case only the hidden lines immediately behind the face need be shown.

10 Bottom Views

A bottom view, or "view looking up," can be used to advantage instead of a top view when the shapes or operations to be shown are on the under side of the part. For example: In a punch and die drawing, the theoretical arrangement of views would be as in Fig. 8 with the view of the bottom of the punch placed in the position of the bottom view, and the top of the die in the position of the top view, each facing the front view.

(a) To conserve space this arrangement is modified by placing the drawing of the bottom of the punch to the right of and in line with the top view of the die, as if it were turned over from the top view, Fig. 9. In drawings where any such arrangement of views is employed the views should

(b) Bottom views (views looking up) should not be used in steel plate and structural drawings. Instead, the view should be shown as a sectional view looking down, the cutting plane passing a little above the bottom, Fig. 10.

11 Auxiliary Views

Objects having inclined faces require auxiliary views to show the true shapes of the inclined surfaces. Partial auxiliary views which show only the inclined faces may be used to advantage in order to simplify the drawing, to eliminate difficult projections, and to show true relationships for dimensioning. The auxiliary plane is revolved into the plane of the paper by considering it to be hinged to the plane to which it is perpendicular. See Figs. 11, 12, and 13.

12 Identification of Views

When any of the standard arrangements described above are used on a drawing, it is unnecessary to identify or name the views. In unusual or special combinations of views, however, the views should be clearly identified as in Fig. 9.

13 Space Between Views

Ample space should be provided between views to permit of placing dimensions without crowding and to preclude the possibility of notes pertaining to one view overlapping or crowding the other views.

14 Hidden Lines

Hidden lines should be indicated by standard type line No. 3, Fig. 18. This

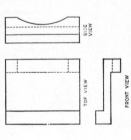

FIG. 6 ALTERNATE ARRANGEMENT OF THREE VIEWS

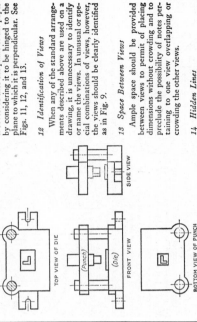

FIG. 7 ARRANGEMENT OF FRONT AND TWO SIDE VIEWS
Top view omitted to save space; two end views illustrate the principle

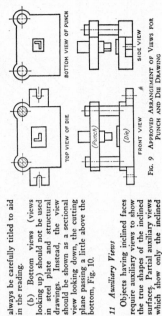

FIG. 8 THEORETICAL ARRANGEMENT OF VIEWS

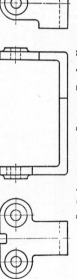

FIG. 9 APPROVED ARRANGEMENT OF VIEWS FOR PUNCH AND DIE DRAWING

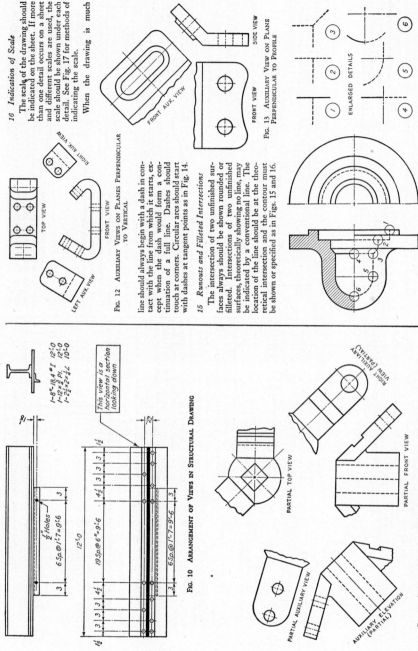

16 Indication of Scale

The scale of the drawing should be indicated on the sheet. If more than one detail occurs on a sheet and different scales are used, the scale should be shown under each detail. See Fig. 17 for methods of indicating the scale.

When the drawing is much

FIG. 12 AUXILIARY VIEWS ON PLANES PERPENDICULAR TO VERTICAL

line should always begin with a dash in contact with the line from which it starts, except when the dash would form a continuation of a full line. Dashes should touch at corners. Circular arcs should start with dashes at tangent points as in Fig. 14.

15 Runouts and Filleted Intersections

The intersection of two unfinished surfaces always should be shown rounded or filleted. Intersections of two unfinished surfaces, theoretically showing no line, may be indicated by a conventional line. The location of the line should be at the theoretical intersection and the contour must be shown or specified as in Figs. 15 and 16.

FIG. 13 AUXILIARY VIEW ON PLANE PERPENDICULAR TO PROFILE

ENLARGED DETAILS

FIG. 14 HIDDEN LINE TECHNIQUE

FIG. 10 ARRANGEMENT OF VIEWS IN STRUCTURAL DRAWING

FIG. 11 PARTIAL AUXILIARY VIEW ON PLANE PERPENDICULAR TO HORIZONTAL

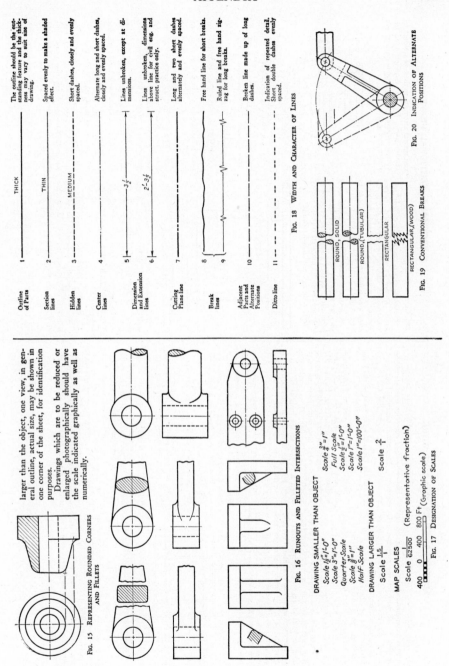

larger than the object, one view, in general outline, actual size, may be shown in one corner of the sheet, for identification purposes.

Drawings which are to be reduced or enlarged photographically should have the scale indicated graphically as well as numerically.

Fig. 15 Representing Rounded Corners and Fillets

Fig. 16 Runouts and Filleted Intersections

DRAWING SMALLER THAN OBJECT

Scale $1\frac{1}{2}"=1'-0"$
Scale $3"=1'-0"$
Quarter Scale
Scale $\frac{3}{8}=1"$
Half Scale

Scale $\frac{3}{4}=1"$
Full Scale
Scale $\frac{1}{2}"=1'-0"$
Scale $1"=1'-0"$
Scale $1"=100'-0"$

DRAWING LARGER THAN OBJECT

Scale $\frac{1}{5}$ Scale $\frac{2}{1}$

MAP SCALES

Scale $\frac{1}{62500}$ (Representative fraction)

400 0 400 800 Ft   (Graphic scale)

Fig. 17 Designation of Scales

		Width and Character of Lines
Outline of Parts	THICK	The outline should be the outstanding feature and the thickness may vary to suit size of drawing.
Section lines	THIN	Spaced evenly to make a shaded effect.
Hidden lines	MEDIUM	Short dashes, closely and evenly spaced.
Center lines		Alternate long and short dashes, closely and evenly spaced.
Dimension and Extension lines	$3\frac{1}{2}$	Lines unbroken, except at dimensions.
	$2'-3\frac{1}{2}$	Lines unbroken, dimensions above line for civil eng. and struct. practice only.
Cutting Plane line		Long and two short dashes alternately and evenly spaced.
Break lines		Free hand line for short break.
		Ruled line and free hand zig-zag for long breaks.
		Broken line made up of long dashes.
Adjacent Parts and Alternate Positions / Ditto line		Indication of repeated detail. Short double dashes evenly spaced.

Fig. 18 Width and Character of Lines

ROUND, SOLID
ROUND (TUBULAR)
RECTANGULAR
RECTANGULAR (WOOD)

Fig. 19 Conventional Breaks

Fig. 20 Indication of Alternate Positions

SECTION 2—LINES AND LINE WORK

17 Line Characteristics

It is recommended that the types shown in Fig. 18 be used for the purposes indicated. All lines should be clean and black. The actual width of each type of line should be governed by the size and style of the drawing, the relative widths of the lines should approximate those shown in Fig. 18.

18 Widths of Lines

Three widths of line, thick, medium and thin, are shown and are considered desirable on finished drawings in ink, both for legibility and appearance, although in rapid practice and in particular on penciled tracings from which prints are to be made this may be simplified to two widths, medium and thin, both of which must be dense black in order to print.

19 Dimension and Extension Lines

Dimension and extension lines should be thin lines. Extension lines should not touch the outlines of the object, Fig. 48.

20 Break Lines Used to Shorten the View of Long Uniform Sections

Break lines may be used on both detail and assembly drawings. On small parts freehand lines are best, (Fig. 18, line 8), while on large parts the second form, made with thin ruled lines with freehand "zigzags," (Fig. 18, line 9) is preferred. When a portion of the lengths of shafts, rods, etc., are broken out to shorten the view, the breaks will be indicated as shown in Fig. 19.

In structural drawing, many parts are not drawn to detail scale in length but no break is shown unless it is necessary to show a revolved section. Symmetrical parts discontinued beyond the center line may have the break made as in Fig. 21 or Fig. 51.

21 Alternate Positions and Adjacent Parts

An alternate position, or indication of the limiting positions of a moving part should be shown by a line made up of long dashes of medium width, Fig. 20.

Adjacent parts added on a drawing to indicate the position or use of the piece represented, are drawn with the same long-dash lines, Fig. 21. This line is also used in showing bosses and lugs cast on for holding purposes, which are to be removed later. On drawings of an illustrative nature adjacent parts may be shown as solid red- or diluted black-ink lines instead of black long-dash lines.

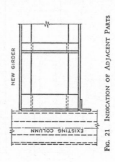

Fig. 21   Indication of Adjacent Parts

For pencil tracings the lines should be in proportion to the ink lines, medium for outlines, hidden, cutting plane, short breaks, adjacent part and alternate position lines; and thin for section, center, extension, dimension, long break, and ditto lines.

SECTION 3—SECTIONAL VIEWS

22 General Principles

Sectional views, commonly called "sections" should be used when the interior construction cannot be shown clearly by outside views. (In assembly drawings they also serve to indicate a difference in materials.)

A sectional view should be made as if on that view the nearest part of the object were cut or broken away. The exposed or cut surface of the material is indicated by "section lining" or "cross-hatching."

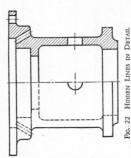

Fig. 22   Hidden Lines in Detail Half Section

Hidden lines behind the cutting plane should be omitted unless required for the necessary description of the object. In half-sectioned detail drawings hidden lines may be shown on the unsectioned side only if needed for dimensioning or clarity, Fig. 22.

23 Symbolic Section Lining

For the graphic indication of various materials of construction symbolic section lining may be used when it is desired to call special attention to them or to identify certain parts, Fig. 25. Symbols used for outside views of certain materials are shown in Fig. 26.

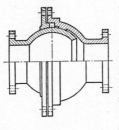

Fig. 23   Hidden Lines Omitted in Half Sectioned Assembly

24 Sectioning in Detail Drawings

If preferred, the section-lining of any metallic piece may be made by equally spaced full lines in one direction as for cast iron. See Figs. 22, 23, and 27. Since the specification of material must usually be more detailed than by name or symbol alone, this practice is recommended. An opening may be left in the sectioning to provide for a reference letter or dimension.

Even when the symbolic types of section lining are used it will be found frequently desirable to use reference letters to indicate the material.

25 Sectioning in Assembly Drawing

In assemblies, when it is desirable to distinguish between different classes of materials without specifying their exact composition, assemblies may be appropriately

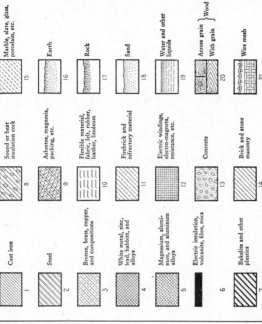

1 Cast iron
2 Steel
3 Bronze, brass, copper, and compositions
4 White metal, zinc, lead, babbitt, and alloys
5 Magnesium, aluminum, and aluminum alloys
6 Electric insulation, vulcanite, fibre, mica
7 Bakelite and other plastics
8 Sound or heat insulation cork
9 Asbestos, magnesia, packing, etc.
10 Flexible material, fabric, felt, rubber, leather, linoleum
11 Firebrick and refractory material
12 Electric windings, electro-magnets, resistance, etc.
13 Concrete
14 Brick and stone masonry
15 Marble, slate, glass, porcelain, etc.
16 Earth
17 Rock
18 Sand
19 Water and other liquids
20 Across grain / With grain } Wood
21 Wire mesh

FIG. 25 SYMBOLS FOR SECTION LINING

Brick
Uncoursed and coursed rubble
Ashlar
Transparent materials, glass, etc.
Marble

FIG. 26 SYMBOLS FOR OUTSIDE VIEWS

cross-sectioned to indicate specified materials, Fig. 24.

Where a large area of a piece is shown in section, it is not necessary to section line the entire area; section lining around the outline of the sectioned area should be sufficient.

26 Full Sections

When the cutting plane extends entirely through the object a "full section" is obtained as in Fig. 27. When the section is on an axis of symmetry it is not necessary to indicate its location.

27 Half Sections

A symmetrical object may be drawn as a "half-section" showing one-half up to the center line,* in section, and the other half in full view. See Figs. 22, 23, and 24. In assemblies it is customary not to show hidden lines on the unsectioned side.

28 Location of Cutting Plane

The cutting plane on which the section is taken should be indicated by type 7 line, Fig. 18, and lettered at the ends as A-A, Fig. 30. Arrows are used to indicate the direction in which the section is viewed. The letters identifying the section may be placed in a circle as the numerator of a fraction whose denominator is the sheet number on which the section will be found, Figs. 28 and 29. When the section is on the same sheet, the sheet number and circle should be omitted. The letters should be large enough to be easily found, Figs. 28 and 30.

On simple symmetrical objects the cutting plane line, letters, and arrows may be omitted when on an axis of symmetry. It is not necessary that the cutting plane be a single continuous plane; it may be bent or offset if by so doing, the construction can be shown to better advantage as, for example A-A or B-B, Fig. 30 and Fig. 29.

* The dividing line between the half-section and full view may be type 1 line, Fig. 18.

The cutting planes line may be shown only at the ends and at changes of direction as in Fig. 28.

29 Revolved Sections

These sections show the shape of the cross-section of a part, such as the arm of a wheel, the cutting plane being rotated in place, Figs. 16 and 31.

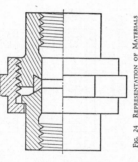

FIG. 24 REPRESENTATION OF MATERIALS IN ASSEMBLY

30 Removed Sections

Removed or "detail sections" should be drawn like revolved sections except that they are placed to one side and often are made to a larger scale than the view on which they are indicated, Section B-B, Fig. 30. Removed sections of symmetrical parts may be placed on an extension of the cutting plane as a center line, Fig. 32.

31 Offset Sections

When the object is not cut by one continuous plane, the section is called an offset section. Its location is shown in the usual way as in Figs. 29 and 30.

32 Broken-Out Sections

Where a sectional view of only a portion of the object is needed, broken-out sections may be used as in Figs. 33 and 36.

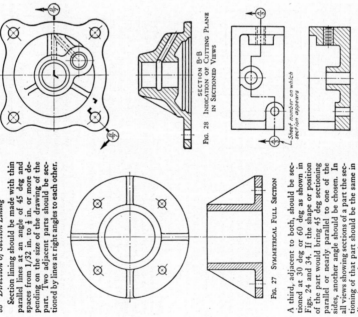

33 *Direction of Section Lining*

Section lining should be made with thin parallel lines at an angle of 45 deg and spaces from 1/32 in. to ⅛ in. or more depending on the size of the drawing of the part. Two adjacent parts should be sectioned by lines at right angles to each other.

A third, adjacent to both, should be sectioned at 30 deg or 60 deg as shown in Figs. 24 and 34. If the shape or position of the part would bring 45 deg sectioning parallel or nearly parallel to one of the sides, another angle should be chosen. In all views showing sections of a part the sectioning of that part should be the same in direction and spacing.

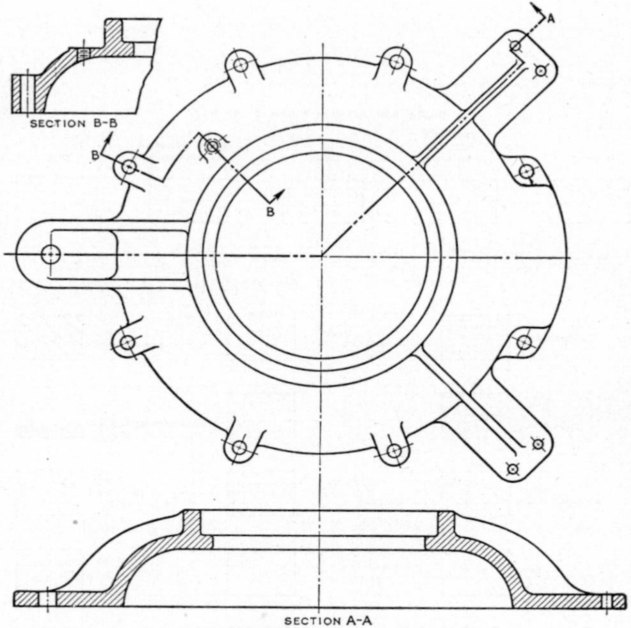

FIG. 30 INDICATION OF CUTTING PLANES

SECTION A-A

SECTION B-B

FIG. 28 INDICATION OF CUTTING PLANE IN SECTIONED VIEWS

SECTION B-B

FIG. 27 SYMMETRICAL FULL SECTION

Sheet number on which section appears

FIG. 29 CROSS-HATCHING AN OFFSET SECTION

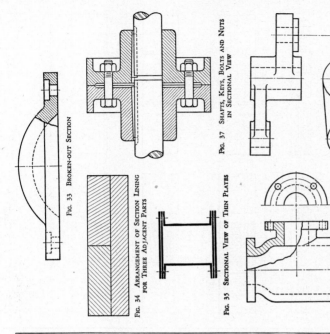

FIG. 33 BROKEN-OUT SECTION

FIG. 34 ARRANGEMENT OF SECTION LINING FOR THREE ADJACENT PARTS

FIG. 35 SECTIONAL VIEW OF THIN PLATES

FIG. 37 SHAFTS, KEYS, BOLTS AND NUTS IN SECTIONAL VIEW

FIG. 38 REVOLUTION OF PARTS TO SHOW TRUE RELATIONSHIPS

FIG. 36 HOLES REVOLVED TO SHOW TRUE DISTANCE FROM CENTER

34 Thin Sections

Sections which are too thin for line sectioning may be shown solid, such as structural shapes, sheet metal, packing, gaskets, etc. Where two or more adjacent parts are shown solid a space should be left between them, Fig. 35.

35 Sections Through Thin Webs, Shafts, Bolts, Pins, Keys, etc.

There is one important violation of the conventional theory which is made in the interest of clearness. When the section or cutting plane passes through a rib, web or similar parallel element, section lines should be omitted from those parts, Figs. 27 and 30.

Shafts, bolts, nuts, rods, rivets, keys, pins and similar solid parts whose axes lie in the cutting plane should not be sectioned, Fig. 37.

36 Treatment of Foreshortened Projections

When the true projection of a piece would result in confusing foreshortening, parts such as ribs or arms, should be rotated until parallel to the plane of the section or projection as shown in Figs. 38 and 40.

Drilled flanges in elevation or section should show the holes at their true distance from the center rather than the true projection, Figs. 27 and 36.

37 Representing Cylindrical Intersections

The intersection of rectangular and circular parts with other circular parts, occurs frequently. Unless very large, these intersections are conventionalized as shown in Fig. 39. The curve of intersection may be drawn as a circular arc.

FIG. 31 REVOLVED SECTIONS

FIG. 32 REMOVED SECTIONS

SECTION 4—SCREW THREAD REPRESENTATION

88 Regular Thread Symbols

Fig. 41 shows threads in section and elevation, with end view.

Fig. 41(a) shows the regular method of representing screw threads recommended for general use on assembly and detail drawings. Except in sections of external threads and hidden internal threads, the threads are indicated by alternate long and short lines at right angles to the axis representing the crests and roots of the thread, the short lines thicker than the long lines, or of equal width if preferred. They need only to approximate the actual pitch, being spaced by eye to look well.

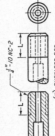
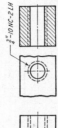

$\frac{3}{4}''$-10NC-2

(a) THREADED ROD

$\frac{3}{4}''$-10NC-2LH

(b) HOLE TAPPED THROUGH

$\frac{3}{4}''$-16NF-3

(c) TAP DRILL SHOWN

$\frac{3}{4}''$-12N-2-$\frac{3}{4}''$Deep

(d) BOTTOMING TAP

FIG. 41 REGULAR THREAD SYMBOL.

FIG. 42 SIMPLIFIED THREAD SYMBOL.

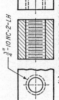

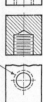

(a) CYLINDRICAL INTERSECTION IN SECTION

1   2   3

(b) EXTERNAL INTERSECTIONS

FIG. 39 REPRESENTING CYLINDRICAL INTERSECTIONS

FIG. 40 SECTION THROUGH SPOKES OF WHEELS

thread and the pitch. For details of modified square and acme threads see American Standard Acme and Other Translating Threads (ASA B1.3—1941).

43 Acme Thread Symbols

Acme threads should be represented as in Fig. 47 with a note specifying the type of thread and the pitch (ASA B1.3—1941).

44 Bolt Heads and Nuts

Exact dimensions of American Standard unfinished, semi-finished, and finished bolt heads and nuts, regular series and heavy series, will be found in the American Standard for Wrench Head Bolts and Nuts and Wrench Openings (ASA B18.2—1941).

FIG. 46 MODIFIED SQUARE THREAD

1½" Square, 4 Th'ds per in.

It is not necessary to indicate taper on standard pipe threads but this may be done if desired. Therefore, when straight pipe threads are specified such threads must be indicated by the symbol NPS. Identification symbols and dimensions of national standard pipe threads, including diameters, form, taper, and length of thread, may be found in the American Standard for Pipe Threads (ASA B2.1—1945).

41 Semi-Conventional Threads or Thread Pictures

When it is desirable to use "thread pictures" it should be done as in Fig. 45. The helices are conventionalized into slanting straight lines and the contour shown as a sharp V at 60 deg although the standard threads are truncated at the top and filled in at the root. Details of standard threads will be found in the American Standard for Screw Threads (ASA B1.1—1935).

42 Square Thread Symbols

Square threads should be shown as in Fig. 46 with a note specifying the type of

1"-8N-2-LH Double

FIG. 45 SEMI-CONVENTIONAL THREAD

1½" Acme, 3 Th'ds per in.

1½" Acme, 3 Th'ds per in.

FIG. 47 ACME THREAD

Fig. 41(b) shows internal threads tapped through. Fig. 41(c) shows internal threads where the tap drill point does not go through. The drill point should be drawn at 60 deg with the center line.

The method shown in Fig. 41(d) should be used to indicate a bottoming tap, when depth of thread is the same as depth of

at the approximate depth of the thread. The size and length of thread and depth of tap should be given on the drawing. Threads are always considered to be "right hand" unless specified as "left hand" or "LH." The letters LH should be added after the class of fit number as shown in Figs. 41(b) or 42(b). Bolt ends should

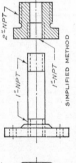
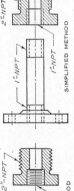
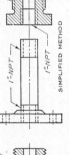

2"-NPT

1"-NPT

SIMPLIFIED METHOD

REGULAR METHOD

1"-NPT

2"-NPT

FIG. 43 PIPE THREADS

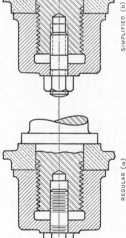
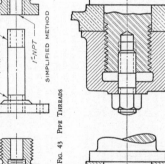

REGULAR (a)　　　SIMPLIFIED (b)

FIG. 44 SCREW THREADS IN ASSEMBLY

drill, or when it is not necessary to specify both depth of drill and depth of threaded parts. The simplified method illustrated should be used with discretion to avoid possible mistakes.

39 Simplified Thread Symbols

Fig. 42 shows the simplified symbol method of screw thread representation. This method may be adopted where it is desirable to simplify drafting work. The threaded portion is indicated by lines made of short dashes drawn parallel to the axis

be shown as flat and chamfered to the thread depth at 45 deg with the flat surface.

Dimensions of screw threads for bolts, nuts, screws and threaded parts may be found in the American Standard for Screw Threads. Identification symbols and methods of designation for drawings may be found in Par. 14 of this bulletin, (ASA B1.1—1935).

40 Pipe Thread Symbols

Pipe threads should be represented in the same manner as bolt threads, Fig. 43.

SECTION 5—DIMENSIONING—GENERAL RULES

45 General Principles of Dimensioning

(a) Economical production and the proper functioning of a part in service are directly dependent upon the method of dimensioning used and the manner in which dimensions are specified on the drawings.

to in actual shop or constructional operation and should be so placed as to minimize the cumulative error.

(d) It is essential that dimensions should be given between those points or surfaces which have a specified relation to each other or which control the location of other component or mating parts.

(e) Dimensions should not be duplicated and none should be given except those required to produce or inspect the part.

46 Technique of Dimensioning

Dimension lines should be thin full lines (broken where dimension is inserted) so as to contrast with the thicker outline of the drawing, Fig. 48. In structural drawings the dimension line is not broken and the figures are placed above the line, Figs. 50, 51, and 52.

minated by carefully made arrowheads whose lengths are approximately three times the spread. The distance from tip to tip of the arrowheads indicates the extent of the dimension as shown in Fig. 48.

Extension lines indicate the distance measured when the dimension is placed outside the view. They are made as thin full lines, should be extended a short distance beyond the arrowhead, and should not touch the view.

In structural drawing the lines along which rivet holes are punched

(b) The dimensions should be so arranged that it never will be necessary to calculate, scale, or assume any dimensions in order to fabricate the specified part.

(c) The dimensions should include those sizes and distances which are worked

are called gage lines. They are drawn as thin solid lines as in Figs. 51 and 52.

Leaders should be thin straight lines terminated by arrowheads. They should not be curved or made freehand, Fig. 49. The leader may terminate in a short horizontal bar at the mid-height of the lettering of the first or last line of the note.

The symbol (") may be used to indicate inches and common and decimal fractions of an inch.

The symbol (') may be used to indicate feet as in Figs. 50, 51, and 52.

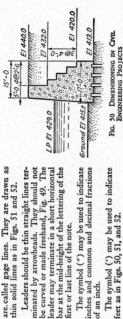

Fig. 50 Dimensioning in Civil Engineering Projects

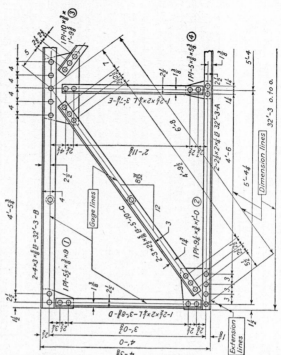

Fig. 51 Dimensioning Assembled Structural Work

Fig. 48 Leaders, Dimension and Extension Lines in Machine Drawing

Fig. 49 Approved Form of Leaders

47 Use of Feet and Inch Symbols

In machine drawing when all dimensions are given in inches the symbol is omitted, unless there is a possibility of misunderstanding, thus 1 valve should be 1" valve or 1 in. valve; 1 bore should be 1" bore.

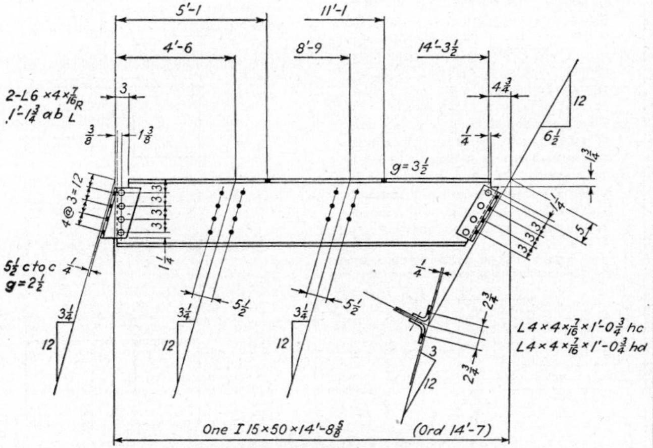

In structural drawing all length dimensions should be expressed in feet and inches. Plate widths are given in inches. Dimensions should be hyphenated thus, 4'-3; 4'-0½; 4'-0 as shown in Fig. 51. When the dimension contains only inches the inch mark may be omitted. In structural draw-

the drawing, Figs. 53 and 55(a). All dimensions are placed so as to read in the direction of the dimension lines as shown in Fig. 55(a). Dimension lines should not run in directions included in the shaded area as shown in Fig. 54, forty-five deg from the vertical, unless unavoidable.

In the aligned system fractions are written with the division bar in line with the dimension line, Fig. 53. The inclined bar or the omission of the bar is not approved.

(b) Unidirectional System. All dimensions are made to read from the bottom of the sheet as shown in Figs. 53 and 55(b). Fractions are written with the division bar horizontal or parallel to the bottom of the sheet. Diameters of circles may be placed in any position, except along center lines.

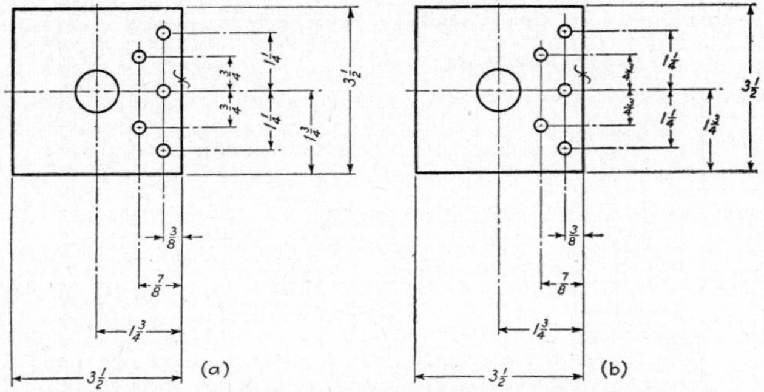

The unidirectional system of dimensioning originated in automobile and aircraft drafting rooms where long drawings made it advantageous. From the standpoint of both making and using a drawing, this system of dimensioning has advantages which

is making its use more widespread, and therefore, acceptable as a method.

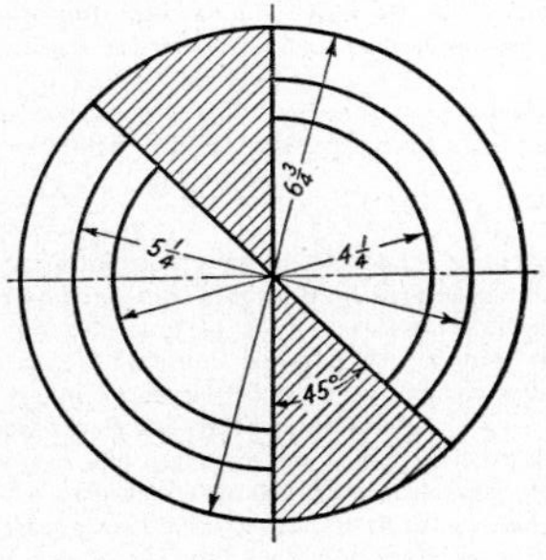

(c) General Rules. The following rules apply to both systems.

(1) The dimension line must not pass through a dimension figure, nor should a dimension figure be placed on the outline of the object.

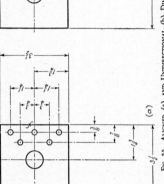

Fig. 54 Area to be Avoided

(a)

(b)

Fig. 55 Aligned (a) and Unidirectional (b) Dimensioning from Center Line and Finished Surface

ing the inch symbol is omitted even though the dimension is in feet and inches, Figs. 51 and 52.

48 Placing Dimensions

Two systems of dimensioning are approved. The older, called the aligned system, and the new, called the unidirectional system, will be found convenient under conditions described in the following:

(a) Aligned System. All dimension lines and their corresponding numbers are placed so that they may be read from the bottom or right-hand edges of

In some industries all dimensions are specified in inches. In others dimensions up to and including 72 in. should be preferably expressed in inches and those greater than that length, in feet and inches.

Fig. 52 Dimensioning Structural Steel Beams

One I 15×50×14'-8⅝

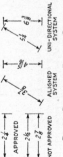

APPROVED

NOT APPROVED

ALIGNED SYSTEM   UNI-DIRECTIONAL SYSTEM

Fig. 53 Position of Fraction Bar

(2) Dimensions should not be placed upon a view unless the drawing becomes clearer by so doing. In general, dimensions should be placed between views as in Figs. 57 and 61.

be one-half inch away from outlines and spaced uniformly at least three-eighths of an inch from each other.

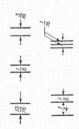

Fig. 56 DIMENSIONING NARROW SPACES

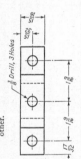

Fig. 57 PLACING OF DIMENSIONS

(3) A center line should never be used as a dimension line. A line of the piece or part illustrated, or an extension of such a line, should never be used as a dimension line.

(4) When there are several parallel dimension lines the figures should be staggered to avoid confusion as shown in Fig. 59.

(5) In general, dimension lines should

(6) Dimensions should be given from a base line, a center line, an important hole or a finished surface that can be readily established (based on design requirements and the relationship of other parts). See Fig. 55. Dimensions for different operations on a piece, as for example, drilling and bending should be kept separate as shown in Fig. 58 if permissible by its design.

(7) For dimensioning in limited space the arrowheads should be reversed and the methods shown in Fig. 56 may be used.

(8) In dimensioning angles an arc should be drawn and the dimension so placed as to read from the bottom of the sheet, Fig. 60. An exception is sometimes made in the dimensioning of large arcs when the dimensions are placed along the arc.

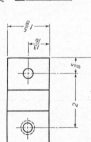

Fig. 58 DIMENSIONS FOR DIFFERENT OPERATIONS SHOULD BE SEPARATED

49 Fractional and Decimal Dimensioning

GENERAL RULES. Dimensions in structural work should be expressed in units and common fractions and in machine drawing, dimensions of parts that can be produced with sufficient accuracy when measured with an ordinary scale, should be dimensioned in the same manner.

(9) Over-all dimensions should be placed outside the intermediate dimensions, Figs. 55, 58 and 77. When an over-all dimension is used, one intermediate distance* should not be dimensioned, unless for reference and so noted as shown in Figs. 57 and 61.

(10) In an object with circular ends an over-all dimension generally need not be given, Figs. 61 and 74.

(11) When the number of dimensions is large and when limited space requires that successive dimensions be given from a common reference point or surface, they may be placed in a single line as shown in Fig. 67. This practice is followed also in structural work as shown in Fig. 52.

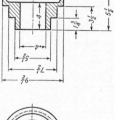

Fig. 59 DIMENSIONING CYLINDERS

Decimal dimensions should be used between finished surfaces and points which it is essential to hold in a specific relation to each other. The fundamental basis of the complete decimal system is the use of a two-place decimal, i.e., a decimal consisting of two figures after the decimal point. In all dimensions where a fraction would

ordinarily be used, the two-place decimal can be applied. The figures after the decimal point, where applicable, should be in fiftieths (e.g., .02, .04, .08, .84) so that when halved (e.g., diameters to radii) two-place decimals will result. Exceptions, of course, will have to be made, but they should be kept to a minimum.

When a decimal value obtained by converting a common fraction to decimals is to be rounded off to a lesser number of places than the total number available, the procedure should be as indicated in ASA Z25.1—1940.

50 Limit Dimensioning

Accurate dimensions which are to be checked with a limit gage or micrometer should be expressed in decimals.

Limits representing the maximum and minimum dimensions allowed shall be specified for all dimensions where the tolerance is other than .01. This (.01) tolerance, or any other predominant tolerance, should be indicated on the drawing

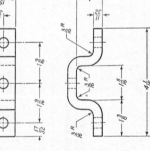

Fig. 60 DIMENSIONING ANGLES WITH LIMIT DIMENSIONS

For parts requiring greater accuracy a complete decimal system of dimensioning will be found advantageous.

* Does not apply to structural dimensioning.

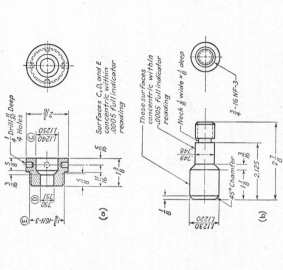

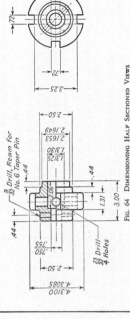

FIG. 63 LIMIT DIMENSIONS FOR CONCENTRICITY

FIG. 64 DIMENSIONING HALF SECTIONED VIEWS

in note form. The method of writing these limits on the drawing should be as shown in Figs. 61 to 64.

For external dimensions the maximum limit is placed above the line and for internal dimensions the minimum limit is placed above the line. This method of writing should be used for smaller parts and where gages are extensively employed.

A second method is to give the calculated or basic size to the required number of decimal places, followed by the tolerance plus and minus with the plus above the minus, as $8.625^{+.002}_{-.000}$.

51 *Dimensioning Fits*

The dimensions and tolerances given in

the detail drawings of the two parts of a cylindrical fit will determine the clearance (or interference) between these parts.

52 *Tolerance of Concentricity*

Mating pairs of two (or more) closely fitting machined cylindrical surfaces must be concentric in order to permit assembly of parts; thus a method of giving the permissible deviation from concentricity, is

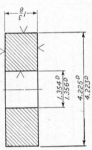

FIG. 62 LIMIT DIMENSIONS FOR CIRCULAR HOLES AND SHAFTS

sometimes necessary. As the center lines of adjoined cylinders coincide on the drawing, the tolerance for concentricity cannot be shown in dimensional form, and must therefore be given by note. One method is to mark the dimensions with reference letter and give the tolerance in a foot-note as in Fig. 63(a). Another method applies the note directly to the surfaces as in Fig. 63(b).

53 *Dimensioning a Half Section*

By a proper use of hidden lines on the external portion of a half section view and the careful observance of the usual rules, dimensioning a half-sectioned drawing becomes a fairly simple matter as shown in Fig. 64. Generous use of notes and careful placement of the dimension lines, leaders and figures will in most cases suffice to make the dimensioning clear.

FIG. 61 DIMENSIONING PART WITH CIRCULAR ENDS

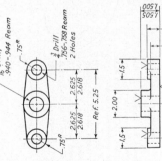

FIG. 63 DIMENSIONING PART WITH CIRCULAR ENDS

A third method, sometimes used, gives the preferred dimension with an unilateral tolerance, either plus or minus (not both) as shown in Fig. 83.

SECTION 6—DIMENSIONING STANDARD DETAILS

54 Circles

A dimension indicating the diameter of a circle should be followed by the letter "D" except when it is obvious from the drawing that the dimension is a diameter, Fig. 62. The dimension of a radius should

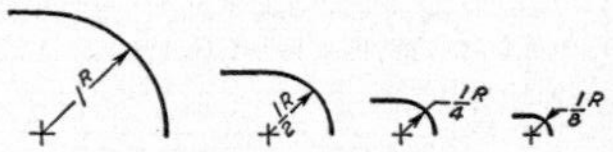

FIG. 65 DIMENSIONING RADII

always be followed by the letter "R," and the radial dimension line should have only one arrowhead, Fig. 65.

A series of concentric circular parts should be dimensioned from the side or sectioned view as in Fig. 59, rather than from the circular view. A large number of dia-

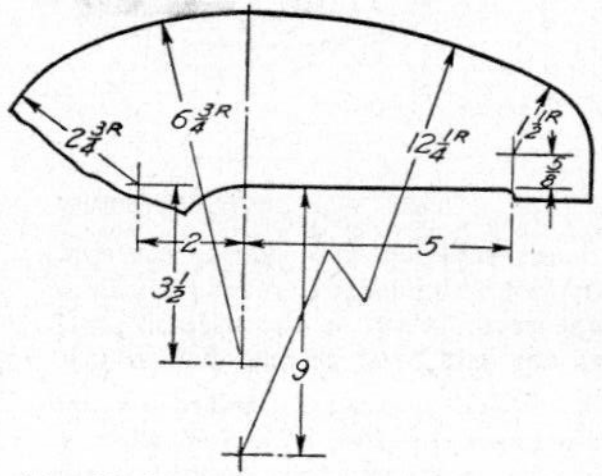

FIG. 66 DIMENSIONING IRREGULAR CURVE WITH RADII

metric dimensions in the circular view is to be avoided.

55 Curves

A curved line may be dimensioned either by radii whose centers are properly located or by offsets, Figs. 66 and 67.

56 Angles

When angular dimensions are necessary a horizontal (or vertical) center line should be used as a base line, but not both, and points located from it, Fig. 68. Angular

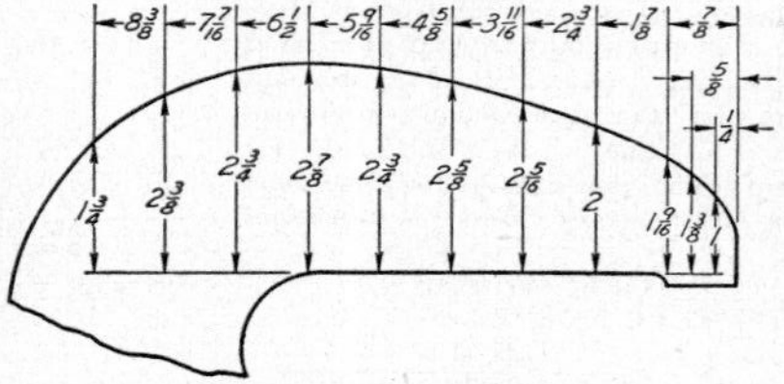

FIG. 67 PROGRESSIVE DIMENSIONING

dimensions should be written as 50°4'; the dash between degrees and minutes should not be used.

When it is necessary to give the accuracy required in an angular dimension, the tolerance is given in degrees; it is written, for example, ±¼°; when given in minutes, ±0°10'; and when given in seconds, ±0°30', as shown in Fig. 60.

In structural drawings angular measurements are shown by giving the ratio of run to rise with the larger side 12 in., Figs. 51 and 52. For steep angles as on retaining walls, the ratio has one factor equal to 1 as shown in Fig. 69.

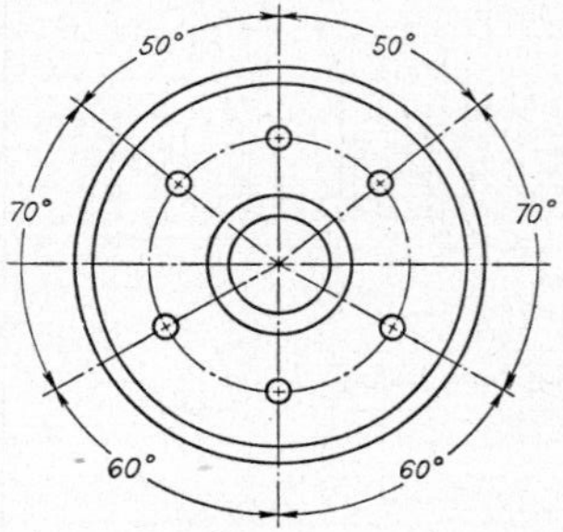

FIG. 68 DIMENSIONING ANGLES

57 Holes—Drilled, Reamed, Punched, Swaged, Cored or Bored

Holes which are to be made by any of these operations should have the diameter given, preferably on a leader, followed by the word indicating the operation, and the number of holes to be made, Fig. 70.

Notes for holes made with drills one-half inch in diameter and smaller should be written as decimal fractions, Figs. 72a, 73, and 75. The drills selected in this range should be the standard diameters given in the American Standard for Straight Shank Twist Drills (ASA B5.12—1940). The indication of the diameters of drills larger than one-half inch should be expressed in units and decimals. If common fractions are employed, the decimal equivalent should be given.

Holes which are to be bored after coring or casting should have finish marks and finished dimensions specified, Fig. 71.

58

For counterbored holes the diameters and depths should be given as shown in Fig. 72.

59

For countersunk and counterdrilled holes the angles and diameters should be given by dimensions or notes as shown in Fig. 73. The value of the countersink angle should be given as the included angle.

60 Tapped Holes

The size and depth of tapped holes should be given by note as shown in Fig. 75 with reference to the American Standard Coarse (NC), American Standard Fine (NF) or American Standard Special (N) Screw Thread Series and the Class of Fit desired. If the American Standard form is desired with a non-standard pitch the symbol is (NS).

See also Fig. 51 and 52

FIG. 69 INDICATING SLOPES ON CIVIL ENGINEERING PROJECTS

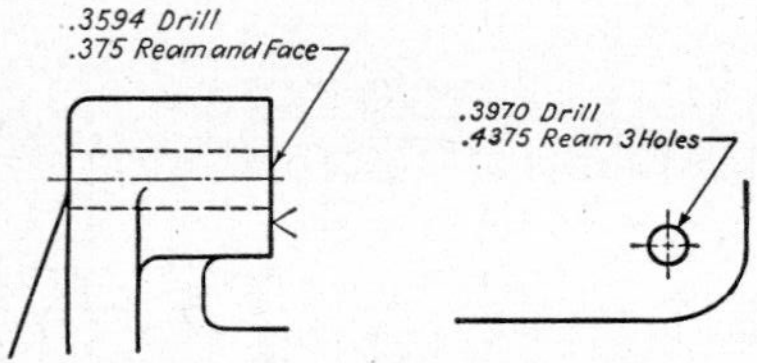

.3594 Drill
.375 Ream and Face

.3970 Drill
.4375 Ream 3 Holes

FIG. 70 DIMENSIONING DRILLED AND REAMED HOLES

61 Location of Holes

Figs. 74, 76, and 77 illustrate the coordinate method of dimensioning holes. The

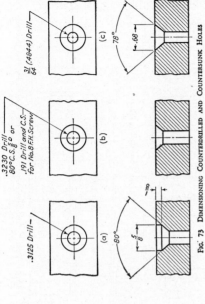

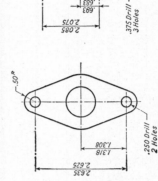

FIG. 73 DIMENSIONING COUNTERDRILLED AND COUNTERSUNK HOLES

FIG. 74 LOCATION DIMENSIONING OF HOLES

3 HOLE FLANGE

2 HOLE FLANGE

---

actual numerical values shown for location of holes in these figures have been included for illustrative purposes only. The alignment of two or more parts requires similar dimensioning from a common datum, line, or plane.

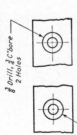

FIG. 71 DIMENSIONING MACHINED HOLES AND CYLINDERS

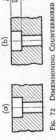

FIG. 72 DIMENSIONING COUNTERBORED HOLES

The use of angular measurements, such as degrees, minutes and seconds to locate holes and parts requiring accurate placement should be avoided as much as possible, Fig. 76.

The ordinate method of dimensioning, as illustrated in the lower right-hand drawing, Fig. 76, is preferred in precision work to the less accurate angular method as illustrated by the three other drawings in Fig. 76.

68 Tapers

The difference in diameter or width in one foot of length is known as the "taper per foot." At least three methods of dimensioning tapers are in general use.

(a) STANDARD TAPERS. Give one diameter or width, the length, and insert note on drawing designating the taper by number taken from ASA B5.10—1943, as shown in Fig. 78.

(b) SPECIAL TAPERS. In dimensioning a taper when the slope is specified, the length and only one diameter should be given or the diameters at both ends of the taper should be given and the length omitted, Fig. 78.

(c) Fig. 79 illustrates the proper method of dimensioning tapered surfaces where accuracy is required so as to obtain a close fit between internal and external tapers. The tolerance on the diameter at the gage line is ±0 and the tolerance on the angle is as shown in the figure. The

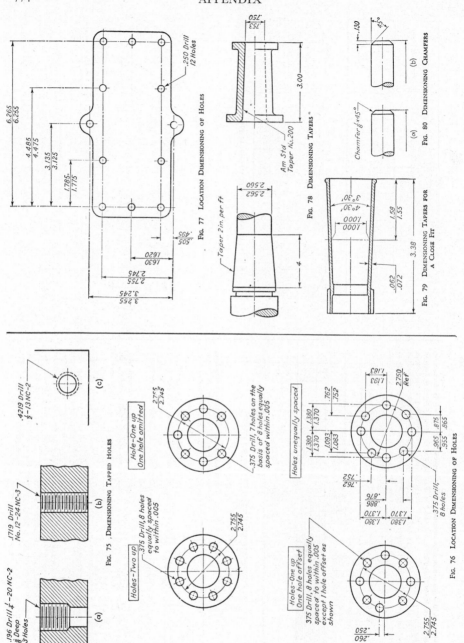

Fig. 77 Location Dimensioning of Holes

Fig. 78 Dimensioning Tapers

Fig. 79 Dimensioning Tapers for a Close Fit

Fig. 80 Dimensioning Chamfers

Fig. 75 Dimensioning Tapped Holes

Fig. 76 Location Dimensioning of Holes

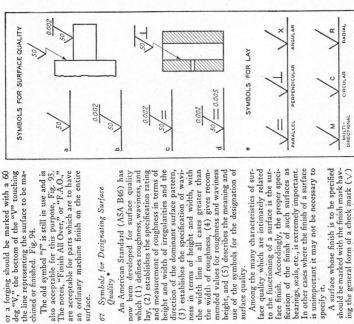

SYMBOLS FOR SURFACE QUALITY

SYMBOLS FOR LAY

PARALLEL	PERPENDICULAR	ANGULAR
MULTI-DIRECTIONAL	CIRCULAR	RADIAL

FIG. 84 SURFACE QUALITY SYMBOLS

tolerance for location of the gage line may be varied to suit the conditions.

63 Chamfers

Ordinary chamfers may be dimensioned as shown in Fig. 80a. More accurate chamfers should be dimensioned as in Fig. 80(b).

64 Knurls

When knurls are used to roughen a surface for the purpose of giving a better grip it is only necessary to specify the pitch of the knurl and show the kind of knurl and the dimensions of the areas as shown in Fig. 81.

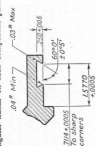

FIG. 81 DIMENSIONING KNURL USED TO PROVIDE GRIP

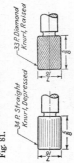

FIG. 82 DIMENSIONING KNURL FOR PRESS FIT

When knurls are used to make a press fit between two parts the original finished surface should be dimensioned with limits and then the minimum acceptable diameter of the knurl should be given in a note together with the pitch and type of knurl, straight or diamond, depressed or raised, as shown in Fig. 82.

65 Dovetail Tongues and Slots

For large quantity production, snug fitting dovetailed parts should be dimensioned as shown in Fig. 83 which provides complete information for the tool and gage maker. The so-called "plug method" is also in common use.

The important contact surfaces should be controlled by dimensions delineated to the same intersection points of mating angular flanks on each component part.

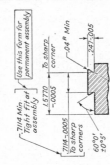

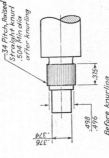

FIG. 83 DIMENSIONING A DOVETAIL TONGUE AND SLOT FOR SNUG FIT

Tolerances should be given on all dimensions including angular dimensions. The radii at corners should be governed by the best requirements of good tool practice and flats may be substituted if desired.

66 Finish Marks

A surface to be machined or "finished" from unfinished material such as a casting or a forging should be marked with a 60 deg "V," the bottom of the "V" touching the line representing the surface to be machined or finished. Fig. 94.

The old symbol "f" is still in use and is also acceptable for this purpose, Fig. 95. The notes, "Finish All Over," or "F.A.O.," are acceptable for parts which are to have an ordinary machine finish on the entire surface.

67 Symbols for Designating Surface Quality *

An American Standard (ASA B46) has now been developed for surface quality which (1) defines roughness, waviness, and lay, (2) establishes the specification rating and measurement of roughness in terms of height and width of irregularities and the direction of the dominant surface pattern, (3) establishes the specification of waviness in terms of height and width, with the width line in all cases greater than the width of roughness, (4) gives recommended values for roughness and waviness height, and (5) describes the meaning and use of the symbols for the designation of surface quality.

Among the many characteristics of surface quality which are intimately related to the functioning of a surface is the surface finish. Accordingly, the proper specification of the finish of such surfaces as bearings, seals, etc., is extremely important. In other cases where the finish of a surface is unimportant it may not be necessary to specify it.

A surface whose finish is to be specified should be marked with the finish mark having the general form of a check mark (√) so that the point of the symbol is

(a) On the line indicating the surface,
(b) On a leader pointing to the surface.

Where it is desired to specify only the surface roughness height, and the width of roughness or direction of tool marks is not important, the simplest form of the symbol should be used. See Fig. 84(a). This height may be either maximum peak to valley height, average peak to valley

* As recommended by the Sectional Committee on the Standardization of Classification and Designation of Surface Qualities (ASA B46).

height, or average deviation from the mean (RMS or arithmetical). The numerical value is placed in the ∨ as shown.

Where it is desired to specify waviness height in addition to roughness height a straight horizontal line should be added to the top of the simple symbol. See Fig. 84(b). The numerical value of height of waviness would be shown above this line.

Then, if the nature of the preferred lay is to be shown in addition to these two characteristics, it will be indicated by the addition of a combination of lines as shown in Fig. 84(c and e). The parallel and perpendicular part of the symbol indicates that the dominant lines on the surface are parallel or perpendicular to the boundary line of the surface in contact with the symbol.

The complete symbol including the roughness width placed to the right of the lay symbol, is shown in Fig. 84(d).

The use of only one number to specify the height or width of roughness or waviness shall indicate the maximum value. Any lesser degree of roughness will be satisfactory. When two numbers are used separated by a dash, they indicate the maximum and minimum permissible values.

68 Bend Allowance

The allowance to be made for bends in sheet metal work or thin steel is shown in Fig. 85. The intersection of the plane sur-

faces adjoining the bend is called a mold or construction line and this line is used in dimensioning rather than the center of the arc.

69 Profile Dimensioning

Parts that are formed by bending are dimensioned as in Fig. 86. The dimensions are given to mold lines. Angles and radii must be shown.

70 Springs

Methods of representing and dimensioning springs are shown in Figs. 90, 91, and

$$\text{Bend allowance (B.A.)} = (.01745\,R + .0078T)\theta$$

FIG. 85 BEND ALLOWANCE

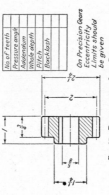

FIG. 86 PROFILE DIMENSIONING

ting data which include the tooth-form standard and method of cutting, and information for measurement and inspection, should be given in a table. Notes for material and heat treatment are also required, Figs. 87 and 88.

72 Keys

Plain square, flat, taper and Gib-head taper stock keys are dimensioned by note giving the width, height and length. Whenever possible, sizes should conform to standards established in the American Standard for Shafting and Stock Keys (ASA B17.1—1943). The keys need not be drawn except for special keys or when limits other than those of the standard are necessary. American Standard Woodruff Keys, Keyslots and Cutter (ASA B17f—1930) may be specified by key number.

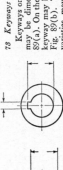

| No. of teeth |
| Pressure angle |
| Addendum |
| Whole depth |
| Pitch |
| Backlash |

On Precision Gears Eccentricity Limits should be given

FIG. 87 DIMENSIONING SPUR PINION

92. Beside the length and controlling diameter (inside or outside) the size and number of turns of wire must be indicated by note. The type of end should be indicated even though standard. If the ends of the spring must be formed to fit some special condition the end must then be dimensioned in detail to secure the desired result. Single line symbols are shown in Fig. 93.

71 Gears

A gear may be shown satisfactorily by a section through the axis, except when additional views may be required to show the construction of a large blank or other details. In principle the dimensions placed on the drawing should be sufficient for machining the gear blank. The gear-cut-

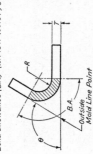

| No. of Teeth |
| Pitch |
| Pressure angle |
| Spiral angle |
| Hand of Spiral |
| Pitch diam |
| Pitch angle |
| Face angle |
| Addendum |
| Whole depth |
| Backlash allowed |

FIG. 88 DIMENSIONING SPIRAL BEVEL PINION

73 Keyways

Keyways on shafts or internal members may be dimensioned as shown in Fig. 89(a). On the hub or external member the keyway may be dimensioned as shown in Fig. 89(b). The key seat for patented varieties may be specified by the key number.

(a)   (b)

FIG. 89 DIMENSIONING KEYWAYS

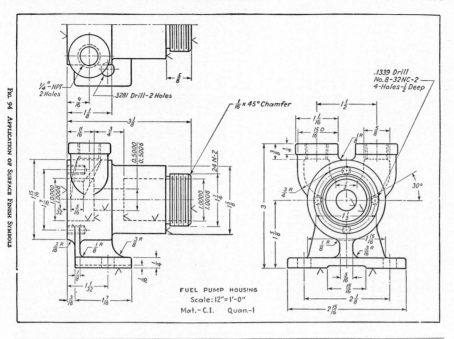

FIG. 94 APPLICATION OF SURFACE FINISH SYMBOLS

FUEL PUMP HOUSING
Scale: 12"=1'-0"
Mat.-C.I.   Quan.-1

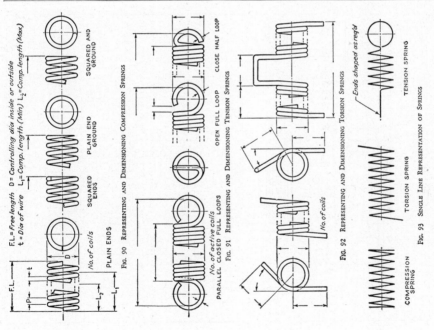

F.L.=Free length   D=Controlling dia inside or outside
t=Dia of wire L_1=Comp.length (Min) L_2=Comp.length (Max)

PLAIN ENDS

SQUARED
ENDS

PLAIN END
GROUND

SQUARED AND
GROUND

FIG. 90 REPRESENTING AND DIMENSIONING COMPRESSION SPRINGS

PARALLEL CLOSED FULL LOOPS

OPEN FULL LOOP   CLOSE HALF LOOP

FIG. 91 REPRESENTING AND DIMENSIONING TENSION SPRINGS

FIG. 92 REPRESENTING AND DIMENSIONING TORSION SPRINGS

TENSION SPRING

TORSION SPRING

COMPRESSION
SPRING

FIG. 93 SINGLE LINE REPRESENTATION OF SPRINGS

SECTION 7—NOTES

¶4   Definition

Notes are supplementary to dimensioning and are used to indicate necessary information on the drawing in a condensed and systematic manner. Notes may be classified as General and Local or Specific, according to their character.

¶5   General Notes

General notes should be placed in the lower right hand corner of the drawing above or to the left of the title block or in a central position below the view of the object to which they apply. General notes, as the name implies, means those notes which refer to the part as a whole, e.g.: "Finish All Over" or "Paint One Coat."

Also classified as general notes, are notes that apply to dimensions of the part and which might be repeated many times if general notes were not used, e.g.: "All draft angles 3° unless otherwise specified" or "Tolerance ±.001 unless shown otherwise."

¶6   Miscellaneous General Notes

The following miscellaneous General Notes are suggested for use where necessary.

(1) Finish All Over.
(2) Finish All Over Except—
(3) Break Sharp Edges .01-.03 Approx. R Unless Otherwise Specified.
(4) Break Sharp Edges On All (Drilled Holes) (Chamfers) (Countersinks) Unless Otherwise Specified.
(5) All (Casting) (Forging) (Finished) Radii .xxx- .xxx Unless Otherwise Specified.

(6) All Draft Angles X° Unless Otherwise Specified.
(7) All Dimensions To Be Met After Plating.
(8) Must Be Flat and Free From Burrs.
(9) All Small Unfinished Radii and Fillets .XX Unless Otherwise Specified.
(10) Remove Burrs.

¶7   Local Notes

Local notes are those that apply to local operations only and should be placed adjacent, connected by a leader, to the point at which such operations are to be performed, e.g.: "248-.255," "Drill, 4 holes." See Figs. 64 and 70 to 75 inclusive, for examples.

¶8   Specification of Materials and Heat Treatments

Many companies have their own method and standards. A method commonly available is to indicate ferrous materials and heat treatments by specifying the steels by the SAE Numbers, and the hardness required by a Rockwell, or Brinell hardness number, as for example:

SAE—1095—Rockwell C 60-64
SAE—3345—Brinell 340-380

For steel in buildings, bridges, boilers, railroads, and reinforced concrete the A.S.T.M. specifications or special specifications prepared by the firm or department making the drawing are used. Treatments such as case-hardening, carburizing (by any method), cyaniding, nitriding, should be indicated by a specific local note completely covering the requirements.

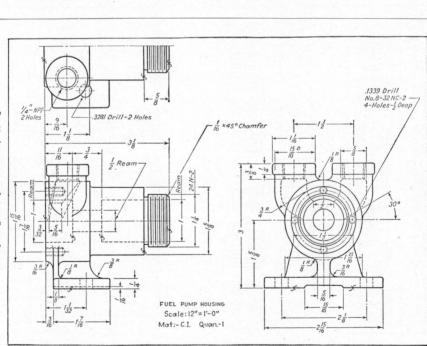

FIG. 95   APPLICATION OF SURFACE FINISH SYMBOLS

FUEL PUMP HOUSING
Scale: 12" = 1'-0"
Mat:- C.I.   Quan.-1

SECTION 8—TRIMMED SIZES OF DRAWING PAPER AND CLOTH. TITLES

79 Sizes of Paper

The recommended standard trimmed sheet sizes of drawing paper and cloth are as follows:

A	$8\frac{1}{2}\times11$	D	22×34
B	11×17	E	34×44
C	17×22		

The use of the basic sheet size $8\frac{1}{2}\times11$ in.

and its multiple permits filing of small tracings and folded prints in commercial standard files with or without correspondence. These sheet sizes also can cut without waste from the present 36 in. rolls of paper and cloth. These standard sizes are based on the dimensions of the commercial letter head, $8\frac{1}{2}\times11$ in., in general use in the United States.

Drawings larger than standard sheet sizes may be made as "rolled" drawings. Widths are controlled by standard paper sizes, and lengths are in multiples of 11 in.

80 Sizes of Paper in the Metric System

For drawings made in the metric system of units or for foreign correspondence it is recommended that the metric standard trimmed sheet sizes be used. These sizes are based on the width to length ratio of 1 to $\sqrt{2}$ and are as follows:

A0	841×1189 mm
A1	594×841 mm
A2	420×594 mm
A3	297×420 mm
A4	210×297 mm
A5	148×210 mm
A6	105×148 mm

81 Title, Change Record and Number Blocks

The title block with appropriate space

for the identifying number should be located at the lower right hand corner of the sheet. Accordion folding of prints with the printed side out is recommended when prints are filed in a standard letter size file as illustrated in Fig. 96.

In order to file prints which have been accordion folded so that the closed fold will be up and the number still be visible, it is necessary to add a supplementary number block (approximately 1.75 in. by .5 in.) to each size sheet as shown in Fig. 96. This supplementary number block may be either parallel or normal to the border line of the drawing. If change notes or general notes reach this supplementary number block a minimum clearance of .25 in. should be left above and below the block.

82 Location of Change Record

The change record should be placed immediately above the title space as shown in Fig. 96. The change record must be "tied in" to the drawing so it can be quickly found. This is particularly necessary on large sheets.

83 Zoning System of Locating Changes

The lower and right hand borders of the

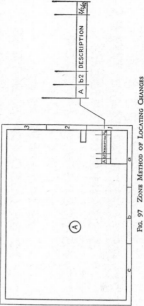

FIG. 97 ZONE METHOD OF LOCATING CHANGES

larger size drawings should be ruled and marked as indicated in Fig. 97 to provide zones for reference purposes. The location of the change on the drawing should be referenced in the change block and identified by a reference letter which should also appear on the drawing near the change and

FIG. 96 TITLE BLOCK, CHANGE RECORD, AND FOLDING

SECTION 9—LETTERING

in a position where it can be readily seen. For example a change referenced (b2) would be found upward from b and over from 2. For purposes of clarity a circle of approximately 5/16 in. diameter should be drawn around the change letter as illustrated in Fig. 97. Letters I, O and Q should not be used to avoid misinterpretation and resultant errors. Other methods not illustrated here are also in common use.

84 The most important requirement for lettering as used on working drawings is legibility. The second is ease and rapidity of execution. These two requirements are met in the single stroke commercial gothic letter, now in almost universal use throughout the technical world. Preference seems to be divided between the vertical and the inclined styles.

The following standard practice is recommended:

(a) That single stroke commercial gothic lettering either vertical or inclined at a slope of 2 in 5 be used on all working drawings for titles, notes, etc.

85 It is not desirable to grade the size of lettering with the size of the drawing except when a reduced photographic reproduction of the drawing is to be made. In other words the size and weight of the lettering should be such as will produce legible prints from tracings either in pencil or in ink.

Lettering should not be underlined except for particular emphasis.

Approved specimens of vertical and inclined letters are shown in Figs. 98 and 99.

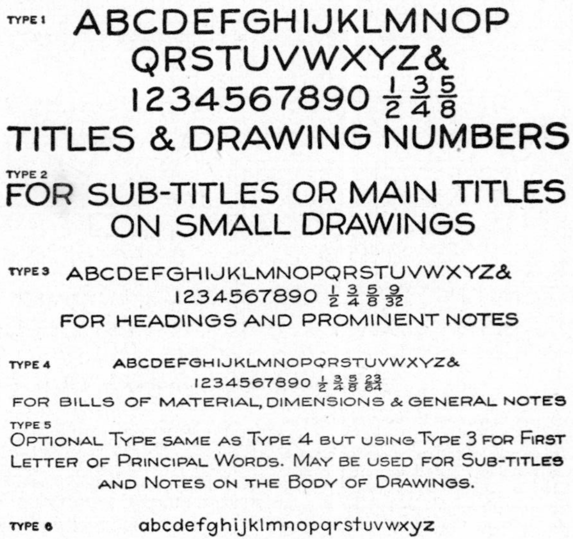

TYPE 1
ABCDEFGHIJKLMNOP QRSTUVWXYZ&
1234567890 $\frac{1}{2}$ $\frac{3}{4}$ $\frac{5}{8}$ $\frac{7}{16}$
TO BE USED FOR MAIN TITLES & DRAWING NUMBERS

TYPE 2
ABCDEFGHIJKLMNOPQR STUVWXYZ&
1234567890 $\frac{13}{64}$ $\frac{5}{8}$ $\frac{4}{82}$
TO BE USED FOR SUB-TITLES

TYPE 3
ABCDEFGHIJKLMNOPQRSTUVWXYZ&
1234567890 $\frac{1}{2}$ $\frac{3}{4}$ $\frac{5}{8}$ $\frac{7}{16}$
FOR HEADINGS AND PROMINENT NOTES

TYPE 4
ABCDEFGHIJKLMNOPQRSTUVWXYZ&
1234567890 $\frac{1}{2}$ $\frac{4}{8}$ $\frac{1}{32}$
FOR BILLS OF MATERIAL, DIMENSIONS & GENERAL NOTES

TYPE 5
OPTIONAL TYPE SAME AS TYPE 4 BUT USING TYPE 3 FOR FIRST LETTER OF PRINCIPAL WORDS. MAY BE USED FOR SUB-TITLES & NOTES ON THE BODY OF DRAWINGS.

TYPE 6
abcdefghijklmnopqrstuvwxyz
Type 6 may be used in place of Type 4 with capitals of Type 3, for Bills of Material and Notes on Body of Drawing.

Fig. 99

TYPE 1
ABCDEFGHIJKLMNOP QRSTUVWXYZ&
1234567890 $\frac{1}{2}$ $\frac{3}{4}$ $\frac{5}{8}$
TITLES & DRAWING NUMBERS

TYPE 2
FOR SUB-TITLES OR MAIN TITLES ON SMALL DRAWINGS

TYPE 3
ABCDEFGHIJKLMNOPQRSTUVWXYZ&
1234567890 $\frac{1}{2}$ $\frac{3}{4}$ $\frac{5}{8}$ $\frac{9}{32}$
FOR HEADINGS AND PROMINENT NOTES

TYPE 4
ABCDEFGHIJKLMNOPQRSTUVWXYZ&
1234567890 $\frac{1}{2}$ $\frac{3}{4}$ $\frac{5}{8}$ $\frac{21}{32}$
FOR BILLS OF MATERIAL, DIMENSIONS & GENERAL NOTES

TYPE 5
OPTIONAL TYPE SAME AS TYPE 4 BUT USING TYPE 3 FOR FIRST LETTER OF PRINCIPAL WORDS. MAY BE USED FOR SUB-TITLES AND NOTES ON THE BODY OF DRAWINGS.

TYPE 6
abcdefghijklmnopqrstuvwxyz

Fig. 98

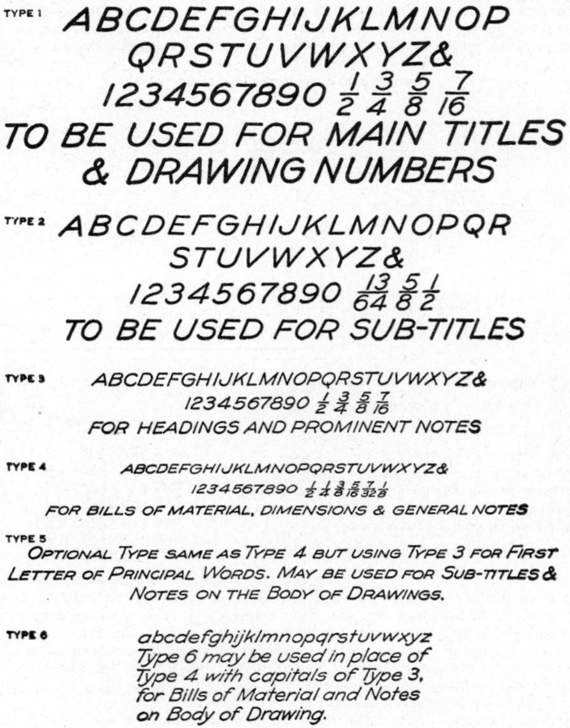

3. AMERICAN STANDARD BASIC GRAPHICAL SYMBOLS FOR ELECTRICAL APPARATUS
(From ASA Z32.12—1947)

ALARM	**COILS**	Grid (Incl. Beam-confining or Beam-forming Electrodes)
Bell_____	Blowout_____	Ignitor
Buzzer_____	Relay_____	Ignitor_____
	(Dot indicates inner end of winding)	
Annunciator_____	Inductor, Reactor, Field, etc. ___ or ___	**ELECTRODE, EMITTING**
Horn, Howler, or Loudspeaker _____	Operating ∧∨ or (*) or ⊔	Cold Cathode (Incl. Ionic Heated Cathode)_____
	*Use identifying legend within or adjacent to circle	Directly Heated Cathode (Filament Type)_____
AMPLIFIER or REPEATER	**CONTACTS**	Indirectly Heated Cathode _____
ANTENNA	Normally Open_____ or	Ionic Heated Cathode with Supplementary Heater_____
Aerial_____	Normally Closed_____ or	Photoelectric Cathode_____
Loop_____	Lever Switch_____	Pool Cathode_____
ARRESTER ELEMENT	Moving Contact or Armature for Relays, Non-Locking Keys, Jacks, etc._____	**ENVELOPE (SHELL)**
General_____	Moving Contact for Locking Keys, Jacks, etc._____	Gas Filled_____
Horn Gap_____	Sleeve_____	Located as convenient
Protective Gap_____	Spring for Telegraph Operation_____	High Vacuum_____
	CORE	
Sphere-gap Element_____	Air (No Symbol; Indicate *Air Core* When Needed) Magnetic (General)_____	Magnetron, Resonant Type_____
Valve or Film Element_____	Relay or Magnet_____	
	CRYSTAL	Electronic Tube, Typical Assembly of Symbols (Triode with In-directly-Heated Cathode and Envelope Connected to Base Terminal)
BATTERY	Detector_____	
Long line always positive	Piezo-Electric_____	
BIMETAL ELEMENT	**ELECTRODE, COLLECTING**	See also Tube Basing Orientation and Tube Terminals
	Anode or Plate (Incl. Collector and Fluorescent ___ Target)	
BUSHING	Target, X-Ray_____	**FUSE**
		General_____
CAPACITOR	**ELECTRODE, COLLECTING and EMITTING**	Thermal Element_____
	Dynode_____	**GENERAL APPARATUS**
CIRCUIT BREAKER	**ELECTRODE, CONTROLLING**	**In all cases indicate type*
Air_____	Deflecting, Reflecting, or Repelling Electrode _____ *(Electrostatic Type)* Excitor	
Oil_____	Excitor (Contactor Type) _____	**GROUND**

3. AMERICAN STANDARD BASIC GRAPHICAL SYMBOLS
FOR ELECTRICAL APPARATUS (*Continued*)
(From ASA Z32.12—1947)

HANDSET	**RECEPTACLE** Non-Polarized or Polarized _ _	**TUBE BASING ORIENTATION**
HEATER ELEMENT	**RECTIFIER** General _ _ _ _ _ _ _ _ _ _ (*Arrow points in direction of low resistance*)	For Keyed Bases _ _ _ _ Key Convention
LAMP General _ _ _ _ _ _ _ _ _ _ _ _ *Identifying designation within* *circle to indicate color* Illuminating _ _ _ _ _ _ _ _ _ _ _ Switchboard (Telephone) _ _ _ _ _ _ _ _ _ _	**REPRODUCER** **RESISTOR, FIXED** —\/\/\— or —▭— *Always use identifying legend* *within or adjacent to rectangle*	For Bayonets, Bosses, and other Reference Points _ _ _ _ _ **TUBE**　Small Pin→ **TERMINALS** Base Terminals _ _ _ _ _
METER OR INSTRUMENT 　　　or *Identifying designation within* *circle or square, as* *A—Ammeter, V—Voltmeter*	**RESISTOR, VARIABLE** Variable or Adjustable *Two-wire or Rheostat* Variable or Adjustable *Three-wire or* *Voltage-Divider*	Large Pin → Rigid Terminals Envelope Terminals _ _ _ _ _ Flexible Leads
MICROPHONE	**RESONATOR**	**VARIABLE** General _ _ _ _ _ _ _ _ _ _ _ _
MOTOR OR GENERATOR Field _ _ or Machine or Rotating Armature _ _ _ _ _ _ _ _ _ _ _ Wound Rotor Induction Motor or Generator _ _ _ _ _ Typical D-C Motor or Generator Ass'y of Symbols _ _ _ _ _ _ _ _ _ Single-Line Diagrams for Motor and Generator Winding Symbols 1 Phase　　2 Phase 3 Phase　　3 Phase Wye　　　　Delta (Undergrounded)		**VOLTAGE, SOURCE** **OF ALTERNATING** **WIRING (See Coils)** Cable Termination _ _ _ _ _ _ _ _ Conduit or Grouping of Leads or　or　or　or Connections _ _ _　or Crossing, Not Connected Electric Conductor _ _ _ Incoming Line _ _ _ _ _ _ Junction or Splice of Conductors _ _ _ _ _ _ _ _ _ _ Outgoing Line _ _ _ _ _ _
	RHEOSTAT OR RESISTOR Adjustable Tap or Side Wire With Leads　With Terminals	
	RINGER	
	SOUNDER, **TELEGRAPH**	
PLUG Disconnecting Device Non-Polarized or Polarized	**SWITCH (Push Button)** See also Contacts Normally Closed _ _ _ _ _ _ _ _ _ Normally Open _ _ _ _ _ _ _ _ _	**Pair**
RECEIVER General _ _ _ _ _ _ _ _ _ _ _ _ _ Hand _ _ _ _ _ _ _ _ _ _ _ _ _ Headset, Single _ _ _ _ _ _ _ _ Headset, Double _ _ _ _ _ _ _ _	**SWITCH HOOK** **THERMOCOUPLE** **TRANSFORMER** 　　　　or **TRANSMITTER** Telephone _ _ _ _ _ _ _ _ _ _	**RADIO FREQUENCY CABLE** Coaxial _ _ _ _ _ _ Twin Conductor _ _ _ _ Tie Lines _ _ _ _ _ _ _ _ _ Underground or in Conduit _ _ _ _ _ _ _ _ Wiring Terminal _ _ _ _ _ _ _ _ _

4. TOPOGRAPHIC SYMBOLS
Board of Surveys and Maps

Highway		National or State Line
Railroad		County Line
Highway Bridge		Township or District Line
Railroad Bridge		City or Village Line
Drawbridges		Triangulation Station
Suspension Bridge	BM	Bench Mark and Elevation
	X	
	1232	
Dam		Any Location Station (WITH EXPLANATORY NOTE)
Telegraph or Telephone Line		Streams in General
Power-Trans. Line		Lake or Pond
Buildings in General		Falls and Rapids
		Contours
Capital		Hachures
County Seat		Sand and Sand Dunes
Other Towns		Marsh
Barbed Wire Fence		Woodland of Any Kind
Smooth Wire Fence		Orchard
Hedge		Grassland in General
Oil or Gas Wells		
Windmill		Cultivated Fields
Tanks		Commercial or Municipal Field
Canal or Ditch		Airplane Landing Field Marked or Emergency
Canal Lock		Mooring Mast
Canal Lock (POINT UPSTREAM)		Airway Light Beacon (ARROWS INDICATE COURSE LIGHTS)
Aqueduct or Water Pipe		Auxiliary Airway Light Beacon, Flashing

5. RAILWAY ENGINEERING SYMBOLS

	Stream		Rubble in Mortar (COURSES MAY BE OMITTED)
	Water Line		Rubble Dry
	Marsh		Crushed Rock
	Cut		Seamy Rock
	Embankment		Solid Rock
	State, County, Township Line		Rockface Ashlar
	City		Dressed Ashlar
	Section Corner		Gravel, Sand
	Stone Monument		Earth
	Iron Monument		Water (MAY BE USED ALTERNATELY)
	Cattle Guard		Cast Iron
	Fire Hydrant		Wrought Iron
	Riser		Cast Steel
	Mile Post		Wrought Steel
	Section Post		Malleable Iron
	Yard Limits		Copper
	Highway Crossing Bell		Brass
	Crossing Sign		Bronze

Standard Sections

	Wood (WITH THE GRAIN)		Metal, Lead, Babbitt, etc.
	Wood (ACROSS THE GRAIN)		Mica, Rubber, Vulcanite
	Brick (COURSES MAY BE OMITTED)		Wool, Felt, Asbestos, etc.
	Plain Concrete		Structural Steel
	Reinforced Concrete (RODS OR BARS)		True and Mag. Meridian
	Reinforced Concrete (METAL MESH)		Graphic Scales

6. AMERICAN STANDARD PIPING SYMBOLS
(From ASA Z32.2—1941)

	FLANGED	SCREWED	BELL & SPIGOT	WELDED	SOLDERED
1. Joint					
2. Elbow—90°					
3. Elbow—45°					
4. Elbow—Turned Up					
5. Elbow—Turned Down					
6. Elbow—Long Radius					
7. Reducing Elbow					
8. Tee					
9. Tee—Outlet Up					
10. Tee—Outlet Down					
11. Side Outlet Tee—Outlet Up					
12. Cross					
13. Reducer, Concentric					
14. Reducer, Eccentric					
15. Lateral					
16. Gate Valve, Elev.					
17. Globe Valve, Elev.					
18. Check Valve					
19. Stop Cock					
20. Safety Valve					
21. Expansion Joint Flanged					
22. Union	(See No. 1)				
23. Sleeve					
24. Bushing					
25. Gate Valve, Plan					
26. Globe Valve, Plan					

7. AMERICAN STANDARD HEATING, VENTILATING, AND DUCTWORK SYMBOLS
(From ASA Z32.2—1941)

High Pressure Steam	Soil, Waste or Leader (Above Grade)
Medium Pressure Return	Cold Water
FOF — Fuel Oil Flow	Hot Water
A — Compressed Air	Hot Water Return
RD — Refrigerant Discharge	F—F Fire Line
RS — Refrigerant Suction	G—G Gas
B — Brine Supply	S Sprinklers—Main Supplies
Wall Radiator, Plan	Volume Damper
Wall Radiator on Ceiling, Plan	*Elev*
Unit Heater (Propeller), Plan	Deflecting Damper
Unit Heater (Centrifugal Fan), Plan	Turning Vanes
Thermostatic Trap	
Thermostatic Float	
Thermometer	Automatic Dampers
Thermostat	
20X12 — Duct Plan (1st Figure, Width; 2nd Depth)	
D — Inclined Drop in Respect to Air Flow	Canvas Connections
S —12X20 Supply Duct Section	
E —12X20 Exhaust Duct Section	
R —12X20 Recirculation Duct Section	Fan and Motor with Belt Guard
F A —12X20 Fresh Air Duct Section	
Supply Outlet	
Exhaust Inlet	
Volume Damper *Plan*	Intake Louvres and Screen

8. AMERICAN STANDARD PLUMBING SYMBOLS
(From ASA Z32.2—1941)

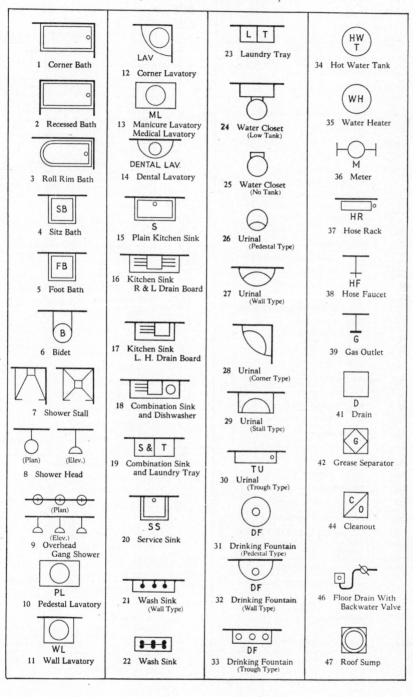

1 Corner Bath	LAV 12 Corner Lavatory	L | T 23 Laundry Tray	HW T 34 Hot Water Tank
2 Recessed Bath	ML 13 Manicure Lavatory Medical Lavatory	24 Water Closet (Low Tank)	WH 35 Water Heater
3 Roll Rim Bath	DENTAL LAV. 14 Dental Lavatory	25 Water Closet (No Tank)	M 36 Meter
SB 4 Sitz Bath	S 15 Plain Kitchen Sink	26 Urinal (Pedestal Type)	HR 37 Hose Rack
FB 5 Foot Bath	16 Kitchen Sink R & L Drain Board	27 Urinal (Wall Type)	HF 38 Hose Faucet
B 6 Bidet	17 Kitchen Sink L. H. Drain Board	28 Urinal (Corner Type)	G 39 Gas Outlet
7 Shower Stall	18 Combination Sink and Dishwasher	29 Urinal (Stall Type)	D 41 Drain
(Plan) (Elev.) 8 Shower Head	S & T 19 Combination Sink and Laundry Tray	T U 30 Urinal (Trough Type)	G 42 Grease Separator
(Plan) (Elev.) 9 Overhead Gang Shower	S S 20 Service Sink	DF 31 Drinking Fountain (Pedestal Type)	C O 44 Cleanout
PL 10 Pedestal Lavatory	21 Wash Sink (Wall Type)	DF 32 Drinking Fountain (Wall Type)	46 Floor Drain With Backwater Valve
WL 11 Wall Lavatory	22 Wash Sink	DF 33 Drinking Fountain (Trough Type)	47 Roof Sump

9. AMERICAN STANDARD ELECTRICAL SYMBOLS
FOR ARCHITECTURAL PLANS (From ASA Z32.9—1943)

GENERAL OUTLETS

O	–O	Outlet.
ⓑ	–ⓑ	Blanked Outlet.
ⓓ		Drop Cord.
ⓔ	–ⓔ	Electrical Outlet; for use only when circle used alone might be confused with columns, plumbing symbols, etc.
ⓕ	–ⓕ	Fan Outlet.
ⓙ	–ⓙ	Junction Box.
ⓛ	–ⓛ	Lamp Holder.
ⓛPS	–ⓛPS	Lamp Holder with Pull Switch.
ⓢ	–ⓢ	Pull Switch.
ⓥ	–ⓥ	Outlet for Vapor Discharge Lamp.
ⓧ	–ⓧ	Exit Light Outlet.
ⓒ	–ⓒ	Clock Outlet. (Specify Voltage.)

CONVENIENCE OUTLETS

	Duplex Convenience Outlet.
$_{1,3}$	Convenience Outlet, not Duplex. 1 = Single, 3 = Triplex, etc.
$_{WP}$	Weatherproof Convenience Outlet.
$_R$	Range Outlet.
$_S$	Switch and Convenience Outlet.
R	Radio and Convenience Outlet.
	Special Purpose Outlet. (Des. in Spec.)
	Floor Outlet.

SWITCH OUTLETS

S	Single Pole Switch.
S_2	Double Pole Switch.
S_3	Three Way Switch.
S_4	Four Way Switch.
S_D	Automatic Door Switch.
S_E	Electrolier Switch.
S_K	Key Operated Switch.
S_P	Switch and Pilot Lamp.
S_{CB}	Circuit Breaker.
S_{WCB}	Weatherproof Circuit Breaker.
S_{MC}	Momentary Contact Switch.
S_{RC}	Remote Control Switch.
S_{WP}	Weatherproof Switch.
S_F	Fused Switch.
S_{WF}	Weatherproof Fused Switch.

SPECIAL OUTLETS

O$_{a,b,c,etc}$	Any Standard Symbol as given above with the addition of a lower case subscript letter may be used to designate some special variation of Standard Equipment of particular interest in a specific set of Architectural Plans.
$_{a,b,c,etc}$	
S$_{a,b,c,etc}$	When used they must be listed in the Key of Symbols on each drawing and if necessary further described in the specifications.
□$_{a,b,c}$	Special Auxiliary Outlets. Subscript letters refer to notes on plans or detailed description in specifications.

PANELS, CIRCUITS, AND MISCELLANEOUS

▬	Lighting Panel.
▨	Power Panel.
——	Branch Circuit; Concealed in Ceiling or Wall.
– – –	Branch Circuit; Concealed in Floor.
-----	Branch Circuit; Exposed.
↦	Home Run to Panel Board. Indicate number of Circuits by number of arrows. NOTE: Any circuit without further designation indicates a two-wire circuit. For a greater number of wires indicate as follows: –///– (3 wires) –////– (4 wires), etc.
▬▬	Feeders. NOTE: Use heavy lines and designate by number corresponding to listing in Feeder Schedule.
▤	Underfloor Duct and Junction Box. Triple System. NOTE: For double or single systems eliminate one or two lines. This symbol is equally adaptable to auxiliary system layouts.
Ⓖ	Generator.
Ⓜ	Motor.
Ⓘ	Instrument.
Ⓣ	Power Transformer. (Or to scale.)
⊠	Controller.
⊏⊐	Isolating Switch.

AUXILIARY SYSTEMS

▣	Push Button.
▱	Buzzer.
▭	Bell.
–◇	Annunciator.
◀	Outside Telephone.
⊲	Interconnecting Telephone.
⊲	Telephone Switchboard.
Ⓣ	Bell Ringing Transformer.
Ⓓ	Electric Door Opener.
Ⓕ	Fire Alarm Bell.
F	Fire Alarm Station.
⊠	City Fire Alarm Station.
FA	Fire Alarm Central Station.
FS	Automatic Fire Alarm Device.
W	Watchman's Station.
W	Watchman's Central Station.
H	Horn.
N	Nurse's Signal Plug.
M	Maid's Signal Plug.
R	Radio Outlet.
SC	Signal Central Station.
□	Interconnection Box.
⑂⑂⑂	Battery.
– – –	Auxiliary System Circuits. NOTE: Any line without further designation indicates a 2-Wire System. For a greater number of wires designate with numerals in manner similar to —•— 12-No. 18W$\frac{3}{4}$″ C., or designate by number corresponding to listing in Schedule.

10. AMERICAN STANDARD WROUGHT-STEEL PIPE[1] AND TAPER PIPE THREADS[2]

Nominal Pipe Size	Outside Diameter[3]	Thds per Inch	Tap Drill Size	Hand-tight Engagement	Effective Thread Length, External	Nominal Wall Thickness, Steel Pipe			Length of Pipe, Feet, per Square Foot External Surface[7]	Length of Standard-weight Pipe, Feet, Containing 1 Cu. Ft.[7]
						Standard Weight Schedule 40[4]	Extra Strong Schedule 80[5]	Double Extra Strong[6]		
	D	N	T	L^1	L^2					
$\frac{1}{8}$	0.405	27	$\frac{11}{32}$	0.180	0.2639	0.068	0.095	....	9.431	2,533.8
$\frac{1}{4}$	0.540	18	$\frac{7}{16}$	0.200	0.4018	0.088	0.119	....	7.073	1,383.8
$\frac{3}{8}$	0.675	18	$\frac{37}{64}$	0.240	0.4078	0.091	0.126	....	5.658	754.36
$\frac{1}{2}$	0.840	14	$\frac{23}{32}$	0.320	0.5337	0.109	0.147	0.294	4.547	473.91
$\frac{3}{4}$	1.050	14	$\frac{59}{64}$	0.339	0.5457	0.113	0.154	0.308	3.637	270.03
1	1.315	$11\frac{1}{2}$	$1\frac{5}{32}$	0.400	0.6828	0.133	0.179	0.358	2.904	166.62
$1\frac{1}{4}$	1.660	$11\frac{1}{2}$	$1\frac{1}{2}$	0.420	0.7068	0.140	0.191	0.382	2.301	96.275
$1\frac{1}{2}$	1.900	$11\frac{1}{2}$	$1\frac{47}{64}$	0.420	0.7235	0.145	0.200	0.400	2.010	70.733
2	2.375	$11\frac{1}{2}$	$2\frac{7}{32}$	0.436	0.7565	0.154	0.218	0.436	1.608	42.913
$2\frac{1}{2}$	2.875	8	$2\frac{5}{8}$	0.682	1.1375	0.203	0.276	0.552	1.328	30.077
3	3.500	8	$3\frac{1}{4}$	0.766	1.2000	0.216	0.300	0.600	1.091	19.479
$3\frac{1}{2}$	4.000	8	$3\frac{3}{4}$	0.821	1.2500	0.226	0.318	0.636	0.954	14.565
4	4.500	8	$4\frac{1}{4}$	0.844	1.3000	0.237	0.337	0.674	0.848	11.312
5	5.563	8	$5\frac{5}{16}$	0.937	1.4063	0.258	0.375	0.750	0.686	7.199
6	6.625	8	$6\frac{5}{16}$	0.958	1.5125	0.280	0.432	0.864	0.576	4.984
8	8.625	8	......	1.063	1.7125	0.322	0.500	0.875	0.443	2.878
10	10.750	8	......	1.210	1.9250	0.365	0.593	....	0.355	1.826
12	12.750	8	......	1.360	2.1250	0.406	0.687	....	0.299	1.273
14 O.D.	14.000	8	......	1.562	2.2500	0.437	0.750	....	0.273	1.065
16 O.D.	16.000	8	......	1.812	2.4500	0.500	0.843	....	0.239	0.815
18 O.D.	18.000	8	......	2.000	2.6500	0.562	0.937	....	0.212	0.644
20 O.D.	20.000	8	......	2.125	2.8500	0.593	1.031	....	0.191	0.518
24 O.D.	24.000	8	......	2.375	3.2500	0.687	1.218	....	0.159	0.358

All dimensions are in inches except those in the last two columns.

[1] From ASA B36.10—1939, which also includes data for welded wrought iron pipe.

[2] From ASA B2.1—1945.

[3] Refer to § 424 and Fig. 771.

[4] American Standard Schedule 40. Thicknesses above 0.406 correspond to "standard weight" pipe.

[5] American Standard Schedule 80. Thicknesses above 0.593 correspond to "extra strong" pipe.

[6] Not American Standard, but included since the pipe is commercially available in wrought iron and steel.

[7] Calculated values for Schedule 40 pipe.

11. COPPER AND BRASS PIPE

Standard dimensions and weights of copper and brass pipe[1]

Pipe size	Outside diameter	REGULAR PIPE			EXTRA-STRONG PIPE		
		Wall thickness	Weight per foot		Wall thickness	Weight per foot	
			Copper	Red brass		Copper	Red brass
in.	*in.*	*in.*	*lb*	*lb*	*in.*	*lb*	*lb*
1/8	0.405	0.062	0.259	0.253	0.100	0.371	0.363
1/4	.540	.082	.457	.447	.123	.625	.611
3/8	.675	.090	.641	.627	.127	.847	.829
1/2	.840	.107	.955	.934	.149	1.25	1.23
3/4	1.050	.114	1.30	1.27	.157	1.71	1.67
1	1.315	.126	1.82	1.78	.182	2.51	2.46
1¼	1.660	.146	2.69	2.63	.194	3.46	3.39
1½	1.900	.150	3.20	3.13	.203	4.19	4.10
2	2.375	.156	4.22	4.12	.221	5.80	5.67
2½	2.875	.187	6.12	5.99	.280	8.85	8.66
3	3.500	.219	8.75	8.56	.304	11.8	11.6
3½	4.000	.250	11.4	11.2	.321	14.4	14.1
4	4.500	.250	12.9	12.7	.341	17.3	16.9
5	5.562	.250	16.2	15.8	.375	23.7	23.2
6	6.625	.250	19.4	19.0	.437	32.9	32.2
8	8.625	.312	31.6	30.9	.500	49.5	48.4
10	10.750	.365	46.2	45.2	.500	62.4	61.1
12	12.750	.375	56.5	55.3	. . . . .	. . . . .	. . . . .

12. COPPER WATER TUBE

Standard dimensions and weights of copper water tube for compression or soldered fittings[1]

Copper water tube size	Outside diameter	WALL THICKNESS			WEIGHT PER FOOT		
		Type K	Type L	Type M	Type K	Type L	Type M
in.	*in.*	*in.*	*in.*	*in.*	*lb*	*lb*	*lb*
3/8	0.500	0.049	0.035	. . . . .	0.269	0.198	. . . . .
1/2	.625	.049	.040	. . . . .	.344	.285	. . . . .
5/8	.750	.049	.042	. . . . .	.418	.362	. . . . .
3/4	.875	.065	.045	. . . . .	.641	.455	. . . . .
1	1.125	.065	.050	. . . . .	.839	.655	. . . . .
1¼	1.375	.065	.055	. . . . .	1.04	.884	. . . . .
1½	1.625	.072	.060	. . . . .	1.36	1.14	. . . . .
2	2.125	.083	.070	. . . . .	2.06	1.75	. . . . .
2½	2.625	.095	.080	0.065	2.93	2.48	2.03
3	3.125	.109	.090	.072	4.00	3.33	2.68
3½	3.625	.102	.100	.083	5.12	4.29	3.58
4	4.125	.134	.110	.095	6.51	5.38	4.66
5	5.125	.160	.125	.109	9.67	7.61	6.66
6	6.125	.192	.140	.122	13.9	10.2	8.92
8	8.125	.271	.200	.170	25.9	19.3	16.5
10	10.125	.338	.250	.212	40.3	30.1	25.6
12	12.125	.405	.280	.254	57.8	40.4	36.7

Tempers for copper water tube: Types K and L—hard and soft; type M—hard only.

[1] Proposed by the Copper & Brass Research Association on behalf of the brass mill industry. Approved for promulgation by the United States Department of Commerce, through the National Bureau of Standards. Effective from March 15, 1946.

13. AMERICAN STANDARD MALLEABLE IRON SCREWED FITTINGS, 150 LB.
(From ASA B16c—1939)

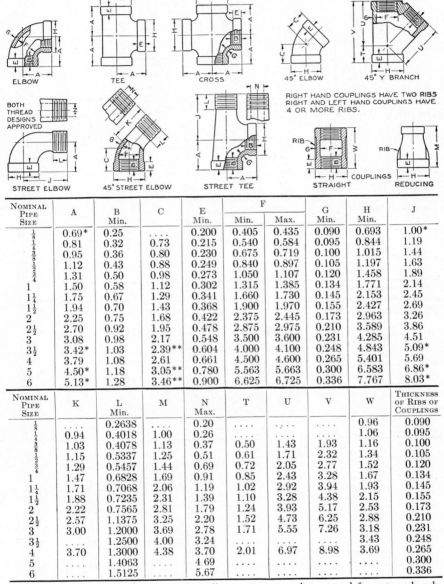

ELBOW   TEE   CROSS   45° ELBOW   45° Y BRANCH

BOTH THREAD DESIGNS APPROVED

STREET ELBOW   45° STREET ELBOW   STREET TEE   STRAIGHT   REDUCING

RIGHT HAND COUPLINGS HAVE TWO RIBS
RIGHT AND LEFT HAND COUPLINGS HAVE 4 OR MORE RIBS.

COUPLINGS

Nominal Pipe Size	A	B Min.	C	E Min.	F Min.	F Max.	G Min.	H Min.	J
⅛	0.69*	0.25	....	0.200	0.405	0.435	0.090	0.693	1.00*
¼	0.81	0.32	0.73	0.215	0.540	0.584	0.095	0.844	1.19
⅜	0.95	0.36	0.80	0.230	0.675	0.719	0.100	1.015	1.44
½	1.12	0.43	0.88	0.249	0.840	0.897	0.105	1.197	1.63
¾	1.31	0.50	0.98	0.273	1.050	1.107	0.120	1.458	1.89
1	1.50	0.58	1.12	0.302	1.315	1.385	0.134	1.771	2.14
1¼	1.75	0.67	1.29	0.341	1.660	1.730	0.145	2.153	2.45
1½	1.94	0.70	1.43	0.368	1.900	1.970	0.155	2.427	2.69
2	2.25	0.75	1.68	0.422	2.375	2.445	0.173	2.963	3.26
2½	2.70	0.92	1.95	0.478	2.875	2.975	0.210	3.589	3.86
3	3.08	0.98	2.17	0.548	3.500	3.600	0.231	4.285	4.51
3½	3.42*	1.03	2.39**	0.604	4.000	4.100	0.248	4.843	5.09*
4	3.79	1.08	2.61	0.661	4.500	4.600	0.265	5.401	5.69
5	4.50*	1.18	3.05**	0.780	5.563	5.663	0.300	6.583	6.86*
6	5.13*	1.28	3.46**	0.900	6.625	6.725	0.336	7.767	8.03*

Nominal Pipe Size	K	L Min.	M	N Max.	T	U	V	W	Thickness of Ribs of Couplings
⅛	....	0.2638	....	0.20	....	....	....	0.96	0.090
¼	0.94	0.4018	1.00	0.26	....	....	....	1.06	0.095
⅜	1.03	0.4078	1.13	0.37	0.50	1.43	1.93	1.16	0.100
½	1.15	0.5337	1.25	0.51	0.61	1.71	2.32	1.34	0.105
¾	1.29	0.5457	1.44	0.69	0.72	2.05	2.77	1.52	0.120
1	1.47	0.6828	1.69	0.91	0.85	2.43	3.28	1.67	0.134
1¼	1.71	0.7068	2.06	1.19	1.02	2.92	3.94	1.93	0.145
1½	1.88	0.7235	2.31	1.39	1.10	3.28	4.38	2.15	0.155
2	2.22	0.7565	2.81	1.79	1.24	3.93	5.17	2.53	0.173
2½	2.57	1.1375	3.25	2.20	1.52	4.73	6.25	2.88	0.210
3	3.00	1.2000	3.69	2.78	1.71	5.55	7.26	3.18	0.231
3½	....	1.2500	4.00	3.24	....	....	....	3.43	0.248
4	3.70	1.3000	4.38	3.70	2.01	6.97	8.98	3.69	0.265
5	....	1.4063	....	4.69	....	....	....	....	0.300
6	....	1.5125	....	5.67	....	....	....	....	0.336

See ASA B16c—1939 for reducing elbows, crosses and tees, and for return bends, locknuts and bushings.

* Street elbow only.
** 45° elbow only.

14. AMERICAN STANDARD SQUARE HEAD PIPE PLUGS*
(From ASA B16e2—1936)

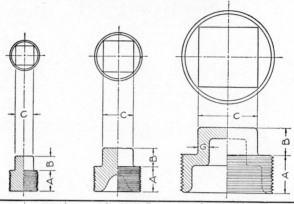

Nominal Pipe Size	A	B	C (Nominal)	G	Nominal Pipe Size	A	B	C	G
$\frac{1}{8}$	0.37	0.24	$\frac{9}{32}$	....	$1\frac{1}{4}$	0.80	0.56	$\frac{15}{16}$	0.22
$\frac{1}{4}$	0.44	0.28	$\frac{3}{8}$	....	$1\frac{1}{2}$	0.83	0.62	$1\frac{1}{8}$	0.24
$\frac{3}{8}$	0.48	0.31	$\frac{7}{16}$	....	2	0.88	0.68	$1\frac{5}{16}$	0.26
$\frac{1}{2}$	0.56	0.38	$\frac{9}{16}$	0.16	$2\frac{1}{2}$	1.07	0.74	$1\frac{1}{2}$	0.29
$\frac{3}{4}$	0.63	0.44	$\frac{5}{8}$	0.18	3	1.13	0.80	$1\frac{11}{16}$	0.31
1	0.75	0.50	$\frac{13}{16}$	0.20	$3\frac{1}{2}$	1.18	0.86	$1\frac{7}{8}$	0.34

* To be used with American Standard 125 lb. and 250 lb. Cast-Iron Screwed Fittings, and 150 lb. Malleable Iron Screwed Fittings. Screw threads are American Standard Taper Pipe Threads (ASA B2).

15. AMERICAN STANDARD CAPS
(From ASA B16c—1939)

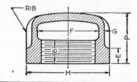

Nominal Pipe Size	B	E	F	G	H	P	Thickness of Ribs
$\frac{1}{2}$	0.43	0.249	0.840	0.105	1.197	0.87	0.105
$\frac{3}{4}$	0.50	0.273	1.050	0.120	1.458	0.97	0.120
1	0.58	0.302	1.315	0.134	1.771	1.16	0.134
$1\frac{1}{4}$	0.67	0.341	1.660	0.145	2.153	1.28	0.145
$1\frac{1}{2}$	0.70	0.368	1.900	0.155	2.427	1.33	0.155
2	0.75	0.422	2.375	0.173	2.963	1.45	0.173
$2\frac{1}{2}$	0.92	0.478	2.875	0.210	3.589	1.70	0.210
3	0.98	0.548	3.500	0.231	4.285	1.80	0.231
$3\frac{1}{2}$	1.03	0.604	4.000	0.248	4.843	1.90	0.248
4	1.08	0.661	4.500	0.265	5.401	2.08	0.265
5	1.18	0.780	5.563	0.300	6.583	2.32	0.300
6	1.28	0.900	6.625	0.336	7.767	2.55	0.336

The outside radius of the top is equal to $3 \times F$.

16. AMERICAN STANDARD CAST IRON PIPE FLANGES AND FLANGED FITTINGS, CLASS 125*
(From ASA B16a—1939)

90° ELBOW — LONG RADIUS ELBOW — 45° ELBOW — REDUCING ELBOW — TEE — CROSS — SIDE OUTLET

SIDE OUTLET — TRUE "Y" — LATERAL — REDUCER — ECCENTRIC REDUCER — FLANGES

Nominal Pipe Size**	A	B	C	D	E	F	G	O	Wall Thickness
1	$3\frac{1}{2}$	5	$1\frac{3}{4}$	$7\frac{1}{2}$	$5\frac{3}{4}$	$1\frac{3}{4}$	...	$4\frac{1}{4}$	$\frac{5}{16}$
$1\frac{1}{4}$	$3\frac{3}{4}$	$5\frac{1}{2}$	2	8	$6\frac{1}{4}$	$1\frac{3}{4}$	...	$4\frac{5}{8}$	$\frac{5}{16}$
$1\frac{1}{2}$	4	6	$2\frac{1}{4}$	9	7	2	...	5	$\frac{5}{16}$
2	$4\frac{1}{2}$	$6\frac{1}{2}$	$2\frac{1}{2}$	$10\frac{1}{2}$	8	$2\frac{1}{2}$	5	6	$\frac{5}{16}$
$2\frac{1}{2}$	5	7	3	12	$9\frac{1}{2}$	$2\frac{1}{2}$	$5\frac{1}{2}$	7	$\frac{5}{16}$
3	$5\frac{1}{2}$	$7\frac{3}{4}$	3	13	10	3	6	$7\frac{1}{2}$	$\frac{3}{8}$
$3\frac{1}{2}$	6	$8\frac{1}{2}$	$3\frac{1}{2}$	$14\frac{1}{2}$	$11\frac{1}{2}$	3	$6\frac{1}{2}$	$8\frac{1}{2}$	$\frac{7}{16}$
4	$6\frac{1}{2}$	9	4	15	12	3	7	9	$\frac{1}{2}$
5	$7\frac{1}{2}$	$10\frac{1}{4}$	$4\frac{1}{2}$	17	$13\frac{1}{2}$	$3\frac{1}{2}$	8	10	$\frac{9}{16}$
6	8	$11\frac{1}{2}$	5	18	$14\frac{1}{2}$	$3\frac{1}{2}$	9	11	$\frac{9}{16}$
8	9	14	$5\frac{1}{2}$	22	$17\frac{1}{2}$	$4\frac{1}{2}$	11	$13\frac{1}{2}$	$\frac{5}{8}$
10	11	$16\frac{1}{2}$	$6\frac{1}{2}$	$25\frac{1}{2}$	$20\frac{1}{2}$	5	12	16	$\frac{3}{4}$
12	12	19	$7\frac{1}{2}$	30	$24\frac{1}{2}$	$5\frac{1}{2}$	14	19	$\frac{13}{16}$

Nominal Pipe Size**	Q Min.	J	Diameter of Holes in Flanges	Number of Bolts for Flanges	Diameter of Bolts for Flanges	Length of Bolts for Flanges	X Min.	Y Min.
1	$\frac{7}{16}$	$3\frac{1}{8}$	$\frac{5}{8}$	4	$\frac{1}{2}$	$1\frac{3}{4}$	$1\frac{15}{16}$	$\frac{11}{16}$
$1\frac{1}{4}$	$\frac{1}{2}$	$3\frac{1}{2}$	$\frac{5}{8}$	4	$\frac{1}{2}$	2	$2\frac{5}{16}$	$\frac{13}{16}$
$1\frac{1}{2}$	$\frac{9}{16}$	$3\frac{7}{8}$	$\frac{5}{8}$	4	$\frac{1}{2}$	2	$2\frac{9}{16}$	$\frac{7}{8}$
2	$\frac{5}{8}$	$4\frac{3}{4}$	$\frac{3}{4}$	4	$\frac{5}{8}$	$2\frac{1}{4}$	$3\frac{1}{16}$	1
$2\frac{1}{2}$	$\frac{11}{16}$	$5\frac{1}{2}$	$\frac{3}{4}$	4	$\frac{5}{8}$	$2\frac{1}{2}$	$3\frac{9}{16}$	$1\frac{1}{8}$
3	$\frac{3}{4}$	6	$\frac{3}{4}$	4	$\frac{5}{8}$	$2\frac{1}{2}$	$4\frac{1}{4}$	$1\frac{3}{16}$
$3\frac{1}{2}$	$\frac{13}{16}$	7	$\frac{3}{4}$	8	$\frac{5}{8}$	$2\frac{3}{4}$	$4\frac{13}{16}$	$1\frac{1}{4}$
4	$\frac{15}{16}$	$7\frac{1}{2}$	$\frac{3}{4}$	8	$\frac{5}{8}$	3	$5\frac{5}{16}$	$1\frac{5}{16}$
5	$\frac{15}{16}$	$8\frac{1}{2}$	$\frac{7}{8}$	8	$\frac{3}{4}$	3	$6\frac{7}{16}$	$1\frac{7}{16}$
6	1	$9\frac{1}{2}$	$\frac{7}{8}$	8	$\frac{3}{4}$	$3\frac{1}{2}$	$7\frac{9}{16}$	$1\frac{9}{16}$
8	$1\frac{1}{8}$	$11\frac{3}{4}$	$\frac{7}{8}$	8	$\frac{3}{4}$	$3\frac{1}{2}$	$9\frac{11}{16}$	$1\frac{3}{4}$
10	$1\frac{3}{16}$	$14\frac{1}{4}$	1	12	$\frac{7}{8}$	$3\frac{3}{4}$	$11\frac{15}{16}$	$1\frac{15}{16}$
12	$1\frac{1}{4}$	17	1	12	$\frac{7}{8}$	$3\frac{3}{4}$	$14\frac{1}{16}$	$2\frac{3}{16}$

* For maximum saturated steam service pressures of 125 lb. per sq. in. (gage) sizes 1 to 5 in., incl.; 100 lb. per sq. in. (gage) sizes 6 to 12 in., incl. For sizes 14 O.D. to 48 O.D., see ASA B16a—1939.

** Also inside diameter of fittings.

17. AMERICAN STANDARD CAST IRON SCREWED FITTINGS, 125 LB.*
(From ASA B16d—1941)

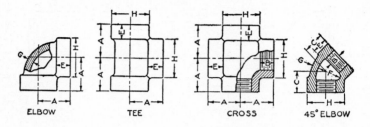

| | ELBOW | | TEE | | CROSS | | 45° ELBOW |

Nominal Pipe Size	A	B Min.	C	E Min.	Inside Diameter of Fittings F Min.	Max.	G Min.	H Min.
¼	0.81	0.32	0.73	0.38	0.540	0.584	0.110	0.93
⅜	0.95	0.36	0.80	0.44	0.675	0.719	0.120	1.12
½	1.12	0.43	0.88	0.50	0.840	0.897	0.130	1.34
¾	1.31	0.50	0.98	0.56	1.050	1.107	0.155	1.63
1	1.50	0.58	1.12	0.62	1.315	1.385	0.170	1.95
1¼	1.75	0.67	1.29	0.69	1.660	1.730	0.185	2.39
1½	1.94	0.70	1.43	0.75	1.900	1.970	0.200	2.68
2	2.25	0.75	1.68	0.84	2.375	2.445	0.220	3.28
2½	2.70	0.92	1.95	0.94	2.875	2.975	0.240	3.86
3	3.08	0.98	2.17	1.00	3.500	3.600	0.260	4.62
3½	3.42	1.03	2.39	1.06	4.000	4.100	0.280	5.20
4	3.79	1.08	2.61	1.12	4.500	4.600	0.310	5.79
5	4.50	1.18	3.05	1.18	5.563	5.663	0.380	7.05
6	5.13	1.28	3.46	1.28	6.625	6.725	0.430	8.28
8	6.56	1.47	4.28	1.47	8.625	8.725	0.550	10.63
10	8.08**	1.68	5.16	1.68	10.750	10.850	0.690	13.12
12	9.50**	1.88	5.97	1.88	12.750	12.850	0.800	15.47

See ASA B16d—1941 for 125 lb. reducing elbows, crosses, tees and couplings, and for 125 lb. caps; also for 250 lb. screwed fittings.

* For maximum saturated steam service pressure (gage) of 125 lb.
** Elbows and tees only.

18. LIMITS FOR METAL FITS
(From ASA B4a—1925)*

Loose Fit (Class 1)—Large Allowance, Interchangeable

This fit provides for considerable freedom and embraces certain fits where accuracy is not essential.

Size		Limits				Tightest Fit	Loosest Fit
From	Up to and Incl.	Hole or External Member		Shaft or Internal Member		Allowance	Allowance + Tolerances
		+		−	−	+	+
0	$\frac{3}{16}$	0.001	0.000	0.001	0.002	0.001	0.003
$\frac{3}{16}$	$\frac{5}{16}$	0.002	0.000	0.001	0.003	0.001	0.005
$\frac{5}{16}$	$\frac{7}{16}$	0.002	0.000	0.001	0.003	0.001	0.005
$\frac{7}{16}$	$\frac{9}{16}$	0.002	0.000	0.002	0.004	0.002	0.006
$\frac{9}{16}$	$\frac{11}{16}$	0.002	0.000	0.002	0.004	0.002	0.006
$\frac{11}{16}$	$\frac{13}{16}$	0.002	0.000	0.002	0.004	0.002	0.006
$\frac{13}{16}$	$\frac{15}{16}$	0.002	0.000	0.002	0.004	0.002	0.006
$\frac{15}{16}$	$1\frac{1}{16}$	0.003	0.000	0.003	0.006	0.003	0.009
$1\frac{1}{16}$	$1\frac{3}{16}$	0.003	0.000	0.003	0.006	0.003	0.009
$1\frac{3}{16}$	$1\frac{3}{8}$	0.003	0.000	0.003	0.006	0.003	0.009
$1\frac{3}{8}$	$1\frac{5}{8}$	0.003	0.000	0.003	0.006	0.003	0.009
$1\frac{5}{8}$	$1\frac{7}{8}$	0.003	0.000	0.004	0.007	0.004	0.010
$1\frac{7}{8}$	$2\frac{1}{8}$	0.003	0.000	0.004	0.007	0.004	0.010
$2\frac{1}{8}$	$2\frac{3}{8}$	0.003	0.000	0.004	0.007	0.004	0.010
$2\frac{3}{8}$	$2\frac{3}{4}$	0.003	0.000	0.005	0.008	0.005	0.011
$2\frac{3}{4}$	$3\frac{1}{4}$	0.004	0.000	0.005	0.009	0.005	0.013
$3\frac{1}{4}$	$3\frac{3}{4}$	0.004	0.000	0.006	0.010	0.006	0.014
$3\frac{3}{4}$	$4\frac{1}{4}$	0.004	0.000	0.006	0.010	0.006	0.014
$4\frac{1}{4}$	$4\frac{3}{4}$	0.004	0.000	0.007	0.011	0.007	0.015
$4\frac{3}{4}$	$5\frac{1}{2}$	0.004	0.000	0.007	0.011	0.007	0.015
$5\frac{1}{2}$	$6\frac{1}{2}$	0.005	0.000	0.008	0.013	0.008	0.018
$6\frac{1}{2}$	$7\frac{1}{2}$	0.005	0.000	0.009	0.014	0.009	0.019
$7\frac{1}{2}$	$8\frac{1}{2}$	0.005	0.000	0.010	0.015	0.010	0.020

All dimensions in inches.

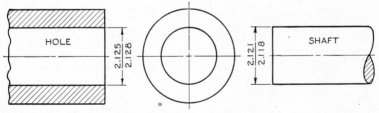

* This standard is now being revised, but the present tables will continue in use for some time until replaced by revised tables. This standard is superceded in part by ASA B4.1—1947 (see p. 803).

18. LIMITS FOR METAL FITS (*Continued*)
(From ASA B4a—1925)

Free Fit (Class 2)—Liberal Allowance, Interchangeable

For running fits with speeds of 600 r.p.m. or over, and journal pressures of 600 lb. per sq. in. or over.

Size		Limits				Tightest Fit	Loosest Fit
From	Up to and Incl.	Hole or External Member		Shaft or Internal Member		Allowance	Allowance + Tolerances
		+		−	−	+	+
0	3/16	0.0007	0.0000	0.0004	0.0011	0.0004	0.0018
3/16	5/16	0.0008	0.0000	0.0006	0.0014	0.0006	0.0022
5/16	7/16	0.0009	0.0000	0.0007	0.0016	0.0007	0.0025
7/16	9/16	0.0010	0.0000	0.0009	0.0019	0.0009	0.0029
9/16	11/16	0.0011	0.0000	0.0010	0.0021	0.0010	0.0032
11/16	13/16	0.0012	0.0000	0.0012	0.0024	0.0012	0.0036
13/16	15/16	0.0012	0.0000	0.0013	0.0025	0.0013	0.0037
15/16	1 1/16	0.0013	0.0000	0.0014	0.0027	0.0014	0.0040
1 1/16	1 3/16	0.0014	0.0000	0.0015	0.0029	0.0015	0.0043
1 3/16	1 3/8	0.0014	0.0000	0.0016	0.0030	0.0016	0.0044
1 3/8	1 5/8	0.0015	0.0000	0.0018	0.0033	0.0018	0.0048
1 5/8	1 7/8	0.0016	0.0000	0.0020	0.0036	0.0020	0.0052
1 7/8	2 1/8	0.0016	0.0000	0.0022	0.0038	0.0022	0.0054
2 1/8	2 3/8	0.0017	0.0000	0.0024	0.0041	0.0024	0.0058
2 3/8	2 3/4	0.0018	0.0000	0.0026	0.0044	0.0026	0.0062
2 3/4	3 1/4	0.0019	0.0000	0.0029	0.0048	0.0029	0.0067
3 1/4	3 3/4	0.0020	0.0000	0.0032	0.0052	0.0032	0.0072
3 3/4	4 1/4	0.0021	0.0000	0.0035	0.0056	0.0035	0.0077
4 1/4	4 3/4	0.0021	0.0000	0.0038	0.0059	0.0038	0.0080
4 3/4	5 1/2	0.0022	0.0000	0.0041	0.0063	0.0041	0.0085
5 1/2	6 1/2	0.0024	0.0000	0.0046	0.0070	0.0046	0.0094
6 1/2	7 1/2	0.0025	0.0000	0.0051	0.0076	0.0051	0.0101
7 1/2	8 1/2	0.0026	0.0000	0.0056	0.0082	0.0056	0.0108

All dimensions in inches.

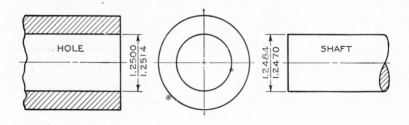

18. LIMITS FOR METAL FITS (*Continued*)
(From ASA B4a—1925)

Medium Fit (Class 3)—Medium Allowance, Interchangeable

For running fits under 600 r.p.m. and with journal pressures less than 600 lb. per sq. in.; also for sliding fits, and the more accurate machine-tool and automotive parts.

Size		Limits				Tightest Fit	Loosest Fit
From	Up to and Incl.	Hole or External Member		Shaft or Internal Member		Allowance	Allowance + Tolerances
		+		−	−	+	+
0	3/16	0.0004	0.0000	0.0002	0.0006	0.0002	0.0010
3/16	5/16	0.0005	0.0000	0.0004	0.0009	0.0004	0.0014
5/16	7/16	0.0006	0.0000	0.0005	0.0011	0.0005	0.0017
7/16	9/16	0.0006	0.0000	0.0006	0.0012	0.0006	0.0018
9/16	11/16	0.0097	0.0000	0.0007	0.0014	0.0007	0.0021
11/16	13/16	0.0007	0.0000	0.0007	0.0014	0.0007	0.0021
13/16	15/16	0.0008	0.0000	0.0008	0.0016	0.0008	0.0024
15/16	1 1/16	0.0008	0.0000	0.0009	0.0017	0.0009	0.0025
1 1/16	1 3/16	0.0098	0.0000	0.0010	0.0018	0.0010	0.0026
1 3/16	1 5/16	0.0009	0.0000	0.0010	0.0019	0.0010	0.0028
1 5/16	1 5/8	0.0009	0.0000	0.0012	0.0021	0.0012	0.0030
1 5/8	1 7/8	0.0010	0.0000	0.0013	0.0023	0.0013	0.0033
1 7/8	2 1/8	0.0010	0.0000	0.0014	0.0024	0.0014	0.0034
2 1/8	2 3/8	0.0010	0.0000	0.0015	0.0025	0.0015	0.0035
2 3/8	2 3/4	0.0011	0.0000	0.0017	0.0028	0.0017	0.0039
2 3/4	3 1/4	0.0012	0.0000	0.0019	0.0031	0.0019	0.0043
3 1/4	3 3/4	0.0012	0.0000	0.0021	0.0033	0.0021	0.0045
3 3/4	4 1/4	0.0013	0.0000	0.0023	0.0036	0.0023	0.0049
4 1/4	4 3/4	0.0013	0.0000	0.0025	0.0038	0.0025	0.0051
4 3/4	5 1/2	0.0014	0.0000	0.0026	0.0040	0.0026	0.0054
5 1/2	6 1/2	0.0015	0.0000	0.0030	0.0045	0.0030	0.0060
6 1/2	7 1/2	0.0015	0.0000	0.0033	0.0048	0.0033	0.0063
7 1/2	8 1/2	0.0016	0.0000	0.0036	0.0052	0.0036	0.0068

All dimensions in inches.

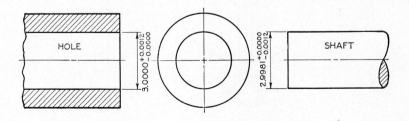

18. LIMITS FOR METAL FITS (*Continued*)
(From ASA B4a—1925)

Snug Fit (Class 4)—Zero Allowance, Interchangeable

This is the closest fit which can be assembled by hand and necessitates work of considerable precision. It should be used where no perceptible shake is permissible and where moving parts are not intended to move freely under load.

Size		Limits				Tightest Fit	Loosest Fit
From	Up to and Incl.	Hole or External Member		Shaft or Internal Member		Allowance	Allowance + Tolerances
		+		−			+
0	3/16	0.0003	0.0000	0.0000	0.0002	0.0000	0.0005
3/16	5/16	0.0004	0.0000	0.0000	0.0003	0.0000	0.0007
5/16	7/16	0.0004	0.0000	0.0000	0.0003	0.0000	0.0007
7/16	9/16	0.0005	0.0000	0.0000	0.0003	0.0000	0.0008
9/16	11/16	0.0005	0.0000	0.0000	0.0003	0.0000	0.0008
11/16	13/16	0.0005	0.0000	0.0000	0.0004	0.0000	0.0009
13/16	15/16	0.0006	0.0000	0.0000	0.0004	0.0000	0.0010
15/16	1 1/16	0.0006	0.0000	0.0000	0.0004	0.0000	0.0010
1 1/16	1 3/16	0.0006	0.0000	0.0000	0.0004	0.0000	0.0010
1 3/16	1 5/16	0.0006	0.0000	0.0000	0.0004	0.0000	0.0010
1 5/16	1 1/2	0.0007	0.0000	0.0000	0.0005	0.0000	0.0012
1 1/2	1 7/8	0.0007	0.0000	0.0000	0.0005	0.0000	0.0012
1 7/8	2 1/8	0.0008	0.0000	0.0000	0.0005	0.0000	0.0013
2 1/8	2 3/8	0.0008	0.0000	0.0000	0.0005	0.0000	0.0013
2 3/8	2 3/4	0.0008	0.0000	0.0000	0.0005	0.0000	0.0013
2 3/4	3 1/4	0.0009	0.0000	0.0000	0.0006	0.0000	0.0015
3 1/4	3 3/4	0.0009	0.0000	0.0000	0.0006	0.0000	0.0015
3 3/4	4 1/4	0.0010	0.0000	0.0000	0.0006	0.0000	0.0016
4 1/4	4 3/4	0.0010	0.0000	0.0000	0.0007	0.0000	0.0017
4 3/4	5 1/2	0.0010	0.0000	0.0000	0.0007	0.0000	0.0017
5 1/2	6 1/2	0.0011	0.0000	0.0000	0.0007	0.0000	0.0018
6 1/2	7 1/2	0.0011	0.0000	0.0000	0.0008	0.0000	0.0019
7 1/2	8 1/2	0.0012	0.0000	0.0000	0.0008	0.0000	0.0020

All dimensions in inches.

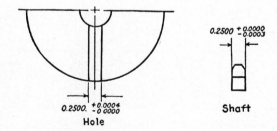

0.2500 +0.0004 −0.0000
Hole

0.2500 +0.0000 −0.0003
Shaft

18.   LIMITS FOR METAL FITS (*Continued*)
(From ASA B4a—1925)

Wringing Fit (Class 5)— Zero to Negative Allowance, Selective Assembly

This is also known as a "tunking fit" and it is practically metal-to-metal. Assembly is usually selective and not interchangeable.

Size		Limits				Tightest Fit	Loosest Fit	Selected Fit
From	Up to and Incl.	Hole or External Member		Shaft or Internal Member		Allowance	Allowance + Tolerances	Average Interference of Metal
		+		+		−	+	
0	3/16	0.0003	0.0000	0.0002	0.0000	0.0002	0.0003	0.0000
3/16	5/16	0.0004	0.0000	0.0003	0.0000	0.0003	0.0004	0.0000
5/16	7/16	0.0004	0.0000	0.0003	0.0000	0.0003	0.0004	0.0000
7/16	9/16	0.0005	0.0000	0.0003	0.0000	0.0003	0.0005	0.0000
9/16	11/16	0.0005	0.0000	0.0003	0.0000	0.0003	0.0005	0.0000
11/16	13/16	0.0005	0.0000	0.0004	0.0000	0.0004	0.0005	0.0000
13/16	15/16	0.0006	0.0000	0.0004	0.0000	0.0004	0.0006	0.0000
15/16	1 1/16	0.0006	0.0000	0.0004	0.0000	0.0004	0.0006	0.0000
1 1/16	1 3/16	0.0006	0.0000	0.0004	0.0000	0.0004	0.0006	0.0000
1 3/16	1 5/16	0.0006	0.0000	0.0004	0.0000	0.0004	0.0006	0.0000
1 5/16	1 5/8	0.0007	0.0000	0.0005	0.0000	0.0005	0.0007	0.0000
1 5/8	1 7/8	0.0007	0.0000	0.0005	0.0000	0.0005	0.0007	0.0000
1 7/8	2 1/8	0.0008	0.0000	0.0005	0.0000	0.0005	0.0008	0.0000
2 1/8	2 3/8	0.0008	0.0000	0.0005	0.0000	0.0005	0.0008	0.0000
2 3/8	2 3/4	0.0008	0.0000	0.0005	0.0000	0.0005	0.0008	0.0000
2 3/4	3 1/4	0.0009	0.0000	0.0006	0.0000	0.0006	0.0009	0.0000
3 1/4	3 3/4	0.0009	0.0000	0.0006	0.0000	0.0006	0.0009	0.0000
3 3/4	4 1/4	0.0010	0.0000	0.0006	0.0000	0.0006	0.0010	0.0000
4 1/4	4 3/4	0.0010	0.0000	0.0007	0.0000	0.0007	0.0010	0.0000
4 3/4	5 1/2	0.0010	0.0000	0.0007	0.0000	0.0007	0.0010	0.0000
5 1/2	6 1/2	0.0011	0.0000	0.0007	0.0000	0.0007	0.0011	0.0000
6 1/2	7 1/2	0.0011	0.0000	0.0008	0.0000	0.0008	0.0011	0.0000
7 1/2	8 1/2	0.0012	0.0000	0.0008	0.0000	0.0008	0.0012	0.0000

All dimensions in inches.

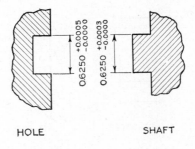

HOLE   SHAFT

18. LIMITS FOR METAL FITS (*Continued*)
(From ASA B4a—1925)

Tight Fit (Class 6)—Slight Negative Allowance, Selective Assembly

Light pressure is required to assemble these fits and the parts are more or less permanently assembled, such as the fixed ends of studs for gears, pulleys, rocker arms, etc.

SIZE		LIMITS				TIGHTEST FIT	LOOSEST FIT	SELECTED FIT
From	Up to and Incl.	Hole or External Member		Shaft or Internal Member		Allowance	Allowance + Tolerances	Average Interference of Metal
		+		+	+	−		−
0	3/16	0.0003	0.0000	0.0003	0.0000	0.0003	+0.0003	0.0000
3/16	5/16	0.0004	0.0000	0.0005	0.0001	0.0005	+0.0003	0.0001
5/16	7/16	0.0004	0.0000	0.0005	0.0001	0.0005	+0.0003	0.0001
7/16	9/16	0.0005	0.0000	0.0006	0.0001	0.0006	+0.0004	0.0001
9/16	11/16	0.0005	0.0000	0.0007	0.0002	0.0007	+0.0003	0.0002
11/16	13/16	0.0005	0.0000	0.0007	0.0002	0.0007	+0.0003	0.0002
13/16	15/16	0.0006	0.0000	0.0008	0.0002	0.0008	+0.0004	0.0002
15/16	1 1/16	0.0006	0.0000	0.0009	0.0003	0.0009	+0.0003	0.0003
1 1/16	1 3/16	0.0006	0.0000	0.0009	0.0003	0.0009	+0.0003	0.0003
1 3/16	1 5/16	0.0006	0.0000	0.0009	0.0003	0.0009	+0.0003	0.0003
1 5/16	1 5/8	0.0007	0.0000	0.0011	0.0004	0.0011	+0.0003	0.0004
1 5/8	1 7/8	0.0007	0.0000	0.0011	0.0004	0.0011	+0.0003	0.0004
1 7/8	2 1/8	0.0008	0.0000	0.0013	0.0005	0.0013	+0.0003	0.0005
2 1/8	2 3/8	0.0008	0.0000	0.0014	0.0006	0.0014	+0.0002	0.0006
2 3/8	2 3/4	0.0008	0.0000	0.0014	0.0006	0.0014	+0.0002	0.0006
2 3/4	3 1/4	0.0009	0.0000	0.0017	0.0008	0.0017	+0.0001	0.0008
3 1/4	3 3/4	0.0009	0.0000	0.0018	0.0009	0.0018	−0.0000	0.0009
3 3/4	4 1/4	0.0010	0.0000	0.0020	0.0010	0.0020	−0.0000	0.0010
4 1/4	4 3/4	0.0010	0.0000	0.0021	0.0011	0.0021	−0.0001	0.0011
4 3/4	5 1/2	0.0010	0.0000	0.0023	0.0013	0.0023	−0.0003	0.0013
5 1/2	6 1/2	0.0011	0.0000	0.0026	0.0015	0.0026	−0.0004	0.0015
6 1/2	7 1/2	0.0011	0.0000	0.0029	0.0018	0.0029	−0.0007	0.0018
7 1/2	8 1/2	0.0012	0.0000	0.0032	0.0020	0.0032	−0.0008	0.0020

All dimensions in inches.

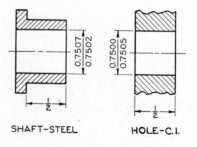

SHAFT-STEEL   HOLE-C.I.

18. LIMITS FOR METAL FITS (*Continued*)
(From ASA B4a—1925)

Medium Force Fit (Class 7)—Negative Allowance, Selective Assembly

Considerable pressure is required to assemble these fits and the parts are considered permanently assembled. These fits are used in fastening locomotive wheels, car wheels, armatures of dynamos and motors, and crank disks to their axles or shafts.

Size		Limits				Tightest Fit	Loosest Fit	Selected Fit
From	Up to and Incl.	Hole or External Member		Shaft or Internal Member		Allowance	Allowance + Tolerances	Average Interference of Metal
		+		+	+	−		−
0	$\frac{3}{16}$	0.0003	0.0000	0.0004	0.0001	0.0004	+0.0002	0.0001
$\frac{3}{16}$	$\frac{5}{16}$	0.0004	0.0000	0.0005	0.0001	0.0005	+0.0003	0.0001
$\frac{5}{16}$	$\frac{7}{16}$	0.0004	0.0000	0.0006	0.0002	0.0006	+0.0002	0.0002
$\frac{7}{16}$	$\frac{9}{16}$	0.0005	0.0000	0.0008	0.0003	0.0008	+0.0002	0.0003
$\frac{9}{16}$	$\frac{11}{16}$	0.0005	0.0000	0.0008	0.0003	0.0008	+0.0002	0.0003
$\frac{11}{16}$	$\frac{13}{16}$	0.0005	0.0000	0.0009	0.0004	0.0009	+0.0001	0.0004
$\frac{13}{16}$	$\frac{15}{16}$	0.0006	0.0000	0.0010	0.0004	0.0010	+0.0002	0.0004
$\frac{15}{16}$	$1\frac{1}{16}$	0.0006	0.0000	0.0011	0.0005	0.0011	+0.0001	0.0005
$1\frac{1}{16}$	$1\frac{3}{16}$	0.0006	0.0000	0.0012	0.0006	0.0012	0.0000	0.0006
$1\frac{3}{16}$	$1\frac{3}{8}$	0.0006	0.0000	0.0012	0.0006	0.0012	0.0000	0.0006
$1\frac{3}{8}$	$1\frac{5}{8}$	0.0007	0.0000	0.0015	0.0008	0.0015	−0.0001	0.0008
$1\frac{5}{8}$	$1\frac{7}{8}$	0.0007	0.0000	0.0016	0.0009	0.0016	−0.0002	0.0009
$1\frac{7}{8}$	$2\frac{1}{8}$	0.0008	0.0000	0.0018	0.0010	0.0018	−0.0002	0.0010
$2\frac{1}{8}$	$2\frac{3}{8}$	0.0008	0.0000	0.0019	0.0011	0.0019	−0.0003	0.0011
$2\frac{3}{8}$	$2\frac{3}{4}$	0.0008	0.0000	0.0021	0.0013	0.0021	−0.0005	0.0013
$2\frac{3}{4}$	$3\frac{1}{4}$	0.0009	0.0000	0.0024	0.0015	0.0024	−0.0006	0.0015
$3\frac{1}{4}$	$3\frac{3}{4}$	0.0009	0.0000	0.0027	0.0018	0.0027	−0.0009	0.0018
$3\frac{3}{4}$	$4\frac{1}{4}$	0.0010	0.0000	0.0030	0.0020	0.0030	−0.0010	0.0020
$4\frac{1}{4}$	$4\frac{3}{4}$	0.0010	0.0000	0.0033	0.0023	0.0033	−0.0013	0.0023
$4\frac{3}{4}$	$5\frac{1}{2}$	0.0010	0.0000	0.0035	0.0025	0.0035	−0.0015	0.0025
$5\frac{1}{2}$	$6\frac{1}{2}$	0.0011	0.0000	0.0041	0.0030	0.0041	−0.0019	0.0030
$6\frac{1}{2}$	$7\frac{1}{2}$	0.0011	0.0000	0.0046	0.0035	0.0046	−0.0024	0.0035
$7\frac{1}{2}$	$8\frac{1}{2}$	0.0012	0.0000	0.0052	0.0040	0.0052	−0.0028	0.0040

All dimensions in inches.

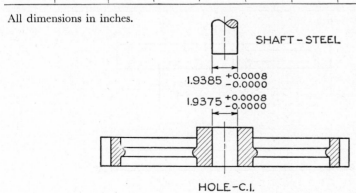

SHAFT – STEEL

$1.9385\ ^{+0.0008}_{-0.0000}$

$1.9375\ ^{+0.0008}_{-0.0000}$

HOLE – C.I.

18. LIMITS FOR METAL FITS (*Continued*)
(From ASA B4a—1925)
Heavy Force and Shrink Fit (Class 8)—Considerable Negative
Allowance, Selective Assembly

These fits are used for steel holes where the metal can be stressed to its elastic limit. These fits cause excessive stress for cast-iron holes. Shrink fits are used where heavy force fits are impractical, as on locomotive wheel tires, heavy crank disks of large engines, etc.

Size		Limits				Tightest Fit	Loosest Fit	Selected Fit
From	Up to and Incl.	Hole or External Member		Shaft or Internal Member		Allowance	Allowance + Tolerances	Average Interference of Metal
		+		+	+	−		−
0	$\frac{3}{16}$	0.0003	0.0000	0.0004	0.0001	0.0004	+0.0002	0.0001
$\frac{3}{16}$	$\frac{5}{16}$	0.0004	0.0000	0.0007	0.0003	0.0007	+0.0001	0.0003
$\frac{5}{16}$	$\frac{7}{16}$	0.0004	0.0000	0.0008	0.0004	0.0008	−0.0000	0.0004
$\frac{7}{16}$	$\frac{9}{16}$	0.0005	0.0000	0.0010	0.0005	0.0010	0.0000	0.0005
$\frac{9}{16}$	$\frac{11}{16}$	0.0005	0.0000	0.0011	0.0006	0.0011	−0.0001	0.0006
$\frac{11}{16}$	$\frac{13}{16}$	0.0005	0.0000	0.0013	0.0008	0.0013	−0.0003	0.0008
$\frac{13}{16}$	$\frac{15}{16}$	0.0006	0.0000	0.0015	0.0009	0.0015	−0.0003	0.0009
$\frac{15}{16}$	$1\frac{1}{16}$	0.0006	0.0000	0.0016	0.0010	0.0016	−0.0004	0.0010
$1\frac{1}{16}$	$1\frac{3}{16}$	0.0006	0.0000	0.0017	0.0011	0.0017	−0.0005	0.0011
$1\frac{3}{16}$	$1\frac{3}{8}$	0.0006	0.0000	0.0019	0.0013	0.0019	−0.0007	0.0013
$1\frac{3}{8}$	$1\frac{5}{8}$	0.0007	0.0000	0.0022	0.0015	0.0022	−0.0008	0.0015
$1\frac{5}{8}$	$1\frac{7}{8}$	0.0007	0.0000	0.0025	0.0018	0.0025	−0.0011	0.0018
$1\frac{7}{8}$	$2\frac{1}{8}$	0.0008	0.0000	0.0028	0.0020	0.0028	−0.0012	0.0020
$2\frac{1}{8}$	$2\frac{3}{8}$	0.0008	0.0000	0.0031	0.0023	0.0031	−0.0015	0.0023
$2\frac{3}{8}$	$2\frac{3}{4}$	0.0008	0.0000	0.0033	0.0025	0.0033	−0.0017	0.0025
$2\frac{3}{4}$	$3\frac{1}{4}$	0.0009	0.0000	0.0039	0.0030	0.0039	−0.0021	0.0030
$3\frac{1}{4}$	$3\frac{3}{4}$	0.0009	0.0000	0.0044	0.0035	0.0044	−0.0026	0.0035
$3\frac{3}{4}$	$4\frac{1}{4}$	0.0010	0.0000	0.0050	0.0040	0.0050	−0.0030	0.0040
$4\frac{1}{4}$	$4\frac{3}{4}$	0.0010	0.0000	0.0055	0.0045	0.0055	−0.0035	0.0045
$4\frac{3}{4}$	$5\frac{1}{2}$	0.0010	0.0000	0.0060	0.0050	0.0060	−0.0040	0.0050
$5\frac{1}{2}$	$6\frac{1}{2}$	0.0011	0.0000	0.0071	0.0060	0.0071	−0.0049	0.0060
$6\frac{1}{2}$	$7\frac{1}{2}$	0.0011	0.0000	0.0081	0.0070	0.0081	−0.0059	0.0070
$7\frac{1}{2}$	$8\frac{1}{2}$	0.0012	0.0000	0.0092	0.0080	0.0092	−0.0068	0.0080

All dimensions in inches.

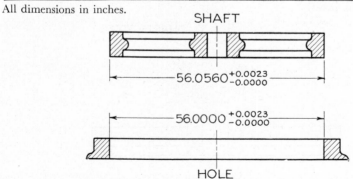

SHAFT

$56.0560^{+0.0023}_{-0.0000}$

$56.0000^{+0.0023}_{-0.0000}$

HOLE

19. AMERICAN STANDARD PREFERRED BASIC SIZES
(From ASA B4.1—1947)

	0.0100	$\frac{5}{16}$	0.3125	$1\frac{7}{8}$	1.8750
	0.0125	$\frac{3}{8}$	0.3750	2	2.0000
$\frac{1}{64}$	0.01562	$\frac{7}{16}$	0.4375	$2\frac{1}{8}$	2.1250
	0.0200	$\frac{1}{2}$	0.5000	$2\frac{1}{4}$	2.2500
	0.0250	$\frac{9}{16}$	0.5625	$2\frac{3}{8}$	2.3750
$\frac{1}{32}$	0.03125	$\frac{5}{8}$	0.6250	$2\frac{1}{2}$	2.5000
	0.0400	$\frac{11}{16}$	0.6875	$2\frac{5}{8}$	2.6250
	0.0500	$\frac{3}{4}$	0.7500	$2\frac{3}{4}$	2.7500
$\frac{1}{16}$	0.0625	$\frac{7}{8}$	0.8750	$2\frac{7}{8}$	2.8750
	0.0800	1	1.0000	3	3.0000
$\frac{3}{32}$	0.09375	$1\frac{1}{8}$	1.1250	$3\frac{1}{4}$	3.2500
	0.1000	$1\frac{1}{4}$	1.2500	$3\frac{1}{2}$	3.5000
$\frac{1}{8}$	0.1250	$1\frac{3}{8}$	1.3750	$3\frac{3}{4}$	3.7500
$\frac{5}{32}$	0.15625	$1\frac{1}{2}$	1.5000	4	4.0000*
$\frac{3}{16}$	0.1875	$1\frac{5}{8}$	1.6250		
$\frac{1}{4}$	0.2500	$1\frac{3}{4}$	1.7500		

* Diameters larger than 4 in. are usually adopted on the basis of engineering considerations. Therefore, no preferred basic sizes in this larger range are included here.

20. AMERICAN STANDARD TOLERANCES AND ALLOWANCES*
(From ASA B4.1—1947)

0.0001	0.0006	0.0025	**0.0100**
0.00015	0.0008	0.0030	0.0120
0.0002	**0.0010**	0.0040	0.0150
0.00025	0.0012	**0.0050**	**0.0200**
0.0003	0.0015	0.0060	0.0250
0.0004	**0.0020**	0.0080	**0.0300**
0.0005			

* The values in heavy type are preferred.

21. AMERICAN STANDARD COARSE AND FINE THREADS
(From ASA B1.1—1935)

With Tap Drill Sizes to Produce Approximately 75% Full Depth of Thread

Size	Basic Major Diameter (Inches)	National Coarse Series NC		Tap Drill	Decimal Equivalent (Inches)	National Fine Series NF		Tap Drill	Decimal Equivalent (Inches)
		Threads per Inch	Basic Minor Diam. (Inches)			Threads per Inch	Basic Minor Diam. (Inches)		
0	0.0600	—	—	—	—	80	0.0438	$\frac{3}{64}$	0.0469
1	0.0730	64	0.0527	No. 53	0.0595	72	0.0550	No. 53	0.0595
2	0.0860	56	0.0628	No. 50	0.0700	64	0.0657	No. 50	0.0700
3	0.0990	48	0.0719	No. 47	0.0785	56	0.0758	No. 45	0.0820
4	0.1120	40	0.0795	No. 43	0.0890	48	0.0849	No. 42	0.0935
5	0.1250	40	0.0925	No. 38	0.1015	44	0.0955	No. 37	0.1040
6	0.1380	32	0.0974	No. 36	0.1065	40	0.1055	No. 33	0.1130
8	0.1640	32	0.1234	No. 29	0.1360	36	0.1279	No. 29	0.1360
10	0.1900	24	0.1359	No. 25	0.1495	32	0.1494	No. 21	0.1590
12	0.2160	24	0.1619	No. 16	0.1770	28	0.1696	No. 14	0.1820
$\frac{1}{4}$	0.2500	20	0.1850	No. 7	0.2010	28	0.2036	No. 3	0.2130
$\frac{5}{16}$	0.3125	18	0.2403	F	0.2570	24	0.2584	I	0.2720
$\frac{3}{8}$	0.3750	16	0.2938	$\frac{5}{16}$	0.3125	24	0.3209	Q	0.3320
$\frac{7}{16}$	0.4375	14	0.3447	U	0.3680	20	0.3725	$\frac{25}{64}$	0.3906
$\frac{1}{2}$	0.5000	13	0.4001	$\frac{27}{64}$	0.4219	20	0.4350	$\frac{29}{64}$	0.4531
$\frac{9}{16}$	0.5625	12	0.4542	$\frac{31}{64}$	0.4844	18	0.4903	$\frac{33}{64}$	0.5156
$\frac{5}{8}$	0.6250	11	0.5069	$\frac{17}{32}$	0.5312	18	0.5528	$\frac{37}{64}$	0.5781
$\frac{3}{4}$	0.7500	10	0.6201	$\frac{21}{32}$	0.6562	16	0.6688	$\frac{11}{16}$	0.6875
$\frac{7}{8}$	0.8750	9	0.7307	$\frac{49}{64}$	0.7656	14	0.7822	$\frac{13}{16}$	0.8125
1	1.0000	8	0.8376	$\frac{7}{8}$	0.8750	14	0.9072	$\frac{15}{16}$	0.9375
$1\frac{1}{8}$	1.1250	7	0.9394	$\frac{63}{64}$	0.9844	12	1.0167	$1\frac{3}{64}$	1.0469
$1\frac{1}{4}$	1.2500	7	1.0644	$1\frac{7}{64}$	1.1094	12	1.1417	$1\frac{11}{64}$	1.1719
$1\frac{3}{8}$	1.3750	6	1.1585	$1\frac{7}{32}$	1.2187	12	1.2667	$1\frac{19}{64}$	1.2969
$1\frac{1}{2}$	1.5000	6	1.2835	$1\frac{11}{32}$	1.3437	12	1.3917	$1\frac{27}{64}$	1.4219
$1\frac{3}{4}$	1.7500	5	1.4902	$1\frac{9}{16}$	1.5625				
2	2.0000	$4\frac{1}{2}$	1.7113	$1\frac{25}{32}$	1.7812				
$2\frac{1}{4}$	2.2500	$4\frac{1}{2}$	1.9613	$2\frac{1}{32}$	2.0312				
$2\frac{1}{2}$	2.5000	4	2.1752	$2\frac{1}{4}$	2.2500				
$2\frac{3}{4}$	2.7500	4	2.4252	$2\frac{1}{2}$	2.5000				
3	3.0000	4	2.6752	$2\frac{3}{4}$	2.7500				
$3\frac{1}{4}$	3.2500	4	2.9252	3	3.0000				
$3\frac{1}{2}$	3.5000	4	3.1752	$3\frac{1}{4}$	3.2500				
$3\frac{3}{4}$	3.7500	4	3.4252	$3\frac{1}{2}$	3.5000				
4	4.0000	4	3.6752	$3\frac{3}{4}$	3.7500				

22. SAE EXTRA-FINE THREADS—NEF

Size	Basic Major Diam.	Threads per Inch	Size	Basic Major Diam.	Threads per Inch	Size	Basic Major Diam.	Threads per Inch
12	0.2160	32	$\frac{5}{8}$	0.6250	24	$1\frac{5}{16}$	1.3125	18
$\frac{1}{4}$	0.2500	32	$\frac{3}{4}$	0.7500	20	$1\frac{3}{8}$	1.3750	18
$\frac{5}{16}$	0.3125	32	$\frac{7}{8}$	0.8750	20	$1\frac{7}{16}$	1.4375	18
$\frac{3}{8}$	0.3750	32	1	1.0000	20	$1\frac{1}{2}$	1.5000	18
$\frac{7}{16}$	0.4375	28	$1\frac{1}{16}$	1.0625	18	$1\frac{9}{16}$	1.5625	18
$\frac{1}{2}$	0.5000	28	$1\frac{1}{8}$	1.1250	18	$1\frac{5}{8}$	1.6250	18
$\frac{9}{16}$	0.5625	24	$1\frac{3}{16}$	1.1875	18	$1\frac{11}{16}$	1.6875	18
$\frac{5}{8}$	0.6250	24	$1\frac{1}{4}$	1.2500	18	$1\frac{3}{4}$	1.7500	16
...	......	..	...	......	..	2*	2.0000	16

* For diameters over 2 in., use 16 threads per inch.

23. AMERICAN STANDARD ACME THREADS*

Size	Major Diam.	Threads per Inch	Size	Major Diam.	Threads per Inch	Size	Major Diam.	Threads per Inch
$\frac{1}{4}$	0.2500	16	1	1.0000	5	$2\frac{1}{2}$	2.5000	3
$\frac{5}{16}$	0.3125	14	$1\frac{1}{8}$	1.1250	5	$2\frac{3}{4}$	2.7500	3
$\frac{3}{8}$	0.3750	12	$1\frac{1}{4}$	1.2500	5	3	3.0000	2
$\frac{7}{16}$	0.4375	12	$1\frac{3}{8}$	1.3750	4	$3\frac{1}{2}$	3.5000	2
$\frac{1}{2}$	0.5000	10	$1\frac{1}{2}$	1.5000	4	4	4.0000	2
$\frac{5}{8}$	0.6250	8	$1\frac{3}{4}$	1.7500	4	$4\frac{1}{2}$	4.5000	2
$\frac{3}{4}$	0.7500	6	2	2.0000	4	5	5.0000	2
$\frac{7}{8}$	0.8750	6	$2\frac{1}{4}$	2.2500	3	...	......	..

* ASA B1.5—1945.

24. SQUARE THREADS

Size	Threads per Inch	Size	Threads per Inch	Size	Threads per Inch	Size	Threads per Inch	Size	Threads per Inch
$\frac{1}{4}$	10	$\frac{5}{8}$	$5\frac{1}{2}$	1	4	$1\frac{3}{4}$	$2\frac{1}{2}$	3	$1\frac{3}{4}$
$\frac{5}{16}$	9	$\frac{11}{16}$	5	$1\frac{1}{8}$	$3\frac{1}{2}$	$1\frac{7}{8}$	$2\frac{1}{2}$	$3\frac{1}{4}$	$1\frac{3}{4}$
$\frac{3}{8}$	8	$\frac{3}{4}$	5	$1\frac{1}{4}$	$3\frac{1}{2}$	2	$2\frac{1}{4}$	$3\frac{1}{2}$	$1\frac{5}{8}$
$\frac{7}{16}$	7	$\frac{13}{16}$	$4\frac{1}{2}$	$1\frac{3}{8}$	3	$2\frac{1}{4}$	$2\frac{1}{4}$	$3\frac{3}{4}$	$1\frac{1}{2}$
$\frac{1}{2}$	$6\frac{1}{2}$	$\frac{7}{8}$	$4\frac{1}{2}$	$1\frac{1}{2}$	3	$2\frac{1}{2}$	2	4	$1\frac{1}{2}$
$\frac{9}{16}$	6	$\frac{15}{16}$	4	$1\frac{5}{8}$	$2\frac{3}{4}$	$2\frac{3}{4}$	2	...	....

25. AMERICAN STANDARD 8-PITCH, 12-PITCH, AND 16-PITCH THREADS (From ASA B1.1—1935)

Size	Major Diam.	8-Pitch Series* Basic Pitch Diam.	Threads per Inch	12-Pitch Series* Basic Pitch Diam.	Threads per Inch	16-Pitch Series** Basic Pitch Diam.	Threads per Inch
1/2	0.5000	......	..	0.4459	12	......	..
9/16	0.5625	......	..	0.5084	12	......	..
5/8	0.6250	......	..	0.5709	12	......	..
11/16	0.6875	......	..	0.6334	12	......	..
3/4	0.7500	......	..	0.6959	12	0.7094	16
13/16	0.8125	......	..	0.7584	12	0.7719	16
7/8	0.8750	......	..	0.8209	12	0.8344	16
15/16	0.9375	......	..	0.8834	12	0.8969	16
1	1.0000	0.9188	8	0.9459	12	0.9594	16
1 1/16	1.0625	......	..	1.0084	12	1.0219	16
1 1/8	1.1250	1.0438	8	1.0709	12	1.0844	16
1 3/16	1.1875	......	..	1.1334	12	1.1469	16
1 1/4	1.2500	1.1688	8	1.1959	12	1.2094	16
1 5/16	1.3125	......	..	1.2584	12	1.2719	16
1 3/8	1.3750	1.2938	8	1.3209	12	1.3344	16
1 7/16	1.4375	......	..	1.3834	12	1.3969	16
1 1/2	1.5000	1.4188	8	1.4459	12	1.4594	16
1 9/16	1.5625	......	..	......	..	1.5219	16
1 5/8	1.6250	1.5438	8	1.5709	12	1.5844	16
1 11/16	1.6875	......	..	......	..	1.6469	16
1 3/4	1.7500	1.6688	8	1.6959	12	1.7094	16
1 13/16	1.8125	......	..	......	..	1.7719	16
1 7/8	1.8750	1.7938	8	1.8209	12	1.8344	16
1 15/16	1.9375	......	..	......	..	1.8969	16
2	2.0000	1.9188	8	1.9459	12	1.9594	16
2 1/16	2.0625	......	..	......	..	2.0219	16
2 1/8	2.1250	2.0438	8	2.0709	12	2.0844	16
2 3/16	2.1875	......	..	......	..	2.1469	16
2 1/4	2.2500	2.1688	8	2.1959	12	2.2094	16
2 5/16	2.3125	......	..	......	..	2.2719	16
2 3/8	2.3750	......	..	2.3209	12	2.3344	16
2 7/16	2.4375	......	..	......	..	2.3969	16
2 1/2	2.5000	2.4188	8	2.4459	12	2.4594	16
2 5/8	2.6250	......	..	2.5709	12	2.5844	16
2 3/4	2.7500	2.6688	8	2.6959	12	2.7094	16
2 7/8	2.8750	......	..	2.8209	12	2.8344	16
3	3.0000	2.9188	8	2.9459	12	2.9594	16
3 1/8	3.1250	......	..	3.0709	12	3.0844	16
3 1/4	3.2500	3.1688	8	3.1959	12	3.2094	16
3 3/8	3.3750	......	..	3.3209	12	3.3344	16
3 1/2	3.5000	3.4188	8	3.4459	12	3.4594	16
3 5/8	3.6250	......	..	3.5709	12	3.5844	16
3 3/4	3.7500	3.6688	8	3.6959	12	3.7094	16
3 7/8	3.8750	......	..	3.8209	12	3.8344	16
4	4.0000	3.9188	8	3.9459	12	3.9594	16
4 1/4	4.2500	4.1688	8	4.1959	12	......	..
4 1/2	4.5000	4.4188	8	4.4459	12	......	..
4 3/4	4.7500	4.6688	8	4.6959	12	......	..
5	5.0000	4.9188	8	4.9459	12	......	..
5 1/4	5.2500	5.1688	8	5.1959	12	......	..
5 1/2	5.5000	5.4188	8	5.4459	12	......	..
5 3/4	5.7500	5.6688	8	5.6959	12	......	..
6	6.0000	5.9188	8	5.9459	12	......	..

* Classes 2 and 3 are standard; class 2 recommended for general use.

** Class 3 only is standard.

26. STANDARDS FOR WIRE GAGES*

Dimensions of Sizes in Decimal Parts of an Inch

No. OF WIRE	AMERICAN OR BROWN & SHARPE FOR NON-FERROUS METALS	BIRMING-HAM, OR STUBS' IRON WIRE	AMERICAN S.&W. CO.'s (WASHBURN & MOEN) STD. STEEL WIRE	AMERICAN S. & W. CO.'s MUSIC WIRE	IMPERIAL WIRE	STUBS' STEEL WIRE	U. S. STD. GAGE FOR SHEET & PLATE IRON & STEEL	No. OF WIRE
7–0's	.651354	...	.4900	...	.500	...	.500	7–0's
6–0's	.580049	...	.4615	.004	.464	...	.46875	6–0's
5–0's	.516549	.500	.4305	.005	.432	...	.4375	5–0's
4–0's	.460	.454	.3938	.006	.400	...	.40625	4–0's
000	.40964	.425	.3625	.007	.372	...	.375	000
00	.3648	.380	.3310	.008	.348	...	.34375	00
0	.32486	.340	.3065	.009	.324	...	.3125	0
1	.2893	.300	.2830	.010	.300	.227	.28125	1
2	.25763	.284	.2625	.011	.276	.219	.265625	2
3	.22942	.259	.2437	.012	.252	.212	.250	3
4	.20431	.238	.2253	.013	.232	.207	.234375	4
5	.18194	.220	.2070	.014	.212	.204	.21875	5
6	.16202	.203	.1920	.016	.192	.201	.203125	6
7	.14428	.180	.1770	.018	.176	.199	.1875	7
8	.12849	.165	.1620	.020	.160	.197	.171875	8
9	.11443	.148	.1483	.022	.144	.194	.15625	9
10	.10189	.134	.1350	.024	.128	.191	.140625	10
11	.090742	.120	.1205	.026	.116	.188	.125	11
12	.080808	.109	.1055	.029	.104	.185	.109375	12
13	.071961	.095	.0915	.031	.092	.182	.09375	13
14	.064084	.083	.0800	.033	.080	.180	.078125	14
15	.057068	.072	.0720	.035	.072	.178	.0703125	15
16	.05082	.065	.0625	.037	.064	.175	.0625	16
17	.045257	.058	.0540	.039	.056	.172	.05625	17
18	.040303	.049	.0475	.041	.048	.168	.050	18
19	.03589	.042	.0410	.043	.040	.164	.04375	19
20	.031961	.035	.0348	.045	.036	.161	.0375	20
21	.028462	.032	.0317	.047	.032	.157	.034375	21
22	.025347	.028	.0286	.049	.028	.155	.03125	22
23	.022571	.025	.0258	.051	.024	.153	.028125	23
24	.0201	.022	.0230	.055	.022	.151	.025	24
25	.0179	.020	.0204	.059	.020	.148	.021875	25
26	.01594	.018	.0181	.063	.018	.146	.01875	26
27	.014195	.016	.0173	.067	.0164	.143	.0171875	27
28	.012641	.014	.0162	.071	.0149	.139	.015625	28
29	.011257	.013	.0150	.075	.0136	.134	.0140625	29
30	.010025	.012	.0140	.080	.0124	.127	.0125	30
31	.008928	.010	.0132	.085	.0116	.120	.0109375	31
32	.00795	.009	.0128	.090	.0108	.115	.01015625	32
33	.00708	.008	.0118	.095	.0100	.112	.009375	33
34	.006304	.007	.0104	...	.0092	.110	.00859375	34
35	.005614	.005	.0095	...	.0084	.108	.0078125	35
36	.005	.004	.0090	...	.0076	.106	.00703125	36
37	.004453	...	.0085	...	.0068	.103	.00664063	37
38	.003965	...	.0080	...	.0060	.101	.00625	38
39	.003531	...	.0075	...	.0052	.099	...	39
40	.003144	...	.0070	...	.0048	.097	...	40

The difference between the Stubs' Iron Wire Gage and the Stubs' Steel Wire Gage should be constantly borne in mind, the first being commonly known as the English Standard Wire, or Birmingham Gage, and which designates the Stubs' soft wire sizes, and the second being used in measuring drawn steel wire or drill rods of Stubs' make.

* Courtesy Brown & Sharpe Mfg. Co.

27. AMERICAN STANDARD REGULAR BOLTS AND NUTS
(From ASA B18.2—1941)

BOLT DIAM. OR MAJOR THREAD DIAM.	BOLT HEADS			NUTS				
	Width Across Flats	HEIGHT*		Width Across Flats	THICKNESS*			
					REGULAR NUTS		REGULAR JAM NUTS	
		Unfinished Square and Hexagon	Semifinished Hexagon		Unfinished Square and Hexagon	Semifinished Hexagon	Unfinished Square and Hexagon	Semifinished Hexagon
1/4	3/8	11/64	5/32	7/16	7/32	13/64	5/32	9/64
5/16	1/2	13/64	3/16	9/16	17/64	1/4	3/16	11/64
3/8	9/16	1/4	15/64	5/8	21/64	5/16	7/32	13/64
7/16	5/8	19/64	9/32	3/4	3/8	23/64	1/4	15/64
1/2	3/4	21/64	19/64	13/16	7/16	27/64	5/16	19/64
9/16	7/8	3/8	11/32	7/8	1/2	31/64	11/32	21/64
5/8	15/16	27/64	25/64	1	35/64	17/32	3/8	23/64
3/4	1 1/8	1/2	15/32	1 1/8	21/32	41/64	7/16	27/64
7/8	1 5/16	19/32	9/16	1 5/16	49/64	3/4	1/2	31/64
1	1 1/2	21/32	19/32	1 1/2	7/8	55/64	9/16	35/64
1 1/8	1 11/16	3/4	11/16	1 11/16	1	31/32	5/8	39/64
1 1/4	1 7/8	47/64	25/32	1 7/8	1 3/32	1 1/16	3/4	23/32
1 3/8	2 1/16	29/32	27/32	2 1/16	1 13/64	1 11/64	13/16	25/32
1 1/2	2 1/4	1	15/16	2 1/4	1 5/16	1 9/32	7/8	27/32
1 5/8	2 7/16	1 3/32	1 3/32	2 7/16	1 27/64	1 25/64	15/16	29/32
1 3/4	2 5/8	1 5/32	1 3/32	2 5/8	1 17/32	1 1/2	1	31/32
1 7/8	2 13/16	1 1/4	1 3/16	2 13/16	1 41/64	1 39/64	1 1/16	1 1/32
2	3	1 11/32	1 7/32	3	1 3/4	1 23/32	1 1/8	1 3/32
2 1/4	3 3/8	1 1/2	1 3/8	3 3/8	1 31/32	1 59/64	1 1/4	1 13/64
2 1/2	3 3/4	1 21/64	1 17/32	3 3/4	2 3/16	2 9/64	1 1/2	1 29/64
2 3/4	4 1/8	1 13/16	1 11/16	4 1/8	2 13/32	2 23/64	1 5/8	1 37/64
3	4 1/2	2	1 7/8	4 1/2	2 5/8	2 37/64	1 3/4	1 45/64

* Over-all distance from the top to the bearing surface including thickness of washer face where provided. Finished bolt heads and nuts are the same as semifinished except that the surfaces other than the bearing surface have been so treated as to provide a special appearance. Such finish must be specified by the purchaser.

28. AMERICAN STANDARD HEAVY BOLTS AND NUTS
(From ASA B18.2—1941)

Bolt Diam. or Major Thread Diam.	Bolt Heads			Nuts				
	Width Across Flats	Height*		Width Across Flats	Thickness*			
		Unfinished Square and Hexagon	Semi-finished Hexagon		Heavy Nuts		Heavy Jam Nuts	
					Unfinished Square and Hexagon	Semi-finished Hexagon	Unfinished Square and Hexagon	Semi-finished Hexagon
$\frac{1}{4}$	. . . .	. . . .	. . . .	$\frac{1}{2}$	$\frac{1}{4}$	$\frac{15}{64}$	$\frac{3}{16}$	$\frac{11}{64}$
$\frac{5}{16}$	. . . .	. . . .	. . . .	$\frac{19}{32}$	$\frac{5}{16}$	$\frac{19}{64}$	$\frac{7}{32}$	$\frac{13}{64}$
$\frac{3}{8}$	. . . .	. . . .	. . . .	$\frac{11}{16}$	$\frac{3}{8}$	$\frac{23}{64}$	$\frac{1}{4}$	$\frac{15}{64}$
$\frac{7}{16}$	. . . .	. . . .	. . . .	$\frac{25}{32}$	$\frac{7}{16}$	$\frac{27}{64}$	$\frac{9}{32}$	$\frac{17}{64}$
$\frac{1}{2}$	$\frac{7}{8}$	$\frac{7}{16}$	$\frac{13}{32}$	$\frac{7}{8}$	$\frac{1}{2}$	$\frac{31}{64}$	$\frac{5}{16}$	$\frac{19}{64}$
$\frac{9}{16}$	$\frac{15}{16}$	$\frac{15}{32}$	$\frac{7}{16}$	$\frac{15}{16}$	$\frac{9}{16}$	$\frac{35}{64}$	$\frac{11}{32}$	$\frac{21}{64}$
$\frac{5}{8}$	$1\frac{1}{16}$	$\frac{17}{32}$	$\frac{1}{2}$	$1\frac{1}{16}$	$\frac{5}{8}$	$\frac{39}{64}$	$\frac{3}{8}$	$\frac{23}{64}$
$\frac{3}{4}$	$1\frac{1}{4}$	$\frac{5}{8}$	$\frac{19}{32}$	$1\frac{1}{4}$	$\frac{3}{4}$	$\frac{47}{64}$	$\frac{7}{16}$	$\frac{27}{64}$
$\frac{7}{8}$	$1\frac{7}{16}$	$\frac{23}{32}$	$\frac{11}{16}$	$1\frac{7}{16}$	$\frac{7}{8}$	$\frac{55}{64}$	$\frac{1}{2}$	$\frac{31}{64}$
1	$1\frac{5}{8}$	$\frac{13}{16}$	$\frac{3}{4}$	$1\frac{5}{8}$	1	$\frac{63}{64}$	$\frac{9}{16}$	$\frac{35}{64}$
$1\frac{1}{8}$	$1\frac{13}{16}$	$\frac{29}{32}$	$\frac{27}{32}$	$1\frac{13}{16}$	$1\frac{1}{8}$	$1\frac{7}{64}$	$\frac{5}{8}$	$\frac{39}{64}$
$1\frac{1}{4}$	2	1	$\frac{15}{16}$	2	$1\frac{1}{4}$	$1\frac{7}{32}$	$\frac{3}{4}$	$\frac{23}{32}$
$1\frac{3}{8}$	$2\frac{3}{16}$	$1\frac{3}{32}$	$1\frac{1}{32}$	$2\frac{3}{16}$	$1\frac{3}{8}$	$1\frac{11}{32}$	$\frac{13}{16}$	$\frac{25}{32}$
$1\frac{1}{2}$	$2\frac{3}{8}$	$1\frac{3}{16}$	$1\frac{1}{8}$	$2\frac{3}{8}$	$1\frac{1}{2}$	$1\frac{15}{32}$	$\frac{7}{8}$	$\frac{27}{32}$
$1\frac{5}{8}$	$2\frac{9}{16}$	$1\frac{9}{32}$	$1\frac{3}{32}$	$2\frac{9}{16}$	$1\frac{5}{8}$	$1\frac{19}{32}$	$\frac{15}{16}$	$\frac{29}{32}$
$1\frac{3}{4}$	$2\frac{3}{4}$	$1\frac{3}{8}$	$1\frac{5}{16}$	$2\frac{3}{4}$	$1\frac{3}{4}$	$1\frac{23}{32}$	1	$\frac{31}{32}$
$1\frac{7}{8}$	$2\frac{15}{16}$	$1\frac{15}{32}$	$1\frac{13}{32}$	$2\frac{15}{16}$	$1\frac{7}{8}$	$1\frac{27}{32}$	$1\frac{1}{16}$	$1\frac{1}{32}$
2	$3\frac{1}{8}$	$1\frac{9}{16}$	$1\frac{7}{16}$	$3\frac{1}{8}$	2	$1\frac{31}{32}$	$1\frac{1}{8}$	$1\frac{3}{32}$
$2\frac{1}{4}$	$3\frac{1}{2}$	$1\frac{3}{4}$	$1\frac{5}{8}$	$3\frac{1}{2}$	$2\frac{1}{4}$	$2\frac{13}{64}$	$1\frac{1}{4}$	$1\frac{13}{64}$
$2\frac{1}{2}$	$3\frac{7}{8}$	$1\frac{15}{16}$	$1\frac{13}{16}$	$3\frac{7}{8}$	$2\frac{1}{2}$	$2\frac{29}{64}$	$1\frac{1}{2}$	$1\frac{29}{64}$
$2\frac{3}{4}$	$4\frac{1}{4}$	$2\frac{1}{8}$	2	$4\frac{1}{4}$	$2\frac{3}{4}$	$2\frac{45}{64}$	$1\frac{5}{8}$	$1\frac{37}{64}$
3	$4\frac{5}{8}$	$2\frac{5}{16}$	$2\frac{3}{16}$	$4\frac{5}{8}$	3	$2\frac{61}{64}$	$1\frac{3}{4}$	$1\frac{45}{64}$

* Over-all distance from the top to the bearing surface including thickness of washer face where provided. Finished bolt heads and nuts are the same as semifinished except that the surfaces other than the bearing surface have been so treated as to provide a special appearance. Such finish must be specified by the purchaser.

29. AMERICAN STANDARD REGULAR AND HEAVY SLOTTED NUTS
(From ASA B18.2—1941)
SEMIFINISHED HEXAGON

Major Thread Diam.	Regular Width Across Flats	Regular Thickness	Heavy Width Across Flats	Heavy Thickness	Slots (Regular and Heavy) Width	Slots (Regular and Heavy) Depth
1/4	7/16	13/64	1/2	15/64	5/64	3/32
5/16	9/16	1/4	19/32	19/64	3/32	3/32
3/8	5/8	5/16	11/16	23/64	1/8	1/8
7/16	3/4	23/64	25/32	27/64	1/8	5/32
1/2	13/16	27/64	7/8	31/64	5/32	5/32
9/16	7/8	31/64	15/16	35/64	5/32	3/16
5/8	1	17/32	1 1/16	39/64	3/16	7/32
3/4	1 1/8	41/64	1 1/4	47/64	3/16	1/4
7/8	1 5/16	3/4	1 7/16	55/64	3/16	1/4
1	1 1/2	55/64	1 5/8	63/64	1/4	9/32
1 1/8	1 11/16	31/32	1 13/16	1 7/64	1/4	11/32
1 1/4	1 7/8	1 1/16	2	1 7/32	5/16	3/8
1 3/8	2 1/16	1 11/64	2 3/16	1 11/32	5/16	3/8
1 1/2	2 1/4	1 9/32	2 3/8	1 15/32	3/8	7/16
1 5/8	2 7/16	1 25/64	2 9/16	1 19/32	3/8	7/16
1 3/4	2 5/8	1 1/2	2 3/4	1 23/32	7/16	1/2
1 7/8	2 13/16	1 39/64	2 15/16	1 27/32	7/16	9/16
2	3	1 23/32	3 1/8	1 31/32	7/16	9/16
2 1/4	3 3/8	1 59/64	3 1/2	2 13/64	7/16	9/16
2 1/2	3 3/4	2 9/64	3 7/8	2 29/64	9/16	11/16
2 3/4	4 1/8	2 23/64	4 1/4	2 45/64	9/16	11/16
3	4 1/2	2 37/64	4 5/8	2 61/64	5/8	3/4
3 1/4	...	...	5	3 3/16	5/8	3/4
3 1/2	...	...	5 3/8	3 7/16	5/8	3/4
3 3/4	...	...	5 3/4	3 11/16	5/8	3/4
4	...	...	6 1/8	3 15/16	5/8	3/4

30. AMERICAN STANDARD LIGHT SERIES NUTS
(From ASA B18.2—1941)
SEMIFINISHED HEXAGON

Major Thread Diam.	Width Across Flats	Thickness: Light Nuts and Light Slotted Nuts	Thickness: Light Jam Nuts	Thickness: Lt. Thick, Lt. Thick Slotted, and Light Castle Nuts	Light Castle Nuts: Height of Flats*	Light Castle Nuts: Diam. Cyl. Part.	Light Castle Nuts: Radius of Fillet	Slots (All Light Series) Width	Slots (All Light Series) Depth
1/4	7/16	7/32	5/32	9/32	3/16	0.371	3/32	5/64	3/32
5/16	1/2	17/64	3/16	21/64	15/64	0.425	3/32	3/32	3/32
3/8	9/16	21/64	7/32	13/32	9/32	0.478	3/32	1/8	1/8
7/16	5/8	3/8	1/4	29/64	19/64	0.531	3/32	1/8	5/32
1/2	3/4	7/16	5/16	9/16	13/32	0.637	1/8	5/32	5/32
9/16	7/8	31/64	5/16	39/64	27/64	0.744	5/32	5/32	3/16
5/8	15/16	35/64	3/8	23/32	1/2	0.797	5/32	3/16	7/32
3/4	1 1/16	21/32	3/8	13/16	9/16	0.903	3/16	3/16	1/4
7/8	1 1/4	49/64	7/16	29/32	21/32	1.063	3/16	3/16	1/4
1	1 7/16	7/8	1/2	1	23/32	1.222	3/16	1/4	9/32
1 1/8	1 5/8	63/64	9/16	1 5/32	13/16	1.382	1/4	1/4	11/32
1 1/4	1 13/16	1 3/32	5/8	1 1/4	7/8	1.541	1/4	5/16	3/8
1 3/8	2	1 13/64	3/4	1 3/8	1	1.700	1/4	5/16	3/8
1 1/2	2 3/16	1 5/16	13/16	1 1/2	1 1/16	1.859	1/4	3/8	7/16

* Height of hexagon portion measured from bearing surface of nut to top of arc.

31. RECOMMENDED MINIMUM THREAD LENGTHS FOR BOLTS
(From ASA B18.2—1941)*

Bolt[1] Length	Nominal Diameter of Bolt: No.10, $\frac{1}{4}$	$\frac{5}{16}$, $\frac{3}{8}$	$\frac{7}{16}$, $\frac{1}{2}$	$\frac{9}{16}$, $\frac{5}{8}$	$\frac{3}{4}$	$\frac{7}{8}$	1	$1\frac{1}{8}$, $1\frac{1}{4}$	$1\frac{3}{8}$, $1\frac{1}{2}$	$1\frac{5}{8}$, $1\frac{3}{4}$	$1\frac{7}{8}$, 2	$2\frac{1}{4}$	$2\frac{1}{2}$	$2\frac{3}{4}$	3
	Minimum Thread Length														
$\frac{3}{4}$	$\frac{1}{2}$	$\frac{1}{2}$	...	...	...	...	...	...	...	...	...	...	...	...	...
1	$\frac{3}{4}$	$\frac{3}{4}$	$\frac{3}{4}$	$\frac{3}{4}$	...	...	...	...	...	...	...	...	...	...	...
$1\frac{1}{4}$	$\frac{3}{4}$	$\frac{3}{4}$	1	1	1	...	...	...	...	...	...	...	...	...	...
$1\frac{1}{2}$	$\frac{3}{4}$	$\frac{7}{8}$	1	$1\frac{1}{8}$	$1\frac{1}{8}$	$1\frac{1}{8}$	...	...	...	...	...	...	...	...	...
$1\frac{3}{4}$	$\frac{3}{4}$	$\frac{7}{8}$	1	$1\frac{3}{16}$	$1\frac{3}{8}$	$1\frac{3}{8}$	$1\frac{3}{8}$	...	...	...	...	...	...	...	...
2	$\frac{3}{4}$	1	$1\frac{1}{4}$	$1\frac{1}{4}$	$1\frac{3}{8}$	$1\frac{9}{16}$	$1\frac{5}{8}$	$1\frac{5}{8}$	...	...	...	...	...	...	...
$2\frac{1}{2}$	$\frac{3}{4}$	1	$1\frac{1}{4}$	$1\frac{1}{2}$	$1\frac{1}{2}$	$1\frac{9}{16}$	$1\frac{3}{4}$	2	2	...	...	...	...	...	...
3	$\frac{7}{8}$	1	$1\frac{1}{4}$	$1\frac{1}{2}$	$1\frac{3}{4}$	$1\frac{3}{4}$	$1\frac{3}{4}$	$2\frac{1}{8}$	$2\frac{1}{2}$	$2\frac{1}{2}$	...	...	...	...	...
4	$\frac{7}{8}$	1	$1\frac{1}{4}$	$1\frac{1}{2}$	$1\frac{3}{4}$	2	$2\frac{1}{4}$	$2\frac{1}{4}$	$2\frac{1}{2}$	$2\frac{7}{8}$	$3\frac{1}{4}$	$3\frac{1}{4}$	$3\frac{1}{4}$	...	...
5	$\frac{7}{8}$	$1\frac{3}{16}$	$1\frac{1}{4}$	$1\frac{1}{2}$	$1\frac{3}{4}$	2	$2\frac{1}{4}$	$2\frac{3}{4}$	$2\frac{3}{4}$	$2\frac{7}{8}$	$3\frac{1}{4}$	$3\frac{5}{8}$	4	$4\frac{1}{8}$	$4\frac{1}{4}$
6	$\frac{7}{8}$	$1\frac{3}{16}$	$1\frac{1}{2}$	$1\frac{1}{2}$	$1\frac{3}{4}$	2	$2\frac{1}{4}$	$2\frac{3}{4}$	$3\frac{1}{4}$	$3\frac{1}{4}$	$3\frac{1}{4}$	$3\frac{5}{8}$	4	$4\frac{1}{8}$	$4\frac{3}{4}$
8	$\frac{7}{8}$	$1\frac{3}{16}$	$1\frac{1}{2}$	$1\frac{13}{16}$	2	2	$2\frac{1}{4}$	$2\frac{3}{4}$	$3\frac{1}{4}$	$3\frac{3}{4}$	4	4	4	$4\frac{1}{8}$	$4\frac{3}{4}$
10	$\frac{7}{8}$	$1\frac{3}{16}$	$1\frac{1}{2}$	$1\frac{13}{16}$	$2\frac{1}{8}$	$2\frac{7}{16}$	$2\frac{1}{2}$	$2\frac{3}{4}$	$3\frac{1}{4}$	$3\frac{3}{4}$	$4\frac{1}{4}$	$4\frac{3}{4}$	$4\frac{3}{4}$	$4\frac{3}{4}$	$4\frac{3}{4}$
12	$\frac{7}{8}$	$1\frac{3}{16}$	$1\frac{1}{2}$	$1\frac{13}{16}$	$2\frac{1}{8}$	$2\frac{7}{16}$	$2\frac{3}{4}$	$2\frac{3}{4}$	$3\frac{1}{4}$	$3\frac{3}{4}$	$4\frac{1}{4}$	$4\frac{3}{4}$	$5\frac{1}{4}$	$5\frac{3}{4}$	$6\frac{1}{4}$
16	1	$1\frac{3}{16}$	$1\frac{1}{2}$	$1\frac{13}{16}$	$2\frac{1}{8}$	$2\frac{7}{16}$	$2\frac{3}{4}$	$3\frac{1}{4}$	$3\frac{1}{4}$	$3\frac{3}{4}$	$4\frac{1}{4}$	$4\frac{3}{4}$	$5\frac{1}{4}$	$5\frac{3}{4}$	$6\frac{1}{4}$
20	1	$1\frac{3}{8}$	$1\frac{1}{2}$	$1\frac{13}{16}$	$2\frac{1}{8}$	$2\frac{7}{16}$	$2\frac{3}{4}$	$3\frac{3}{8}$	4	$4\frac{5}{8}$	$4\frac{3}{4}$	$4\frac{3}{4}$	$5\frac{1}{4}$	$5\frac{3}{4}$	$6\frac{1}{4}$
30	...	...	$1\frac{3}{4}$	$1\frac{13}{16}$	$2\frac{1}{8}$	$2\frac{7}{16}$	$2\frac{3}{4}$	$3\frac{3}{8}$	4	$4\frac{5}{8}$	$5\frac{1}{4}$	$5\frac{7}{8}$	$6\frac{1}{2}$	$6\frac{1}{2}$	$6\frac{1}{2}$

Minimum thread length is measured from the end of the bolt to the last complete thread.

For bolts too short for the specified minimum thread lengths, threads shall be cut or rolled to within $\frac{1}{4}$ in. of head or neck on sizes up to and including $\frac{1}{2}$ in., $\frac{3}{8}$ in. on sizes $\frac{9}{16}$ to 1 in., inclusive; $\frac{1}{2}$ in. on sizes $1\frac{1}{8}$ to 2 in., inclusive; and $\frac{3}{4}$ in. on sizes $2\frac{1}{8}$ to 3 in., inclusive.

Length of incomplete threads shall not exceed $2\frac{1}{2}$ threads.

Bolt length is measured from the greatest diameter of the under surface of the head to the end of the bolt.

The thread lengths shown in this table have been inserted as showing the usual practice followed by manufacturers when American Standard bolts are ordered and are applicable to both Regular and Heavy series.

* This table is included in the Appendix of the Standard for information only and is not a part of the Standard itself.

[1] For intermediate bolt lengths, the minimum thread length shall be the same as that specified in the table for the next shorter length of bolt of the same diameter.

32. AMERICAN STANDARD CAP SCREWS

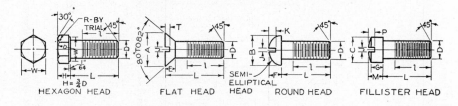

HEXAGON HEAD   FLAT HEAD   SEMI-ELLIPTICAL HEAD   ROUND HEAD   FILLISTER HEAD

Body Diam.	Hexagon Head*		Flat Head**			Round Head**			Fillister Head**				Widths of all Slots
	Width Across Flats	Height of Head	Diam. of Head	Height of Head	Depth of Slot	Diam. of Head	Height of Head	Depth of Slot	Diam. of Head	Height of Head	Total Ht. of Head	Depth of Slot	
D	W	H	A	E	T	B	F	K	C	G	M	P	J
$\frac{1}{4}$	$\frac{7}{16}$	$\frac{3}{16}$	0.500	0.140	0.069	0.437	0.191	0.117	0.375	0.172	0.216	0.097	0.075
$\frac{5}{16}$	$\frac{1}{2}$	$\frac{15}{64}$	0.625	0.176	0.086	0.562	0.246	0.151	0.437	0.203	0.253	0.115	0.084
$\frac{3}{8}$	$\frac{9}{16}$	$\frac{9}{32}$	0.750	0.210	0.103	0.625	0.273	0.168	0.562	0.250	0.314	0.143	0.094
$\frac{7}{16}$	$\frac{5}{8}$	$\frac{21}{64}$	0.8125	0.210	0.103	0.750	0.328	0.202	0.625	0.297	0.368	0.168	0.094
$\frac{1}{2}$	$\frac{3}{4}$	$\frac{3}{8}$	0.875	0.210	0.103	0.812	0.355	0.219	0.750	0.328	0.412	0.188	0.106
$\frac{9}{16}$	$\frac{13}{16}$	$\frac{27}{64}$	1.000	0.245	0.120	0.937	0.410	0.253	0.812	0.375	0.466	0.214	0.118
$\frac{5}{8}$	$\frac{7}{8}$	$\frac{15}{32}$	1.125	0.281	0.137	1.000	0.438	0.270	0.875	0.422	0.521	0.240	0.133
$\frac{3}{4}$	1	$\frac{9}{16}$	1.375	0.352	0.171	1.250	0.547	0.337	1.000	0.500	0.612	0.283	0.149
$\frac{7}{8}$	$1\frac{1}{8}$	$\frac{21}{32}$	1.625	0.423	0.206	....	....	....	1.125	0.594	0.720	0.334	0.167
1	$1\frac{5}{16}$	$\frac{3}{4}$	1.875	0.494	0.240	....	....	....	1.312	0.656	0.802	0.372	0.188
$1\frac{1}{8}$	$1\frac{1}{2}$	$\frac{27}{32}$	....	....	....	....	....	....	....	....	....	....	....
$1\frac{1}{4}$	$1\frac{11}{16}$	$\frac{15}{16}$	....	....	....	....	....	....	....	....	....	....	....

Threads: Use either Coarse or Fine thread series, Class 3 fit. Thread length $l = 2D + \frac{1}{4}''$. Screws too short for formula length of thread should be threaded as close as practicable to the head for the hexagon head screw and to within $2\frac{1}{2}$ threads of the head for the slotted head screws.

Lengths of Screws: The difference between consecutive lengths of screws (L) shall be $\frac{1}{8}''$ for screw lengths $\frac{1}{4}''$ to 1", $\frac{1}{4}''$ for screw lengths 1" to 4", and $\frac{1}{2}''$ for screw lengths 4" to 6".

* From ASA B18.2—1941. Head height includes $\frac{1}{64}''$ washer face.
** From ASA B18.6—1947.

33. AMERICAN STANDARD HEXAGON SOCKET CAP SCREWS
(From ASA B18.3—1947)

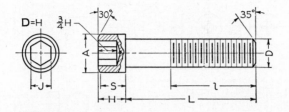

Body Diam. D Nom.	Body Diam. D Max.	Head Diam. A*	Side Height S	Socket Width J	Body Diam. D	Max.	Head Diam. A*	Side Height S	Socket Width J
2	0.0860	0.140	0.0788	$\frac{1}{16}$	$\frac{7}{16}$	0.4375	$\frac{5}{8}$	0.4010	$\frac{5}{16}$
3	0.0990	0.161	0.0907	$\frac{5}{64}$	$\frac{1}{2}$	0.5000	$\frac{3}{4}$	0.4583	$\frac{3}{8}$
4	0.1120	0.183	0.1026	$\frac{5}{64}$	$\frac{9}{16}$	0.5625	$\frac{13}{16}$	0.5156	$\frac{3}{8}$
5	0.1250	0.205	0.1146	$\frac{3}{32}$	$\frac{5}{8}$	0.6250	$\frac{7}{8}$	0.5729	$\frac{1}{2}$
6	0.1380	0.226	0.1265	$\frac{3}{32}$	$\frac{3}{4}$	0.7500	1	0.6875	$\frac{9}{16}$
8	0.1640	0.270	0.1503	$\frac{1}{8}$	$\frac{7}{8}$	0.8750	$1\frac{1}{8}$	0.8020	$\frac{9}{16}$
10	0.1900	$\frac{5}{16}$	0.1741	$\frac{5}{32}$	1	1.0000	$1\frac{5}{16}$	0.9166	$\frac{5}{8}$
12	0.2160	$\frac{11}{32}$	0.1980	$\frac{5}{32}$	$1\frac{1}{8}$	1.1250	$1\frac{1}{2}$	1.0312	$\frac{3}{4}$
$\frac{1}{4}$	0.2500	$\frac{3}{8}$	0.2291	$\frac{3}{16}$	$1\frac{1}{4}$	1.2500	$1\frac{3}{4}$	1.1457	$\frac{3}{4}$
$\frac{5}{16}$	0.3125	$\frac{7}{16}$	0.2864	$\frac{7}{32}$	$1\frac{3}{8}$	1.3750	$1\frac{7}{8}$	1.2604	$\frac{3}{4}$
$\frac{3}{8}$	0.3750	$\frac{9}{16}$	0.3437	$\frac{5}{16}$	$1\frac{1}{2}$	1.5000	2	1.3750	1

Lengths of Screws: The difference in consecutive lengths of screws (L) shall be $\frac{1}{8}''$ for screw lengths $\frac{1}{4}''$ to $1''$, $\frac{1}{4}''$ for screw lengths $1''$ to $4''$, and $\frac{1}{2}''$ for screw lengths $4''$ to $6''$.

Threads: For National Coarse Threads, the length of thread l equals $2D + \frac{1}{2}''$ where this length of thread would be greater than half the screw length; and l equals $\frac{1}{2}L$ where this length of thread would be greater than $2D + \frac{1}{2}''$.

For National Fine Threads, length of thread l equals $1\frac{1}{2}D + \frac{1}{2}''$ where this length of thread would be greater than $\frac{3}{8}$ the screw length; and l equals $\frac{3}{8}L$ where this length of thread would be greater than $1\frac{1}{2}D + \frac{1}{2}''$.

Screws too short for the formula thread lengths are threaded as close to the head as practicable.

* Head height H equals head diameter D for all sizes.

34. AMERICAN STANDARD MACHINE SCREWS
(From ASA B18.6—1947)

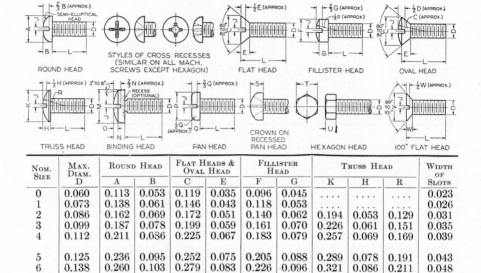

ROUND HEAD · STYLES OF CROSS RECESSES (SIMILAR ON ALL MACH. SCREWS EXCEPT HEXAGON) · FLAT HEAD · FILLISTER HEAD · OVAL HEAD

TRUSS HEAD · BINDING HEAD · PAN HEAD · CROWN ON RECESSED PAN HEAD · HEXAGON HEAD · 100° FLAT HEAD

Nom. Size	Max. Diam. D	Round Head		Flat Heads & Oval Head		Fillister Head		Truss Head			Width of Slots
		A	B	C	E	F	G	K	H	R	
0	0.060	0.113	0.053	0.119	0.035	0.096	0.045	....	....	....	0.023
1	0.073	0.138	0.061	0.146	0.043	0.118	0.053	....	....	....	0.026
2	0.086	0.162	0.069	0.172	0.051	0.140	0.062	0.194	0.053	0.129	0.031
3	0.099	0.187	0.078	0.199	0.059	0.161	0.070	0.226	0.061	0.151	0.035
4	0.112	0.211	0.086	0.225	0.067	0.183	0.079	0.257	0.069	0.169	0.039
5	0.125	0.236	0.095	0.252	0.075	0.205	0.088	0.289	0.078	0.191	0.043
6	0.138	0.260	0.103	0.279	0.083	0.226	0.096	0.321	0.086	0.211	0.048
8	0.164	0.309	0.120	0.332	0.100	0.270	0.113	0.384	0.102	0.254	0.054
10	0.190	0.359	0.137	0.385	0.116	0.313	0.130	0.448	0.118	0.283	0.060
12	0.216	0.408	0.153	0.438	0.132	0.357	0.148	0.511	0.134	0.336	0.067
$\frac{1}{4}$	0.250	0.472	0.175	0.507	0.153	0.414	0.170	0.573	0.150	0.375	0.075
$\frac{5}{16}$	0.3125	0.590	0.216	0.635	0.191	0.518	0.211	0.698	0.183	0.457	0.084
$\frac{3}{8}$	0.375	0.708	0.256	0.762	0.230	0.622	0.253	0.823	0.215	0.538	0.094
$\frac{7}{16}$	0.4375	0.750	0.328	0.812	0.223	0.625	0.265	0.948	0.248	0.619	0.094
$\frac{1}{2}$	0.500	0.813	0.355	0.875	0.223	0.750	0.297	1.073	0.280	0.701	0.106
$\frac{9}{16}$	0.5625	0.938	0.410	1.000	0.260	0.812	0.336	1.198	0.312	0.783	0.118
$\frac{5}{8}$	0.625	1.000	0.438	1.125	0.298	0.875	0.375	1.323	0.345	0.863	0.133
$\frac{3}{4}$	0.750	1.250	0.547	1.375	0.372	1.000	0.441	1.573	0.410	1.024	0.149

Nom. Size	Max. Diam. D	Binding Head			Pan Head			Hexagon Head		100° Flat Head		Width of Slots
		M	N	O	P	Q	S	T	U	V	W	
2	0.086	0.181	0.046	0.018	0.167	0.053	0.062	0.125	0.050	....	....	0.031
3	0.099	0.208	0.054	0.022	0.193	0.060	0.071	0.187	0.055	....	....	0.035
4	0.112	0.235	0.063	0.025	0.219	0.068	0.080	0.187	0.060	0.225	0.048	0.039
5	0.125	0.263	0.071	0.029	0.245	0.075	0.089	0.187	0.070	....	....	0.043
6	0.138	0.290	0.080	0.032	0.270	0.082	0.097	0.250	0.080	0.279	0.060	0.048
8	0.164	0.344	0.097	0.039	0.322	0.096	0.115	0.250	0.110	0.332	0.072	0.054
10	0.190	0.399	0.114	0.045	0.373	0.110	0.133	0.312	0.120	0.385	0.083	0.060
12	0.216	0.454	0.130	0.052	0.425	0.125	0.151	0.312	0.155	....	....	0.067
$\frac{1}{4}$	0.250	0.513	0.153	0.061	0.492	0.144	0.175	0.375	0.190	0.507	0.110	0.075
$\frac{5}{16}$	0.3125	0.641	0.193	0.077	0.615	0.178	0.218	0.500	0.230	0.635	0.138	0.084
$\frac{3}{8}$	0.375	0.769	0.234	0.094	0.740	0.212	0.261	0.562	0.295	0.762	0.165	0.094

Length of Thread: On screws 2″ long and shorter, the threads extend to within two threads of the head and closer if practicable; longer screws have minimum thread length of $1\frac{3}{4}″$.

Points: Machine screws are regularly made with plain sheared ends, not chamfered.

Threads: Either Coarse or Fine Thread Series, Class 2 fit.

Recessed Heads: Two styles of cross recesses are available on all screws except hexagon head.

35. AMERICAN STANDARD SQUARE AND FLAT KEYS, PLAIN TAPER KEYS, AND GIB HEAD KEYS
(From ASA B17.1—1943)

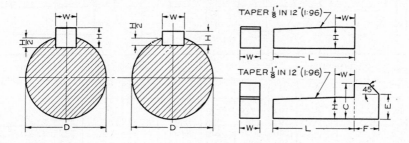

Shaft Diame- ters	Square Stock Key	Flat Stock Key	Gib Head Taper Stock Key					
			Square			Flat		
			Height	Length	Height to Chamfer	Height	Length	Height to Chamfer
D	W = H	W × H	C	F	E	C	F	E
$\frac{1}{2} - \frac{9}{16}$	$\frac{1}{8}$	$\frac{1}{8} \times \frac{3}{32}$	$\frac{1}{4}$	$\frac{7}{32}$	$\frac{5}{32}$	$\frac{3}{16}$	$\frac{1}{8}$	$\frac{1}{8}$
$\frac{5}{8} - \frac{7}{8}$	$\frac{3}{16}$	$\frac{3}{16} \times \frac{1}{8}$	$\frac{5}{16}$	$\frac{9}{32}$	$\frac{7}{32}$	$\frac{1}{4}$	$\frac{3}{16}$	$\frac{5}{32}$
$\frac{15}{16}-1\frac{1}{4}$	$\frac{1}{4}$	$\frac{1}{4} \times \frac{3}{16}$	$\frac{7}{16}$	$\frac{11}{32}$	$\frac{11}{32}$	$\frac{5}{16}$	$\frac{1}{4}$	$\frac{3}{16}$
$1\frac{5}{16}-1\frac{3}{8}$	$\frac{5}{16}$	$\frac{5}{16} \times \frac{1}{4}$	$\frac{9}{16}$	$\frac{13}{32}$	$\frac{13}{32}$	$\frac{3}{8}$	$\frac{5}{16}$	$\frac{1}{4}$
$1\frac{7}{16}-1\frac{1}{4}$	$\frac{3}{8}$	$\frac{3}{8} \times \frac{1}{4}$	$\frac{11}{16}$	$\frac{15}{32}$	$\frac{15}{32}$	$\frac{7}{16}$	$\frac{3}{8}$	$\frac{5}{16}$
$1\frac{13}{16}-2\frac{1}{4}$	$\frac{1}{2}$	$\frac{1}{2} \times \frac{3}{8}$	$\frac{7}{8}$	$\frac{19}{32}$	$\frac{5}{8}$	$\frac{5}{8}$	$\frac{1}{2}$	$\frac{7}{16}$
$2\frac{5}{16}-2\frac{3}{4}$	$\frac{5}{8}$	$\frac{5}{8} \times \frac{7}{16}$	$1\frac{1}{16}$	$\frac{23}{32}$	$\frac{3}{4}$	$\frac{3}{4}$	$\frac{5}{8}$	$\frac{1}{2}$
$2\frac{7}{8} -3\frac{1}{4}$	$\frac{3}{4}$	$\frac{3}{4} \times \frac{1}{2}$	$1\frac{1}{4}$	$\frac{7}{8}$	$\frac{7}{8}$	$\frac{7}{8}$	$\frac{3}{4}$	$\frac{5}{8}$
$3\frac{3}{8} -3\frac{3}{4}$	$\frac{7}{8}$	$\frac{7}{8} \times \frac{5}{8}$	$1\frac{1}{2}$	1	1	$1\frac{1}{16}$	$\frac{7}{8}$	$\frac{3}{4}$
$3\frac{7}{8} -4\frac{1}{2}$	1	$1 \times \frac{3}{4}$	$1\frac{3}{4}$	$1\frac{3}{16}$	$1\frac{3}{16}$	$1\frac{1}{4}$	1	$1\frac{3}{16}$
$4\frac{3}{4} -5\frac{1}{2}$	$1\frac{1}{4}$	$1\frac{1}{4} \times \frac{7}{8}$	2	$1\frac{7}{16}$	$1\frac{7}{16}$	$1\frac{1}{2}$	$1\frac{1}{4}$	1
$5\frac{3}{4} -6$	$1\frac{1}{2}$	$1\frac{1}{2} \times 1$	$2\frac{1}{2}$	$1\frac{3}{4}$	$1\frac{3}{4}$	$1\frac{3}{4}$	$1\frac{1}{2}$	$1\frac{1}{4}$

Stock Lengths for Plain Taper and Gib Head Taper Keys: Minimum stock length equals 4W, and the maximum equals 16W. The increments of increase of length equal 2W.

Gib Head Taper Square and Flat Keys have the same dimensions as the Square and Flat Stock Keys, with the addition of a taper on top, and of a gib head.

Plain Taper Square and Flat Keys have the same dimensions as the Gib Head Taper Square and Flat Keys, with the exception of the gib head.

36. AMERICAN STANDARD WOODRUFF KEYS

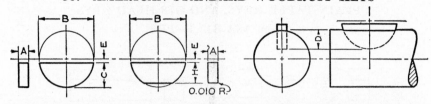

KEY No.	NOMINAL SIZES		MAX. SIZES			KEY No.	NOMINAL SIZES		MAX. SIZES		
	$A \times B$	E	H	D	C		$A \times B$	E	H	D	C
204	$\frac{1}{16} \times \frac{1}{2}$	$\frac{3}{64}$	.194	.1718	0.203	808	$\frac{1}{4} \times 1$	$\frac{1}{16}$	.428	.3130	.438
304	$\frac{3}{32} \times \frac{1}{2}$	$\frac{3}{64}$	.194	.1561	.203	809	$\frac{1}{4} \times 1\frac{1}{8}$	$\frac{5}{64}$	.475	.3590	.484
305	$\frac{3}{32} \times \frac{5}{8}$	$\frac{1}{16}$	.240	.2031	.250	810	$\frac{1}{4} \times 1\frac{1}{4}$	$\frac{5}{64}$	.537	.4220	.547
404	$\frac{1}{8} \times \frac{1}{2}$	$\frac{3}{64}$	.194	.1405	.203	811	$\frac{1}{4} \times 1\frac{3}{8}$	$\frac{3}{32}$	.584	.4690	.594
405	$\frac{1}{8} \times \frac{5}{8}$	$\frac{1}{16}$	.240	.1875	.250	812	$\frac{1}{4} \times 1\frac{1}{2}$	$\frac{7}{64}$	.631	.5160	.641
406	$\frac{1}{8} \times \frac{3}{4}$	$\frac{1}{16}$	.303	.2505	.313	1008	$\frac{5}{16} \times 1$	$\frac{1}{16}$	.428	.2818	.438
505	$\frac{5}{32} \times \frac{5}{8}$	$\frac{1}{16}$	.240	.1719	.250	1009	$\frac{5}{16} \times 1\frac{1}{8}$	$\frac{5}{64}$	.475	.3278	.484
506	$\frac{5}{32} \times \frac{3}{4}$	$\frac{1}{16}$	.303	.2349	.313	1010	$\frac{5}{16} \times 1\frac{1}{4}$	$\frac{5}{64}$	.537	.3908	.547
507	$\frac{5}{32} \times \frac{7}{8}$	$\frac{1}{16}$	.365	.2969	.375	1011	$\frac{5}{16} \times 1\frac{3}{8}$	$\frac{3}{32}$	.584	.4378	.594
606	$\frac{3}{16} \times \frac{3}{4}$	$\frac{1}{16}$	.303	.2193	.313	1012	$\frac{5}{16} \times 1\frac{1}{2}$	$\frac{7}{64}$	.631	.4848	.641
607	$\frac{3}{16} \times \frac{7}{8}$	$\frac{1}{16}$	.365	.2813	.375	1210	$\frac{3}{8} \times 1\frac{1}{4}$	$\frac{5}{64}$	.537	.3595	.547
608	$\frac{3}{16} \times 1$	$\frac{1}{16}$	.428	.3443	.438	1211	$\frac{3}{8} \times 1\frac{3}{8}$	$\frac{3}{32}$	.584	.4065	.594
609	$\frac{3}{16} \times 1\frac{1}{8}$	$\frac{5}{64}$	.475	.3903	.484	1212	$\frac{3}{8} \times 1\frac{1}{2}$	$\frac{7}{64}$	.631	.4535	.641
807	$\frac{1}{4} \times \frac{7}{8}$	$\frac{1}{16}$	.365	.2500	.375	...	...	...	...	...	...

Key numbers indicate the nominal key dimensions. The last two digits give the nominal diameter (B) in eighths of an inch, and the digits preceding the last two give the nominal width (A) in thirty-seconds of an inch.

37. STANDARD TAPER PINS

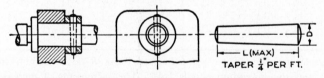

TAPER $\frac{1}{4}$" PER FT.

PIN No.	DIAM. D	SHAFT DIAM. (Approx.)	LENGTH	DRILL SIZE (Before Reamer)	PIN No.	DIAM. D	SHAFT DIAM.	LENGTH	DRILL SIZE (Before Reamer)
000000	0.078	$\frac{7}{32}$	$\frac{3}{8}-\frac{3}{4}$	0.0595	3	0.219	$\frac{3}{4}$	$\frac{3}{4}-1\frac{3}{4}$	0.1890
00000	0.094	$\frac{1}{4}$	$\frac{1}{2}-1$	0.0785	4	0.250	$\frac{13}{16}$	$\frac{3}{4}-2$	0.2130
0000	0.109	$\frac{5}{16}$	$\frac{1}{2}-1$	0.0935	5	0.298	$\frac{7}{8}$	$1-2\frac{1}{4}$	$\frac{1}{4}$
000	0.125	$\frac{3}{8}$	$\frac{1}{2}-1$	0.1040	6	0.341	1	$1\frac{1}{4}-3$	$\frac{9}{32}$
00	0.141	$\frac{7}{16}$	$\frac{1}{2}-1\frac{1}{4}$	0.1200	7	0.409	$1\frac{1}{4}$	$2-3\frac{1}{2}$	$\frac{11}{32}$
0	0.156	$\frac{1}{2}$	$\frac{1}{2}-1\frac{1}{4}$	0.1405	8	0.492	$1\frac{1}{2}$	$2-4\frac{1}{2}$	$\frac{13}{32}$
1	0.172	$\frac{9}{16}$	$\frac{5}{8}-1\frac{1}{4}$	0.1495	9	0.591	2	$2\frac{3}{4}-5\frac{1}{4}$	$\frac{31}{64}$
2	0.193	$\frac{5}{8}$	$\frac{3}{4}-1\frac{1}{2}$	0.1660	10	0.706	$2\frac{1}{2}$	$3\frac{1}{2}-6$	$\frac{19}{32}$

38. PRATT AND WHITNEY ROUND END KEYS

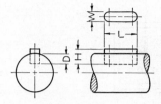

KEYS MADE WITH ROUND ENDS AND KEYWAYS CUT IN SPLINE MILLER

Key No.	L	W or D	H	Key No.	L	W or D	H
1	$\frac{1}{2}$	$\frac{1}{16}$	$\frac{3}{32}$	22	$1\frac{3}{8}$	$\frac{1}{4}$	$\frac{3}{8}$
2	$\frac{1}{2}$	$\frac{3}{32}$	$\frac{9}{64}$	23	$1\frac{3}{8}$	$\frac{5}{16}$	$\frac{15}{32}$
3	$\frac{1}{2}$	$\frac{1}{8}$	$\frac{3}{16}$	F	$1\frac{3}{8}$	$\frac{3}{8}$	$\frac{9}{16}$
4	$\frac{5}{8}$	$\frac{3}{32}$	$\frac{9}{64}$	24	$1\frac{1}{2}$	$\frac{1}{4}$	$\frac{3}{8}$
5	$\frac{5}{8}$	$\frac{1}{8}$	$\frac{3}{16}$	25	$1\frac{1}{2}$	$\frac{5}{16}$	$\frac{15}{32}$
6	$\frac{5}{8}$	$\frac{5}{32}$	$\frac{15}{64}$	G	$1\frac{1}{2}$	$\frac{3}{8}$	$\frac{9}{16}$
7	$\frac{3}{4}$	$\frac{1}{8}$	$\frac{3}{16}$	51	$1\frac{3}{4}$	$\frac{1}{4}$	$\frac{3}{8}$
8	$\frac{3}{4}$	$\frac{5}{32}$	$\frac{15}{64}$	52	$1\frac{3}{4}$	$\frac{5}{16}$	$\frac{15}{32}$
9	$\frac{3}{4}$	$\frac{3}{16}$	$\frac{9}{32}$	53	$1\frac{3}{4}$	$\frac{3}{8}$	$\frac{9}{16}$
10	$\frac{7}{8}$	$\frac{5}{32}$	$\frac{15}{64}$	26	2	$\frac{3}{16}$	$\frac{9}{32}$
11	$\frac{7}{8}$	$\frac{3}{16}$	$\frac{9}{32}$	27	2	$\frac{1}{4}$	$\frac{3}{8}$
12	$\frac{7}{8}$	$\frac{7}{32}$	$\frac{21}{64}$	28	2	$\frac{5}{16}$	$\frac{15}{32}$
A	$\frac{7}{8}$	$\frac{1}{4}$	$\frac{3}{8}$	29	2	$\frac{3}{8}$	$\frac{9}{16}$
13	1	$\frac{3}{16}$	$\frac{9}{32}$	54	$2\frac{1}{4}$	$\frac{1}{4}$	$\frac{3}{8}$
14	1	$\frac{7}{32}$	$\frac{21}{64}$	55	$2\frac{1}{4}$	$\frac{5}{16}$	$\frac{15}{32}$
15	1	$\frac{1}{4}$	$\frac{3}{8}$	56	$2\frac{1}{4}$	$\frac{3}{8}$	$\frac{9}{16}$
B	1	$\frac{5}{16}$	$\frac{15}{32}$	57	$2\frac{1}{4}$	$\frac{7}{16}$	$\frac{21}{32}$
16	$1\frac{1}{8}$	$\frac{3}{16}$	$\frac{9}{32}$	58	$2\frac{1}{2}$	$\frac{5}{16}$	$\frac{15}{32}$
17	$1\frac{1}{8}$	$\frac{7}{32}$	$\frac{21}{64}$	59	$2\frac{1}{2}$	$\frac{3}{8}$	$\frac{9}{16}$
18	$1\frac{1}{8}$	$\frac{1}{4}$	$\frac{3}{8}$	60	$2\frac{1}{2}$	$\frac{7}{16}$	$\frac{21}{32}$
C	$1\frac{1}{8}$	$\frac{5}{16}$	$\frac{15}{32}$	61	$2\frac{1}{2}$	$\frac{1}{2}$	$\frac{3}{4}$
19	$1\frac{1}{4}$	$\frac{3}{16}$	$\frac{9}{32}$	30	3	$\frac{3}{8}$	$\frac{9}{16}$
20	$1\frac{1}{4}$	$\frac{7}{32}$	$\frac{21}{64}$	31	3	$\frac{7}{16}$	$\frac{21}{32}$
21	$1\frac{1}{4}$	$\frac{1}{4}$	$\frac{3}{8}$	32	3	$\frac{1}{2}$	$\frac{3}{4}$
D	$1\frac{1}{4}$	$\frac{5}{16}$	$\frac{15}{32}$	33	3	$\frac{9}{16}$	$\frac{27}{32}$
E	$1\frac{1}{4}$	$\frac{3}{8}$	$\frac{9}{16}$	34	3	$\frac{5}{8}$	$\frac{15}{16}$

The length L may vary from the table, but equals at least 2W.

Max. length of slot is $4''$ + W. Note that key is sunk two-thirds into shaft in all cases.

39. CENTER HOLE SIZES*

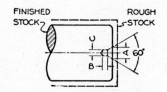

FINISHED SIZE OF SHAFT		A	B	C
From	To			
$\frac{1}{8}$	$\frac{5}{32}$	$\frac{3}{64}$	$\frac{1}{16}$	$\frac{3}{64}$
$\frac{3}{16}$	$\frac{7}{32}$	$\frac{5}{64}$	$\frac{1}{16}$	$\frac{3}{64}$
$\frac{1}{4}$	$\frac{11}{32}$	$\frac{3}{32}$	$\frac{1}{16}$	$\frac{3}{64}$
$\frac{3}{8}$	$\frac{17}{32}$	$\frac{1}{8}$	$\frac{5}{64}$	$\frac{1}{16}$
$\frac{9}{16}$	$\frac{25}{32}$	$\frac{3}{16}$	$\frac{3}{32}$	$\frac{5}{64}$
$\frac{13}{16}$	$1\frac{3}{32}$	$\frac{1}{4}$	$\frac{3}{32}$	$\frac{3}{32}$
$1\frac{1}{8}$	$1\frac{15}{32}$	$\frac{5}{16}$	$\frac{3}{32}$	$\frac{5}{32}$
$1\frac{1}{2}$	$1\frac{31}{32}$	$\frac{3}{8}$	$\frac{5}{32}$	$\frac{5}{32}$
2	$2\frac{31}{32}$	$\frac{7}{16}$	$\frac{3}{16}$	$\frac{7}{32}$
3	$3\frac{31}{32}$	$\frac{1}{2}$	$\frac{7}{32}$	$\frac{7}{32}$
4	and over	$\frac{9}{16}$	$\frac{7}{32}$	$\frac{7}{32}$

*Brown & Sharpe Mfg. Co.

40. SAE STANDARD PLAIN WASHERS[1]

Size	Light			Medium			Heavy		
	I.D.	O.D.	Thickness	I.D.	O.D.	Thickness	I.D.	O.D.	Thickness
$\frac{3}{16}$ (.187)	$\frac{7}{32}$	$\frac{7}{16}$	.049	$\frac{7}{32}$	$\frac{1}{2}$	.049	...	...	...
10 (.190)	$\frac{7}{32}$	$\frac{7}{16}$	.049	$\frac{1}{4}$	$\frac{9}{16}$	.049	...	...	...
11 (.203)	$\frac{15}{64}$	$\frac{17}{32}$	.049	$\frac{1}{4}$	$\frac{9}{16}$	.049	...	...	...
12 (.216)	$\frac{1}{4}$	$\frac{1}{2}$	.049	$\frac{1}{4}$	$\frac{9}{16}$	.049	$\frac{1}{4}$	$\frac{9}{16}$	.065
14 (.242)	$\frac{17}{64}$	$\frac{5}{8}$	.049	$\frac{5}{16}$	$\frac{3}{4}$	.065	$\frac{5}{16}$	$\frac{7}{8}$	.065
$\frac{1}{4}$ (.250)	$\frac{9}{32}$	$\frac{5}{8}$	.065	$\frac{5}{16}$	$\frac{3}{4}$	.065	$\frac{5}{16}$	$\frac{7}{8}$	.065
16 (.268)	$\frac{9}{32}$	$\frac{5}{8}$	.065	$\frac{5}{16}$	$\frac{3}{4}$	.065	$\frac{5}{16}$	$\frac{7}{8}$	.065
18 (.294)	$\frac{5}{16}$	$\frac{3}{4}$	.065	$\frac{3}{8}$	$\frac{3}{4}$	.065	$\frac{3}{8}$	$\frac{7}{8}$	.083
$\frac{5}{16}$ (.3125)	$\frac{11}{32}$	$\frac{11}{16}$	.065	$\frac{3}{8}$	$\frac{3}{4}$	.065	$\frac{3}{8}$	$\frac{7}{8}$	.083
20 (.320)	$\frac{11}{32}$	$\frac{11}{16}$	.065	$\frac{3}{8}$	$\frac{3}{4}$	.065	$\frac{3}{8}$	$\frac{7}{8}$	.083
24 (.372)	$\frac{13}{32}$	$\frac{13}{16}$	.065	$\frac{7}{16}$	$\frac{7}{8}$	.083	$\frac{7}{16}$	1	.083
$\frac{3}{8}$ (.375)	$\frac{13}{32}$	$\frac{13}{16}$	.065	$\frac{7}{16}$	$\frac{7}{8}$	.083	$\frac{7}{16}$	1	.083
$\frac{7}{16}$ (.4375)	$\frac{15}{32}$	$\frac{59}{64}$	.065	$\frac{1}{2}$	$1\frac{1}{8}$	.083	$\frac{1}{2}$	$1\frac{1}{4}$	.083
$\frac{1}{2}$ (.5000)	$\frac{17}{32}$	$1\frac{1}{16}$	.095	$\frac{9}{16}$	$1\frac{1}{4}$	.109	$\frac{9}{16}$	$1\frac{3}{8}$	.109
$\frac{9}{16}$ (.5625)	$\frac{19}{32}$	$1\frac{3}{16}$	.095	$\frac{5}{8}$	$1\frac{3}{8}$	.109	$\frac{5}{8}$	$1\frac{1}{2}$	.109
$\frac{5}{8}$ (.625)	$\frac{21}{32}$	$1\frac{5}{16}$	.095	$\frac{11}{16}$	$1\frac{1}{2}$	.134	$\frac{11}{16}$	$1\frac{3}{4}$	.134
$\frac{3}{4}$ (.750)	$\frac{13}{16}$	$1\frac{1}{2}$	.134	$\frac{13}{16}$	$1\frac{3}{4}$	.148	$\frac{13}{16}$	2	.148
$\frac{7}{8}$ (.875)	$\frac{15}{16}$	$1\frac{3}{4}$	.134	$\frac{15}{16}$	2	.165	$\frac{15}{16}$	$2\frac{1}{4}$	.165
1 (1.000)	$1\frac{1}{16}$	2	.134	$1\frac{1}{16}$	$2\frac{1}{4}$	.165	$1\frac{1}{16}$	$2\frac{1}{2}$	.165
$1\frac{1}{8}$ (1.125)	...	...	...	$1\frac{3}{16}$	$2\frac{1}{2}$	.165	$1\frac{1}{4}$	$2\frac{3}{4}$	.165
$1\frac{1}{4}$ (1.250)	...	...	...	$1\frac{5}{16}$	$2\frac{3}{4}$	.165	$1\frac{3}{8}$	3	.165
$1\frac{3}{8}$ (1.375)	...	...	...	$1\frac{7}{16}$	3	.180	$1\frac{1}{2}$	$3\frac{1}{4}$	.180
$1\frac{1}{2}$ (1.500)	...	...	...	$1\frac{9}{16}$	$3\frac{1}{4}$	.180	$1\frac{5}{8}$	$3\frac{1}{2}$	.180
$1\frac{5}{8}$ (1.625)	...	...	...	$1\frac{11}{16}$	$3\frac{1}{2}$	.180	$1\frac{3}{4}$	$3\frac{3}{4}$	.180
$1\frac{3}{4}$ (1.750)	...	...	...	$1\frac{13}{16}$	$3\frac{3}{4}$	.180	$1\frac{7}{8}$	4	.180

[1] For sizes less than $\frac{3}{16}$ or over $1\frac{3}{4}$, see SAE HANDBOOK.

41. SAE SPRING LOCK WASHERS[1]

Nominal Size	Min. I.D.	Medium		Light		Heavy		Extra Heavy	
		Thickness	Max. O.D.	Thickness	Max. O.D.	Thickness	Max. O.D.	Thickness	Max. O.D.
6 (.138)	0.141	0.031	0.251	0.025	0.237	0.040	0.267	0.045	0.315
8 (.168)	0.168	0.040	0.296	0.031	0.280	0.047	0.310	0.057	0.378
10 (.190)	0.194	0.047	0.337	0.040	0.323	0.056	0.353	0.068	0.437
12 (.216)	0.221	0.056	0.380	0.047	0.364	0.063	0.394	0.080	0.500
$\frac{1}{4}$	0.255	0.062	0.493	0.047	0.489	0.077	0.495	0.084	0.539
$\frac{5}{16}$	0.319	0.078	0.591	0.056	0.575	0.097	0.601	0.108	0.627
$\frac{3}{8}$	0.382	0.094	0.688	0.070	0.678	0.115	0.696	0.123	0.746
$\frac{7}{16}$	0.446	0.109	0.784	0.085	0.780	0.133	0.792	0.143	0.844
$\frac{1}{2}$	0.509	0.125	0.879	0.099	0.877	0.151	0.889	0.162	0.945
$\frac{9}{16}$	0.573	0.141	0.979	0.113	0.975	0.170	0.989	0.182	1.049
$\frac{5}{8}$	0.636	0.156	1.086	0.126	1.082	0.189	1.100	0.202	1.164
$\frac{11}{16}$	0.700	0.172	1.184	0.138	1.178	0.207	1.200	0.221	1.266
$\frac{3}{4}$	0.763	0.188	1.279	0.153	1.277	0.226	1.299	0.241	1.369
$\frac{13}{16}$	0.827	0.203	1.377	0.168	1.375	0.246	1.401	0.261	1.473
$\frac{7}{8}$	0.890	0.219	1.474	0.179	1.470	0.266	1.504	0.285	1.586
$\frac{15}{16}$	0.954	0.234	1.570	0.191	1.562	0.284	1.604	0.308	1.698
1	1.017	0.250	1.672	0.202	1.656	0.306	1.716	0.330	1.810
$1\frac{1}{16}$	1.081	0.266	1.768	0.213	1.746	0.326	1.820	0.352	1.922
$1\frac{1}{8}$	1.144	0.281	1.865	0.224	1.837	0.345	1.921	0.375	2.031
$1\frac{3}{16}$	1.208	0.297	1.963	0.234	1.923	0.364	2.021	0.396	2.137
$1\frac{1}{4}$	1.271	0.312	2.058	0.244	2.012	0.384	2.126	0.417	2.244
$1\frac{5}{16}$	1.335	0.328	2.156	0.254	2.098	0.403	2.226	0.438	2.350
$1\frac{3}{8}$	1.398	0.344	2.253	0.264	2.183	0.422	2.325	0.458	2.453
$1\frac{7}{16}$	1.462	0.359	2.349	0.273	2.269	0.440	2.421	0.478	2.555
$1\frac{1}{2}$	1.525	0.375	2.446	0.282	2.352	0.458	2.518	0.496	2.654

[1] For sizes under No. 6, see SAE HANDBOOK.

42. SAE STANDARD COTTER PINS

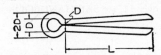

Diam. D	Nominal Trade Diameter D																	
	$\frac{5}{16}$	$\frac{7}{16}$	$\frac{1}{2}$	$\frac{5}{8}$	$\frac{3}{4}$	$\frac{7}{8}$	1	$1\frac{1}{8}$	$1\frac{1}{4}$	$1\frac{3}{8}$	$1\frac{1}{2}$	$1\frac{5}{8}$	$1\frac{3}{4}$	2	$2\frac{1}{4}$	$2\frac{1}{2}$	$2\frac{3}{4}$	3
$\frac{1}{16}$	*	*	*	*	*	*												
$\frac{3}{32}$			*	*	*	*	*	*										
$\frac{1}{8}$					*	*	*	*	*	*	*	*						
$\frac{5}{32}$							*	*	*	*	*	*	*					
$\frac{3}{16}$									*	*	*	*	*	*				
$\frac{7}{32}$													*	*	*	*	*	*
$\frac{1}{4}$															*	*	*	*
$\frac{5}{16}$																*	*	*

43. ABBREVIATIONS FOR USE ON DRAWINGS
(Compiled from ASA Z32.13—1946)

Absolute	ABS	Bracket	BRKT
Account	ACCT	Brass	BRS
Accumulate	ACCUM	Break	BRK
Actual	ACT.	Brinell Hardness	BH
Addendum	ADD.	Broach	BRO
Addition	ADD.	Bronze	BRZ
Adjust	ADJ	Building	BLDG
Advance	ADV	Button	BUT.
Aeronautical Standards	AS		
After	AFT.	Cap Screw	CAP.SCR
Air Blast	AB	Carburize	CARB
Alteration	ALTN	Case Harden	CH
Alternate	ALT	Cast Iron	CI
Altitude	ALT	Cast Steel	CS
Aluminum	AL	Casting	CSTG
American Standard	AMER STD	Center	CTR
Amount	AMT	Center Line	CL
Anneal	ANL	Center to Center	C to C
Anti-Friction Bearing	AFB	Chamfer	CHAM
Apparatus	APP	Chord	CHD
Appendix	APPX	Circle	CIR
Approved	APPD	Clear	CLR
Approximate	APPROX	Coated	CTD
Arc Weld	ARC/W	Cold Drawn	CD
Area	A	Cold Rolled	CR
Asbestos	ASB	Cold Rolled Steel	CRS
Assemble	ASSEM	Company	CO
Assembly	ASSY	Concentric	CONC
Attach	ATT	Concrete	CONC
Automatic	AUTO	Condition	COND
Auxiliary	AUX	Construction	CONST
Average	AVG	Correct	CORR
		Counterbore	CBORE
Babbitt	BAB	Counterdrill	CDRILL
Ball Bearing	BB	Countersink	CSK
Bearing	BRG	Coupling	CPLG
Between	BET.	Cross Section	X-SECT
Between Centers	BC		
Bevel	BEV	Decimal	DEC
Bill of Material	B/M	Degree	(°) DEG
Birmingham Wire Gage	BWG	Department	DEPT
Blueprint	BP	Design	DSGN
Boiler	BLR	Detail	DET
Bolt Circle	BC	Diagonal	DIAG
Bottom	BOT	Distance	DIST

43. ABBREVIATIONS FOR USE ON DRAWINGS (*Continued*)

Dovetail	DVTL	Harden	HDN
Dowel	DWL	Head	HD
Down	DN	Headless	HDLS
Drafting	DFTG	Heat	HT
Draftsman	DFTSMN	Heat Treat	HT TR
Drawing	DWG	Heavy	HVY
Drill	DR	Height	HGT
Drive	DR	Hexagon	HEX
Drive Fit	DF	High-Speed Steel	HSS
Drop Forge	DF	Horizontal	HOR
		Hot Rolled Steel	HRS
Each	EA		
Eccentric	ECC	Illustrate	ILLUS
Elbow	ELL	Inch	(") IN.
Electric	ELEC	Inside Diameter	ID
Elevation	EL	Instrument	INST
Engine	ENG	Intersect	INT
Engineer	ENGR	Iron	I
Equal	EQ	Journal	JNL
Equipment	EQUIP.		
External	EXT	Key	K
		Keyseat	KST
Fabricate	FAB	Keyway	KWY
Feed	FD		
Feet	(') FT	Left Hand	LH
Feet per Minute	FPM	Length	LG
Feet per Second	FPS	Length Over All	LOA
Figure	FIG.	Line	L
Fillet	FIL	Long	LG
Fillister	FIL		
Finish	FIN.	Machine	MACH
Finish All Over	FAO	Machine Steel	MS
Fixture	FIX.	Malleable	MALL
Flange	FLG	Malleable Iron	MI
Flat Head	FH	Manufacture	MFR
Foot	(') FT	Material	MATL
Forged Steel	FST	Maximum	MAX
Forging	FORG	Mechanical	MECH
Forward	FWD	Metal	MET.
		Millimeter	MM
Gage or Gauge	GA	Minimum	MIN
Galvanize	GALV	Miscellaneous	MISC
General	GENL		
Glass	GL	National	NATL
Grade	GR	Nominal	NOM
Grind	GRD	Normal	NOR
		Not to Scale	NTS
Half-Round	H RD	Number	NO.

43. ABBREVIATIONS FOR USE ON DRAWINGS (*Continued*)

Obsolete	OBS	Set Screw	SS
Octagon	OCT	Shaft	SFT
On Center	OC	Sheet	SH
Opening	OPNG	Sketch	SK
Opposite	OPP	Socket	SOC
Original	ORIG	Special	SPL
Outside Diameter	OD	Spherical	SPHER
Outside Radius	OR	Spindle	SPDL
Overall	OA	Spot Faced	SF
		Spring	SPG
Pair	PR	Square	SQ
Parallel	PAR.	Stainless Steel	SST
Part	PT	Station	STA
Pattern	PATT	Steel	STL
Perpendicular	PERP	Stock	STK
Piece	PC	Straight	STR
Pierce	PRC	Structural	STR
Pitch	P	Supersede	SUPSD
Plate	PL	Support	SUPT
Point	PT	Surface	SUR
Polish	POL	Switch	SW
		Symbol	SYM
Quadrant	QUAD	Symmetrical	SYM
Quantity	QTY		
Quarter	QTR	Tangent	TAN.
		Taper	TPR
Radial	RAD	Technical	TECH
Radius	R	Template	TEMP
Ream	RM	That is	IE
Rectangle	RECT	Thick	THK
Reference	REF	Thread	THD
Relief	REL	Threads per Inch	TPI
Required	REQD	Tolerance	TOL
Revolution	REV	Tool Steel	TS
Revolutions per Minute	RPM	Tooth	T
Right	RT	Typical	TYP
Right Hand	RH		
Rivet	RIV	United States Standard	USS
Rockwell Hardness	RH	Vandyke	VD
Rough	RGH	Vertical	VERT
Round	RD	Volume	VOL
		Weight	WT
Sand Blast	SD BL	Width	W
Scleroscope Hardness	SCLER	Woodruff	WDF
Screw	SCR	Wrought	WRT
Second	SEC	Wrought Iron	WI
Section	SECT		

44. BIBLIOGRAPHY OF TECHNICAL DRAWING
AND RELATED SUBJECTS

AERONAUTICAL DRAFTING

Anderson, Newton. *Aircraft Layout and Detail Design.* McGraw-Hill.

Davis, D. J., and Goen, C. H. *Aircraft Mechanical Drawing.* McGraw-Hill.

Faulconer, Thomas. *Introduction to Aircraft Design.* McGraw-Hill.

Katz, Hyman H. *Aircraft Drafting.* Macmillan.

Meadowcraft, Norman. *Aircraft Detail Drafting.* McGraw-Hill.

Nelson, William. *Airplane Lofting.* McGraw-Hill.

SAE Aeronautical Drafting Manual. Society of Automotive Engineers, Inc., 29 West 39th Street, New York.

Svensen, C. L., *A Manual of Aircraft Drafting.* D. Van Nostrand.

AMERICAN STANDARDS

Below is a selected list of American Standards related to drafting as presented in this text. A complete list, with prices, can be obtained from the American Standards Association, 70 East 45th Street, New York 17, New York.

Abbreviations

Abbreviations for Use on Drawings, Z32.13—1946

Abbreviations for Scientific and Engineering Terms, Z10.1—1941

Bolts and Screws

Plow Bolts, B18F—1928

Round Unslotted Head Bolts, B18.5—1939

Socket Head Cap Screws and Socket Set Screws, B18.3—1947

Slotted and Recessed-Head Screws, Machine, Cap, Wood, Tapping and Slotted Headless Types, B18.6—1947

Track Bolts and Nuts, B18d—1930

Wrench-Head Bolts and Nuts and Wrench Openings, B18.2—1941

Charts and Graphs

Engineering and Scientific Charts for Lantern Slides, Z15.1—1932

Engineering and Scientific Graphs for Publications, Z15.3—1943

Time-Series Charts, Z15.2—1938

Dimensioning and Surface Finish

Design and Dimensioning, Z14.

Limits and Fits, B4.1—1947

Surface Roughness, B46.1—1947

Drawings

Drawings and Drafting Room Practice, Z14.1—1946

Gears

Gear Tolerances and Inspection, B6.6—1947
Letter Symbols for Gear Engineering, B6.5—1943
Spur Gear Tooth Form, B6.1—1932

Graphical Symbols

Basic Graphical Symbols for Electric Apparatus, Z32.12—1947
Graphical Symbols for Use on Drawings in Mechanical Engineering, Z32.2—1941
Graphical Symbols for Power and Control, Z32.3—1946
Graphical Symbols for Telephone, Telegraph, and Radio Use, Z32.5—1944
Graphical Electrical Symbols for Architectural Plans, Z32.9—1943
Graphical Symbols for Electronic Devices, Z32.10—1948
Welding Symbols and Instructions for their Use, Z32.1—1942

Keys

Shafting and Stock Keys, B17.1—1943
Woodruff Keys, Keyslots, and Cutters, B17f—1930

Piping

Cast Iron Pipe Flanges and Flanged Fittings (25 lb.), B16b2—1931
Cast Iron Pipe Flanges and Flanged Fittings (125 lb.), B16a—1939
Cast Iron Pipe Flanges and Flanged Fittings (250 lb.), B16b—1944
Cast Iron Pipe Flanges and Flanged Fittings (800 lb.), B16b1—1931
Cast Iron Screwed Fittings, 125 and 250 lb., B16d—1941
Ferrous Plugs, Bushings, Locknuts and Caps, B16.14—1943
Malleable-Iron Screwed Fittings, 150 lb., B16c—1939
Scheme for Identification of Piping Systems, A13—1928
Steel Pipe Flanges and Flanged Fittings, B16e—1939
Wrought-Iron and Wrought-Steel Pipe, B36.10—1939

Rivets

Large Rivets, B18.4—1937
Small Rivets, B18a—1927
Tinners', Coopers', and Belt Rivets, B18g—1929

Small Tools

Twist Drills, Straight Shank, B5.12—1940
Machine Tapers, Self-Holding, and Steep Taper Series, B5.10—1943
Milling Cutters, B5c—1930
Reamers, B5.14—1941
Taps, Cut and Ground Threads, B5.4—1948

Threads

Acme Threads, B1.5—1945
Screw Threads for Bolts, Nuts, Machine Screws and Threaded Parts, B1.1—1935
Screw Threads of Truncated Whitworth Form, B1.6—1944
Straight Screw Threads for High-Temperature Bolting, B1.4—1945
Unified and American Screw Threads, B1.1—1949

ARCHITECTURAL DRAWING

Cram, T., *Architectural Construction.* John Wiley.

Field, W. B. *An Introduction to Architectural Drawing.* McGraw-Hill.

Pickering, E. *Architectural Design.* John Wiley.

Ramsey, C. G., and Sleeper, H. R. *Architectural Graphic Standards.* John Wiley.

Sleeper, H. R. *Architectural Specifications.* John Wiley.

Svensen, C. L. and Shelton, E. D. *Architectural Drafting.* D. Van Nostrand.

Sweets Catalogue. F. W. Dodge Corporation (Yearly).

BLUEPRINT READING

DeVette, W. A. and Kellogg, D. E. *Blueprint Reading for the Metal Trades.* Bruce Pub. Company, Milwaukee.

Ihne, R. W. and Streeter, W. E. *Machine Trades Blueprint Reading.* Amer. Tech. Society, Chicago.

Norcross, C. *Aircraft Blueprints & How to Read Them.* McGraw-Hill.

Owens, A. A. and Slingluff, B. F. *How to Read Blueprints.* John C. Winston Co., Philadelphia.

Simple Blueprint Reading. Lincoln Electric Company, Cleveland.

Spencer, H. C. and Grant, H. E. *The Blueprint Language.* Macmillan.

Svensen, C. L. and Street, W. E. *A Manual of Blueprint Reading.* D. Van Nostrand.

CHARTS AND GRAPHS

Dingman, C. F. *Plan Reading and Quantity Surveying.* McGraw-Hill.

Douglas, R. D. and Adams, D. P. *Elements of Nomography.* McGraw-Hill.

Haskell, A. C. *How to Make and Use Graphic Charts.* Codex Book Co., New York.

Karsten, K. G. *Charts and Graphs.* Prentice-Hall.

Levens, A. S. *Nomography.* John Wiley.

Mackay, C. O. *Graphical Solutions.* John Wiley.

Mavis, F. T. *The Construction of Nomographic Charts.* Int. Textbook Co.

Swett, G. W. *Construction of Alignment Charts.* John Wiley.

DESCRIPTIVE GEOMETRY

Giesecke, F. E. and Mitchell, A. *Descriptive Geometry.* F. E. Giesecke, New Braunfels, Tex.

Higbee, F. G. *Drawing-Board Geometry.* John Wiley.

Hood, George J. *Geometry of Engineering Drawing.* McGraw-Hill.

Jordan, H. H. and Porter, F. M. *Descriptive Geometry.* Ginn.

Levens, A. S. and Eggers, H. C. T. *Descriptive Geometry.* Harper.

Millar, A. V. and Shiels, K. G. *Descriptive Geometry.* D. C. Heath.

Rowe, C. E. *Engineering Descriptive Geometry.* D. Van Nostrand.

Rusinoff, S. E. *Practical Descriptive Geometry.* Amer. Tech. Society, Chicago.

Street, W. E. *Technical Descriptive Geometry.* D. Van Nostrand.

Vaughn, W. *Aircraft Descriptive Geometry.* Aircraft Pub. Co., Glendale, Cal.

Warner, F. M. *Applied Descriptive Geometry.* McGraw-Hill.

Wellman, B. Leighton. *Technical Descriptive Geometry.* McGraw-Hill.

DESCRIPTIVE GEOMETRY PROBLEMS

Giesecke, F. E. and Mitchell, A. *Descriptive Geometry Problems.* F. E. Giesecke, New Braunfels, Tex.

Grant, H. E. *Practical Descriptive Geometry Problems.* H. E. Grant, Washington Univ., St. Louis.

Paré, Eugene, Loving, R. O., and Hill, I. L. *Descriptive Geometry Problems.* E. Paré, Ill. Inst. of Tech., Chicago.

Rowe, C. E. and McFarland, J. D. *Engineering Descriptive Geometry Problems.* D. Van Nostrand.

Street, W. E., Perryman, C. C. and McGuire, J. G. *Technical Descriptive Geometry Problems.* D. Van Nostrand.

Turner, W. W. and Buck, C. P. *Basic Problems in Descriptive Geometry.* Ronald Press.

Uhler, E. H. *Problems in Descriptive Geometry for Engineers.* Int. Textbook Co.

DRAWING INSTRUMENTS AND SUPPLIES

Eugene Dietzgen & Co., Chicago.

Frederick Post Co., Chicago.

Keuffel & Esser Co., Hoboken, N. J.

Theodore Alteneder & Sons, 1217 Spring Garden St., Philadelphia.

ELECTRICAL DRAWING

Bishop, C. C. *Electrical Drafting and Design.* McGraw-Hill.

Carini, L. F. B. *Drafting for Electronics.* McGraw-Hill.

Kocher, S. E. *Electrical Drafting.* Int. Textbook Co.

Van Gieson, D. W. *Electrical Drafting.* McGraw-Hill.

ENGINEERING AS A VOCATION

Carlisle, N. D. *Your Career in Engineering.* E. P. Dutton and Co.

Grinter, L. E., Spencer, H. C., et al. *Engineering Preview.* Macmillan.

Williams, C. C. *Building an Engineering Career.* McGraw-Hill.

ENGINEERING DRAWING

Carter, I. N. and Thompson, H. L. *Engineering Drawing.* Int. Textbook Co.

French, T. E. *Engineering Drawing.* McGraw-Hill.

French, T. E. and Svensen, C. L. *Mechanical Drawing.* McGraw-Hill.

Giesecke, F. E., Mitchell, A. and Spencer, H. C. *Technical Drawing.* Macmillan.

Hobart, D. E. *Engineering Drawing.* D. C. Heath.

Jordan, H. H. and Hoelscher, R. P. *Engineering Drawing.* John Wiley.

Luzadder, W. J. *Fundamentals of Engineering Drawing.* Prentice-Hall.

Orth, H. D., Worsencroft, R. R., and Doke, H. B. *Basic Engineering Drawing.* Irwin-Farnham, Chicago.

Sahag, L. M. *Engineering Drawing.* Ronald Press.

Schumann, C. H. *Technical Drafting.* Harper.

Svensen, C. L. *Drafting for Engineers.* D. Van Nostrand

Svensen, C. L. *Essentials of Drafting.* D. Van Nostrand.

ENGINEERING DRAWING PROBLEMS

French, T. E. and McCully, H. M. *Engineering Drawing Sheets*. McGraw-Hill.

Giesecke, F. E., Mitchell, A. and Spencer, H. C. *Technical Drawing Problems*. Macmillan.

Higbee, F. G. and Russ, John. *Engineering Drawing Problems*. John Wiley.

Orth, H. D., Worsencroft, R. R. and Doke, H. B. *Problems in Basic Engineering Drawing*. Irwin-Farnham, Chicago.

Spencer, H. C. and Grant, H. E. *Technical Drawing Problems—Series 2*. Macmillan.

Svensen, C. L., Schumann, C. H. and Street, W. E. *Drafting Problem Layouts*. D. Van Nostrand.

Tozer, E. F. and Paré, E. G. *Engineering Drawing Problems—Series M*. D. Van Nostrand.

Williams, E. L. and Spencer, H. C. *Technical Drawing for High Schools, Workbooks I and II*. Macmillan.

HANDBOOKS

A Manual of Standard Practice for Detailing Reinforced Concrete Structures. American Concrete Institute.

Colvin, F. H. and Stanley, F. A. *American Machinists' Handbook*. McGraw-Hill.

American Society of Heating and Ventilating Engineers' Guide. Amer. Soc. of Heating and Ventilating Engineers, 29 W. 39th St., N. Y.

Colvin, F. H. *Aircraft Handbook*. McGraw-Hill.

Kent, William. *Mechanical Engineer's Handbook*. John Wiley.

Kidder, F. E. *Architects' and Builders' Handbook*. John Wiley.

Knowlton, A. E. *Standard Handbook for Electrical Engineers*. McGraw-Hill.

Oberg, E. and Jones, F. D. *Machinery's Handbook*. The Industrial Press.

Marks, L. S. *Mechanical Engineers' Handbook*. McGraw-Hill.

Merriman, T. and Wiggin, T. H. *American Civil Engineers' Handbook*. John Wiley.

O'Rourke, C. E. *General Engineering Handbook*. McGraw-Hill.

Perry, J. H. *Chemical Engineers' Handbook*. McGraw-Hill.

SAE Handbook. Society of Automotive Engineers, 29 W. 39th St., N. Y.

Steel Construction. American Institute of Steel Construction, N. Y.

Urquhart, L. C. *Civil Engineering Handbook*. McGraw-Hill.

Wagener, A. M. *The Machinists' and Draftsman's Handbook*. D. Van Nostrand.

INDUSTRIAL DESIGN

Bel Geddes, N. *Horizons*. Little, Brown & Co.

Holme, G. *Industrial Design*. Studio Publications.

Read, H. *Art and Industry*. Harcourt, Brace.

Van Doren, H. *Industrial Design*. McGraw-Hill.

LETTERING

French, T. E. and Meiklejohn, R. *Essentials of Lettering*. McGraw-Hill.

French, T. E. and Turnbull, W. D. *Lessons in Lettering, Books 1 and 2*. McGraw-Hill.

George R. F. *Modern Lettering for Pen and Brush Poster Design*. Hunt Pen Co., Camden, N. J.

Giesecke, F. E., Mitchell, A. and Spencer, H. C. *Lettering Exercises*. Macmillan.

Hornung, C. P. *Lettering from A to Z*. Ziff-Davis Pub. Co., N. Y.

Ogg, Oscar. *An Alphabet Source Book*. Harper.

Svensen, C. L. *The Art of Lettering*. D. Van Nostrand.

MACHINE DESIGN AND MECHANISM

Albert, C. D. *Machine Design and Drawing Room Problems*. John Wiley.

Faires, V. M. *Design of Machine Elements*. Macmillan.

Ham, C. W. and Crane, E. J. *Mechanics of Machinery*. McGraw-Hill.

Keon, R. M. and Faires, V. M. *Mechanism*. McGraw-Hill.

Leutwiler, O. A. *Elements of Machine Design*. McGraw-Hill.

Norman, C. A., Ault, S. and Zarobsky, I. *Fundamentals of Machine Design*. Macmillan.

Schwamb, Peter, Merrill, A. L. and James, W. H. *Elements of Mechanism*. John Wiley.

Vallance, A. *Design of Machine Members*. McGraw-Hill.

Winston, S. E. *Machine Design*. D. Van Nostrand.

MACHINE DRAWING

Snow, G. C. and Russell, J. C. *Machine Drafting*. Manual Arts Press, Peoria, Ill.

Svensen, C. L. *Machine Drawing*. D. Van Nostrand.

Tozer, E. F. and Rising, H. A. *Machine Drawing*. McGraw-Hill.

MAP DRAWING

Deetz, Charles H. *Elements of Map Projection*. U.S. Gov. Printing Office.

Finch, J. K. *Topographic Maps and Sketch Mapping*. John Wiley.

Greitzer, S. L. *Elementary Topography and Map Reading*. McGraw-Hill.

Hinks, A. R. *Maps and Surveys*. Macmillan.

Sloan, R. C. and Montz, J. M. *Elements of Topographic Drawing*. McGraw-Hill.

PATENT DRAWINGS

Radzinsky, Harry. *Making Patent Drawings*. Macmillan.

Rules of Practice. U. S. Patent Office, Washington, D. C.

PERSPECTIVE

Freese, E. I. *Perspective Projection*. Reinhold Pub. Corp.

Lawson, P. J. *Practical Perspective Drawing*. McGraw-Hill.

Lubschez, B. *Perspective*. D. Van Nostrand.

Norling, E. *Perspective Made Easy*. Macmillan.

Turner, W. W. *Simplified Perspective*. Ronald Press.

PIPING DRAWING

Crane & Company, Chicago (Catalogue).

Walworth Company, Boston (Catalogue).

Crocker, S. *Piping Handbook*. McGraw-Hill.

PRODUCTION ILLUSTRATION

Hoelscher, R. P., Springer, C. H. |and Pohle, R. F. *Industrial Production Illustration*. McGraw-Hill.

Tharratt, George. *Aircraft Production Illustration*. McGraw-Hill.
Treacy, John. *Production Illustration*. John Wiley.

SHEET METAL DRAFTING

Dougherty, J. S. *Sheet-Metal Pattern Drafting and Shop Problems*. Manual Arts Press.
Jenkins, Rolland. *Sheet Metal Pattern Layout*. Prentice-Hall.
Kidder, F. S. *Triangulation Applied to Sheet Metal Pattern Cutting*. Sheet Metal Pub. Co., N. Y.
Kittredge, G. W. *The New Metal Worker Pattern Book*. Scientific Book Corp., N. Y.
Longfield, E. M. *Sheet Metal Drafting*. McGraw-Hill.
Neubecker, William. *The Universal Sheet Metal Pattern Cutter, Vols. I and II*. Metal Pub. Co., N. Y.
Neubecker, William. *Sheet Metal Work*. Amer. Tech. Society, Chicago.
O'Rourke, F. J. *Sheet Metal Pattern Drafting*. McGraw-Hill.
Paull, J. H. *Industrial Sheet Metal Drawing*. D. Van Nostrand.

SHOP PROCESSES AND MATERIALS

Arc Welding in Design, Manufacturing and Construction. Lincoln Arc Welding Foundation.
Begeman, M. L. *Manufacturing Processes*. John Wiley.
Boston, O. W. *Metal Processing*. John Wiley.
Campbell, H. L. *Metal Castings*. John Wiley.
Clapp, W. H. and Clark, D. S. *Engineering Materials and Processes*. Int. Textbook Co.
Dubois, J. H. *Plastics*. Amer. Tech. Society, Chicago.
Hesse, H. C. *Engineering Tools and Processes*. D. Van Nostrand.
Hinman, C. W. *Die Engineering Layouts and Formulas*. McGraw-Hill.
Johnson, C. G. *Forging Practice*. Amer. Tech. Society, Chicago.
Wendt, R. E. *Foundry Work*. McGraw-Hill.
Young, J. F. *Materials and Processes*. John Wiley.

SKETCHING

Guptill, A. L. *Drawing with Pen and Ink*. Reinhold Pub. Corp.
Guptill, A. L. *Sketching and Rendering in Pencil*. Reinhold Pub. Corp.
Jones, F. D. *How to Sketch Mechanisms*. The Industrial Press.
Kautsky, T. *Pencil Broadsides*. Reinhold Pub. Corp.
Zipprich, A. E. *Freehand Drafting*. D. Van Nostrand.

SLIDE RULE

Cooper, H. O. *Slide Rule Calculations*. Oxford Univ. Press.
Harris, C. O. *Slide Rule Simplified*. Amer. Tech. Society, Chicago.
Mackay, C. O. *Graphical Solutions*. John Wiley.

STRUCTURAL DRAWING AND DESIGN

Bishop, C. T. *Structural Design*. John Wiley.
Bishop, C. T. *Structural Drafting*. John Wiley.
Manual of Standard Practice for Detailing Reinforced Concrete Structures. American Concrete Institute.

TOOL DESIGN

Bloom, R. R. *Principles of Tool Engineering*. McGraw-Hill.
Cole, C. B. *Tool Design*. Amer. Tech. Society, Chicago.

WELDING

Elzea, L. S. *Aircraft Welding*. McGraw-Hill.
Fish, G. D. *Arc Welded Steel Frame Structures*. McGraw-Hill.
Procedure Handbook of Arc Welding Design and Practice. Lincoln Electric Co., Cleveland.

APPENDIX

45. DECIMAL EQUIVALENTS

		$\frac{1}{64}$	.015625			$\frac{33}{64}$	.515625
	$\frac{1}{32}$		.03125		$\frac{17}{32}$		.53125
		$\frac{3}{64}$	.046875			$\frac{35}{64}$	.546875
$\frac{1}{16}$			.0625	$\frac{9}{16}$			.5625
		$\frac{5}{64}$	.078125			$\frac{37}{64}$	.578125
	$\frac{3}{32}$		.09375		$\frac{19}{32}$		.59375
		$\frac{7}{64}$	.109375			$\frac{39}{64}$	.609375
$\frac{1}{8}$			.125	$\frac{5}{8}$			.625
		$\frac{9}{64}$	.140625			$\frac{41}{64}$	.640625
	$\frac{5}{32}$		.15625		$\frac{21}{32}$		.65625
		$\frac{11}{64}$	.171875			$\frac{43}{64}$	.671875
$\frac{3}{16}$			.1875	$\frac{11}{16}$			.6875
		$\frac{13}{64}$	.203125			$\frac{45}{64}$	.703125
	$\frac{7}{32}$		.21875		$\frac{23}{32}$		.71875
		$\frac{15}{64}$	.234375			$\frac{47}{64}$	.734375
$\frac{1}{4}$			.25	$\frac{3}{4}$			.75
		$\frac{17}{64}$	.265625			$\frac{49}{64}$	.765625
	$\frac{9}{32}$		.28125		$\frac{25}{32}$		.78125
		$\frac{19}{64}$	.296875			$\frac{51}{64}$	.796875
$\frac{5}{16}$			.3125	$\frac{13}{16}$			.8125
		$\frac{21}{64}$	.328125			$\frac{53}{64}$	.828125
	$\frac{11}{32}$		.34375		$\frac{27}{32}$		.84375
		$\frac{23}{64}$	.359375			$\frac{55}{64}$	.859375
$\frac{3}{8}$			.375	$\frac{7}{8}$			.875
		$\frac{25}{64}$	.390625			$\frac{57}{64}$	.890625
	$\frac{13}{32}$		.40625		$\frac{29}{32}$		.90625
		$\frac{27}{64}$	.421875			$\frac{59}{64}$	.921875
$\frac{7}{16}$			.4375	$\frac{15}{16}$			.9375
		$\frac{29}{64}$	.453125			$\frac{61}{64}$	.953125
	$\frac{15}{32}$		.46875		$\frac{31}{32}$		.96875
		$\frac{31}{64}$	.484375			$\frac{63}{64}$	.984375
$\frac{1}{2}$			.5	1			1.

INDEX

Scales (use of)
Spacing of Drawing
Lead Of Screw Threads
Drawing Ellipses
Projections
True Length lines
Cavalier & Cabinet Proj.

Oblique — 45
Isometric 30°